The Chemistry of
Nucleosides and Nucleotides

The Chemistry of
Nucleosides and Nucleotides

A. M. MICHELSON

Institut de Biologie Physico-Chimique, Paris, France

1963

ACADEMIC PRESS
London and New York

ACADEMIC PRESS INC. (LONDON) LTD.
Berkeley Square House
Berkeley Square
London, W.1

U.S. Edition published by
ACADEMIC PRESS INC.
111 Fifth Avenue
New York 3, New York

*Printed in Great Britain
by The Whitefriars Press Ltd.,
London and Tonbridge*

PREFACE

"... one can only hope that if we have not reached the last chapter in an interesting series of researches which was initiated by Miescher many years ago, we must be somewhat near the penultimate one."

W. D. HALLIBURTON

[Annual Reports on the Progress of Chemistry, **6**, 170, (1909)]

This book presents an attempt to describe the general chemistry of nucleosides and nucleotides and their major derivatives, the nucleotide coenzymes and nucleic acids, and also those biochemical aspects that are so intimately connected with the chemical approach that segregation becomes absurd. No description of carbohydrate or purine and pyrimidine chemistry *per se* has been essayed, since such topics are covered to a large extent by standard texts. Apart from giving, in the words of the publishers, " a bird's-eye-view of the subject of value to advanced students " it is hoped that this volume will be of some use to the numerous experimentalists whose efforts render the task of writing such an account both necessary and possible.

Paris
October 1962

A. M. MICHELSON

ACKNOWLEDGMENTS

The Author wishes to make the acknowledgments listed below for permissions to use certain diagrams.

Chapter 8, Figure 1: *Journal of the Chemical Society*, The Chemical Society, from the paper by A. M. Michelson (1959). Figure 5: *Journal of the Chemical Society*, The Chemical Society, from the paper by A. M. Michelson (1959). Figure 8: *Biochimica et Biophysica Acta*, Elsevier Publishing Company, from the paper by M. N. Lipsett, L. A. Heppel and D. F. Bradley (1960). Figure 9: Proceedings of the 4th International Congress of Biochemistry, Pergamon Press, from the paper by A. Rich (1958). Figure 10: *Biochimica et Biophysica Acta*, Elsevier Publishing Company, from the paper by G. Felsenfeld and A. Rich (1957). Figure 11: *Nature*, Macmillan and Company, from the paper by A. Rich (1958) and the paper by D. R. Davies (1960). Figure 12: *Reviews of Modern Physics*, American Society of Physics, from the paper by P. Doty (1959). Figure 13: *Journal of Molecular Biology*, Academic Press, from the paper by A. Rich, D. R. Davies, F. H. C. Crick and J. D. Watson (1961), and *Biochimica et Biophysica Acta*, Elsevier Publishing Company, from the paper by A. Rich (1958). Figure 16: *Nature*, Macmillan and Company, from the paper by J. D. Watson and F. H. C. Crick (1953). Figure 17: *Journal of the Chemical Society*, The Chemical Society, from the paper by A. R. Peacocke and B. N. Preston (1959). Figure 21: *Biochimica et Biophysica Acta*, Elsevier Publishing Company, from the paper by S. Zamenhof, G. Griboff and N. Marullo (1954). Figure 22: *Proceedings of the National Academy of Sciences of the U.S.A.*, University of Chicago Press, from the paper by P. Doty, H. Boedtker, J. R. Fresco, R. Haselkorn and M. Litt (1959). Figure 23: *Nature*, Macmillan and Company, from the paper by J. Marmur and P. Doty (1959). Figure 24: *Nature*, Macmillan and Company, from the paper by N. Sueoka, J. Marmur and P. Doty (1959). Figure 25: *Proceedings of the National Academy of Sciences of the U.S.A.*, University of Chicago Press, from the paper by P. Doty, H. Boedtker, J. R. Fresco, R. Haselkorn and M. Litt (1959). Figure 26: *Journal of Biological Chemistry*, American Society of Biological Chemists Inc., from the paper by J. Shack (1958). Figure 27: *Biochimica et Biophysica Acta*, Elsevier Publishing Company, from the paper by R. Thomas (1954). Figure 29: *Journal of Molecular Biology*, Academic Press, from the paper by H. Boedtker (1960). Figure 30: *Journal of Molecular Biology*, Academic Press, from the paper by H. Boedtker (1960). Figure 31: *Doklady Akademii Nauk*

S.S.S.R., The Academy of Sciences of the U.S.S.R., from the paper by A. S. Spirin, L. P. Gavrilova and A. N. Belozersky (1959). Figure 32: *Journal of Molecular Biology*, Academic Press, from the paper by H. Boedtker (1960). Figure 33: *Journal of Molecular Biology*, Academic Press, from the paper by A. S. Spirin (1960). Figure 34: *Biochimica et Biophysica Acta*, Elsevier Publishing Company, from the paper by U. Z. Littauer and H. Eisenberg (1959). Figure 35: *Proceedings of the National Academy of Sciences of the U.S.A.*, University of Chicago Press, from the paper by P. Doty, H. Boedtker, J. R. Fresco, R. Haselkorn and M. Litt (1959). Figure 36: *Journal of Molecular Biology*, Academic Press, from the paper by R. A. Cox and U. Z. Littauer (1960). Figure 37: *Journal of Molecular Biology*, Academic Press, from the paper by M. Grunberg-Manago (1959). Figure 38: *Nature*, Macmillan and Company, from the paper by J. R. Fresco, B. M. Alberts and P. Doty (1960). Figure 39: R. Haselkorn, Thesis, Harvard University (1959).

CONTENTS

A*

CONTENTS

Chapter 1

INTRODUCTION

The biological significance of nucleosides, nucleotides and their derivatives is attested by the numerous publications now appearing. In large measure this renaissance is based on the emergence of a number of techniques which have facilitated the separation and identification of substances that were not amenable to treatment by the classical methods of organic chemistry, partly owing to the hybrid character of their properties and partly because of the relatively low stability of some of the linkages involved. A nucleotide is best defined as the phosphate ester of a sugar in glycosyl combination with a base molecule derived from purine or pyrimidine, that is, it is the phosphate ester of a nucleoside. In the naturally occurring compounds the nucleoside moiety is generally a β-D-ribofuranosyl or β-D-2-deoxyribofuranosyl derivative. Common usage embraces such substances as nicotinamide mononucleotide and riboflavin mononucleotide. The simplest units include adenosine-5′ phosphate, adenosine-5′ pyrophosphate and adenosine-5′ triphosphate as well as the mononucleotides obtained by degradative hydrolysis of nucleic acids. Others of a rather more complex nature are the diesterified pyrophosphate derivatives active as coenzymes, such as flavin adenine dinucleotide, coenzyme A, uridine diphosphate glucose and diphosphopyridine nucleotide, examples that also illustrate the somewhat haphazard nomenclature now prevalent. Finally, the polymeric nucleotide derivatives known as nucleic acids have molecular weights of up to several million, and exhibit biological properties close to life itself as components of chromosomes and viruses, and as agents in cell growth.

The earliest isolation of polynucleotide material reflects a connection with medical science that has grown significantly in recent times, many purine and pyrimidine derivatives being of considerable chemotherapeutic value. In 1869 Miescher[1] attempted the extraction of nuclear substances from pus cells (obtained from discarded surgical bandages) by digesting the cells with pepsin and dilute hydrochloric acid for prolonged periods, and then shaking the mixture with ether, when practically pure nuclear material settled at the bottom of the aqueous phase. From this he prepared a rather unusual acidic substance, *nuclein*, that contained a large amount of phosphorus, was insoluble in the usual organic solvents and in dilute acids, but was readily soluble

1

in dilute alkali.   Although the scepticism of Hoppe-Seyler delayed publication for two years, until he and two of his research students could confirm and expand the work, further investigations by Miescher on his return to Basel soon showed that salmon sperm was a convenient source of high molecular weight nuclein and of a basic protein, which he named *protamine*, that could be extracted readily from the sperm with dilute acid. In later work by Altmann[2] (who introduced the term *nucleic acid* in 1889) and others, general methods were developed for the isolation of nucleic acids from yeast and a number of animal tissues, and in 1891 Kossel[3] described the hydrolysis of protein free nucleic acid. The existence of two main types of nucleic acid, now known as ribonucleic acid and deoxyribonucleic acid, was recognised at an early date in the pioneer work of Miescher and Kossel and later developed in the work of Hammarsten, Jones, Levene, and others. Historically, the subject has endured more disputes than usual, such as the controversy raised in 1899 by Bang's description of " guanylic acid " as a complex containing four guanine molecules, four phosphate groups joined together, three glycerols, and three pentoses; a controversy at times coloured with undue bitterness. Strong differences of opinion were expressed in the contest between a trinucleotide theory of nucleic acid advanced by Steudel and by Jones versus the tetranucleotide theory proposed by Levene, and an even more acrimonious discussion between Levene in the U.S.A., Gulland in Great Britain, and Bredereck in Germany ensued over an apocryphal guanine-uridylic acid.[4–11] The meretricious appeal of oversimplification has all too often succeeded in the absence of sound experimental evidence; in view of the nature of the problems involved and the techniques available, this is perhaps not too surprising.

Although inosinic acid was discovered by Liebig[12] in 1847 (the structure was not fully determined till some 90 years later) it was not until the isolation of muscle adenylic acid in 1927 by Embden and Zimmerman[13] and of adenosine triphosphate two years later by Lohmann[14] and by Fiske and Subbarow,[15] that a second major branch of nucleotide derivatives began to be explored. This group of compounds, loosely classified as nucleotide coenzymes, has grown considerably in the past decade, while the central significance of adenosine-5′ triphosphate in a multitude of biochemical reactions continues to be demonstrated, undiminished by the recognition of di- and triphosphates of the other major nucleosides. Methods of isolation, characterisation, and synthesis have now become routine, a marked contrast to the situation less than fifteen years ago when the chemical synthesis of adenosine triphosphate was regarded as a somewhat ludicrous and futile ambition.

REFERENCES

1. Miescher, F., *Hoppe-Seyler's Med. chem. Unters.*, 441 (1871).
2. Altmann, R., *Arch. Anat. u. Physiol., Physiol. Abt.*, 524 (1889).
3. Kossel, A., *Arch. Anat. u. Physiol., Physiol. Abt.*, 181 (1891).
4. Bredereck, H., and Richter, G., *Chem. Ber.*, **69**, 1129 (1936).
5. Bredereck, H., Köthnig, M., and Lehmann, G., *Chem. Ber.*, **71**, 2613 (1938).
6. Bredereck, H., *Fortschr. Chem. org. Naturstoffe*, **1**, 121 (1938).
7. Bredereck, H., Berger, E., and Richter, F., *Chem. Ber.*, **74**, 338 (1941).
8. Tipson, R. S., and Levene, P. A., *J. Biol. Chem.*, **127**, 105 (1939).
9. Tipson, R. S., and Levene, P. A., *Chem. and Ind.* (*London*), **58**, 1010 (1939).
10. Falconer, R., Gulland, J. M., Hobday, G. I., and Jackson, E. M., *J. Chem. Soc.*, **907** (1939).
11. Gulland, J. M., *Chem. and Ind.* (*London*), **59**, 321 (1940).
12. Liebig, J. von, *Ann.*, **62**, 257 (1847).
13. Embden, G., and Zimmermann, M., *Z. physiol. Chem.*, **167**, 137 (1927).
14. Lohmann, K., *Naturwissenschaften*, **17**, 624 (1929).
15. Fiske C. H., and Subbarow, Y., *Science*, **70**, 381 (1929).

Chapter 2

CHEMISTRY OF NUCLEOSIDES*

The name *nucleoside*, introduced by Levene and Jacobs in 1909, was originally applied to the purine–carbohydrate derivatives isolated from alkaline hydrolysates of yeast ribonucleic acid.[1]

ISOLATION

Although nucleosides can be obtained either enzymically or by chemical means from any type of naturally occurring nucleotide material, the main sources of these glycosyls are the nucleic acids isolated from various tissues and organisms. Degradation of ribonucleic acid to a mixture of the component nucleosides can be accomplished in a number of ways, among which may be mentioned hydrolysis with dilute ammonia at elevated temperatures,[2] treatment with aqueous pyridine under reflux for several days,[3] and hydrolysis catalysed by various metal ions.[4] In a recently described method,[5] the ribonucleic acid (or mononucleotide) is refluxed in aqueous formamide for several hours at pH 4. Separation and isolation of the nucleosides has been greatly improved by the application of ion exchange methods.[6]

Chemical methods for the hydrolysis of deoxyribonucleic acids to deoxynucleosides have been unsuccessful for a variety of reasons; a rather laborious enzymic digestion with deoxyribonuclease, diesterase, and monophosphatase must therefore be used.[7] Again, the earlier isolation procedures have been considerably simplified by the application of ion exchange chromatography.[8]

A number of nucleosides, including some with antibiotic activity, occur naturally as such and can be extracted directly without previous hydrolytic procedures.

STRUCTURE

The major nucleosides obtained from ribonucleic acids are the purine derivatives, adenosine and guanosine, and the ribosyl pyrimidines, cytidine and uridine. In addition, certain ribonucleic acids contain a relatively high proportion of an isomer of uridine, pseudouridine.

---

* The older numbering system is used for pyrimidine derivatives, in conformity with purines. There seems little point in excepting the latter class from standard rules, but not the former.

Various ribonucleosides derived from methylated purines and pyrimidines, including thymine, 5-methylcytosine, 1-methyladenine, 2-methyladenine, 6-methylaminopurine, 6-dimethylaminopurine, 1-methylguanine, 6-hydroxy-2-methylaminopurine, and 6-hydroxy-2-dimethylaminopurine (the so-called minor bases), occur in small amounts.[9] Nucleosides substituted at the sugar 2' hydroxyl group have also been isolated.[10, 11] They are probably 2'-O-methyl derivatives.

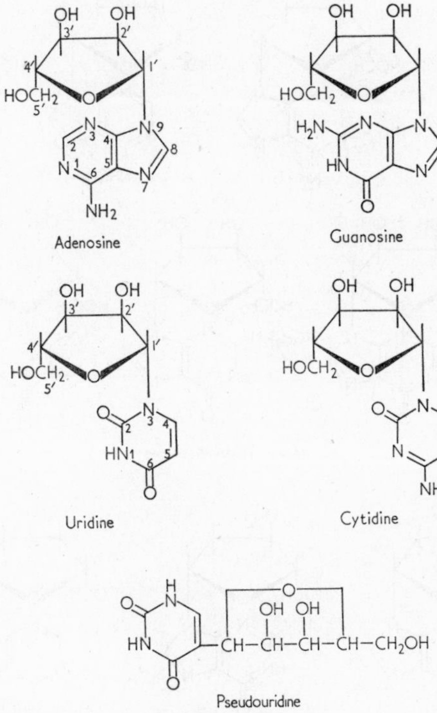

Adenosine

Guanosine

Uridine

Cytidine

Pseudouridine

Major Ribonucleosides

Deoxyribonucleic acids contain deoxyadenosine, deoxyguanosine, deoxycytidine, and thymidine as major nucleosides except in *Escherichia coli* T *even* numbered bacteriophage deoxynucleic acids where the cytosine is entirely replaced by 5-hydroxymethylcytosine[12] (or the 5-glucoside of 5-hydroxymethylcytosine). Deoxyribosyl-5-methylcytosine occurs in some deoxynucleic acids, particularly those from wheat germ,[13, 14] and small amounts of deoxyribosyl-6-methylaminopurine have been identified in deoxyribonucleic acids from various bacteria and bacteriophage.[15]

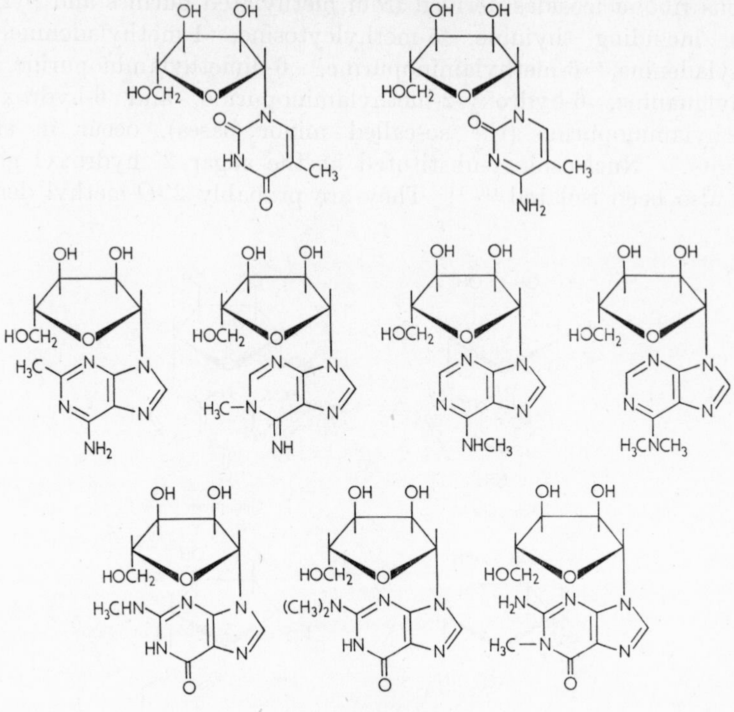

Minor ribonucleosides

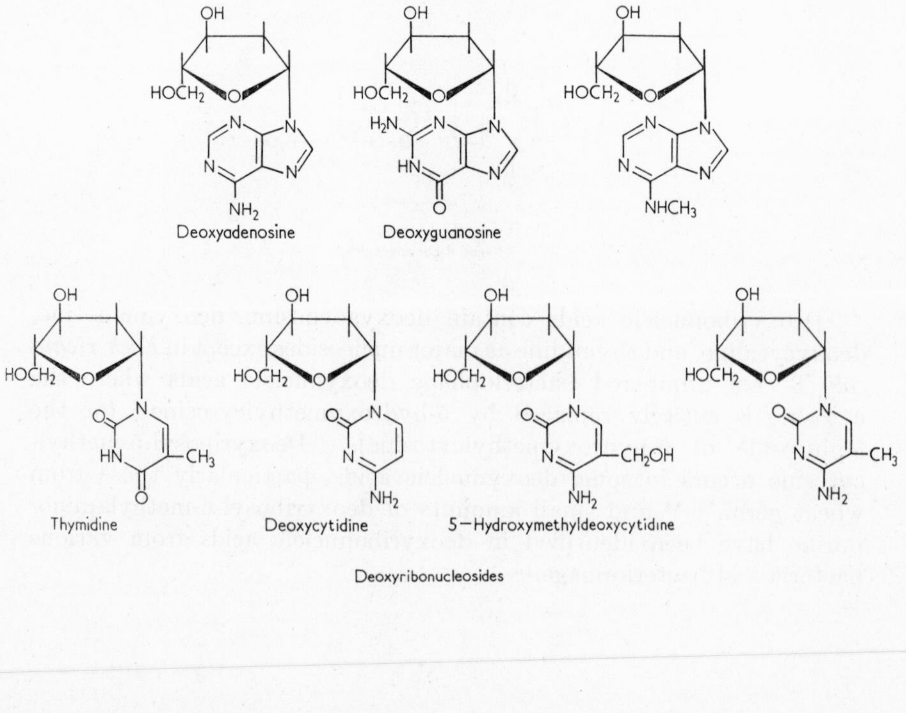

Deoxyadenosine   Deoxyguanosine

Thymidine   Deoxycytidine   5−Hydroxymethyldeoxycytidine

Deoxyribonucleosides

Deoxyuridine has been isolated from deoxynucleic acids of rather doubtful history[16] but is probably an artefact arising from deamination of cytosine residues.*

Complete knowledge of the structure of nucleosides involves the determination of (i) the nature of the base, (ii) the nature of the sugar, (iii) the mode of union and position of attachment of the sugar to base, (iv) the lactol structure of the sugar, and (v) the configuration at the sugar-base linkage.

Since the bases of the " classical " ribonucleosides—adenosine, guanosine, cytidine, and uridine—are readily obtained by acidic hydrolysis, they were early identified as adenine, guanine, cytosine, and uracil respectively.[17] In like manner, the bases present in deoxy-nucleosides and in the "newer" ribonucleosides (except pseudo-uridine) were isolated and identified after liberation by acidic hydrolysis. Comparison and identification with known purines and pyrimidines can now be made with extremely small amounts of material, using ultraviolet absorption spectra at several pH values, paper chromato-graphy, paper electrophoresis, and ion exchange chromatography, techniques which have greatly facilitated the recognition and isolation of purine and pyrimidine derivatives that are present in nucleic acids in minor proportions.

The sugar moiety of adenosine and guanosine remained unidentified for many years until in 1911 Levene and Jacobs isolated it in crystalline form, and succeeded in characterising it as D-ribose, hitherto unknown.[18] Uridine and cytidine proved more difficult to investigate as the hydro-lytic conditions necessary to rupture the glycosyl linkage are sufficiently vigorous to degrade the liberated sugar. However, preliminary hydro-genation gave a glycosyl-4,5-dihydropyrimidine that could be hydro-lysed with dilute acid to yield D-ribose; in addition, simultaneous hydrolysis and oxidation of uridine with hydrobromic acid and bromine gave D-ribonic acid.[19] Confirmation of the presence of D-ribose in these four nucleosides was obtained by Gulland and co-workers,[20] who converted the sugar components into D-ribobenzimidazole, though this evidence was somewhat ambiguous owing to epimerisation reactions. As yet, no sugar other than D-ribose has been observed in a nucleoside shown to be derived from ribonucleic acid.

Considerable difficulty was encountered in determining the structure of the sugar component in the deoxynucleosides, as application of the hydrolytic conditions used on the purine ribonucleosides invariably yielded levulinic acid, and for some time the sugar was considered to be a hexose. However, Levene and his co-workers eventually isolated a crystalline deoxypentose by extremely mild acidic hydrolysis of deoxy-guanosine.[21] The sugar did not form an osazone, showed many of the

* More recently it has been found that thymine is replaced by uracil in DNA from the *Bacillus subtilis* bacteriophage SP2 ; in another bacteriophage with the same host 5-hydroxymethyluracil is present instead of thymine.[369]

D–Ribose

properties characteristic of 2-deoxysugars, and was identical with synthetic L-2-deoxyribose except that the specific rotation, while of the same numerical value, was opposite in sign.[22] More recently the crystalline benzyl mercaptal of D-2-deoxyribose has been isolated directly from deoxyribonucleic acid by mercaptanolysis,[23] and the sugar of the purine deoxynucleosides in a number of deoxynucleic acids (isolated from different sources) has been shown to be chromatographically identical with 2-deoxyribose.[24] Reduction of thymidine and deoxycytidine with sodium and ethanol, or with sodium amalgam in water, followed by mild acidic hydrolysis also yields D-2-deoxyribose,[25-27] while D-2-deoxyribose benzylphenylhydrazone has been prepared from deoxyadenosine, deoxyguanosine, deoxycytidine, and thymidine.[28] In the absence of contrary evidence it is generally assumed that the sugar in deoxynucleic acids is uniformly D-2-deoxyribose.

The rapid acidic hydrolysis of purine nucleosides suggested that the sugar was linked to the base as a ring N-glycosyl rather than via a C—C linkage, the amino groups of adenosine and guanosine being excluded since both substances could be deaminated (to inosine and xanthosine respectively) without loss of the sugar residue. Since xanthosine could be methylated to give ribosyl theophylline, positions 1 and 3 were eliminated leaving only N7 or N9 as the point of attachment.[29]

Inosine   Xanthosine   Ribosyltheophylline

Whereas the ultraviolet absorption spectra of xanthosine are quite unlike those of 7-methylxanthine (or 1- or 3-methylxanthine) they closely resemble spectra of the 9-methyl derivative. Similarly, ultra-violet absorption spectra of adenosine, inosine, and guanosine are very similar to those of 9-methyladenine, 9-methylhypoxanthine, and 9-methylguanine respectively, rather than the 7-methyl derivatives.[30-32] These results strongly indicated that the purine nucleosides are 9-ribo-sylpurines, a proof that is also valid for deoxyadenosine and deoxy-guanosine since these substances show ultraviolet absorption spectra almost identical with those of adenosine and guanosine. Confirmation of the location of the sugar at position 9 in the purine nucleosides was provided by Todd and his co-workers through the unambiguous synthesis of 9-D-mannopyranosyladenine.[33] Periodate oxidation of this nucleoside gave a dialdehyde identical with that obtained from adenosine.

9-D-Mannopyranosyladenine   Adenosine

Since deamination of cytidine gives uridine, it is clear that the glycosyl linkage in the pyrimidine nucleosides does not involve C6, and bromination (or nitration) or uridine to the 5-bromo (or 5-nitro) derivative eliminates position 5. The action of phenylhydrazine on uridine previously treated with bromine gives 4,5-diphenylhydra-zinouridine indicating the absence of substituents at position 4; the known instability of uracil O^2-glycosides towards dilute acids leaves only N1 and N3 as the point of glycosyl linkage.[34] Methylation of 2′,3′-di-O-acetyl-5′-O-trityluridine with diazomethane gave the N-methylated derivative which could be hydrolysed to 1-methyluracil, and therefore uridine and cytidine are 3-glycosyls.[35]

The isolation of 1-methylthymine from the hydrolysis products of methylated deoxyribonucleic acid indicates, but does not prove, that thymidine is likewise a 3-glycosyl pyrimidine,[36] and the similarity in ultraviolet absorption spectra of cytidine and deoxycytidine provides evidence for the structure of the latter nucleoside. Confirmation of the structure of all these nucleosides is provided by the synthetic studies and interconversions described later. The structure of pseudouridine, a naturally occurring ribosyl pyrimidine containing a C—C glycosyl linkage, will be considered separately.

The furanose nature of the ribosyl residue in adenosine, guanosine, and uridine (and hence cytidine) was decisively demonstrated by Levene and Tipson.[37] Simultaneous methylation and deacetylation of tri-*O*-acetyladenosine gave a tri-*O*-methyl-*N*-methyladenosine that on acidic hydrolysis yielded 6-methylaminopurine and a trimethylribose, identified as 2,3,5-trimethyl-D-ribofuranose by oxidation first to trimethyl-γ-D-ribonolactone and then to *meso*-dimethoxysuccinic acid. The same oxidation products were obtained from methylated guanosine and methylated dihydrouridine. Subsequent synthesis of 2,3,5-trimethyl-D-ribofuranose gave final proof of the assigned structures.[38]

A more convenient proof of the ribofuranosyl structure of these nucleosides is provided by periodate titration.[39] A pentofuranosyl derivative consumes one molar equivalent of periodate on oxidation to the dialdehyde, as do the natural ribonucleosides; with pyranose isomers, two mols of periodate are consumed and one mol of formic acid is liberated. Periodate titration also indicated the absence of a pair of adjacent hydroxyl groups in thymidine, deoxycytidine, deoxyguanosine, and deoxyinosine (derived from deoxyadenosine by deamination), and therefore these deoxynucleosides have furanose structures,[40] in agreement with the observation that they do not increase the conductivity of a boric acid solution in the Böeseken test for *cis*-1,2-glycol systems.[41, 42] Syntheses of thymidine, deoxyuridine, and deoxyadenosine provide rigorous proof of the furanose nature of the sugar.

The configuration of the glycosyl linkage in the naturally occurring nucleosides remained unknown until 1946, when Todd and his coworkers demonstrated the identity of the dialdehyde obtained by periodate oxidation of adenosine with that resulting from similar treatment of 9-β-D-glucopyranosyladenine, the β-configuration of which was established by synthesis of the compound from α-acetobromo-D-glucose.[43]

That uridine and cytidine are likewise β(-D-) glycosyl compounds was established by comparison of the dialdehydes formed by periodate oxidation of the nucleosides with those obtained from 3-β-D-glucopyranosyluracil and 3-β-D-glucopyranosylcytosine respectively. An independent proof of the β(-D-) configuration arose from the discovery of 5'-cyclonucleosides derived from cytidine and adenosine, since, owing to steric requirements, cyclisation from the 5'-position can occur only with β(-D-) compounds.[44] The formation of 5'-cyclonucleosides from uridine and guanosine, and from thymidine, deoxycytidine, and deoxyadenosine established the configuration of these nucleosides, and it is likely that nucleic acids are built up entirely of β-D-glycosyl monomers.

X-ray analysis of a number of ribo- and deoxyribo-nucleosides and derivatives thereof fully confirmed the structural features elucidated by chemical methods. Further detail was also provided by the X-ray diffraction studies which showed that the slightly nonplanar sugar is almost perpendicular to the planar purine (or pyrimidine) ring system, the glycosyl bond lying in the same plane as the base.[45] Infrared absorption spectra, particularly of solutions of the nucleosides in deuterium oxide, have yielded information on the tautomeric structure of the bases under various conditions.[46, 47]

PSEUDOURIDINE

Apart from the variety of relatively orthodox " minor constituents " of ribonucleic acids that have been identified[9, 48-53] in recent years, a " fifth " component, present in fairly high concentration in " soluble ribonucleic acids ", has been isolated. Distinguished by being the first to be observed supplemental to the " classical " ribonucleosides, this component was additionally uncommon in that both the nucleoside and the nucleotide from which it was derived resisted the conventional methods for the determination of structure. The nucleotide, liberated from yeast ribonucleic acid by treatment with ribonuclease (or by alkaline hydrolysis, as a mixture of the -2' and -3' phosphates), could be converted into a -2',3' cyclic phosphate that was susceptible to the action of ribonuclease. On the basis of ribonuclease specificity, this suggested a pyrimidine derivative, and indeed the free nucleoside was found to have an elementary composition identical with that of uridine. However, ultraviolet absorption spectra were closely similar to those of 5-hydroxymethyluracil rather than of a 3-glycosyluracil. Hydrazinolysis suggested the presence of ribose, and periodate oxidation of the nucleoside indicated a furanose structure. Nevertheless, hydrogenation or bromination followed by treatment with acid or alkali did not liberate a sugar, while the free base could not be obtained by vigorous acidic hydrolysis, by oxidation, or by alkaline or acidic hydrolysis of the dialdehyde produced by periodate oxidation of the nucleoside. Treatment of this dialdehyde with bromine, however, gave uracil and 5-bromouracil. Methylation studies eliminated positions 1, 2, 3 and 6 of the pyrimidine ring for the glycosyl bond.[54-57] A C5 rather than a C4 linkage was indicated by sodium borohydride reduction of the previously mentioned dialdehyde to a product which was periodate-oxidised to an aldehydrouracil; this on reduction gave 5-hydroxymethyluracil.[54, 55] Conclusive proof of the structure of pseudouridine as 5-ribofuranosyluracil was provided by nuclear magnetic resonance spectra which indicated the presence of a C4 proton and absence of a C5 proton. In addition, changes in the character of protons at C4 and C1′ consonant with a C5—C1′ linkage, compared with the N3—C1′ bond in uridine, were observed.[54, 55] In accord with this structure, methylation of the free nucleoside with diazomethane readily gave a dimethyl (i.e. N^1 and N^3) pseudouridine. Under the same conditions only one methyl group is introduced into uridine to give N^1-methyluridine.[54, 55] The effects of ultraviolet irradiation on aqueous solutions of pseudouridine resemble those obtained with thymine rather than uridine, in that photolysis (which presumably involves addition of water across the 4,5 double bond) is irreversible.[58]

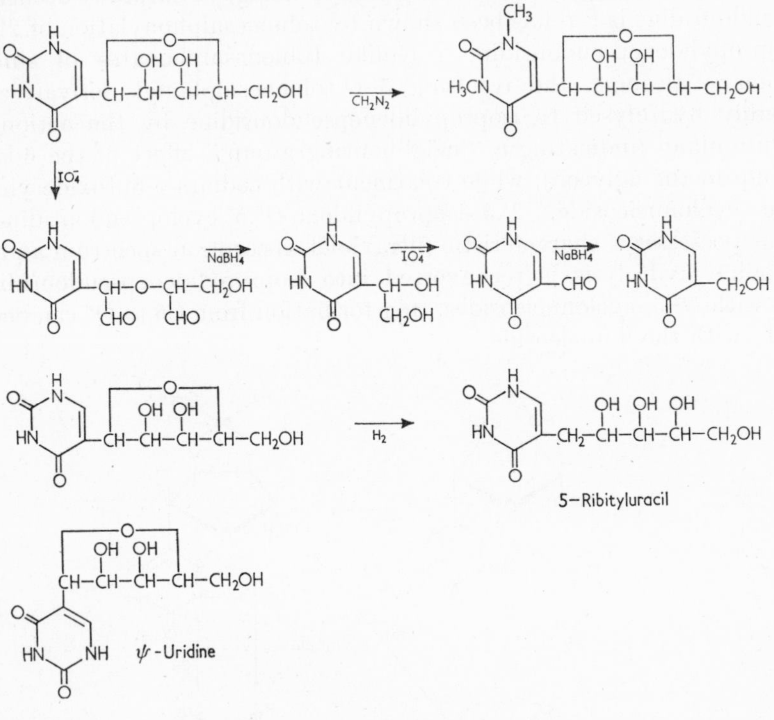

5−Ribityluracil

ψ -Uridine

Isomeric nucleosides are formed by the action of alkali on pseudouridine. Acidic treatment of pseudouridylic acid gives rise to a rather large number of isomers as may be expected from α and β mutarotation, furanose, pyranose, and acyclic interconversions, and phosphate migration.[55]

Whereas pseudouridine gives an orcinol test characteristic of neuraminic acids, the dihydronucleoside, formed without loss of ultraviolet absorption, does not. Dihydropseudouridine is therefore 5-ribityluracil, and reduction is by hydrogenolysis rather than by saturation of the 4,5 double bond (c.f. hydrogenolysis of allyl and benzyl ethers and of 5-hydroxymethyluracil).[54]

Pseudouridine C (the naturally occurring nucleoside) has been synthesised by reaction between 2,6-dimethoxypyrimidine-5-lithium (obtained by treating 2,6-dimethoxy-5-bromopyrimidine with n-butyl-lithium) and 2,3,5-tri-O-benzoyl-D-ribofuranosyl chloride, followed by removal of protecting groups from the product and then separation of the four possible isomers (α and β, furanose and pyranose).[59] Despite the extremely low yield, this synthesis does confirm the 5-D-ribofuranosyl structure assigned to the nucleoside.

That the configuration of the glycosyl linkage in naturally occurring pseudouridine is β-D has been shown by toluenesulphonylation of 2',3'-isopropylidenepseudouridine. Unlike toluenesulphonates of simple primary alcohols, the resulting 5'-O-toluenesulphonyl derivative is readily hydrolysed to isopropylidenepseudouridine by the action of dilute alkali (indicating a " neighbouring group " effect of the 6-keto group in the aglycon), while treatment with sodium t-butoxide yields the cyclonucleoside, 2',3'-isopropylidene-O^6,5'-cyclopseudouridine.[60] This possesses a characteristic ultraviolet absorption spectrum and on alkaline hydrolysis is reconverted into isopropylidenepseudouridine. As with O^2,5'-cyclonucleosides, ring formation from C5 to O^6 can occur only with the β-nucleoside.

CYCLONUCLEOSIDES*

The conversion of certain nucleoside esters into cyclonucleoside derivatives was first observed in 1951, when 5'-O-toluene-p-sulphonyl-2',3'-O-isopropylideneadenosine was found to isomerise readily to an ionic tosylate, particularly on heating solutions of the covalent compound.[44] Ultraviolet absorption spectra and a cryoscopic determination of molecular weight indicated intramolecular alkylation of the adenine moiety. X-Ray crystallographic examination of the corresponding iodide fully established that a new ring was formed and that the ionic

* The original *cyclo* terminology is considered preferable to the *anhydro* convention promulgated by Fox and Wempen [*Advances in Carbohydrate Chemistry* 14, 283 (1959)]. "Anhydro" possesses several connotations in carbohydrate chemistry, but is seldom applied to amino derivatives or to alkyl (aryl) ethers. On the other hand, "cyclo" is used in the appropriate sense, as in cyclodextrins.

tosylate was $2',3'-O$-isopropylidene-$N^3,5'$-cycloadenosine tosylate.[44] The unprotected cyclonucleoside has been prepared via $5'-O$-toluene-p-sulphonyladenosine.[61]   Similarly, warming a solution of covalent $5'-O$-'toluene-p-sulphonyl-$2',3'-O$-isopropylidenecytidine gave the ionic $2',3'-O$-isopropylidene-$O^2,5'$-cyclocytidine tosylate as indicated by changed ultraviolet absorption spectra and by acidic hydrolysis of the compound to cytidine.[44]

Cyclonucleosides were likewise obtained from $3'-O$-acetyl-$5'-O$-toluene-p-sulphonyl-$2'$-deoxyadenosine and from $5'-O$-toluene-p-sul-phonyl-$2'$-deoxycytidine.[62]   As with the ribonucleosides, cyclisation established the β configuration of the glycosyl linkage on stereochemical grounds. Confirmation of the β-glycosyl nature of the aminonucleoside moiety of puromycin was also obtained by analogous formation of a cyclonucleoside salt from the $5'-O$-methanesulphonate.[63]   Intra-molecular alkylation in these cases is presumably facilitated to some extent by the basic character of the purine or pyrimidine ring; nucleo-philic attack at C5$'$ will also depend on the strength of the acid with which the sugar hydroxyl group is esterified. Thus the $5'-O$-toluene-p-sulphonates of inosine, uridine, and thymidine are somewhat resistant to cyclisation, and $N^6,3'-O$-di-acetyl-$5'$-toluene-p-sulphonyl-$2'$-deoxy-cytidine is markedly more stable than the deacetylated product. The action of heat on $2',3'-O$-isopropylideneguanosine-$5'$di-(p-nitrophenyl)-phosphate, or treatment with sodium benzoxide in benzyl alcohol, readily effects intramolecular alkylation to yield a cycloguanosine derivative;[64] $O^2,2'$-cyclouridine and $O^2,2'$-cyclocytidine phosphates have been obtained by treating the nucleoside with polyphosphoric acid.[65]

Methods for the preparation of cyclo derivatives of the less basic nucleosides were first developed when it was found that treatment of $5'$-iodo-$5'$-deoxythymidine with silver acetate (in the presence of a base) gave the corresponding $O^2,5'$-cyclothymidine, as shown by the general physical properties of the product.[66] Alkaline hydrolysis gave thymidine, but acidic hydrolysis cleaved the glycosyl bond as well as the $O^2,5'$ ether linkage, to yield thymine. The instability of the N3—C1$'$ linkage, previously noted with $O^2,5'$-cyclo-$2'$-deoxycytidine which in contrast with the ribose derivative is so unstable as to preclude isolation, is possibly due to the presence of a CH_2 group β to a positively charged nitrogen atom. Similar treatment of $3'$-iodo-$3'$-deoxythymidine with silver acetate caused cyclisation with inversion to yield $O^2,3'$-cyclo-thymidine. This was readily converted by alkaline hydrolysis into 3-β-D-$2'$-deoxyxylofuranosylthymine or, by treatment with acid, into a mixture of thymine and the sugar residue. Molecular models indicated that the ease of formation of these cyclonucleosides should be in the

R = CH₃SO₂

order $O^2,3' > O^2,5'$ and that in the ribose series an $O^2,2'$ cyclisation should be even more facile. This proved to be the case, and to some extent the same order is reflected in the relative stabilities of the compounds to ring opening.[66] Although 5'-O-sulphonyl derivatives of thymidine are resistant to the action of weak bases, the 3'esters are readily converted into the cyclonucleoside. Thus treatment of 3',5'-di-O-methanesulphonylthymidine with alcoholic ammonia gives 5'-O-methanesulphonyl-$O^2,3'$-cyclothymidine.[66]

Later work showed that 5'-iodo-5'deoxyuridine derivatives were also readily cyclised by the action of silver acetate, although neither 5'-O-toluene-p-sulphonyluridine nor 5'-iodo-5'deoxyuridine gave cyclo compounds when heated, or treated with certain bases.[67]

In contrast with the rapid conversion of 3'-O-methanesulphonyl-thymidine derivatives into $O^2,3'$-cyclonucleosides by the action of alcoholic ammonia, 3'-O-toluene-p-sulphonyluridine was unaffected by this reagent. However, similar treatment of 3',5'-di-O-acetyl-2'-O-toluene-p-sulphonyluridine gave $O^2,2'$-cyclouridine.[68] Related $O^2,2'$-cyclonucleosides have been obtained from 2'-O-methanesulphonyl esters of 3-β-D-ribofuranosylthymine[69] and 3-β-D-xylofuranosyl-thymine.[70] Cyclisation of 5'-O-trityl-2'-O-methanesulphonyl-5-methyl-2-thiouridine to give an $S^2,2'$-cyclo derivative occurred extremely readily,[71] as might be expected, since the thiocarbonyl function would be even more effective than the carbonyl group in nucleophilic attack at C2' with expulsion of a methanesulphonate ion. A general and convenient method for the preparation of $O^2,2'$-cyclonucleosides from ribosyl pyrimidines lies in direct sulphonylation of the 5'-O-trityl (or acetyl) nucleoside followed by treatment of the crude product with alcoholic ammonia, the intermediate material being mainly the 2'-O-sulphonyl derivative, though small amounts of the 3'-isomer can also be formed.

The 5'-O-sulphonyl derivatives of both thymidine and uridine are readily converted into $O^2,5'$-cyclonucleosides by the action of sodium t-butoxide, displacement of the sulphonyloxy group by nucleophilic attack of the aglycon 2-carbonyl group at C5' being aided by removal of a proton from the pyrimidine base.[72] Cyclisations of 3'-O-toluene-p-sulphonyluridine to $O^2,3'$-cyclouridine[72] and 5'-O-toluene-p-sulphonyl-2',3'-isopropylidenepseudouridine to 2',3'-isopropylidene-$O^6,5'$-cyclo-pseudouridine[60] are likewise effected by this reagent. Sodium benzoate in dimethylformamide converts 2',5'-di-O-trityl-3'-O-methanesulphonyl-uridine (but not the detritylated compound) into the corresponding $O^2,3'$-cyclonucleoside.[73]

The reactivity of cyclonucleosides has been demonstrated in a number of ways. Treatment of a 6-dimethylaminopurine cyclo-

R = H or CH$_3$ Tr = triphenylmethyl

R′ = CH$_3$SO$_2$ or CH$_3$—⟨⟩—SO$_2$

Ts = toluene-p-sulphonyl
t-BuONa = sodium t-butoxide

nucleoside with dilute alkali caused rapid cleavage of the pyrimidine ring to give $5',N^4$-cyclo-3-(2',3'-carbonyl-3'-amino-3'-deoxy-β-D-ribofuranosyl) -4-formamidoimidazole-5- (N,N-dimethyl)-carboxamidine methanesulphonate which on further treatment with alkali yielded $5',N^4$-cyclo-3-(2',3'-carbonyl-3'-amino-3'-deoxy-β-D-ribofuranosyl)-4-aminoimidazole-5-carboxamide.[63] Similarly, elimination of C2 from 2',3'-isopropylidene-N^3,5'-cycloadenosine toluene-p-sulphonate by reaction with base gave the imidazole derivative.[74]

Pyrimidine cyclonucleosides have been of considerable value for the synthesis, by inversion at C2', of *cis*-C1—C2 glycosyl derivatives (not generally obtained by reaction of the halogenose with a suitable pyrimidine derivative) as well as for conversion into 2'-deoxynucleosides. The reactions of cyclouridines with a variety of reagents have been examined in detail; in general the O^2,5'-cyclo compounds are considerably more reactive than the O^2,2'-isomers. Base-catalysed methanolysis (or ethanolysis) of 2',3'-O-isopropylidene-O^2,5'-cyclouridine gave 2',3'-O-isopropylidene-O^2-methyl-(or ethyl)-uridine which on

2',3'-O-Isopropylidene-
pseudocytidine

further treatment with alcoholic ammonia yielded 2',3'-isopropylidene-isocytidine, readily converted into isocytidine, the structure of which was confirmed by deamination of the nucleoside to uridine.[67] Similarly, treatment of 2',3'-O-isopropylidene-O^6,5'-cyclopseudouridine with methanolic ammonia yielded 2',3'-O-isopropylidenepseudocytidine.[60] The reaction has been further extended to the synthesis of isopropylidene-N-butylisocytidine and isopropylidene-N,N-diethylisocytidine by direct action of the relevant amines on 2',3'-O-isopropylidene-O^2,5'-cyclo-uridine.[75]

Similar treatment of O^2,2'-cyclouridine with methanolic ammonia yielded 3-β-D-arabinofuranosylisocytosine,[76] analogous to the formation of 3-β-D-arabinofuranosyluracil by hydrolysis with dilute acid.[68]

In addition to ring opening by nucleophilic attack at C2 of the pyrimidine, alkyl-oxygen fission can be effected by nucleophilic displacement at a sugar carbon atom. Whereas treatment of 2',3'-O-isopropylidene-O^2,5'-cyclouridine with hydrogen sulphide and triethylamine yielded the 2-thiouridine derivative and related polysulphides, reaction with the more powerful nucleophilic reagent sodium ethyl sulphide gave 5'-deoxy-5'-ethylthio-2',3'-isopropylideneuridine.[76]

However, application of the same reaction to O^2,2'-cyclouridine yielded 3'-deoxy-3'-ethylthio-uridine (presumably via a 2',3'-anhydro-uridine anion) since treatment of the acetylated product with Raney nickel followed by deacetylation gave 3'-deoxyuridine.[76]

Nucleophilic attack at C2′ in $O^2,2′$-cyclouridine by halides is described in connection with the synthesis of 2′-deoxynucleosides. (See also p. 68 for other reactions of cyclonucleosides.)

PROPERTIES

The chemical and physical properties of nucleosides reflect those of the bases and sugars involved. As glycosyl derivatives they are optically active, the value being dependent on pH. However, apart from the sugar dissociation (pK ~ 12 to 13), the nature of the base (and of its dissociation constants) also has a significant influence on the optical activity and presumably all pKs could be estimated from a knowledge of the variation of rotation with pH.

Acylation of the sugar moiety occurs readily; in the deoxyribose series a pronounced selectivity is shown for the 5′-hydroxyl group on partial acylation.[77] With ribose derivatives, partial acetylation of the 5′-O-acetylnucleoside gives the 3′,5′-di-O-acetyl compound rather than the 2′,5′-diacetate,[78] either through marked specificity of reaction or, more probably, as a result of rapid and easy acetyl migration. Whereas partial deacetylation of acetylated deoxynucleosides gives rise to both 5′-O-acetyl and 3′-O-acetyl compounds,[79] the same procedure applied to 2′,3′,5′-tri-O-acetyladenosine gives 5′-O-acetyladenosine as the major, if not only, monoacetyl derivative,[80] and no 2′(or 3′),5′-di-O-acetyladenosine is formed, indicating that a 2′ or 3′ acyl group is markedly less stable when adjacent to a free cis-hydroxyl group. Transacetylation occurs when 5′-O-acetyladenosine is treated with 2′,3′,5′-tri-O-acetyladenosine, the 3′,5′-di-O-acetyl compound being obtained.[80] Amino-acylation of nucleosides and nucleotides has been achieved in rather low yield by treatment with thiophenyl esters of the amino acids in di-methyl sulphoxide at 120°.[81-83] Milder approaches generally involve prior formation of a protected aminoacyl anhydride such as the ethyl carbonate derivative (from the carbobenzyloxyamino acid and ethyl chloroformate)[75] or *in situ* formation of an anhydride by means of dicyclohexylcarbodi-imide or N,N'-carbonyl di-imidazole.[84]

Although O-trimethylsilyl derivatives of pentoses and hexoses have been described, no reports of the action of trimethylsilyl chloride on nucleosides have appeared. Since the trimethylsilyl group is readily removed by hydrolysis in water (at neutral pH) it could offer possible advantages over other protecting agents.

The nucleosides generally form 5'-O-trityl derivatives by treatment with triphenylmethyl chloride, though this reagent, while preferential, is not entirely specific for the primary hydroxyl group.[85-88] Indeed, uridine forms a ditrityl derivative,[89] the structure of which has been shown to be 2',5'-di-O-trityluridine.[73] Some 3',5'-di-O-trityluridine is also formed.

Ribonucleosides react with benzaldehyde to give 2',3'-O-benzylidene derivatives (either of the diastereoisomers resulting from introduction of the asymmetric benzylidene carbon atom can be obtained by the use of appropriate reaction temperatures),[90, 91] and with acetone to give 2',3'-O-isopropylidene nucleosides. The latter are readily prepared by treatment of the ribonucleoside with di-p-nitrophenyl phosphate and 2,2-dimethoxypropane in acetone,[92] or simply by acid-catalysed con-densation with acetone.[73, 87, 93-96] Yields by the first method (the dimethoxypropane maintains anhydrous conditions) are virtually quantitative for a wide range of nucleosides and analogues.[92]

Generally, all hydroxyl groups can be toluene-(or methane)-sul-phonylated under suitable conditions.[87] Selective sulphonylation at the 2'- rather than the 3'-hydroxyl group (a reflection of relative nucleo-philic character) has been mentioned previously.* The influence of the base on the reactivity of sugar hydroxyl groups towards certain re-agents is demonstrated by the guanine nucleosides; despite repeated attempts to prepare sulphonyl derivatives, they have not been described as yet. (Another example lies in the much greater ease of phosphoryla-tion of 2',3'-O-isopropylidene adenosine compared with the 6-dimethyl-

---

* Reports in the literature describing selective phosphorylation of the 3'-hydroxyl group in 5'-protected ribonucleosides are not necessarily correct in view of later develop-ments in the chemistry of nucleotides. Indeed, it is likely that preferential phosphoryla-tion of the 2'-hydroxyl group would occur, at least with mild reagents, under conditions precluding cyclic phosphate formation and phosphate migration. Compare tritylation and tosylation (migration unlikely) with acetylation (transfer and migration to give a more stable ester established in numerous cases). The 2'-hydroxyl group in ribonucleo-sides is known to be more " acidic " than that at the 3'-position

aminopurine[97] or guanine[94] analogues using a mild reagent such as dibenzyl phosphorochloridate.) Whereas the 5'-O-alkane (or arane)-sulphonyl derivatives of the more basic nucleosides form cyclonucleoside salts on treatment with sodium iodide[98] or lithium bromide, a 5'-sulphonyloxy group in uridine, thymidine, or inosine is replaced by halogen. This reaction, normally indicative of esterification of a primary hydroxyl group, has no such value when applied to nucleosides since both 2'-iodo-2'-deoxyuridine and 3'-iodo (or bromo)-3'-deoxythymidine have been prepared by this procedure, presumably via cyclonucleoside intermediates. Catalytic reduction of the halogenodeoxy nucleosides gives the corresponding deoxy compounds. In addition to the synthesis of naturally occurring 2'-deoxynucleosides this procedure has been

T = Thymine   Tr = Triphenylmethyl

Ms = CH$_3$SO$_2$ Ts = CH$_3$C$_6$H$_4$SO$_2$

used to prepare 5'-deoxyuridine,[75, 99] 3'-deoxythymidine, 5'-deoxy-thymidine, and 3-β-D-2',3',5'-trideoxyribofuranosylthymine (3',5'-di-deoxythymidine),[66] the last by stepwise catalytic reductive dehalogena-tion of 3',5'-dibromo-3',5'-dideoxythymidine.

The stability of the glycosyl linkage towards hydrolysis by acid varies widely and is dependent on both the nature of the base (and its substituents) and on the nature of the sugar (and its substituents). Thus the deoxynucleosides are less stable than the ribonucleosides, while within each class stability is in the order uracil (or thymine) > cytosine > adenine > guanine nucleoside. Acylation of the heterocyclic base can have a marked effect on the rate of acidic cleavage of the glycosyl linkage,[100, 101] notwithstanding implications to the contrary.[102] Esterification of sugar hydroxyl groups also affects the stability of the glycosyl bond as shown by the behaviour of O-acetyl-2'-deoxyguano-sines,[79] thymidine phosphates,[103] and 2'-O-toluene-p-sulphonyl adeno-sine,[78] and by the remarkable stability of 2',3',5'-tri-O-(3,5-dinitro-benzoyl)-uridine.[99] Acidic hydrolysis of nucleosides probably involves three major factors,[104, 105] though others may well be significant. For hydrolysis to occur at an appreciable rate the proton must become attached to the ring oxygen of the glycosyl moiety. When addition of the first proton is to a nitrogen atom of the base, hydrolysis occurs if ready transfer of this proton to the ring oxygen of the sugar is possible. If this transfer cannot take place hydrolysis still occurs if the charge is so widely distributed that a second proton can be added. The ease of transfer of a proton from the base to the ring oxygen is particularly important. Thus N3 of the purine ring, an amino substituent at C2 of the pyrimidine ring and an amino substituent at C5 of the imidazole ring can all lie close to this oxygen, hence facilitating the transfer. In accord with this concept, the purine nucleosides and 5-amino-1-β-D-ribofuranosylimidazoles are readily hydrolysed, and isocytidine is hydrolysed much more rapidly than cytidine. The stability of the " natural " pyrimidine nucleosides may be attributed to the poor capacity of the C2 carbonyl oxygen for protonation. Minor differences among related purine nucleosides may be a result of variation in the charge location and tautomeric forms of the protonated bases. A kinetic study of the hydrolysis of α and β-anomers of the nucleosides would be of interest.

In general, nucleosides are very resistant to alkaline hydrolysis. However, a number of exceptions to this are known where the glycosyl bond is readily broken without degradation of the purine or pyrimidine. (In other cases, described later, cleavage of the pyrimidine or imidazole ring system occurs.) Thus both adenosine-3',5' cyclic phosphate and 2',3'-anhydro-9-β-D-lyxofuranosyladenine are hydrolysed to the free base by aqueous sodium hydroxide, possibly because of a strained conformation induced in the sugar. Sulphonium ribonucleosides, for example, S-(5'-deoxyadenosine-5')-dimethylsulphonium iodide and the corresponding uridine and inosine derivatives, decompose in cold dilute alkali to give the free base and a sulphonium sugar. Both lyxose and ribose derivatives are formed[234] owing to intermediate formation of a 4,5 double bond and consequent loss of asymmetry at C4. Liberation of adenine from vitamin B_{12} coenzyme in weakly alkaline potassium cyanide solution probably occurs by a similar mechanism.[213] (See also the base catalysed hydrolysis of psicofuranine.)[190]

Except for the rather special case of pseudouridine (glycosyl linkage to an " ethylenic " carbon atom) no convincing evidence of anomerisation in a naturally occurring nucleoside (N-glycosyl) has been observed.

Halogenation of the pyrimidine nucleosides occurs readily at C5. A photocatalytic process with the halogen in pyridine-acetic acid has been used for the preparation of 5-chloro and 5-bromo analogues of uracil and cytosine nucleosides (both ribo- and 2'-deoxyribo-).[106, 107] Treatment of uridine and 2'-deoxyuridine with iodine gives the corresponding 5-iodo derivatives.[108] Direct chlorination in acetic acid is effective; bromination and iodination are best achieved by action of the halogen on the nucleoside in aqueous dioxan containing a small amount of nitric acid.[109] The 5-fluoro analogues have been synthesised via 5-fluouracil. Subsequent conversions of the halogenonucleosides are possible, though reactivity is low. Treatment of 5-bromonucleosides with liquid ammonia yields the 5-amino compounds; the halogen can also be replaced by hydroxyl. Further reaction of 5-aminouridine with nitrous acid gives diazouridine.[110, 111] Conversion of 5-bromouridine into 5-morpholinouridine (by treatment with morpholine) has also been reported.[112]

Additional evidence that position 5 is particularly susceptible to electrophilic substitution lies in nitration of 2',3',5'-tri-O-(3,5'-dinitrobenzoyl)-uridine to the 5-nitro derivative, from which 5-nitrouridine is obtained by de-acylation. Reduction of the nitro compound gives 5-aminouridine. Under the same nitration conditions, uridine is oxidised to 5-nitrouracil-3-β-D-ribonic acid.[99, 113] (See also the action of formaldehyde on uracil nucleosides, p. 83.)

Addition to the 4,5 double bond in pyrimidine nucleosides can occur in a number of ways. Reduction has been mentioned previously as a means of decreasing the stability of the glycosyl linkage, platinum or palladium catalysts being used by the earlier workers. More effective hydrogenation under mild conditions is possible if a rhodium catalyst is employed,[114] and a number of nucleosides (and nucleotides) including thymidine, deoxycytidine, cytidine, 5-hydroxymethyl-2'-deoxyuridine, and 5-hydroxymethyl-2′-deoxycytidine have been reduced in this way to the corresponding 4,5-dihydro compounds. The 6-amino group in dihydrocytosine derivatives is very unstable, and indeed dihydrouridylic acid was obtained on catalytic hydrogenation of either uridylic or cytidylic acid, while similar reduction of 2′deoxycytidine-5′ phosphate gave 4,5-dihydro-2′-deoxyuridylic acid.[114, 115] Mild alkaline treatment of dihydrouridylic acid gave the N-ribosyl phosphate of β-ureidopropionic acid.[114]

The course of hydrogenation of 5-hydroxymethyl derivatives is markedly dependent on the pH of the solvent when a rhodium–alumina catalyst is used. Hydrogenation in water gives a 4,5-dihydro-5-hydroxymethyl pyrimidine which is then resistant to further reduction, but in 50% acetic acid the hydroxymethyl residue is selectively

$R' = H$ or CH_3

reduced (hydrogenolysed) to a methyl group. The double bond can then be hydrogenated after a change of solvent.[116, 117]

Saturation of the 4,5 double bond by the action of bromine water gives a 5,5-dibromo-4-hydroxy-dihydro compound which on treatment with alkali yields glycosyl derivatives (probably acyclic) from which the sugar is readily liberated by acidic hydrolysis.[118, 119] In contrast, regeneration of the ultraviolet light-absorbing system with formation of a 5-bromonucleoside occurs when the dibromo-hydroxy derivative is treated with acids.[120, 121]

Other examples of addition to the 4,5 double bond include the behaviour of 2',3'-O-isopropylidene-5'-thiouridine in acid and in alkali,[122] and the reversible photolysis of pyrimidine nucleosides with ultraviolet irradiation. Addition of water across the double bond occurs in the latter case;[123, 124] the primary process probably involves polarisation to an ionic intermediate.[125] A similar mechanism gives rise to hydroperoxides on irradiation by X-rays in the presence of oxygen.[126–128]

Cleavage of the pyrimidine ring in nucleosides can be accomplished by various means. Treatment of uridine with hydrazine hydrate gives pyrazolone and ribosylurea;[129] the instability of the ring system in 4,5-dihydronucleosides towards alkali has been mentioned previously.

Methylation of thymidine and uridine with diazomethane yields the respective N^1-methyl nucleosides;[130] prolonged treatment of uridine with diazomethane gives the dimethyl derivative, $N^1,2'$-O-dimethyluridine,[75, 131] in accord with the greater acidity of the 2'-hydroxyl group relative to those at C3' and C5'. Methylation of cytidine (with dimethyl sulphate in dimethylformamide) likewise yields N^1-methylcytidine.

Acetylation of the 6-amino function in cytidine and deoxycytidine occurs readily;[100] a number of N^6-aminoacyl and peptide derivatives of 3-β-D-glucopyranosylcytosine and cytidine have also been prepared.[132–134] Removal of the carbobenzyloxy protecting group from these derivatives decreases the stability of the cytosine-N^6 amide bond which is then rapidly cleaved by alkali. Similar compounds were obtained from N^6- and N^2- aminoacylation of adenosine and 9-β-D-glucopyranosylguanine respectively.[135] Aminopurines react with organic isocyanates to give ureidopurine derivatives. The corresponding nucleosides behave similarly but apparently reaction with sugar hydroxyl groups also occurs. Thus 2′,3′-O-isopropylideneadenosine and ethyl isocyanatoacetate readily formed the diester shown, from which the free dicarboxylic acid was obtained by successive hydrolyses with dilute acetic acid (to remove the isopropylidene residue) and alkali.[136]

While most nucleosides are relatively stable to alkali, certain purine nucleosides undergo rupture of the imidazole ring, analogous to the degradation of 9-methylpurine to 5-amino-4-methylaminopyrimidine (purine itself is stable). Thus 9-β-D-ribofuranosylpurine (nebularine) is rapidly broken down in dilute alkali to 4,5-diaminopyrimidine and ribosyl derivatives thereof; similar degradation of 6-methylnebularine gives ribosyl derivatives of 4-amino-5-formamido-6-methylpyrimidine initially, with subsequent deformylation. Stabilisation of the formylated intermediate is also evident with nebularine-5′ phosphate.[137, 138]

Since instability towards alkali is also shown by 9-glycosyl derivatives of 6-chloro- and 6-methylmercapto-purine, but not by the 6-dimethylamino-, 6-methylamino-, 6-amino- or 6-hydroxy-compounds, it is likely that the initial degradative step is nucleophilic attack by hydroxide ion at C8, the electron density at this carbon being dependent on substituents in the pyrimidine ring.[139] A similar cleavage of the imidazole ring has been observed on alkaline treatment of the methiodides of 1-methylbenzimidazole and 1,2-dimethylbenzimidazole,[140] and 7,9-di-(2-hydroxyethyl) guanine.[141]

Irradiation of guanosine with 15 MeV electrons opens the imidazole ring and 2-amino-4-ribosylamino-5-formamido-6-hydroxypyrimidine is formed.[142] A similar ring-opening occurs when an aqueous solution of xanthosine is irradiated; the products include xanthine, 2,6-dihydroxy-4-amino-5-formamidopyrimidine and its ribosyl.[143]

An alternate degradation of purine nucleosides involves ring opening of the pyrimidine section of the purine base. This can occur readily if the nucleoside is " oxygenated " or alkylated at N1 (e.g. the conversion of 1-benzylinosine to a ribosylimidazole derivative)[144] or alkylated at N3 (e.g. cyclonucleoside degradation). Presumably most, if not all, of these degradations involve initial nucleophilic attack by hydroxide ion at C2 to give an intermediate formyl derivative coincident with ring cleavage. Again, substituents at N1 or N3 are likely to influence the ease of attack at C2 and cleavage of the C2—N1 bond, particularly when the ring carries a positive charge as in cycloadenosine compounds.

Similarly, alkaline hydrolysis of N^1-toluene-p-sulphonylinosine gives 1-ribosyl-5-aminoimidazole-4-(N-tosyl)-carboxamide.[145] Migration of the methyl group from N1 to the extranuclear amino group occurs on alkaline treatment of 1-methyladenylic acid,[146] presumably by ring opening and reclosure. However, acidic hydrolysis of the methylation products from adenosine (using dimethyl sulphate) gives a mixture of 1- and 3-methyladenine, 1,3-dimethyladenine and 5-aminoimidazole-4-(N-methyl)-carboxamidine, the last arising from acidic degradation of 1-methyladenine.

It may be noted[146] that whereas adenine nucleosides and nucleotides are alkylated on the pyrimidine segment, alkylation of the imidazole moiety (N^7) occurs with the corresponding guanine derivatives[141, 147–149] in accord with theoretical estimates of the relative reactivity of the ring nitrogen atoms of the two purines.[150] Alkylation of guanosine with difunctional reagents also gives di(guanin-7-yl) derivatives.[141] Treatment of adenosine with ethylene oxide in aqueous media gives N^1(2-hydroxyethyl)-adenosine which on warming in dilute alkali is converted into 6-(2-hydroxyethylamino)-9-β-D-ribofuranosylpurine.[151] Similar N^1 hydroxyethylation occurs with adenosine-5′ triphosphate (as well as monoesterification of the γ phosphate group) and coenzyme I (nicotinamide adenine dinucleotide, NAD).

Oxidation of adenine, adenosine, and the adenylic acids with hydrogen peroxide gives the respective N-oxides, shown by degradation studies to be 1-N-oxides.[152, 153] Deoxyadenosine-1-N-oxide and the 5′ phosphate have also been prepared.[154] Acidic hydrolysis of adenosine-1-N-oxide yields adenine-1-N-oxide which on further hydrolysis gives 5-aminoimidazole-4-carboxamidoxime, ring opening by loss of C2

occurring much more readily than with adenine itself. Alkaline hydrolysis of adenosine-1-N-oxide and adenylic acid 1-N-oxide gives the
1-ribosyl and 1-phosphoribosyl derivatives of 5-aminoimidazole-4-
carboxamidoxime respectively.[152, 153]   Further treatment of 1-β-D-
ribofuranosyl 5-aminoimidazole-4-carboxamidoxime with nitrous acid
yields 2-aza-adenosine 1-N-oxide.[155]

Bromination of guanosine with dioxan bromide gives 8-bromo-
guanosine.[75] The guanine nucleotides are somewhat more resistant, but
likewise yield the 8-bromo derivatives.

As previously mentioned, periodate oxidation of the ribonucleosides
(and derivatives containing free 2' and 3' hydroxyl groups) gives dialdehyde products. These form bisphenylhydrazones which react
further with hydrazine to give the free heterocyclic base.[156] The
glycosyl C—N linkage in the dialdehydo compounds is considerably
less stable than in the parent nucleosides and the heterocyclic moiety is
liberated under mild hydrolytic conditions, particularly in the presence
of primary amines. Both aldehydo groups are reduced to the alcohol
by alkaline sodium borohydride. In contrast with the acyclic trihydroxy
ether from uridine, the cytosine derivative is resistant to vigorous
acidic hydrolysis; the purine compounds are readily hydrolysed by
dilute acids to give the free base, glycolaldehyde and glycerol, cleavage
of the ether linkage occurring after fission of the C—N bond.[156]

Selective reduction of a single aldehydo group of periodate oxidised
nucleosides can be achieved by treatment with sodium borohydride in
dilute acid, only the aldehydo group distal to the purine or pyrimidine
ring being converted into the alcohol. Further treatment with phenyl-

hydrazine gives quantitative yields of the purine or pyrimidine base, the phenylosazone of glyoxal and free glycerol.[156]

Catalytic (platinum) oxidation of ribo- and deoxyribonucleosides at pH 9 gives the corresponding 5'-carboxylic acids, adenosine and guanosine being oxidised somewhat more slowly than uridine and thymidine. Thymidine-3' phosphate is oxidised in the same way in acidic solution and the results indicate a possible procedure for the stepwise degradation of polydeoxynucleotides by simple or decarboxylative elimination of phosphate.[157] The procedure has been improved by use of a deactivated catalyst (to prevent irreversible adsorption of oligmer) and hydrogen peroxide (instead of oxygen).[158] In this way thymidylyl-3' : 5'-thymidine was oxidised to the 5'-uronic acid. This was somewhat resistant to alkaline hydrolysis, but after conversion of the carboxylate into an alkali-labile propylamide, almost quantitative (overall) degradation to thymidine-5' phosphate was achieved. Other products were thymine, N-propylfuramide and some anhydrothymidine uronic acid.

Oxidation of ribo- and deoxyribo-nucleosides to 5'-carboxylic acids has also been achieved by the use of chromium trioxide–pyridine

at room temperature. The 3′-hydroxyl group is quite stable since
5′-O-tritylthymidine is unaffected. Treatment of the cetrimide (Cetav-
lon) salt of deoxynucleic acid with the reagent caused no spectroscopic
changes in the recovered DNA, indicating that the heterocyclic bases
are not oxidised under the conditions employed.[159]

The purine or pyrimidine component of nucleosides is responsible
for the ultraviolet absorption of these compounds. The nature of this
absorption is dependent on the substituents in the base and the pH of
the solution, since ionisation of the base or its substituents alters the
resonance possibilities in addition to effecting tautomeric changes.
Apparent pKs (including that of the sugar) can be determined readily by
spectrophotometric methods as well as by titration.[160] Since the tautomeric form is controlled by the environmental conditions and each form
is itself a hybrid of many resonance structures, representation by the
normal methods is to some extent misleading. The physical properties of
nucleosides suggest that the contribution of zwitterionic structures is
considerable, particularly in cyclonucleosides such as $O^2,5′$-cyclo-
thymidine. This compound may be more correctly represented as
(I) rather than (II) in view of the solubility properties, much higher
decomposition point (rather than a melting point) than thymidine, and
paper chromatographic and electrophoretic behaviour.

I   II

A further point in the fine structure of nucleosides is the interaction between unionised sugar hydroxyl groups and the aglycon. In the pyrimidine nucleosides, hydrogen bonding between the 2-carbonyl group of the pyrimidine and the sugar hydroxyl groups has been observed spectroscopically[161, 162] and photochemically.[163] In guanosine the lowered pK of the 2-amino group and the decreased rate of reaction with formaldehyde, relative to 2'-deoxyguanosine, suggest that the 2'-hydroxyl group of the sugar is hydrogen bonded to the extranuclear 2-amino group.[164] Such interaction may be evident in a chemical sense in terms of the diverse reactivity of sugar hydroxyl groups in different nucleosides.

Infrared absorption spectra of nucleosides and nucleotides in deuterim oxide indicate that in neutral aqueous solution thymidine and uridine probably exist in the diketo tautomeric form, and cytidine and adenosine exist in the amino form.[46] Spectra of the ionised forms have also been examined.[165] It is clear that apparent pKs refer, not to a substituent group, but to that group and the neighbouring portion of the purine or pyrimidine ring system. The nature of these groups is of considerable importance with regard to hydrogen bonding between purine and pyrimidine derivatives and to the macromolecular structure of nucleic acids.

Examination of the proton magnetic resonance spectra of purines, pyrimidines, nucleosides, and nucleotides in deuterium oxide at different hydrogen ion concentrations suggested definite tautomeric structures for the cations of cytidine (protonation at N^1), adenosine (protonation at N^1, the positive charge being distributed among the nitrogen atoms of the adenine ring system) and guanosine-5' triphosphate ion (protonation at N^7).[166] A concentration dependence of the proton shifts, different for the various protons of a given purine, was observed. Since this effect was also observed with purine itself, hydrogen bonding at high concentrations is not the cause. A possible explanation for the concentration dependence of the shifts is that for a preferred arrangement of molecules in solution the protons of a given molecule may experience to different extents the diamagnetic shielding effect of the secondary magnetic field arising from neighbouring anisotropic molecules. Proton magnetic resonance studies also indicated that the conformation of the ribose ring in nucleosides and nucleotides was dependent on the purine or pyrimidine nature of the aglycon.[167, 168] Thus in the purine nucleosides C2' is out of the plane defined by C1, 0 and C4' (or by C1', 0, C3' and C4') while in the pyrimidine nucleosides C3' is out of the plane defined by C1', 0 and C4' (or by C1', C2', 0 and C4') as previously shown by X-ray crystal structure determinations. This difference in conformation of the ribose moiety of purine and pyrimidine nucleosides suggests an explanation for the rather striking differences in optical rotation of purine nucleoside derivatives (negative specific rotations) and the pyrimidine compounds (positive specific rotations).[167] Analysis of nuclear magnetic resonance spectra of deoxynucleosides and doxynucleotides indicates that the ring oxygen and possibly C1' may be twisted out of the plane of the five membered ring.[169]

Nucleosides, particularly the purine compounds, readily form metal ion complexes.[170] Thus adenosine and guanosine (and to a greater extent the corresponding deoxynucleosides) form cupric chelates presumably involving the imidazole nitrogen and the 6-substituent. Similar metal coordination probably participates in the catalytic decomposition of 6-succinaminopurine to adenine in neutral solution using divalent ions such as copper and manganese.[171] Under basic conditions hypoxanthine and adenine are obtained, whereas acidic hydrolysis yields 5-aminoimidazole-4-carboxamide.[172, 173] Treatment of adenosine with ketopentose (or fructose or glycol aldehyde), inorganic pyrophosphate and cupric ions at 70° yields small amounts of 5-amino-1-ribosylimidazole. Two other adenosine derivatives, probably substituted 6-amino deratives, were also observed.[174]

Examination of various metal complexes with adenine-1-N-oxide and adenosine-1-N-oxide indicated that in the former case binding with N7 and the 6-amino group occurred, but with adenosine-1-N-oxide co-ordination of the metal was between the 6-amino group and the oxide oxygen, by means of a tautomeric shift.[175]

The naturally occurring ribonucleosides are of therapeutic value in cases of bacterial alcoholism, in that they prevent the inhibition of growth of *Lactobacillus arabinosus* 17–5 by ethanol or other simple alcohols.[176]

NUCLEOSIDE ANTIBIOTICS

Cordycepin, isolated[177] from the mould *Cordyceps militaris* is active against strains of *B. subtilis* and an avian tubercle bacillus. Acidic hydrolysis gives adenine and cordycepose; ultraviolet absorption spectra of the compound indicate a 9-glycosyl linkage.[178] Extracts from mycelia of *Cordyceps militaris* also contain **3'-(homocitrullyl-amino)-3'-deoxyadenosine.**[179] Hydrolysis of the nucleoside with sodium hydroxide in methanol gives 3'-amino-3'-deoxyadenosine; acidic hydrolysis gives adenine, 3-amino-3-deoxyribose, and L-homo-citrulline.

Nebularine, 9-β-D-ribofuranosylpurine, isolated from the mushroom *Agaricus (Clytocybe) nebularis,*[180] and from culture media filtrates of a *Streptomyces,*[181] shows activity against mycobacteria and mouse Sarcoma 180, but is highly toxic to mice (although purine itself is not). The usual degradation methods suggested the structure. This was confirmed by synthesis of the nucleoside from 6-chloro-9-β-D-ribo-furanosylpurine (an intermediate that is readily converted into adenosine, thus fixing the 9-β-D configuration) by reductive dehalogenation. In an alternative synthesis the compound was obtained directly from the chloromercuri derivative of purine and 2,3,5,-tri-O-acetylribo-furanosyl chloride.[182]

Nucleocidin, a *Streptomyces* product, shows "phenomenal" anti-trypanosomal activity as well as possessing broad-spectrum anti-bacterial properties. The partial structure shown is suggested by degradation studies.[183]

Amicetin is an antitubercular antibiotic produced by *Streptomyces vinacensdrappus* and *Streptomyces fasciculatis.*[184] Strong acidic hydrolysis liberates cytosine; further degradation studies have shown that amicetin has the structure indicated.[185]

Angustmycin A has been identified as 6-amino-9-L-2'-keto-(1',2'-enediol)-fucopyranosylpurine. Acidic hydrolysis gives adenine and L-2-keto-fucopyranose. The latter compound on reduction with sodium borohydride yields a mixture of L-fucitol and 6-deoxy-L-talitol. Acetylation of the nucleoside gives a tetra-acetate ($N^6,2',3',4'$); catalytic hydrogenation of this to the dihydro derivative followed by acidic cleavage of the glycosyl linkage then gives adenine and 6-deoxytalose.[186]

Angustmycin C,[187] **Psicofuranine,**[188] 6-amino-9-β-D-psicofuranosyl-purine gives adenine and psicose on acidic hydrolysis. The antibiotic was isolated from culture filtrates of *Streptomyces hygroscopicus* var. *decoyinine*; it shows antibacterial and antitumour activity. *In vivo* and

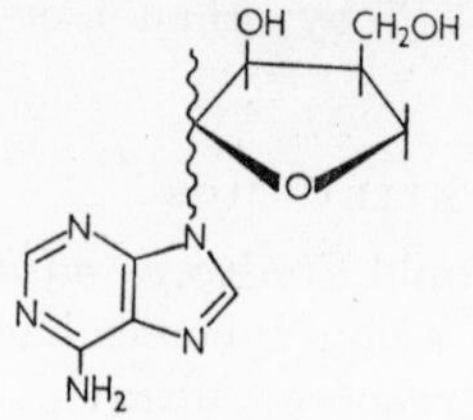

Cordycepin

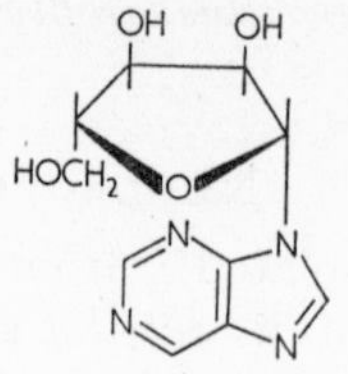

Nebularine

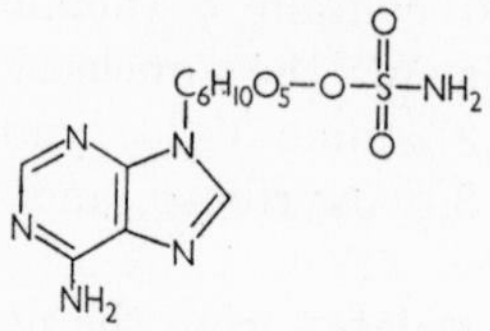

Nucleocidin

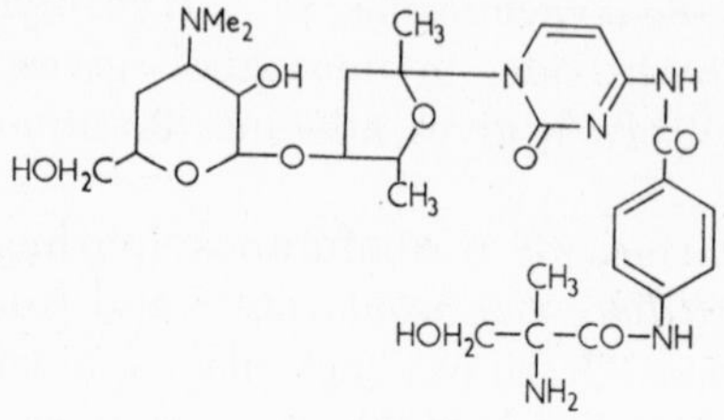

Amicetin

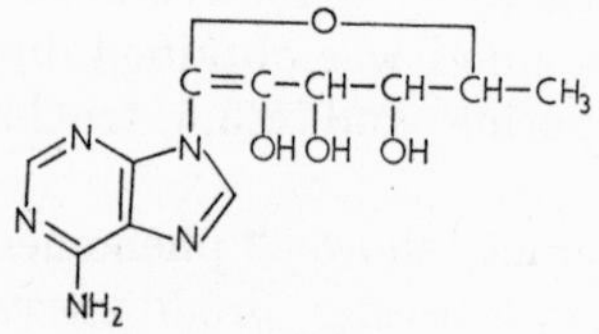

Angustmycin A

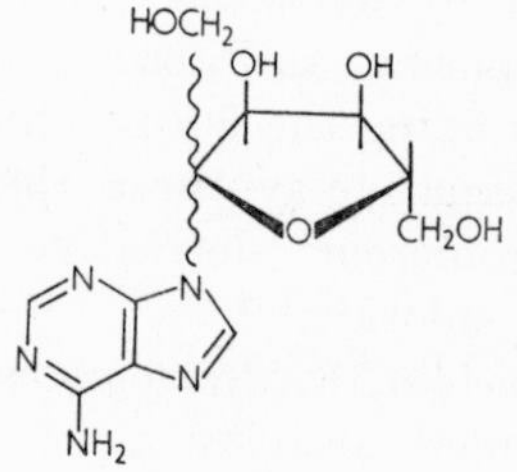

Psicofuranine

in vitro studies of the action of psicofuranine have shown that the antibiotic inhibits xanthosine-5' phosphate aminase.[189] The structure assigned has been confirmed by synthesis of the nucleoside from chloromercuri 6-acetamidopurine and tetra-*O*-acetyl-D-psicosyl chloride, followed by deacetylation of the product and purification by counter current distribution.[188] Hydrolysis of the nucleoside is subject to specific catalysis by both acids and bases.[190]

Toyocamycin, isolated[191] from *Streptomyces toyocaensis*, is a cyano derivative of 7-deaza-adenosine.[192] Hydrolysis with Dowex 50 gives D-ribose. The compound is active against *Mycobacterium tuberculosis* and *Candida albicans*.

Puromycin, produced by *Streptomyces alboniger*, is a broad-spectrum antibiotic which is active against *Trypanosoma equiperdum* and other protozoa, and inhibits the growth of a mammary adenocarcinoma in mice.[193] Cleavage of the nucleoside with ethanolic hydrogen chloride gave 6-dimethylaminopurine, *p*-methoxy-L-phenylalanine and an aminosugar identified as D-3-amino-3-deoxyribose by comparison with a synthetic specimen. Ultraviolet absorption spectra indicated a 9-glycosyl linkage, and the β-configuration and furanose nature of the sugar were established by periodate titration. Puromycin itself does not consume periodate, showing that the free amino group of the antibiotic is in the p-methoxyphenylalanine component rather than the sugar. However, removal of the amino acid residue gave a 6-dimethylamino-9-(3'-amino-3'-deoxyribosyl)-purine that consumed one mole of periodate (establishing a furanose structure) to give the same dialdehyde as that obtained by periodate oxidation of 6-dimethylamino-9-β-D-glucopyranosylpurine. Puromycin is therefore 6-dimethylamino-9-(3'-deoxy-3'-p-methoxy-L-phenylalanylamino-β-D-ribofuranosyl)-purine.[193] This structure has been confirmed by an ingenious synthesis of puromycin by Baker and his collaborators.[194]

Methyl 2,3-anhydro-D-lyxofuranoside was prepared from 3,5-O-

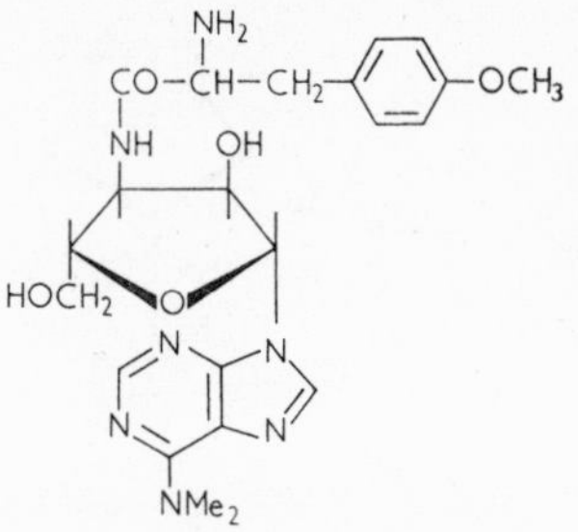

Puromycin

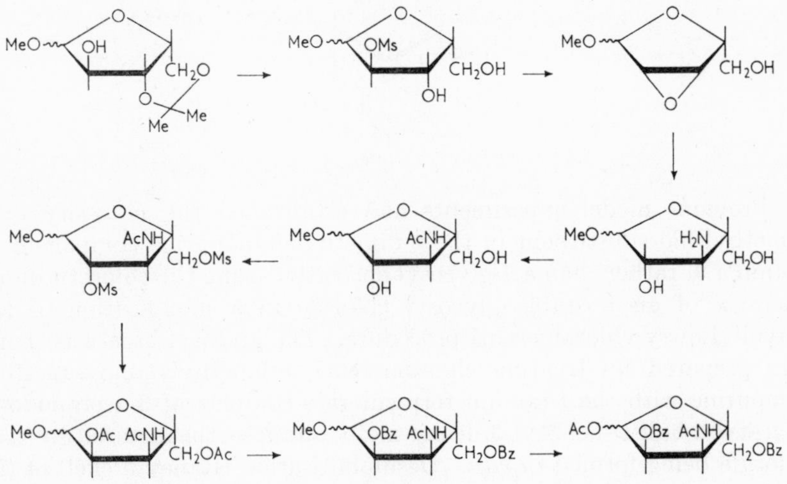

Ms = CH$_3$SO$_2$

isopropylidene methyl D-xylofuranoside by methanesulphonylation, removal of the isopropylidene group and treatment of the resulting methyl 2-*O*-methanesulphonyl-D-xylofuranoside with sodium methoxide. The oxide ring was cleaved with ammonia to give a 3-amino-3-deoxyarabinose derivative which was N-acetylated to yield methyl 3-acetamido-3-deoxy-D-arabinofuranoside. Inversion at C2 was effected by methanesulphonylation to the 2,5-di-*O*-methanesulphonyl compound followed by treatment with wet sodium acetate, both sulphonyloxy groups being displaced, that at C2 by neighbouring group effect, to give a ribose derivative isolated after acetylation of the 2'-hydroxyl group, as methyl 3-acetamido-3-deoxy-2,5-di-*O*-acetyl-D-ribofuranoside. This was converted into a mixture of the anomeric 3-acetamido-1-*O*-acetyl-2,5-di-*O*-benzoyl-3-deoxyribofuranoses by *O*-deacetylation, followed by benzoylation, and then cleavage of the methyl group by hydrochloric or hydrobromic acid in acetic acid, and a final acetylation of the 1-hydroxyl group.

Previous model experiments had established the necessity of a 2-methylthio substituent in the 6-dimethylaminopurine component to obtain a 9- rather than a 7-glycosyl derivative using the chlorotitanium complex of an unstable glycosyl chloride in a modification of the Davoll–Lowry chloromercuri procedure. The glycosyl-base was therefore prepared by treating chloromercuri 6-dimethylamino-2-methylthiopurine with the titanium tetrachloride complex of 3-acetamido-1-*O*-acetyl-2,5-di-*O*-benzoyl-3-deoxy-D-ribofuranose, the required glycosyl chloride being formed *in situ*. Desulphurisation (Raney nickel) of the crude nucleoside followed by debenzoylation and de-N-acetylation gave 6-dimethylamino-9-(3'-amino-3'-deoxy-β-D-ribofuranosyl)-purine identical with the aminonucleoside obtained by degradation of puromycin. Finally, the aminonucleoside was treated with the mixed anhydride of ethyl hydrogen carbonate and N-benzyloxycarbonyl-p-methoxy-L-phenylalanine and the benzyloxycarbonyl group removed from the product by hydrogenolysis to give puromycin.[194] Numerous isomers and analogues of puromycin and of the aminonucleoside moiety have been synthesised.

OTHER NUCLEOSIDES

Crotonoside (isolated from croton beans) is hydrolysed to D-ribose and isoguanine, and can be deaminated to xanthosine. It is therefore 9-β-D-ribofuranosyl-isoguanine.[195] This structure has been confirmed by synthesis of the nucleoside via 9-β-D-ribofuranosyl-2,6-diamino-purine.[196]

Acidic[197] or enzymic[198] hydrolysis of **uric acid riboside** (isolated from beef blood[197] and from diapausing pupae of *Sphingidae* moths[199]) gives D-ribose and uric acid. Comparison of the ultraviolet absorption spectra, spectroscopically determined apparent pK values, colour reactions, and rate of decomposition in alkali with the properties of 3-, 7- and 9-methyluric acids indicates that the nucleoside is 3-ribosyluric acid[198] and not the isomeric 9-ribosyl derivative as previously claimed.[200]

Orotidine (isolated from a pyrimidine requiring mutant of the red bread mould *Neurospora crassa*) is hydrolysed by dilute acid much more readily than is uridine, to give orotic acid and ribose.[201] Spectroscopic evidence shows that it is a 3-ribosyl derivative;[202] periodate oxidation

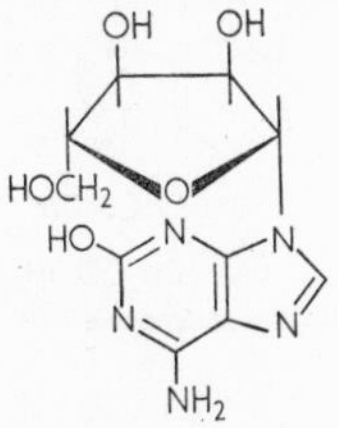

Crotonoside

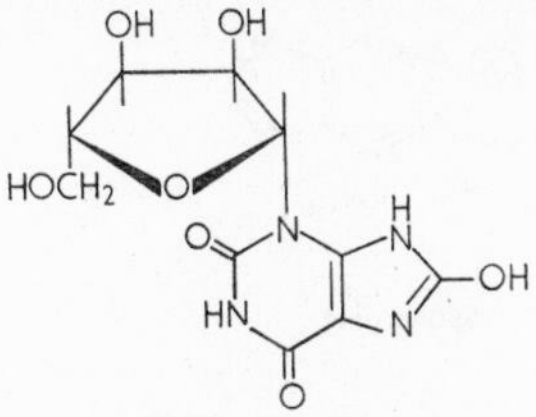

Ribosyl uric acid

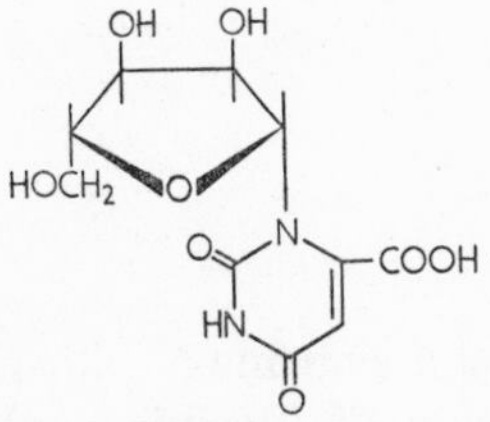

Orotidine

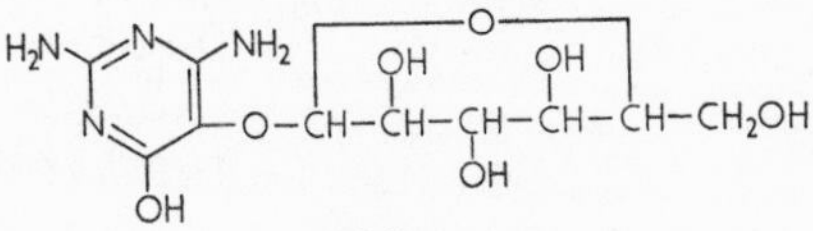

Vicine

and enzymic synthesis (of the nucleotide) and conversion into uridine show that orotidine is 3-β-D-ribofuranosylorotic acid.

Vicine (from vetch meal)[203] on the basis of enzymatic hydrolysis (emulsin) and chemical and spectral comparisons with analogous compounds is 5-O-β-D-glucopyranosyl-2,4-diamino-5,6-dihydroxypyrimidine.[204]

Several nucleosides have been isolated by direct extraction of sponges.[205] **Spongothymidine** and **spongouridine** were shown to be 3-β-D-arabinofuranosyl derivatives of thymine and uracil, respectively. Both have been synthesised by inversion of the 2′ hydroxyl group of the 3-β-D-ribofuranosyl pyrimidines via O^2,2′-cyclonucleosides.[68, 69] The structure of **spongosine** (9-β-D-ribofuranosyl-2-methoxyadenine) was established by synthesis of the nucleoside by selective methylation of silver crotonoside, or from chloromercuri 2-methoxyadenine and 2,3,5-tri-O-benzoyl-D-ribosyl chloride.[206]

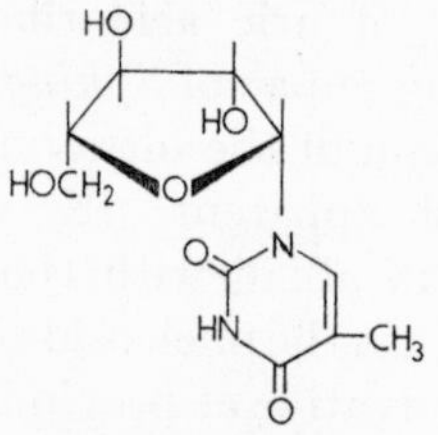

Spongothymidine

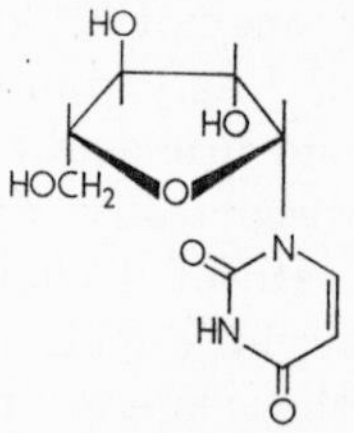

Spongouridine

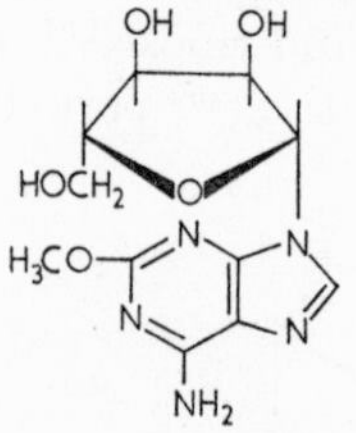

Spongosine

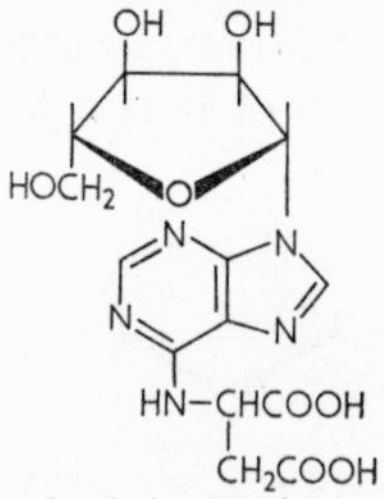

Succinyl adenosine

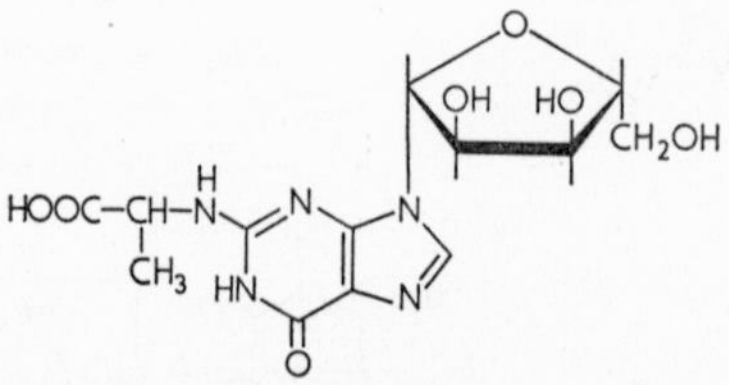

Propionyl guanosine

Succinyl adenosine is derived from succinyl adenosine-5′ phosphate, an intermediate in the biochemical conversion of inosinic acid into adenylic acid. The nucleoside was synthesised by reaction of 6-methyl-mercapto-9-β-D-ribofuranosylpurine with aspartic acid in alkaline solution.[207]

A purine nucleoside isolated from *Fusarium* species has been tentatively identified as 2-(1-carboxyethylamino)-6-hydroxy-9-β-D-ribofuranosylpurine.* Acidic hydrolysis liberates ribose and a purine derivative that on further treatment gives guanine.[208] The free base, 2(α-propionamino)-6-hydroxypurine,* has also been isolated from acidic hydrolysates of a reaction mixture obtained by treating guanine with mycelial extracts of *Eremothecium ashbyii*.[209] A nucleotide or nucleoside derivative is probably formed initially. Guanine propionate* is not deaminated by nitrous acid. Rather vigorous acidic hydrolysis (refluxing in 6N-hydrochloric acid for 60 hours) gives xanthine, alanine, glycine, and lactic acid, but hydrolysis between pH 3 and 12 yields guanine and L-lactic acid.[210]

Vitamin B_{12} coenzyme contains **5'-deoxyadenosine** bound to cobalt through the 5'-carbon atom.[211] Mild acidic hydrolysis of the coenzyme,[212] or treatment with potassium cyanide, cleaves the glycosyl linkage to liberate adenine and D-*erythro*-2,3-dihydroxypenten-4-al. Photolysis of the coenzyme at room temperature gives " adenosine-5' carboxylic acid ";[213] the corresponding 5'-aldehyde is also formed.[368]

"ACTIVE METHIONINE" AND
ADENINE THIOMETHYL PENTOSIDE

Adenine thiomethyl pentoside was first isolated[214] from yeast in 1912, but it was not until forty years later that the significance of the nucleoside was made clear, when it was discovered that biological methylations

* All three systems of nomenclature have appeared in the literature.

by methionine required an activated sulphonium intermediate, formed by interaction of the amino acid with adenosine-5' triphosphate. Acidic hydrolysis of adenine thiomethyl pentoside gave adenine and 5-deoxy-5-methylthioribose. The structure of the latter was proven in a number of ways, and ultraviolet absorption spectra of the nucleoside indicated a 9-glycosyl linkage.[215–219] That this was of β-configuration was decisively shown by the synthesis of " hypoxanthine thiomethyl pentoside " from inosine.[220, 221] Treatment of 2',3'-*O*-isopropylidene-5'-toluene-*p*-sulphonylinosine with potassium methyl mercaptide yielded 2',3'-*O*-isopropylidene-5'-methylthio-5'-deoxyinosine. Removal of the isopropylidene group gave 5'-methylthio-5'-deoxyinosine, identical with the product obtained by nitrous acid treatment[222] of adenine thiomethyl pentoside. The nucleoside is therefore 9-(5'-methylthio-5'-deoxy-β-D-ribofuranosyl)-adenine.

$Ts = CH_3C_6H_4SO_2$

A similar synthetic route from 2′,3′-*O*-isopropylidene-5′-toluene-*p*-sulphonyladenosine gave adenine thiomethyl pentoside in good yield, using appropriate reaction conditions.[223] In an alternate synthesis the compound has been obtained by condensing 2,3-di-*O*-acetyl-5-methyl-thio-5-deoxy-D-ribofuranosyl chloride with 6-acetamidopurine followed by removal of protecting groups.[224]

As previously mentioned, acidic hydrolysis of the nucleoside gives adenine and 5-deoxy-5-methylthioribose. Further treatment with hydriodic acid causes migration of the thiomethyl group from C5 to C1 of the ribose.[225]

" **Active methionine** " acts as methyl donor in a number of biological reactions, such as the methylation of several 2-aminopurines to 2-methylaminopurines;[226] it is probably involved in the metabolism of the methylated purines and pyrimidines present in certain ribonucleic acids. The compound is also an intermediate in the biosynthesis of spermidine. Decarboxylation of " active methionine " yields the propylamine derivative which then alkylates 1,4-diaminobutane to yield spermidine and methylthioadenosine.[227]

Enzymic synthesis of the activated amino acid from L-methionine and adenosine-5′ triphosphate is accompanied by stoichiometric liberation of all the phosphate of the adenosine-5′ triphosphate to give a phosphate free product possessing ultraviolet absorption spectra characteristic of adenosine derivatives. Treatment of " active methionine " with nitrous acid effects deamination (to a hypoxanthine derivative), and acidic hydrolysis gives adenine, homoserine and

$$\text{A}-5'-\overset{+}{\underset{\underset{RNH_2}{|}}{\underset{CH_3}{S}}}-CH_2-CH_2-\underset{\underset{COOH}{|}}{CH}-NH_2 \longrightarrow \text{A}-5'-S-CH_2-CH_2-\underset{\underset{COOH}{|}}{CH}-NH_2$$

$$+$$
$$RNHCH_3 + H^+$$

A = Adenosine

$$\text{A}-5'-\overset{+}{\underset{\underset{CH_3}{|}}{S}}-CH_2-CH_2-\underset{\underset{COOH}{|}}{CH}-NH_2 \longrightarrow \text{A}-5'-\overset{+}{\underset{\underset{CH_3}{|}}{S}}-CH_2-CH_2-CH_2-NH_2$$

$$NH_2-(CH_2)_4-NH_2$$

$$\text{A}-5'-S-CH_3 + NH_2-(CH_2)_4-NH-(CH_2)_3-NH_2 + H^+$$

methylthioribose. Hydrolysis at pH 6 gives homoserine and 5'-deoxy-5'-methylthioadenosine. These results indicate an S-adenosylmethionine structure,[228, 229] confirmation of which was obtained by synthesis of " active methionine ". Reaction of 5'-deoxy-5'-methylthioadenosine with DL-α-amino-γ-bromobutyric acid hydrobromide gave a low yield of a product that was biologically active.[223] In a more successful approach, 2',3'-O-isopropylidene-5'-O-toluene-p-sulphonyladenosine was treated with sodium homocysteine to give, after removal of the isopropylidene group from the product, S-(5'-deoxyadenosine-5')-homocysteine identical with the product from " active methionine " after enzymic transmethylation. Methylation of the S-adenosyl homocysteine gave S-adenosylmethionine in good yield.[230, 231]

Since a new asymmetric centre is introduced, methyl iodide treatment of S-adenosyl-L-homocysteine gives a mixture of the two sulphonium diastereoisomers, that is, $(\pm)$-S-adenosyl-L-methionine. Biological resolution of the mixture yielded $(+)$-S-adenosyl-L-methionine. This was quite inactive in the enzymic systems studied, but was chemically identical (except for optical rotation) with enzymatically synthesised "active methionine", $(-)$-S-adenosyl-L-methionine.[232]

Dimethyladenosyl thetin

The chemical properties of S-adenosylmethionine are of some interest and are identical for all four of the possible diastereoisomers. As previously mentioned, hydrolysis at pH 4 to 7 yields homoserine and methylthioadenosine, the latter being further degraded to adenine and methylthioribose on more vigorous treatment with acid. Mild alkaline treatment at 0° cleaves the nucleoside glycosyl linkage to give adenine and S-ribosylmethionine; the latter is further degraded to methionine with hot alkali. Extreme sensitivity to alkali was also observed with dimethyladenosylthetin (5′-dimethylthio-5′-deoxyadenosine) which was likewise readily degraded to adenine, although both adenosine and 5′-methylthio-5′-deoxyadenosine are stable.[233] Further studies on the alkaline hydrolysis of sulphonium nucleosides have shown that both lyxose and ribose derivatives are formed on cleavage of the glycosyl linkage, partial inversion at C4 occurring as a result of intermediate formation of a 4,5 double bond.[234]

" Active methionine " can also be cleaved enzymically to 5′-methyl-thio-5′-deoxyadenosine and α-amino-γ-butyrolactone by a mechanism involving displacement by nucleophilic attack of the carboxyl anion at the carbon atom adjacent to the sulphonium centre, no tritium being incorporated when the reaction was done in tritiated water.[235]

The mechanism of the enzymatic synthesis of " active methionine " has not been elucidated as yet. Glutathionine and magnesium ions are required, a carboxyl activated intermediate is not involved, and stoichiometric amounts of inorganic pyrophosphate and orthophosphate are formed.[236] Tracer studies (^{18}O and ^{32}P) showed that the inorganic pyrophosphate retained all seven of its original oxygen atoms and was derived entirely from the α- and β-phosphates of the adenosine-5′ triphosphate consumed; the γ-phosphate gave rise to orthophosphate with incorporation of ^{18}O.

Kinetin (6-furfurylaminopurine) is a " wound hormone " plant cell-division factor present in coconuts. More potent sources are old deoxyribonucleic acid, and solutions of deoxynucleic acid that have been autoclaved[237] at pH 4. The factor has been synthesised from 6-methylthiopurine (or 6-chloropurine) and furfurylamine,[238] from adenine and 2-furoic anhydride followed by reduction of the acylaminopurine with lithium aluminium anhydride,[239] and by ring closure of 4,5-diamino-6-furfurylaminopyrimidine with ethyl orthoformate and acetic anhydride.[240] A convenient synthesis of kinetin involving exchange amination has been described.[241] Adenine is simply heated with furfurylamine (together with some of the hydrochloride).

The 9-β-D-ribofuranosyl derivative, " kinetin nucleoside ", has been prepared from tri-O-benzoyl-β-D-ribofuranosyl-6-chloropurine and from tri-O-acetyl-β-D-ribofuranosyl-6-methylthiopurine, both these nucleosides being obtained via the chloromercuri procedure.[242, 243]

SYNTHESIS OF NUCLEOSIDES

Since the early work of E. Fischer and B. Helferich, considerable effort has been expended on the synthesis of nucleosides, partly as a complementary method to degradation studies for the elucidation of the structure of the naturally occurring compounds (and hence of nucleotides and nucleic acids), and partly to provide analogues of value for the interpretation of biological action in terms of chemical structure. More recently, the incentive offered by the isolation of nucleoside antibiotics, as well as the possible utility of " abnormal " nucleosides as chemotherapeutic agents against neoplastic diseases, has intensified this effort and led to the rapid development of methods by means of which almost any nucleoside, natural or unnatural, may be synthesised. These methods fall into three main classes. In the first, a preformed purine or pyrimidine derivative is treated with a suitably reactive form of the sugar, commonly a glycosyl halide; secondly, the purine or pyrimidine ring system is constructed from a simple N-glycosyl precursor; in the third a preformed nucleoside is modified either in the sugar moiety or in the purine or pyrimidine base. All three types of method have been used with success for the synthesis of naturally occurring nucleosides, and all three categories have their biochemical analogies. A possible fourth method, fabrication of the sugar on a simple N-alkyl (or acyl) purine or pyrimidine base has not been observed in metabolic processes, nor has it been used in a chemical sense.

Class 1. Coupling of sugar with preformed base. The earliest work on nucleoside synthesis is that of Emil Fischer and his collaborators who used a method that, with a number of modifications and refinements, has had wide application. In this classical approach, an appropriate silver purine was condensed with an acetohalogeno-sugar and the product deacetylated.[244] Whereas theobromine gave O-glycosides, and theophylline formed 7-glycosyl derivatives,[245] treatment of silver 2,8-dichloroadenine (or 2,6,8-trichloropurine) with acetobromoglucose gave the 9-glucosyl compound, though the position of the glycosyl linkage was not established until much later.[246] Dehalogenation of 2,8-dichloro-9-glucosyladenine gave 9-β-D-glucopyranosyladenine.[244]

Application of the same method to the synthesis of pyrimidine nucleosides by treatment of a silver pyrimidine with an acetohalogen sugar was less successful, since with pyrimidines containing a lactam-lactim tautomeric system either an O-glycoside was obtained (e.g. with uracil) or else no coupling occurred (e.g. with cytosine).[247, 248] However, by restricting this prototropic change through the use of 2,6-dialkoxy-pyrimidines, Hilbert and Johnson were able to prepare glycosyl-pyrimidines that, by analogy with the product from methyl iodide and 2,6-diethoxypyrimidine, were N^3-glycosyl derivatives.[249] Thus treatment of 2,6-diethoxypyrimidine with acetobromoglucose gave a product from which the ethyl and acetyl groups could be removed by methanolic hydrogen chloride to yield 3-D-glucosyluracil, or by methanolic ammonia to give 3-D-glucosylcytosine.[249, 250] Numerous glycopyranosyl pyrimidines were prepared in this fashion, but the method could not be applied to the synthesis of a naturally occurring nucleoside until development of the required ribofuranosyl halide. In 1947 Howard, Lythgoe and Todd obtained cytidine (and hence uridine by deamination) starting from acetobromoribofuranose and 2,6-diethoxypyrimidine.[251]

Adenosine and guanosine were then prepared by adaptation of the original Fischer–Helferich procedures, using tri-O-acetyl-D-ribofuranosyl chloride and silver 2,8-dichloroadenine.[252] Complete hydrogenolytic dehalogenation of the intermediate 9-β-D-ribofuranosyl-2,8-dichloro-adenine gave adenosine. Partial dehalogenation (the 8-chloro atom is more reactive than the 2-chloro) yielded 2-chloroadenosine; deamination with nitrous acid then gave a 2-chloro-6-hydroxypurine nucleoside which on treatment with ammonia was converted into guanosine.

These approaches, while representing the first syntheses of natural ribonucleosides, were somewhat limited in that low yields were generally obtained, and also they could not be applied to purines containing an amino group basic enough to react with the glycosyl halide. The latter drawback was overcome by prior acylation of the amino group, and yields were greatly increased by the use of chloromercuri purines rather than silver derivatives.[253] Improved preparations of tri-O-acylribo-furanosyl halides have also contributed to making this method the most convenient and efficient synthetic route to naturally occurring nucleosides as well as a host of analogues. These latter include 9-

glycosyl purines derived from D-ribopyranose,[254] D-glucofuranose,[255] L-talofuranose,[256] L-rhamnopyranose,[257] L-rhamnofuranose,[258] 6-deoxy-D-glucofuranose,[259] 6-deoxy-L-idofuranose,[260] 6-deoxy-D-allofuranose,[261] tritiated D-ribofuranose,[262] 5-deoxy-D-ribofuranose,[263] 5-deoxy-5-fluoro-D-ribofuranose,[264] lactose,[265] maltose,[266] cellobiose,[266] digitoxose,[267] 2-deoxyglucose,[267] and a number of analogues of the aminonucleoside derived from puromycin,[268, 269] such as 3′-amino-3′-deoxyadenosine.[270] In like manner, treatment of 6-acetamido-chloromercuripurine with the acyclic sugar derivative 1-chloro-1-deoxy-1-O-methyl-penta-O-acetyl-aldehydo-D-galactose aldehydrol followed by deacetylation gave the α and β anomers of 1-(9-adenyl)-1-deoxy-1-O-methyl-aldehydo-D-galactose aldehydrol.[271] Extensive variation of the purine moiety has also been used[272–274] for the preparation of nucleosides such as 1- and 2-β-D-ribofuranosylpyrazolo-[3,4-d]-pyrimidines,[275] and the 8-aza analogues of adenosine, guanosine, inosine, and xanthosine.[276]

The differential stability of acetamido substituents to deacetylation, and of the amino groups to treatment with nitrous acid[253, 277] led to syntheses of guanosine and isoguanosine via the O-acetylribofuranosyl-2,6-diacetamidopurine;[253] the differential reactivities of 2- and 6-chloro substituents have also been utilised.[278, 279] Under suitable conditions, diazotisation of 2,6-diamino-9-β-D-ribofuranosylpurine, and thio-guanosine, in fluoboric acid gives the 2-fluoro derivatives. The 2-flouro substituted nucleosides are much more active than the corresponding 2-chloro compounds, and 2-fluoroadenosine is readily converted into 2-butylaminoadenosine by treatment with butylamine.[280] Methylthio derivatives of purines have proved useful in a number of ways and in certain cases, for example the reaction of chloromercuri-2,8-dimethylthioadenine with 2,3,5-tri-O-benzoyl ribofuranosyl chloride, protection of the 6-amino group is not necessary. Desulphurisation of the intermediate 9-β-D-tri-O-benzoylribofuranosyl-2,8-dimethylthio-6-aminopurine with Raney nickel yielded adenosine after removal of the benzoyl groups.[281]

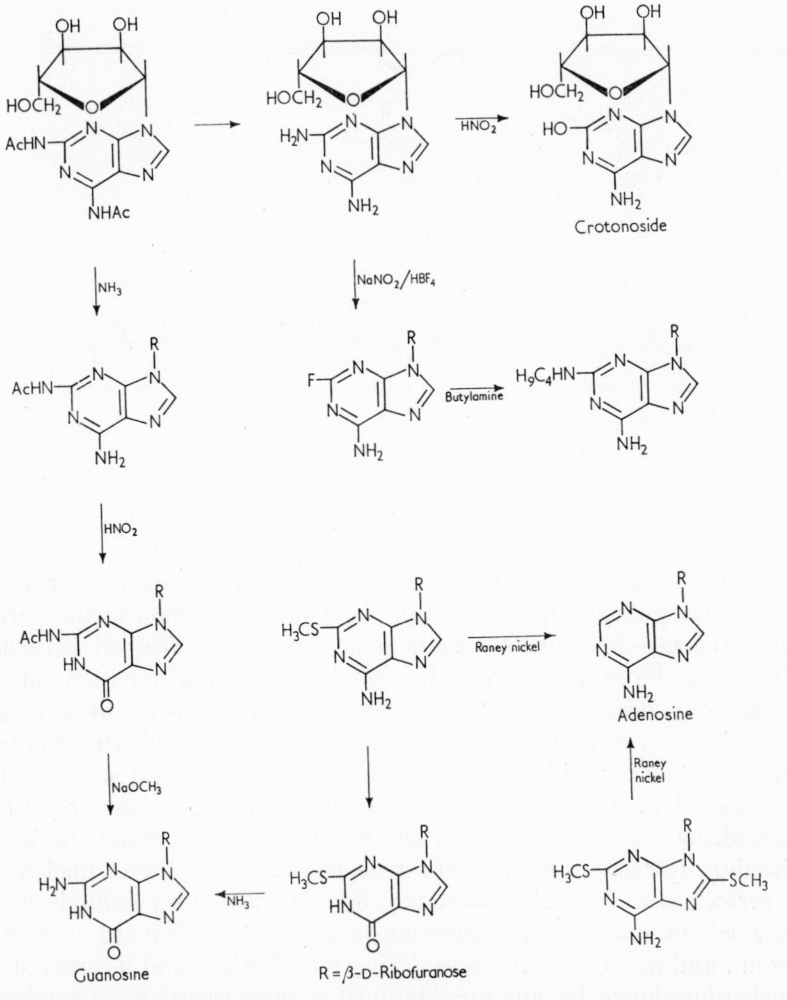

Crotonoside

Adenosine

Guanosine   R = β-D-Ribofuranose

That the stereochemistry of the glycosyl linkage in this type of synthesis is controlled by the 2-acyloxy group of the sugar moiety was recognised in a most useful rule proposed by Baker and his co-workers[282] in 1954. This states that condensation of a heavy metal salt of a purine (or pyrimidine) with an acylated glycosyl halide will form a nucleoside with a C1–C2-*trans*-configuration in the sugar moiety regardless of the

R = β –D–Ribofuranose

original configuration at C1–C2. Whereas halogenosugars with a C1–C2-*cis*-configuration react with simple Walden inversion in the normal way, the C1–C2-*trans*-halosugars react by double Walden inversion, C1 being initially inverted by neighbouring participation of the C2-acyloxy group to give an *ortho*-ester ion, followed by a second inversion on reaction with the purine. In the main, this rule has been shown to have a wide validity, and indeed is now used as a proof of configuration. Occasionally, small amounts of the anomer are formed in addition to a good yield of the expected isomer, while the use of titanium tetrachloride gives rise to a mixture of α- and β-nucleosides in certain cases. Since the directive effect of a 2-acyloxy group is absent in a ribofuranosyl halide carrying a 2,3-cyclic carbonate protecting group, and in 2-deoxy-D-ribose derivatives, both α- and β-forms of the nucleoside should be, and are, obtained in these cases. Thus condensation of 5-O-benzoyl-D-ribofuranosyl bromide 2,3-cyclic carbonate with chloromercuri-6-benzamidopurine followed by removal of the protecting groups yielded both adenosine and the α-nucleoside, 9-α-D-ribofuranosyl adenine.[283]

Although earlier approaches to direct coupling of metal-pyrimidine and sugar to form N^3-glycosyls failed, Fox and co-workers were able to extend the chloromercuri method to the synthesis of pyrimidine nucleosides, in spite of possible lactim–lactam tautomerism.[284] Condensation of dithyminylmercury with an acylated sugar halide followed by removal of protecting groups from the product gave the N^3-glycosyl pyrimidine in good yield. In this way 3-β-D-ribofuranosylthymine and the analogous 3-β-D-xylofuranosyl derivative were prepared. (All four possible 3-β-D-aldopentofuranosylthymines have been synthesised, the β-arabinofuranosyl and β-lyxofuranosyl derivatives by inversion at C2' of the ribo and xylo nucleosides respectively). Determination of the configuration of the products by the usual methods showed that the *trans rule* was also applicable to synthesis of pyrimidine nucleosides. Considerable success has been obtained in application of the procedure to the syntheses of N^3-glycosyl pyrimidines (uracil, cytosine and thymine) including 3'- and 5'-aminonucleosides[285] and 5'-fluoro-5'-deoxynucleosides[264] using the appropriate halogenose. Ribofuranosyl (3-β-D-) derivatives of 5-fluorouracil,[286] 6-deoxyuracil (2-oxo-2,3-dihydropyrimidine)[287, 288] and the isomeric 4-oxo-3,4-dihydropyrimidine,[288] 4-azathymine[289] and 4-azauracil[290] have been prepared by this route. Azapyrimidines give a mixture of 1- and 3-ribofuranosyl derivatives. A somewhat better synthesis of the N^3-glycosyl lies in the use of N^1-diphenylmethyl-4-azauracil (obtained by the action of diphenyldiazomethane on 3-acetyl-4-azauracil and then hydrolysis of the acetyl group) followed by hydrogenolytic removal of the benzhydryl group.[291] A related approach has been used for the synthesis of α and β anomers of 2'-deoxy-4-azauridine.[292] The general method has also been applied to the synthesis of 3-β-D-lactosyl and 3-β-D-cellobiosylcytosine using mercuri N-acetylcytosine and the halogenose. Acidic hydrolysis of these disaccharide nucleosides yielded 3-β-D-glucopyranosylcytosine.[293]

While prior acylation of the amino group of cytosine itself is necessary,[294] protection of aminopyrimidines is not always essential. Thus chloromercuri 5-carbethoxycytosine[295] and 5-nitrocytosine[296] have been used directly to yield the corresponding 5-substituted cytosine nucleosides; presumably the basicity of the amino group is sufficiently diminished by the neighbouring substituents to eliminate interference with the halogenose. Another route to cytosine derivatives lies in the use of chloromercuri 6-ethoxy-2(3H)-pyrimidinone. The intermediate from condensation with the halogenose can be converted into a cytosine nucleoside by the action of ammonia, or alternatively into a uracil derivative by acidic treatment.[294]

More recently, the mercuri procedure has been applied to the synthesis of the naturally occurring 2'-deoxynucleosides. Earlier attempts at deoxynucleoside synthesis using a protected 2-deoxyhalogenofuranose were unsuccessful largely owing to the instability of the halogenose. However, dehydrohalogenation can be avoided by the use of 3,5-di-O-p-nitrobenzoyl-2-deoxy-D-ribofuranosyl chloride.[297] This was obtained from 2-deoxy-D-ribose di-isobutyl dithioacetal by mono p-nitrobenzoylation to the 5-O-p-nitrobenzoyl derivative followed by demercaptalation and then complete p-nitrobenzoylation to give a mixture of the anomeric 1,3,5-tri-O-p-nitrobenzoyl-2-deoxy-D-ribo-

R=Tetra-acetylglucose or 2,3,5-tri-O-benzoyl-D-ribofuranose

furanoses which was converted into the deoxyribosyl chloride in the usual way. Condensation of the halogenose with chloromercuri-6-benzamidopurine in dimethyl sulphoxide, followed by deacylation of the product, gave a mixture of 2'-deoxyadenosine and the unnatural α-anomer, separated by chromatography. Crystalline 3,5-di-O-p-chloro-(or p-methyl)-benzoyl-2-deoxy-D-ribofuranosyl chlorides have also been used.[298–300] These were prepared in high yield by acylation of methyl 2-deoxy-(α, β)-D-ribofuranoside followed by treatment of the product with hydrogen chloride–acetic acid in ether. Condensation of the halogenose with suitable mercuri pyrimidines (the monomercury derivatives are somewhat more reactive than the chloromercuri or mercuridipyrimidyl compounds) gave excellent yields of thymidine, and deoxycytidine, after removal of protecting groups, together with smaller amounts of the α-anomers.[300] In a similar fashion, 5-fluoro analogues of deoxyuridine and deoxycytidine (both α- and β-nucleosides) were synthesised.

The synthesis in very low yield of 2'-deoxyadenosine and 2'-deoxyguanosine (and hence the hypoxanthine and xanthine deoxynucleosides) from silver 2,8-dichloroadenine and 3,5-di-O-acetyl-2-deoxyribofuranosyl chloride (1,3,5-tri-O-acetyl-2-deoxyribose and ethereal hydrogen chloride) has been reported.[301] Treatment of the resultant 9-(3',5'-di-

O-acetyl-2'-deoxy-D-ribofuranosyl)-2,8-dichloroadenine by procedures previously applied to the synthesis of adenosine and guanosine from 2,8-dichloroadenine gave the naturally occurring deoxynucleosides. The α- and β-anomers of 2'-deoxyadenosine have also been synthesised by condensation of chloromercuri-6-benzamidopurine with 5-benzoyl-2-deoxy-D-ribose di-isopropyl dithioacetal.[302]

A novel approach, which may be applicable to the synthesis of 2'-deoxynucleosides, has been used for the preparation of 9-(tetrahydro-2'-furyl)-purines from 6-chloropurine and 2,3-dihydrofuran in the presence of an acidic catalyst.[303] Similarly, 2,3-dihydropyran reacts with 6-chloropurine (in the presence of toluene sulphonic acid) to give 6-chloro-9-(tetrahydro-2'-pyranyl)-purine. Further treatment of this " nucleoside " with ammonia, methylamine, dimethylamine or thiols gives the corresponding 6-substituted derivatives; the 6-aziridinyl compound is obtained by the action of ethylenimine. In like manner, 2-acetoxymethyl-2,3-dihydropyran gives 9-(2'-hydroxymethyl-tetrahydro-6'-pyranyl)-purines after removal of the acetyl group.[304]

Ethyl polyphosphate is a useful reagent for the synthesis of nucleosides. A mixture of the unprotected purine, or pyrimidine, and the polyphosphate ester is treated with the unprotected sugar to give good yields of the natural nucleosides in an extremely direct fashion.[305] For example, 9-β-D-ribofuranosyladenine is obtained from adenine and ribose; the one-step reaction also gives deoxyadenosine (from adenine and 2-deoxyribose) in about 30% yield. A number of other natural and unnatural nucleosides have been prepared by this approach, and it is likely that full elaboration of the work will provide explanations for preferential formation of the naturally occurring isomers (rather than the extremely complex mixture that might be expected) and hence for the evolutionary biosynthesis of nucleosides with specific structures. Small amounts of the mononucleotides are also obtained.

A synthesis of triacanthine (6-amino-3-γ,γ-dimethylallylpurine) by alkylation of adenine with γ,γ-dimethylallyl bromide has been described.[365] Similarly, treatment of adenine with 2,3,5-tri-O-acetyl (or benzoyl)-ribofuranosyl bromide in dimethylformamide gave 3-ribofuranosyladenine (after removal of acyl groups) among other products.[366]

Class 2. Construction of nucleoside from simple glycosyl derivative. This type of synthesis, first successfully developed by Todd and his collaborators, provided unambiguous evidence of the position of the glycosyl residue in the natural purine nucleosides and, as a general method, was used for the preparation of a number of 9-glycosyl purines, culminating in the synthesis of adenosine.[306] In the particular approach that was used, purine nucleosides were formed from pyrimidyl glycosylamines by completion of the imidazole ring. Treatment of 4,6-diamino-

2-methylthiopyrimidine (the 2-methylthio substituent increases the reactivity of the aminopyrimidine) with 2,3,4-tri-O-acetyl-5-O-benzyl-D-ribose (the 5-benzyl group prevents furanose–pyranose isomerisation) gave a Schiff base which on deacetylation rearranged to the 5′-O-benzyl-D-ribofuranosyl derivative.   This was coupled with diazotised 2,5-dichloroaniline and the crude azo compound acetylated, purified by chromatography, and reduced with zinc and acetic acid to the 5-amino compound which was then thioformylated with dithioformic acid. The resultant 2-methylthio-4-(5′-O-benzyl-D-ribofuranosylamino)-5-thioformamido-6-aminopyrimidine was cyclised using sodium methoxide, the product reacetylated and the 2-methylthio and 5′-benzyl groups were removed by treatment with Raney nickel. Deacetylation then gave adenosine, not unexpectedly, in rather low overall yield.

A related approach has been used for the preparation of 9-hydroxy-alkylpurines by treatment of 4,6-dichloro-5-aminopyrimidine with an α-amino-ω-hydroxyalkane followed by ring closure with acetic anhydride and ethyl orthoformate to give the 9-substituted-6-chloropurine.[307] The method is presumably applicable to the synthesis of purine nucleosides from ribosylamine. (See also p. 68.)

An alternate route begins with a glycosylimidazole from which the glycosylpurine is obtained by completion of the pyrimidine ring.

Interaction of 2,3,5-tri-O-acetyl-D-ribofuranosyl chloride and silver 4,5-dicarbomethoxyimidazole gave a product which on treatment with ammonia yielded 1-D-ribofuranosylimidazole-4,5-dicarboxamide. A modified Hofmann reaction with alkaline hypobromite effected ring closure of this compound to xanthosine.[308] More recently, a variation of the method has been used for the synthesis of 7- and 9-glycosyl (including β-D-ribofuranosyl) derivatives of 8-azaxanthine from the glycosyl azide and the dimethyl ester of acetylene dicarboxylate.[309, 310] Re-examination of the ring closure of 1-β-D-glucopyranosylimidazole-4,5-dicarboxyamide showed that in addition to 9-β-D-glucopyranosyl-xanthine, small amounts of the 7-glycosyl were also formed.[310]

In a related approach, the silver or mercury salt of methyl 5-nitro-imidazole-4-carboxylate was treated with 2,3,5-tri-O-benzoyl-D-ribo-furanosyl chloride to give a mixture of ribosyl derivatives (glycosyl linkage at either of the ring nitrogens) which with methanolic ammonia was converted into the corresponding nitro-amides. These were sepa-rated by countercurrent distribution. Catalytic reduction of 1-β-D-ribofuranosyl-5-nitroimidazole-4-carboxamide gave 1-ribosyl-5-amino-imidazole-4-carboxamide; this was converted into inosine via the formyl derivative.[311]

R = β-D-Ribofuranose

A metabolite of histamine, 1-β-D-ribofuranosyl-imidazole-4(5)-acetic acid, was likewise synthesised from chloromercuri 4(5)-cyanomethylimidazole[312] (or methyl imidazole-4(5)-acetate)[313] and tri-O-benzoyl-β-D-ribofuranosyl chloride followed by mild hydrolysis of the product.

The application of glycosyl azide intermediates, mentioned previously, was further developed by Baddiley and his co-workers in chemical studies paralleling the biosynthetic route to purine nucleotides. Treatment of 2,3,5-tri-O-benzoyl-β-D-ribofuranosyl chloride with sodium azide gave the glycosyl-β-azide, the configuration of which was demonstrated by periodate oxidation of the debenzoylated compound to yield a dialdehyde identical with that obtained from β-D-glucopyranosyl azide. Catalytic reduction of 2,3,5-tri-O-benzoyl-β-D-ribofuranosyl azide gave an anomeric mixture of ribosylamines which on treatment with benzyloxycarbonylglycyl chloride (or the ethyl carbonate) followed by debenzoylation with sodium methoxide yielded the α- and β-anomers of N-(benzyloxycarbonylglycyl)-D-ribofuranosyl-amine. These were separated readily by crystallisation. Hydrogenolysis then gave the N-glycylribofuranosylamines, the α- and β-forms of which were relatively stable, unlike the ribofuranosylamines which readily mutarotate.[314]

Ring closure of a glycosylamine derivative has been used to prepare pyrimidine nucleosides. Various 5-cyano-3-D-glycosyluracils[315] were obtained by the reaction of D-glycosylamines with α-cyano-β-ethoxy-N-ethoxycarbonylacrylamide; uridine was synthesised in similar fashion from β-ethoxy-N-ethoxycarbonylacrylamide and tri-O-benzoyl-D-ribofuranosylamine (a mixture of the α- and β-anomers) followed by debenzoylation of the product.[316]

An analogous reaction of tri-O-benzoyl-D-ribofuranosylamine with β-ethoxyacryloyl isothiocyanate or β-methoxy-α-methylacryloyl iso-

R=H, R′= ribo-, xylo-, galacto-, gluco-, and 2-deoxyglucopyranosyls
R=H, R′= ribofuranosyl
R=CH₃, R′= ribo-, xylo-, galacto-, and glucopyranosyls

thiocyanate yielded 2-thiouridine (converted into uridine by the action of aqueous chloracetic acid) or 5-methyl-2-thiouridine respectively, after removal of the benzoyl groups.[316]

In all cases only the β-nucleoside was obtained, none of the isomeric α-compounds being detected. It is likely that pyrimidine nucleoside formation via linear precursors of the type ribose—NH.CH=CR.CO.-NHCOOEt follows a general rule to give a 1,2-*trans* configuration at the glycosyl linkage; molecular models suggest that the β-linear forms should cyclise more readily than the α anomers in which steric hindrance of the NH group by the 2′-O-benzoyl group occurs.[316]

An alternate synthesis of 5-amino-1-β-D-ribofuranosylimidazole-4-carboxamide also makes use of a linear ribofuranosylamine derivative. Reaction of the imino-ether ethyl-N-(carbamoylcyanomethyl) formimidate (readily prepared from ethyl formimidate hydrochloride and α-amino-α-cyanoacetamide in aqueous solution) with 2,3,5-tri-O-benzoylribofuranosylamine and debenzoylation of the product gave a good yield of 5-amino-1-β-D-ribofuranosylimidazole-4-carboxamide, the structure of which was established by conversion of the compound into inosine on treatment with formic acid and acetic anhydride.[317]   A similar reaction sequence involving a formimidate prepared from methyl α-amino-α-cyanoacetate instead of α-amino-α-cyanoacetamide gave methyl 5-amino-β-D-ribofuranosylimidazole-4 carboxylate.[318] This was converted into 5-amino-1-β-D-ribofuranosylimidazole-4 carboxylic acid 5′-phosphate by standard methods. Similarly, treatment of 5-amino-2′,3′-O-isopropylidene-1-β-D-ribofuranosylimidazole-4 carboxylate with dimethyl L-aspartate and dicyclohexylcarbodi-imide, followed by phosphorylation of the resultant succinyl derivative (with 2-cyanoethyl phosphate and dicyclohexylcarbodi-imide) and removal of protecting groups gave N-(5-amino-1-β-D-ribofuranosyl-4-imidazolylcarbonyl)-L-aspartic acid-5′ phosphate (i.e. succinyl aminoimidazole carboxamide ribonucleotide, another intermediate in the biosynthesis of purine nucleotides) in good overall yield.[319]

RNH₂ = 2,3,5 – Tri – O – benzoylribofuranosylamine

The synthesis of several 3-D-glycosyl derivatives of 4-aminouracil by a Traube reaction of O-acylglycosylureas with cyanoacetic acid, has been reported.[320] A related approach has also been used for the synthesis of thymidine.[321] Urea was condensed with 3,5-di-O-benzoyl (or p-toluoyl, anisoyl, p-chlorobenzoyl, or p-nitrobenzoyl)-2-deoxy-D-ribofuranose and the resultant deoxyribofuranosylurea treated with β-ethyoxy-α-methylacryloyl chloride to give 1-(β-ethoxy-α-methyl-acryloyl)-3-(3′,5′-di-O-benzoyl-2′-deoxy-D-ribofuranosyl)-urea. Cyclisation then yielded the 3′,5′-di-O-acylthymidine from which the free deoxynucleoside was obtained in the usual manner.

R′=3,5-D₁-O-benzoyl-2-deoxy-D-ribofuranose

Various glycitylpurines and glycityltriazolopyrimidines, have been synthesised by ring closure of appropriate 5-amino-4-glycitylamino-pyrimidines. These are readily obtained by treating a 4-chloro-5-nitropyrimidine with the glycitylamine in aqueous solution followed by reduction of the nitro group.[322] Thus reduction of the product from 6-amino-4-chloro-5-nitropyrimidine and D-ribitylamine gave 5,6-di-amino-4-D-ribitylaminopyrimidine which on ring closure yielded 9-D-ribityladenine. In a similar fashion 9-ribitylguanine was obtained from 2,5-diamino-6-hydroxy-4-D-ribitylaminopyrimidine.

R = D-Ribityl

Class 3. Alteration of base or sugar moieties of preformed nucleoside. Inversion of a sugar hydroxyl group via cyclonucleoside formation was first observed with O^2,3′-cyclothymidine, which on alkaline hydrolysis gave 3-β-D-2′-deoxyxylofuranosylthymine.[323] Subsequently, similar results were obtained with ribonucleosides. As a general approach, the formation of O^2,2′ cyclonucleosides, and subsequent ring opening, is of considerable value for the synthesis of glycosyl anomers that, because of the C1—C2 *trans* rule, would not be obtained readily by previously described methods. In this way spongouridine,[324] 3-β-D-arabino-furanosylthymine (spongothymidine),[325] 3-β-D-arabinofuranosyl-5-fluorouracil,[326] and 3-β-D-lyxofuranosylthymine[327] were prepared from suitable sulphonyl-ribosyl (or xylosyl in the last case) derivatives.

R = H or CH₃; X = CH₃SO₂ or CH₃C₆H₄SO₂

In similar fashion, 3-β-D-xylofuranosyluracil was converted into the lyxosyl nucleoside via 2'-O-methanesulphonyl-3-β-D-xylofuranosyl-uracil. With one equivalent of alkali this gave an $O^2,2'$-cyclonucleoside (of lyxo configuration) isomeric with $O^2,2'$-cyclouridine (arabino configuration). Further action of alkali yielded 3-β-D-lyxofuranosyl-uracil. Boiling an aqueous solution of the 2'-O-methanesulphonyl nucleoside also yielded $O^2,2'$-cyclo-3-β-D-lyxofuranosyluracil; prolonged reaction led to 3-β-D-lyxofuranosyluracil as a result of acidic hydrolysis of the cyclonucleoside by the liberated methanesulphonic acid.[328]

More conveniently, 3-β-D-lyxofuranosyluracil has been obtained simply by boiling an aqueous solution of 3',5'-di-O-methanesulphonyl-$O^2,2'$-cyclouridine (readily obtained by treatment of 2',3',5'-tri-O-methanesulphonyluridine with one equivalent of sodium hydroxide) or 5'-O-benzoyl-3'-O-methanesulphonyl-$O^2,2'$-cyclouridine. The re-action sequence involves formation of 3'-O-methanesulphonyl-3-β-D-

NUCLEOSIDES AND NUCLEOTIDES

arabinofuranosyluracil and $O^2,3'$-cyclolyxofuranosyluracil intermediates, the latter being hydrolysed under the acidic conditions (resulting from liberation of methanesulphonic acid) to lyxofuranosyluracil derivatives.[329]

Ms = CH_3SO_2
R = CH_3SO_2 or PhCO
Also related reaction sequence with
5'- deoxy derivatives i.e. −OR = −H

The versatility of 2',3',5'-tri-O-methanesulphonyluridine as an intermediate for the synthesis of isomeric pentofuranosyluracils has been amply demonstrated.[330] Displacement of all three sulphonyloxy groups by nucleophilic attack can occur under mild conditions. Treatment with sodium benzoate in dimethylformamide gave 3',5'-di-O-benzoyl-O^2,2'-cyclouridine and 2',3',5'-tri-O-benzoyl-3-β-D-xylofuranosyluracil; in addition, alkaline hydrolysis of the reaction mixture (after removal of the previously named compounds) yielded all four possible 3-β-D-pentofuranosyluracils (ribosyl, arabinosyl, xylosyl, and lyxosyl). Plausible mechanisms for the formation of these compounds have been advanced, among which may be mentioned the suggestion

Ms = CH₃SO₂
Bz = C₆H₅CO

of anchimeric assistance from a C_2—O—C_2' oxygen of a cyclonucleoside in the formation of the 3',5'-di-O-benzoyl O^2,2'-cyclouridine. Here the oxygen exerts a nucleophilic influence on C3' assisting in the elimination of the 3'-methanesulphonyloxy group and resulting in the formation of a transitory cyclic oxonium ion intermediate. Attack by benzoate ion (preferentially at C3′ rather than C2′ in accord with the behaviour of 2′,3′ epoxide derivatives of nucleosides) then gives a product with no net inversion at C3′, the result of two successive inversions.[330]

Treatment of 2′,3′,5′-tri-O-methanesulphonyluridine with three equivalents of aqueous sodium hydroxide yields a nucleoside epoxide, 5′-O-methanesulphonyl-2′,3′-anhydro-3-β-D-lyxofuranosyluracil, via 3′,5′-di-O-methanesulphonyl-O^2,2′-cyclouridine and 3′,5′-di-O-methane-sulphonyl-3-β-D-arabinofuranosyluracil.[331] Similarly, acidic hydrolysis of 5′-O-benzoyl-3′-O-methanesulphonyl-O^2,2′-cyclouridine gives the benzoyl methanesulphonylarabinosyl nucleoside which on treatment with dilute ammonia yields 5′-O-benzoyl-2′,3′-anhydro-3-β-D-lyxo-furanosyluracil. Removal of the benzoyl group, followed by a further treatment with ammonia gives an aminonucleoside, 3′-amino-3′-deoxy-3-β-D-arabinofuranosyluracil.[331]

Ms = CH_3SO_2

An alternate route to β-arabinosyl pyrimidine nucleosides involves synthesis of the O^2,2′-cyclonucleoside via a 2′,3′-anhydroribosyl derivative. Condensation of 2-O-acetyl-3-O-toluene-p-sulphonyl-5-O-

methoxycarbonyl-xylofuranosyl chloride with dithyminyl mercury (or with monomercury 5-fluorouracil) gives the β-nucleoside which, treated directly with sodium methoxide, is converted into an $O^2,2'$-cyclonucleoside, the intermediate $2',3'$-anhydronucleoside being readily interconvertible with the cyclonucleoside.[332] Owing to the influence of the pyrimidine 2-keto group the behaviour of the $2',3'$-anhydroribosyl is atypical in that opening of the epoxide ring occurs by attack at C2' rather than at C3' to give an arabinosyl derivative and not a xylosyl nucleoside.

R = CH₃ or F
Ts = CH₃C₆H₄SO₂

As previously mentioned, $3'-O$-sulphonylthymidine derivatives are readily converted into deoxyxylofuranosyl nucleosides via an $O^2,3'$-cyclonucleoside that is readily formed by the action of weak bases.[323] The same procedure has been applied to uridine derivatives, though somewhat stronger reagents must be used for the preparation of the cyclonucleoside. Under suitable conditions tritylation of uridine gives $2',5'$-di-O-trityluridine (readily separated from the contaminating isomeric $3',5'$-ditrityl derivative by crystallisation); further treatment with methanesulphonyl chloride gives the $3'-O$-methanesulphonyl derivative and this is converted into $2',5'$-di-O-trityl-$O^2,3'$-cyclouridine by the action of sodium benzoate in dimethylformamide. Alkaline hydrolysis of the protected cyclonucleoside (or more directly of $2',5'$-di-O-trityl-$3'-O$-methanesulphonyluridine) followed by removal of the trityl groups then gives 3-β-D-xylofuranosyluracil.[328] Curiously, $3'-O$-methanesulphonyluridine (obtained by detritylation of the pro-

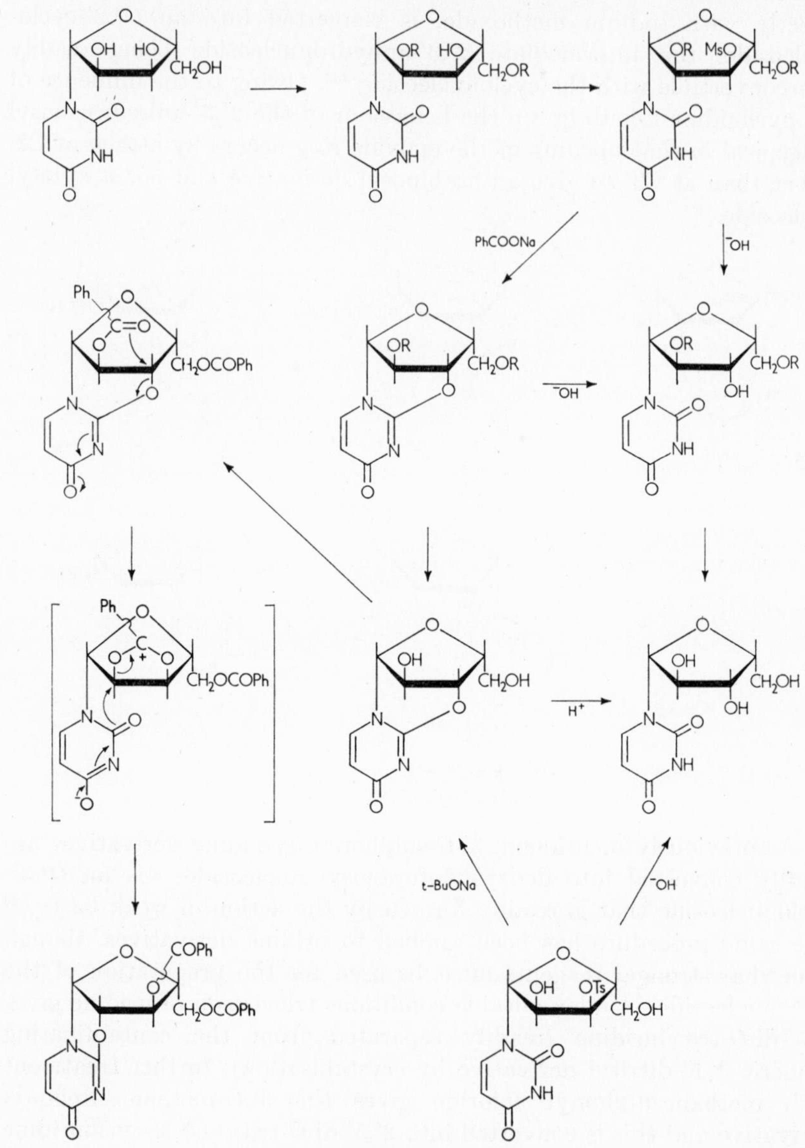

R = Triphenylmethyl
Ms = CH$_3$SO$_2$
Ts = CH$_3$C$_6$H$_4$SO$_2$

tected derivative) was resistant to treatment with sodium benzoate in dimethylformamide and the free $O^2,3'$-cyclonucleoside was obtained by detritylation of the ditrityl-$O^2,3'$-cyclouridine.[328] However, formation of $O^2,3'$-cyclouridine by the action of sodium t-butoxide on $3'$-O-toluene-p-sulphonyluridine has been reported.[333] Direct alkaline hydrolysis of the sulphonyl derivative yields 3-β-D-xylofuranosyl-uracil;[333] this is also obtained by acidic hydrolysis of $O^2,3'$-cyclouridine.[328]

Heating $2',5'$-di-O-benzoyl-$O^2,3'$-cyclouridine to the melting point causes rapid isomerisation to $3',5'$-di-O-benzoyl-$O^2,2'$-cyclouridine, possibly via an orthoester ion. The $O^2,3'$-cyclonucleoside thus serves as an intermediate for both xylofuranosyl and arabinosyl nucleosides.[328]

Although $O^2,2'$-cyclouridine is hydrolysed to 3-β-D-arabinofuranosyl-uracil (spongouridine), acidic hydrolysis of $3',5'$-di-O-acetyl-$O^2,2'$-cyclouridine yields a mixture of uridine and spongouridine, the former presumably arising through intervention of the neighbouring acyl group to give an intermediate ion.[334]

Ts $=$ $CH_3C_6H_4SO_2$

Prolonged treatment of cytidine with polyphosphoric acid followed by dephosphorylation of the product gives $O^2,2'$-cyclocytidine. This is hydrolysed by alkali to 3-β-D-arabinofuranosylcytosine which on deamination yields spongouridine, also obtained by an analogous polyphosphoric acid treatment of uridine.[335]

Apart from their use for specific inversion of sugar hydroxyl groups, pyrimidine $O^2,2'$-cyclonucleosides have proved strikingly successful as intermediates in the synthesis of $2'$-deoxynucleosides. Treatment of $5'$-O-acetyl-$2'$-O-toluene-p-sulphonyluridine with sodium iodide gave

5'-O-acetyl-2'-deoxy-2'-iodouridine from which 2'-deoxyuridine was obtained by hydrogenation and deacetylation.[336] The same iodo derivative (of ribo-configuration) was formed by the action of sodium iodide and acetic acid on 5'-O-acetyl-O^2,2'-cyclouridine, into which it could be reconverted by treatment with base.[334] This cyclonucleoside was probably an intermediate in the replacement of the toluene-p-sulphonyloxy group by iodine, the final product being the result of two displacements with inversion at C2'. The same procedures applied to 5'-O-acetyl-3-β-D-ribofuranosylthymine yielded thymidine.[336]

Similar ring opening of O^2,2'-cyclouridine (involving nucleophilic attack at C2') by treatment with anhydrous hydrogen halide gave 2'-fluoro-2'-deoxyuridine, 2'-chloro-2'-deoxyuridine, and 2'-bromo-2'-deoxyuridine, all of ribo configuration.[337]

In an alternate approach, 5'-O-trityl-5-methyl-2-thiouridine was treated with methanesulphonyl chloride in pyridine to give the cyclonucleoside directly in this case. Ring opening by acidic hydrolysis

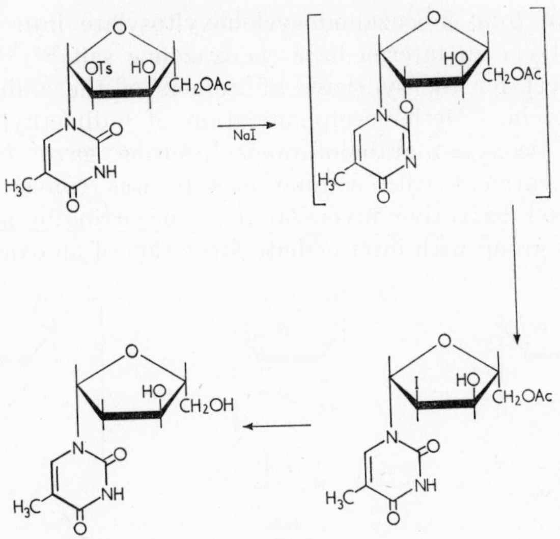

Ts = CH₃C₆H₄SO₂

followed by desulphurisation with Raney nickel in alkali gave a small yield of thymidine.[338]

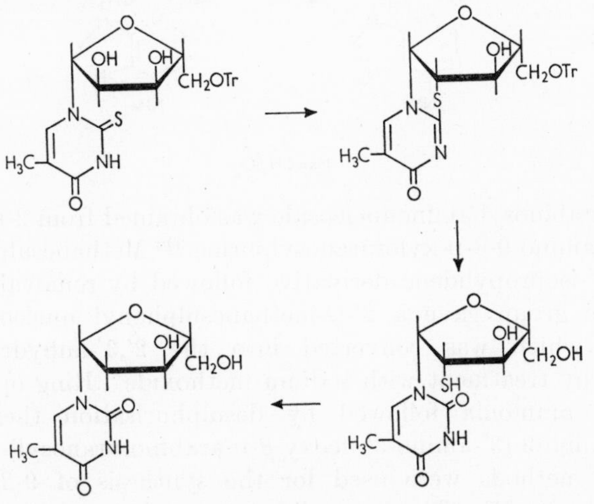

Tr = triphenylmethyl

With glycosylpurines, stereochemical considerations preclude the formation of cyclonucleosides involving 2′-hydroxyl groups, and in any case, cleavage of the purine ring would presumably occur as with the N^3,5′-cyclonucleoside salts. However, Baker and his co-workers have used reactions analogous to cyclonucleoside formation (and to the conversion of *trans*-2-benzamidocyclohexyltosylate into *cis*-2-amino-cyclohexanol via an intermediate *cis*-oxazoline salt)[339, 340] with considerable effect for the synthesis of isomers of the aminonucleoside from puromycin. Methanesulphonylation of 6-dimethylamino-9-(3'-acetamido-3'-deoxy-α-D-arabinofuranosyl)-purine gave a dimesylate which on treatment with sodium acetate was converted into an α-ribofuranosyl derivative, inversion at C2' occurring by attack of the 3'-acetamido group with intermediate formation of an oxazoline.[341]

Ms = CH₃SO₂

The β-arabinosyl aminonucleoside was obtained from 2-methylthio-6-dimethylamino-9-β-D-xylofuranosylpurine.[342] Methanesulphonylation of the 3',5'-isopropylidene derivative followed by removal of the iso-propylidene group gave a 2'-O-methanesulphonyl nucleoside (xylo-furanosyl) which was converted into the 2',3'-anhydro-D-lyxosyl compound by treatment with sodium methoxide. Ring opening with methanolic ammonia followed by desulphurisation then gave 6-dimethylamino-9-(3'-amino-3'-deoxy-β-D-arabinofuranosyl)-purine.

Similar methods were used for the synthesis of 9-β-D-arabino-furanosyladenine.[343] (The more direct route from arabinohalogenose and metalo-purine gives the α-anomer.) Methanesulphonylation of 9-(3',5'-O-isopropylidene-β-D-xylofuranosyl)-adenine followed by re-moval of the isopropylidene group gave the 2'-O-methanesulphonyl nucleoside which on treatment with base gave 9-(2',3'-anhydro-β-D-lyxofuranosyl)-adenine. However, application of the usual hydrolytic procedure with alkali resulted in glycosyl cleavage and liberation of

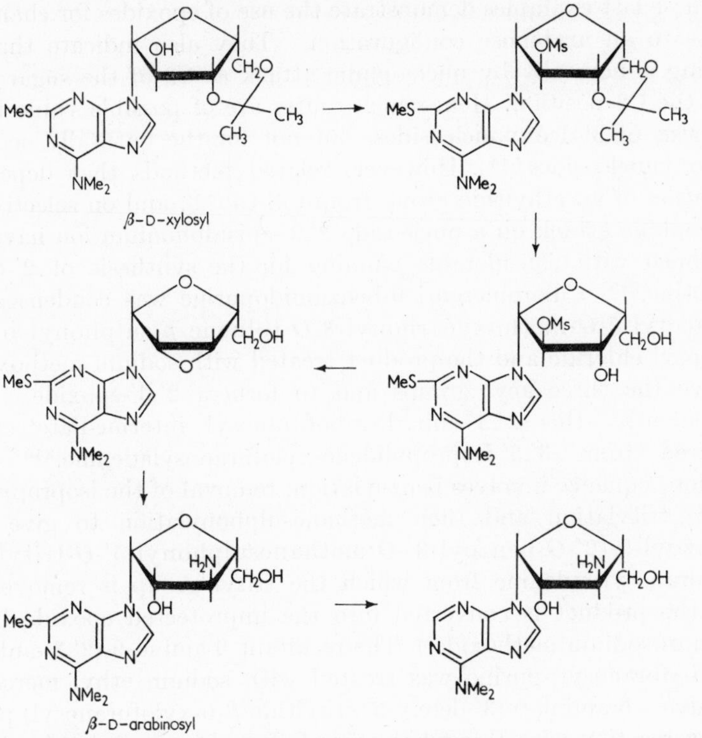

β-D-xylosyl

β-D-arabinosyl

adenine. The anhydronucleoside was resistant to hot acetic acid, but treatment with the powerful nucleophilic reagent, sodium benzoate in wet dimethylformamide, gave a good yield of 9-β-D-arabinofuranosyl-adenine with only a trace of the xylofuranosyl derivative.

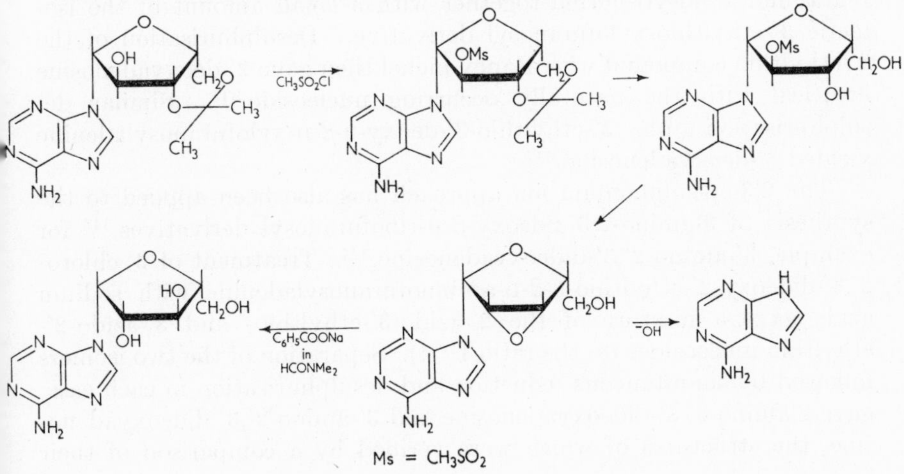

Ms = CH₃SO₂

These last examples demonstrate the use of epoxides for changing a xylose to an arabinose configuration. They also indicate that ring opening is normally by nucleophilic attack at C3 of the sugar rather than the C2 position. Hence such routes are of possible value for the synthesis of 3'-deoxynucleosides, but not for the naturally occurring 2'-deoxynucleosides.[344] However, related methods that depend on migration of an ethylthio group from C3' to C2', and on selectivity of nucleophilic attack on a nucleoside 2',3'-episulphonium ion have been developed with considerable cunning for the synthesis of 2'-deoxy-adenosine.[345] Chloromercuri 6-benzamidopurine was condensed with 2-O-acetyl-5-O-methoxycarbonyl-3-O-toluene-p-sulphonyl-D-xylo-furanosyl chloride and the product treated with sodium methoxide to remove the three acyl groups and to form a 2',3'-epoxide. (More conveniently, this 2',3'-anhydroribofuranosyl intermediate can be prepared from 3',5'-isopropylidene-xylofuranosyladenine.[346] The reaction sequence involves benzoylation, removal of the isopropylidene group, tritylation and then methanesulphonylation to give N,N-dibenzoyl-9-(2'-O-benzoyl-3'-O-methanesulphonyl-5'-O-trityl-β-D-xylofuranosyl)-adenine from which the trityl group is removed and then the product is converted into the unprotected epoxide by the action of sodium methoxide.) The resultant 6-amino-9-(2',3'-anhydro-β-D-ribofuranosyl)-purine was treated with sodium ethyl mercaptide to give 6-amino-9-(3'-deoxy-3'-ethylthio-β-D-xylofuranosyl)-purine; this on reaction with thionyl chloride followed by sodium bicarbonate yielded 6-amino-9-(3'chloro-2',3'-dideoxy-2'-ethylthio-β-D-arabino-furanosyl)-purine.

"Acetolysis" of this chloronucleoside with sodium acetate in 95% aqueous methyl Cellosolve gave 6-amino-9-(2'-deoxy-2'-ethylthio-β-D-arabinofuranosyl)-purine together with a small amount of the iso-meric 3'-ethylthio-xylofuranosyl derivative. Desulphurisation of the 2'-ethylthio compound with Raney nickel then gave 2'-deoxyadenosine identical with the naturally occurring nucleoside.[345] Similar de-sulphurisation of 3'-ethylthio-3'-deoxy-9-β-D-xylofuranosyladenine yielded 3'-deoxyadenosine.[347]

The 2,3-episulphonium ion approach has also been applied to the synthesis of 3-amino-2,3-dideoxy-β-D-ribofuranosyl derivatives,[348] for example, 3'-amino-2',3'-dideoxyadenosine.[347] Treatment of 3'-chloro-2',3'-dideoxy-2'-ethylthio-9-β-D-arabinofuranosyladenine with sodium azide gave a mixture of the 2'-azido-3'-ethylthio- and 3'-azido-2'-ethylthio-nucleosides (in the ratio 1 : 4). Separation of the two isomers followed by simultaneous reduction and desulphurisation in each case, gave 2'amino-2',3'-dideoxyadenosine and 3'-amino-2',3'-dideoxyadeno-sine, the structures of which were verified by a comparison of their nuclear magnetic resonance spectra with those of 3′-deoxyadenosine and 2′-deoxyadenosine.

Direct replacement of a secondary sulphonyloxy group proved successful in an alternate synthesis of 3′-deoxyadenosine.[349] Treatment of 5′-O-acetyladenosine with p-nitrobenzenesulphonyl chloride followed by removal of the acetyl group gave a mixture of 2′- and 3′-O-p-nitrobenzenesulphonyladenosine. These were separated by fractional crystallisation, the 2′-ester being sparingly soluble in propan-2-ol.

Reaction of 3'-O-p-nitrobenzenesulphonyladenosine with sodium iodide under rather vigorous conditions then gave the 3'-iodo-3'-deoxynucleoside (presumably of xylo configuration) which was hydrogenolysed to 3'-deoxyadenosine. A similar procedure applied to 2'-O-p-nitrobenzenesulphonyladenosine was unsuccessful, possibly owing to steric hindrance.

R = H or H_2N

As with changes in the sugar moiety, modification of substituents in the purine or pyrimidine base is closely associated with the synthetic methods previously described, particularly the mercuri condensation procedure. In this section, therefore, chemical alteration of the base in naturally occurring nucleosides only, will be considered.

The direct conversion of inosine and guanosine into thioinosine
(9-β-D-ribofuranosyl-6-mercaptopurine) and thioguanosine (9-β-D-ribo-
furanosyl-2-amino-6-mercaptopurine) respectively by thiation (earlier
applied to purines and pyrimidines) provides a simple route to compounds of possible importance as anti-tumour agents and bacterial
growth antagonists.[350] Treatment of 2′,3′,5′-tri-O-benzoylinosine with
phosphorus pentasulphide in pyridine gave the 6-mercapto analogue
from which thioinosine was obtained by deacylation. Reduction of
thioinosine gave nebularine, while treatment with methyl iodide gave
the 6-methylmercapto derivative from which adenosine was obtained
by the action of alcoholic ammonia. In like manner, conversion of
guanosine into thioguanosine followed by desulphurisation yielded
2-amino-9-β-D-ribofuranosylpurine.[350] Thioinosine is conveniently
labelled by means of an exchange reaction that occurs on refluxing the
nucleoside with elementary ^{35}S in pyridine.[351]

Chlorination of 2′,3′,5′-tri-O-acetylinosine and 2′,3′,5′-tri-O-acetyl-
guanosine gives the corresponding 6-chloro derivatives from which the
6-thio compounds can be obtained by treatment with sodium thioacetate
followed by deacetylation.[352] Reconversion of 6-thio and 6-methylthio
purine nucleosides into the corresponding 6-chloro derivatives is readily
achieved by treatment with chlorine at low temperatures.[353]

Application of the thiation procedure to both ribo- and deoxyribo-
pyrimidine nucleosides gave reactive intermediates from which not
only the naturally occurring basic nucleosides were obtained, but also a
host of 6-substituted analogues.[354] Thus thiation of 3′,5′-di-O-benzoyl-
thymidine gave the 6-thio compound which on treatment with alcoholic
ammonia yielded 5-methyl-2′-deoxycytidine. In the same way,
uridine and 3-β-D-ribofuranosylthymine were converted into cytidine
and 5-methylcytidine respectively; extension to 5-fluorouridine and
5-fluoro-2′-deoxyuridine yielded the corresponding glycosyl-5-fluoro-
cytosines.[355] Similarly, 4-azacytidine has been obtained by successive
thiation, amination and debenzoylation of tri-O-benzoyl-4-
azauridine.[356, 357] Treatment of acylated 6-thio-nucleosides (including
the 2′-deoxy derivatives) with suitable reagents yielded 6-alkylamino,
6-hydrazino, 6-hydroxylamino and other analogues.[354] Complete
hydrogenation of the heterocyclic nucleus to give 2-oxo-hexahydro-
pyrimidine nucleosides occurred on desulphurisation of 6-thiothymidine
or 6-thiouridine with activated Raney nickel. This facile extensive reduction is characteristic of 6-thiouracils and 2-hydroxypyrimidines,
but not of 2-thiouracil or 6-hydroxypyrimidines.[358]

The addition of formaldehyde to pyrimidine nucleotides to form
5-hydroxymethyl and 5-methyl derivatives is of importance in the
metabolism of nucleic acids. Chemically, the reaction of uracil nucleo-

sides with formaldehyde, as with other electrophilic reagents, is selective for C5 of the pyrimidine ring. Treatment of uridine or 2'-deoxyuridine with formaldehyde in the presence of hydrochloric acid gave the 5-hydroxymethyl compound which on hydrogenation yielded 3-β-D-ribofuranosylthymine (5-methyluridine) or thymidine respectively.[359] Condensation of the 5-hydroxymethyl-nucleosides with acids and alcohols occurred readily, and catalytic oxidation gave 5-formyl derivatives.

Related procedures have been developed for the aminomethylation and chloromethylation of uracil, and it is likely that they could be extended to pyrimidine nucleosides and deoxynucleosides. Thus the reaction of uracil with morpholine and formalin gives 5-morpholino-methyluracil; 5-chloromethyluracil is obtained by an analogous treatment with formalin and hydrochloric acid. Both compounds yield thymine on hydrogenolysis. The chlorine atom in 5-chloromethyluracil is remarkably reactive and silver carbonate converts the compound into 5-hydroxymethyluracil.[360]

An alternate approach has been used for the conversion of deoxyuridine into thymidine. Treatment of 5-bromo-2′-deoxyuridine with butyl lithium (to give the 5-lithium compound) followed by reaction with methyl iodide gave thymidine in some 10% yield.[361] This type of reaction has also been applied to the synthesis of pseudouridine.

Conversion of pyrimidine cyclonucleosides into O^2-alkyl and 2-amino derivatives has been described earlier (p. 20).

Synthesis of purine nucleosides via ribosylimidazoles has been described; the procedure can be reversed to obtain 5-amino-1-β-D-ribofuranosylimidazole-4-carboxamide from a readily available ribonucleoside. Benzylation of inosine gave N^1-benzylinosine from which

C2 was readily eliminated by alkaline degradation to give 5-amino-1-β-D-ribofuranosylimidazole-4-N-benzylcarboxamide. Removal of the benzyl group was achieved by treatment with sodium in liquid ammonia.[362]

More conveniently, the ribosyl-5-aminoimidazole-4-carboxamide, and derivatives thereof, can be prepared from N^1-toluene-p-sulphonyl-inosine.[363] Treatment of 2',3',5'-tri-O-acetylinosine with sodium hydride gave the sodio derivative which on reaction with toluene-p-sulphonyl chloride yielded the N^1-toluene-p-sulphonyl nucleoside. Alkaline hydrolysis produced 1-β-D-ribosyl-5-aminoimidazole-4-(N-tosyl)-carboxamide from which the carboxyhydrazide was obtained by hydrazinolysis. Hydrogenolysis of 1-ribosyl-5-aminoimidazole-4-carboxyhydrazide then gave the carboxamide derivative.[363] Treatment of 1-ribosyl-5-aminoimidazole-4-carboxyhydrazide with one equivalent of nitrous acid resulted in selective reaction at the hydrazide group to yield the azide. Further reaction with L-aspartic acid gave 1-β-D-ribosyl-5-aminoimidazole-4-carbonyl-L-aspartic acid.[364]

A related approach has been used for the synthesis of 1-β-D-ribo-furanosyl-5-aminoimidazole-4-carboxamide-5' phosphate. Alkylation at N^1 of 2',3'-isopropylidene-inosine-5' di-(p-nitrophenyl) phosphate with chloromethyl methyl ether followed by alkaline ring opening (under the conditions employed, concomitant hydrolysis of the methoxymethyl group also occurred) gave an intermediate from which the free nucleotide was obtained on removal of all protecting groups.[364]

The utility of the interconversions described in this section can be appreciated when it is realised that any synthesis of, for example, uridine, is in effect a synthesis of 2'-deoxyuridine, cytidine, 2'-deoxy-cytidine, 5-methyluridine, thymidine, 5-methylcytidine, and 5-methyl-deoxycytidine, in addition to the 5-hydroxymethyl derivatives. Together with deamination of the basic nucleosides and the synthesis of two or more nucleosides (e.g. adenosine and guanosine) from a common intermediate, these conversions provide convincing confirmation of the structures assigned to the naturally occurring nucleosides.

REFERENCES

1. Levene, P. A., and Jacobs, W. A., *Chem. Ber.*, **42**, 2475 (1909).
2. Levene, P. A., and Jacobs, W. A., *Chem. Ber.*, **43**, 3150 (1910).
3. Bredereck, H., Martini, A., and Richter, F., *Chem. Ber.*, **74**, 694 (1941).
4. Allen, F. W., and Bacher, J. E., *J. Biol. Chem.*, **188**, 59 (1951).
5. Hayes, D. H., *J. Chem. Soc.*, 1184 (1960).
6. Elmore, D. T., *J. Chem. Soc.*, 2084 (1950).
7. Schindler, O., *Helv. Chim. Acta*, **32**, 979 (1949).
8. Andersen, W., Dekker, C. A., and Todd. A. R., *J. Chem. Soc.*, 2721 (1952).
9. Dunn, D. B., *Biochim. et Biophys. Acta*, **34**, 286 (1959).
10. Smith, J. D., and Dunn, D. B., *Biochim. et Biophys. Acta*, **31**, 573 (1959).
11. Biswas, B. B., and Myers, J., *Nature*, **186**, 238 (1960).
12. Wyatt, G. R., and Cohen, S. S., *Biochem. J.*, **55**, 774 (1953).
13. Dekker, C. A., and Elmore, D. T., *J. Chem. Soc.*, 2864 (1951).
14. Wyatt, G. R., *Biochem. J.*, **48**, 581, 584 (1951).
15. Dunn, D. B., and Smith, J. D., *Biochem. J.*, **68**, 627 (1958).
16. Dekker, C. A., and Todd, A. R., *Nature*, **166**, 557 (1950).
17. Levene, P. A., and London, E. S., *J. Biol. Chem.*, **83**, 793 (1929).
18. Levene, P. A., and Jacobs, W. A., *Chem. Ber.*, **44**, 746 (1911).
19. Levene, P. A., and La Forge, F. B., *Chem. Ber.*, **45**, 608 (1912).
20. Barker, G. R., Farrar, K. R., and Gulland, J. M., *J. Chem. Soc.*, 21 (1947).
21. Levene, P. A., and Mori, T., *J. Biol. Chem.*, **83**, 803 (1929).
22. Levene, P. A., Mikeska, L. A., and Mori, T., *J. Biol. Chem.*, **85**, 785 (1930).
23. Kent, P. W., *Nature*, **166**, 442 (1950).
24. Vischer, E., Zamenhof, S., and Chargaff, E., *J. Biol. Chem.*, **177**, 429 (1949).
25. Burke, D. C., *Chem. and Ind.* (*London*), 1393 (1954).
26. Laland, S. G., and Roth, E., *Acta Chem. Scand.*, **10**, 1058 (1956).
27. Haavaldsen, L., Laland, S. G., McKee, J. M., and Roth, E., *Biochim. et Biophys. Acta*, **33**, 201 (1959).

28. Walker, I. G., and Butler, G. C., *Canadian J. Chem.*, **34,** 1168 (1956).
29. Levene, P. A., *J. Biol. Chem.*, **55,** 437 (1923).
30. Gulland, J. M., and Holiday, E. R., *J. Chem. Soc.*, 765 (1936).
31. Gulland, J. M., and Story, L. F., *J. Chem. Soc.*, **259,** 692 (1938).
32. Gulland, J. M., Holiday, E. R., and Macrae, T. F., *J. Chem. Soc.*, 1639 (1934).
33. Lythgoe, B., Smith, H., and Todd, A. R., *J. Chem. Soc.*, 355 (1947).
34. Levene, P. A., *J. Biol. Chem.*, **63,** 653 (1925).
35. Levene, P. A., and Tipson, R. S., *J. Biol. Chem.*, **104,** 385 (1934).
36. Bredereck, H., Müller, G., and Berger, E., *Chem. Ber.*, **73,** 1058 (1940).
37. Levene, P. A., and Tipson, R. S., *J. Biol. Chem.*, **94,** 809 (1932); **97,** 491 (1932); **101,** 529 (1933).
38. Levene, P. A., and Stiller, E. T., *J. Biol. Chem.*, **102,** 187 (1933).
39. Lythgoe, B., and Todd, A. R., *J. Chem. Soc.*, 592 (1944).
40. Brown, D. M., and Lythgoe, B., *J. Chem. Soc.*, 1990 (1940).
41. Levene, P. A., and Tipson, R. S., *Z. physiol. Chem.*, **234,** V (1935).
42. Makino, K., *Biochem. Z.*, **282,** 263 (1935).
43. Davoll, J., Lythgoe, B., and Todd, A. R., *J. Chem. Soc.*, 833 (1946).
44. Clark, V. M., Todd, A. R., and Zussman, J., *J. Chem. Soc.*, 2952 (1951).
45. Furberg, S., *Acta Chem. Scand.*, **4,** 751 (1950).
46. Miles, H. T., *Biochim. et Biophys. Acta*, **22,** 247 (1956); **27,** 46 (1958).
47. Angell, C. L., *J. Chem. Soc.*, 504 (1951).
48. Littlefield, J. W., and Dunn, D. B., *Biochem J.*, **70,** 642 (1958).
49. Smith, J. D., and Dunn, D. B., *Biochem. J.*, **72,** 294 (1959).
50. Kemp, J. W., and Allen, F. W., *Biochim. et Biophys. Acta*, **28,** 51 (1958).
51. Amos, H., and Korn, M., *Biochim. et Biophys. Acta*, **29,** 444 (1958).
52. Davis, F. F., Carlucci, A. F., and Roubein, I. F., *J. Biol. Chem.*, **234,** 1525 (1959).
53. Adler, M., Weissmann, B., and Gutman, A. B., *J. Biol. Chem.*, **230,** 717 (1958).
54. Cohn, W. E., *Biochim. Biophys. Acta*, **32,** 569 (1959).
55. Cohn, W. E., *J. Biol. Chem.*, **235,** 1488 (1960).
56. Yu, C., and Allen, F. W., *Biochim. et Biophys. Acta*, **32,** 393 (1959).
57. Scannell, J. P., Crestfield, A. M., and Allen, F. W., *Biochim. et Biophys. Acta*, **32,** 406 (1959).
58. Lis, A. W., and Allen, F. W., *Biochim. et Biophys. Acta*, **49,** 190 (1961).
59. Shapiro, R., and Chambers, R. W., *J. Am. Chem. Soc.*, **83,** 3920 (1961).
60. Michelson, A. M., and Cohn, W. E., *J. Biochem.*, **1,** 490 (1962).
61. Mudd, S. H., Jamieson, G. A., and Cantoni, G. L., *Biochim. et Biophys. Acta*, **38,** 164 (1960).
62. Andersen, W., Hayes, D. H., Michelson, A. M., and Todd, A. R., *J. Chem. Soc.*, 1882 (1954).
63. Baker, B. R., and Joseph, J. P., *J. Am. Chem. Soc.*, **77,** 15 (1955).
64. Chambers, R. W., Moffatt, J. G., and Khorana, H. G., *J. Am. Chem. Soc.*, **79,** 3747 (1957).
65. Walwick, E. R., Roberts, W. K., and Dekker, C. A., *Proc. Chem. Soc.*, 84 (1959).
66. Michelson, A. M., and Todd, A. R., *J. Chem. Soc.*, 816 (1955).
67. Brown, D. M., Todd, A. R., and Varadarajan, S., *J. Chem. Soc.*, 868 (1957)
68. Brown, D. M., Todd, A. R., and Varadarajan, S., *J. Chem. Soc.*, 2388 (1956).

69. Fox, J. J., Yung, N. C., and Bendich, A., *J. Am. Chem. Soc.*, **79**, 2775 (1957).
70. Fox, J. J., Codington, J. F., Yung, N. C., Kaplan, L., and Lampen, J. O., *J. Am. Chem. Soc.*, **80**, 5155 (1958).
71. Shaw, G., and Warrener, R. N., *J. Chem. Soc.*, 50 (1959).
72. Letters, R., and Michelson, A. M., *J. Chem. Soc.*, 1410 (1961).
73. Yung, N. C., and Fox, J. J., *J. Am. Chem. Soc.*, **83**, 3060 (1961).
74. Neilson, A. H., and Todd, A. R., unpublished work.
75. Michelson, A. M., unpublished work.
76. Brown, D. M., Parihar, D. B., Todd, A. R., and Varadarajan, S., *J. Chem. Soc.*, 3028 (1958).
77. Hayes, D. H., Michelson, A. M., and Todd, A. R., *J. Chem. Soc.*, 808 (1955).
78. Brown, D. M., Fasman, G. D., Magrath, D. I., and Todd, A. R., *J. Chem. Soc.*, 1448 (1954).
79. Michelson, A. M., *Tetrahedron*, **2**, 333 (1948).
80. Michelson, A. M., Szabo, L., and Todd, A. R., *J. Chem. Soc.*, 1546 (1956).
81. Wieland, T., Jaenicke, F., Merz, H., and Ossorio, M., *Ann.*, **613**, 95 (1958).
82. Wieland, T., Merz, H., and Pfleiderer, G., *Chem. Ber.*, **93**, 1816 (1960).
83. Zachau, H. G., *Chem. Ber.*, **93**, 1822 (1960).
84. Zachau, H. G., and Karau, W., *Chem. Ber.*, **93**, 1830 (1960).
85. Bredereck, H., *Chem. Ber.*, **66**, 198 (1933).
86. Levene, P. A., and Tipson, R. S., *J. Biol. Chem.*, **105**, 419 (1934).
87. Levene, P. A., and Tipson, R. S., *J. Biol. Chem.*, **121**, 131 (1937).
88. Michelson, A. M., and Todd, A. R., *J. Chem. Soc.*, 2476 (1949)
89. Levene, P. A., and Tipson, R. S., *J. Biol. Chem.*, **105**, 419 (1934).
90. Lipkin, D., and McElheny, G. C., *Nature*, **167**, 238 (1951).
91. Lipkin, D., Phillips, B., and Hunter, W. H., *Tetrahedron Letters*, *No.* 21, 18 (1959).
92. Hampton, A., *J. Am. Chem. Soc.*, **83**, 3640 (1961).
93. Levene, P. A., and Tipson, R. S., *J. Biol. Chem.*, **106**, 113 (1934).
94. Michelson, A. M., and Todd, A. R., *J. Chem. Soc.*, 2476 (1949).
95. Baker, B. R., and Schaub, R. E., *J. Am. Chem. Soc.*, **77**, 5900 (1955).
96. Hampton, A., and Magrath, D. I., *J. Am. Chem. Soc.*, **79**, 3250 (1957).
97. Andrews, K. J. M., and Barber, W. E., *J. Chem. Soc.*, 2768 (1958).
98. Levene, P. A., and Tipson, R. S., *J. Biol. Chem.*, **105**, 419 (1934).
99. Wempen, I., Doerr, I. L., Kaplan, L., and Fox, J. J., *J. Am. Chem. Soc.*, **82**, 1624 (1960).
100. Michelson, A. M., and Todd, A. R., *J. Chem. Soc.*, 34 (1954).
101. Khorana, H. G., Turner, A. F., and Vizsolyi, J. P., *J. Am. Chem. Soc.*, **83**, 686 (1961).
102. Gilham, P. T., and Khorana, H. G., *J. Am. Chem. Soc.*, **80**, 6212 (1958).
103. Shapiro, H. S., and Chargaff, E., *Biochim. et Biophys. Acta*, **26**, 596 (1957); **39**, 62 (1960).
104. Kenner, G. W., *Ciba Foundation Symposium*, " *Chemistry and Biology of Purines*," 312 (1957).
105. Dekker, C. A., *Ann. Revs. Biochem.*, **29**, 463 (1960).
106. Fukuhara, T. K., and Visser, D. W., *J. Am. Chem. Soc.*, **77**, 2393 (1955).
107. Frisch, D. M., and Visser, D. W., *J. Am. Chem. Soc.*, **81**, 1756 (1959).
108. Prusoff, W. H., *Biochim. et Biophys. Acta.* **32**, 295 (1959).
109. Michelson, A. M., Dondon, J., and Grunberg-Manago, M., *Biochim. et Biophys. Acta*, **55**, 529 (1962).

90   NUCLEOSIDES AND NUCLEOTIDES

110. Roberts, M., and Visser, D. W., *J. Am. Chem. Soc.*, **74**, 668 (1952).
111. Beltz, R. E., and Visser, D. W., *J. Biol. Chem.*, **226**, 1035 (1957).
112. Ueda, T., *Chem. and Pharm. Bull. (Tokyo)*, **8**, 455 (1960).
113. Levene, P. A., and La Forge, F. B., *Chem. Ber.*, **45**, 608 (1912).
114. Cohn, W. E., and Doherty, D. G., *J. Am. Chem. Soc.*, **78**, 2863 (1956).
115. Green, M., and Cohen, S. S., *J. Biol. Chem.*, **228**, 601 (1957).
116. Cline, R. E., Fink, R. M., and Fink, K., *J. Am. Chem. Soc.*, **81**, 2521 (1959).
117. Cohen, S. S., Green, M., and Barner, H. D., *Biochim. et Biophys. Acta*, **22**, 210 (1956).
118. Levene, P. A., and La Forge, F. B., *Chem. Ber.*, **45**, 615 (1912).
119. Cohn, W. E., *Biochem. J.*, **64**, 28P (1956).
120. Wang, S. Y., *Nature*, **180**, 91 (1957).
121. Moore, A. M., and Anderson, S. M., *Canadian J. Chem.*, **37**, 590 (1959).
122. Bannister, B., and Kagan, F., *J. Am. Chem. Soc.*, **82**, 3363 (1960).
123. Moore, A. M., and Thomson, C. H., *Science*, **122**, 594 (1955); *Canadian J. Chem.*, **35**, 163 (1957).
124. Wang, S. Y., Apicella, M., and Stone, B. R., *J. Am. Chem. Soc.*, **78**, 4180 (1956).
125. Wang, S. Y., *J. Am. Chem. Soc.*, **80**, 6196 (1958).
126. Scholes, G., Weiss, J., and Wheeler, C. M., *Nature*, **178**, 157 (1956).
127. Ekert, B., and Monier, R., *Nature*, **184**, 58 (1959).
128. Scholes, G., and Weiss, J., *Nature*, **185**, 305 (1960).
129. Levene, P. A., and Bass, L. W., *J. Biol. Chem.*, **71**, 167 (1926).
130. Miles, H. T., *Biochim. et Biophys. Acta*, **22**, 247 (1956); *J. Am. Chem. Soc.*, **79**, 2565 (1957).
131. Szer, W., and Shugar, D., *Biokhimiya*, **26**, 840 (1961).
132. Shabarova, Z. A., Sokolova, N. I., Boikova, L. A., and Prokof'ev, M. A., *Zhur. Obshei Khim.*, **29**, 2917 (1959).
133. Shabarova, Z. A., and Prokof'ev, M. A., *Doklady Akad. Nauk. S.S.S.R.*, **109**, 340 (1956).
134. Shabarova, Z. A., Sokolova, N. I., and Prokof'ev, M. A., *Zhur. Obshehei Khim.*, **27**, 2891 (1957); **29**, 539 (1959).
135. Prokof'ev, M. A., Shabarova, Z. A., and Sokolova, N. I., *Vestnik Moskov. Univ. Ser. Mat., Mekh., Astron., Fiz., Khim.*, **12**, 215 (1957).
136. Huber, G., *Angew. Chem.*, **69**, 642 (1957).
137. Gordon, M. P., Weliky, V. S., and Brown, G. B., *J. Am. Chem. Soc.*, **79**, 3245 (1957).
138. Magrath, D. I., and Brown, G. B., *J. Am. Chem. Soc.*, **79**, 3252 (1957).
139. Brown, G. B., Gordon, M. P., Magrath, D. I., and Hampton, A., *Ciba Foundation Symposium, " Chemistry and Biology of Purines,"* 192 (1957).
140. Porai-Koshits, B. A., and Muravich, K. L., *Zhur. Obshchei Khim.*, **26**, 2487 (1956).
141. Brookes, P., and Lawley, P. D., *J. Chem. Soc.*, 3923 (1961).
142. Hems, G., *Nature*, **181**, 1721 (1958).
143. Hems, G., *Nature*, **185**, 525 (1960).
144. Shaw, E., *J. Am. Chem. Soc.*, **80**, 3899 (1958).
145. Shaw, E., *J. Am. Chem. Soc.*, **81**, 6021 (1959).
146. Brookes, P., and Lawley, P. D., *J. Chem. Soc.*, 539 (1960).
147. Lawley, P. D., *Biochim. et Biophys. Acta*, **26**, 450 (1957).
148. Lawley, P. D., and Wallick, C. A., *Chem. and Ind. (London)*, 633 (1957).
149. Reiner, B., and Zamenhof, S., *J. Biol. Chem.*, **228**, 475 (1957).

150. Pullman, B., *J. Chem. Soc.*, 1621 (1959).
151. Windmueller, H. G., and Kaplan, N. O., *J. Biol. Chem.*, **236**, 2716 (1961).
152. Stevens, M. A., Magrath, D. I., Smith, H. W., and Brown, G. B., *J. Am. Chem. Soc.*, **80**, 2755 (1958).
153. Stevens, M. A., Smith, H. W., and Brown, G. B., *J. Am. Chem. Soc.*, **81**, 1734 (1959).
154. Klenow, H., and Frederiksen, S., *Biochim. et Biophys. Acta*, **52**, 384 (1961).
155. Stevens, M. A., Smith, H. W., and Brown, G. B., *J. Am. Chem. Soc.*, **82**, 3189 (1960).
156. Khym, J. X., and Cohn, W. E., *J. Am. Chem. Soc.*, **82**, 6380 (1960).
157. Reese, C. B., Schofield, K., Shapiro, R., and Todd, A. R., *Proc. Chem. Soc.*, 290 (1960).
158. Vizsolyi, J. P., and Tener, G. M., *Chem. and Ind. (London)*, 263 (1962).
159. Jones, A. S., and Williamson, A. R., *Chem. and Ind. (London)*, 1624 (1960).
160. Shugar, D., and Fox, J. J., *Biochim. et Biophys. Acta*, **9**, 199 (1952).
161. Fox, J. J., and Shugar, D., *Biochim. et Biophys. Acta*, **9**, 369 (1952).
162. Fox, J. J., Praag, D. V., Wempen, I., Doerr, I. L., Cheong, L., Knoll, J. E., Eidinoff, M. L., Bendich, A., and Brown, G. B., *J. Am. Chem. Soc.*, **81**, 178 (1959).
163. Wierzchowski, K. L., and Shugar, D., *Biochim. et Biophys. Acta*, **25**, 355 (1957).
164. Grossman, L., Levine, S. S., and Allison, W. S., *J. Mol. Biol.*, **3**, 47 (1961).
165. Tsuboi, M., Kyogoku, Y., and Shimanouchi, T., *Biochim. et Biophys. Acta*, **55**, 1 (1962).
166. Jardetzky, C. D., and Jardetzky, O., *J. Am. Chem. Soc.*, **82**, 222 (1960).
167. Jardetzky, C. D., *J. Am. Chem. Soc.*, **82**, 229 (1960).
168. Jardetzky, C. D., *J. Am. Chem. Soc.*, **84**, 62 (1962).
169. Jardetzky, C. D., *J. Am. Chem. Soc.*, **83**, 2919 (1961).
170. Frieden, E., and Alles, J., *J. Biol. Chem.*, **230**, 797 (1958).
171. Baddiley, J., Buchanan, J. G., and Stephenson, J. E., *Arch. Biochem. Biophys.*, **83**, 54 (1959).
172. Carter, C. E., *J. Biol. Chem.*, **223**, 139 (1956).
173. Baddiley, J., Buchanan, J. G., Hawker, F. J., and Stephenson, J. E., *J. Chem. Soc.*, 4659 (1956).
174. King, M. E., and Carter, C. E., *Biochim. et Biophys. Acta*, **44**, 232 (1960).
175. Perrin, D. D., *J. Am. Chem. Soc.*, **82**, 5642 (1960).
176. Lansford, E. M., Hill, I. D., and Shive, W., *J. Biol. Chem.*, **235**, 3551 (1960).
177. Cunningham, K. G., Hutchinson, S. A., Manson, W., and Spring, F. S., *J. Chem. Soc.*, 2299 (1951).
178. Bentley, H. R., Cunningham, K. G., and Spring, F. S., *J. Chem. Soc.*, 2301 (1951).
179. Kredich, N. M., and Guarino, A. J., *J. Biol. Chem.*, **236**, 3300 (1961).
180. Lüfgren, N., and Lüning, B., *Acta Chem. Scand.*, **7**, 225 (1953).
181. Isono, K., and Suzuki, S., *J. Antibiotics (Japan)*, **13A**, 270 (1960).
182. Brown, G. B., and Weliky, V. S., *J. Biol. Chem.*, **204**, 1019 (1953).
183. Waller, C. W., Patrick, J. B., Fulmor, W., and Meyer, W. E., *J. Am. Chem. Soc.*, **79**, 1011 (1957).
184. Flynn, E. H., Hinman, J. W., Caron, E. L., and Woolf, D. O., *J. Am. Chem. Soc.*, **75**, 5867 (1953).

185. Stevens, C. L., Gasser, R. J., Mukherjee, T. K., and Haskell, T. H., *J. Am. Chem. Soc.*, **78**, 6212 (1956).
186. Yünsten, H., *J. Antibiotics (Japan)*, **11A**, 77, 79, 233 (1958).
187. Yünsten, H., *J. Antibiotics (Japan)*, **11A**, 244 (1958).
188. Schroeder, W., and Hoeksema, H., *J. Am. Chem. Soc.*, **81**, 1767 (1959).
189. Slechta, L., *Biochem. Biophys. Research Communs.*, **3**, 596 (1960).
190. Garrett, E. R., *J. Am. Chem. Soc.*, **82**, 827 (1960).
191. Nishimura, H., Katagioi, K., Sato, K., Mayama, M., and Shimaoka, N., *J. Antibiotics (Japan)*, **9A**, 60 (1956).
192. Ohkuma, K., *J. Antibiotics (Japan)*, **13A**, 361 (1960).
193. Waller, C. W., Fryth, P. W., Hutchings, B. L., and Williams, J. H., *J. Am. Chem. Soc.*, **75**, 2025 (1953).
194. Baker, B. R., Schaub, R. E., and Williams, J. H., *J. Am. Chem. Soc.*, **77**, 7 (1955) ; Baker, B. R., Schaub, R. E., Joseph, J. P., and Williams, J. H., *J. Am. Chem, Soc.*, **77**, 12 (1955).
195. Cherbuliez, E., and Bernhard, K., *Helv. Chim. Acta*, **15**, 464 (1932).
196. Davoll, J., *J. Am. Chem. Soc.*, **73**, 3174 (1951).
197. Davis, A. R., Newton, E. B., and Benedict, S. R., *J. Biol. Chem.*, **54**, 595 (1922).
198. Forrest, H. S., Hatfield, D. L., and Lagowski, J. M., *J. Chem. Soc.*, 963 (1961).
199. Heller, J., and Jezewska, M. M., *Acta Biochim. Polon.*, **7**, 469 (1960).
200. Falconer, R., and Gulland, J. M., *J. Chem. Soc.*, 1369 (1939).
201. Michelson, A. M., Drell, W., and Mitchell, H. K., *Proc. Natl. Acad. Sci. U.S.A.*, **37**, 396 (1951).
202. Fox, J. J., Yung, N., and Wempen, I., *Biochim. et Biophys. Acta*, **23**, 295 (1957).
203. Ritthausen, H., *Chem. Ber.*, **29**, 894, 2108 (1896).
204. Bendich, A., and Clements, G. C., *Biochim. et Biophys. Acta*, **12**, 462 (1953).
205. Bergmann, W., and Feeney, R. J., *J. Am. Chem. Soc.*, **72**, 2809 (1950).
206. Bergmann, W., and Stempien, M. F., *J. Org. Chem.*, **22**, 1575 (1957).
207. Hampton, A., *J. Am. Chem. Soc.*, **79**, 503 (1957).
208. Ballio, A., Delfini, C., and Russi, S., *Nature*, **186**, 968 (1960).
209. Al-Khalidi, U., and Greenberg, G. R., *J. Biol. Chem.*, **236**, 189 (1961).
210. Al-Khalidi, U., and Greenberg, G. R., *J. Biol. Chem.*, **236**, 192 (1961).
211. Lenhert, P. G., and Hodgkin, D. C., *Nature*, **192**, 937 (1961).
212. Hogenkamp, H. P. C., and Barker, H. A., *J. Biol. Chem.*, **236**, 3097 (1961).
213. Johnson, A. W., and Shaw, N., *Proc. Chem. Soc.*, **447** (1961).
214. Mandel, J. A., and Dunham, E. K., *J. Biol. Chem.*, **11**, 85 (1912).
215. Levene, P. A., and Sobotka, H., *J. Biol. Chem.*, **65**, 551 (1925).
216. Wendt, G., *Z. physiol. Chem.*, **272**, 152 (1942).
217. Satoh, K., and Makino, K., *Nature*, **165**, 769 (1950).
218. Weyand, F., Trauth, O., and Löwenfeld, R., *Chem. Ber.*, **83**, 563 (1950).
219. Falconer, R., and Gulland, J. M., *J. Chem. Soc.*, 1912 (1937).
220. Baddiley, J., *J. Chem. Soc.*, 1348 (1951).
221. Satch, K., and Makino, K., *Nature*, **167**, 238 (1951).
222. Kuhn, R., and Henkel, K., *Z. physiol. Chem.*, **269**, 41 (1941).
223. Baddiley, J., and Jamieson, G. A., *J. Chem. Soc.*, 4280 (1954).
224. Kanazawa, T., *Nippon Kagaku Zasshi*, **81**, 516 (1960).
225. Lavine, T. F., Floyd, N. F., and Cammaroti, M. S., *Biochem. Biophys. Research Communs.*, **1**, 156 (1959).
226. Remy, C. N., *J. Biol. Chem.*, **234**, 1485 (1959).

227. Tabor, H., Rosenthal, S. M., and Tabor, C. W., *J. Biol. Chem.*, **233**, 907 (1958).
228. Cantoni, G. L., *J. Am. Chem. Soc.*, **74**, 2942 (1952); *J. Biol. Chem.*, **204**, 403 (1953).
229. Baddiley, J., Cantoni, G. L., and Jamieson, G. A., *J. Chem. Soc.*, 2662 (1953).
230. Baddiley, J., and Jamieson, G. A., *J. Chem. Soc.*, 1085 (1955).
231. Shunk, C. H., and Richter, J. W., *U.S.* **2**, 969, 353, Jan. 24th, 1961 [*Chem. Abstr.*, 55, 14490 (1961)].
232. de la Haba, G., Jamieson, G. A., Mudd, S. H., and Richards, H. H., *J. Am. Chem. Soc.*, **81**, 3975 (1959).
233. Parks, L. W., and Schlenk, F., *J. Biol. Chem.*, **230**, 295 (1958).
234. Frank, W., Wieczotkowski, J., Hughes, N. A., and Baddiley, J., *Proc. Chem. Soc.*, 449 (1961) ; *J. Chem. Soc.*, 1999 (1962).
235. Mudd, S. H., *J. Biol. Chem.*, **234**, 1784 (1959).
236. Cantoni, G. L., and Durell, J., *J. Biol. Chem.*, **225**, 1033 (1957).
237. Miller, C. O., Skoog, F., von Saltza, M. H., and Strong, F. M., *J. Am. Chem. Soc.*, **77**, 1392 (1955).
238. Miller, C. O., Skoog, F., Okumura, F. S., von Saltza, M. H., and Strong, F. M., *J. Am. Chem. Soc.*, **77**, 2662 (1955).
239. Baizer, M. M., Clark, J. R., Dub, M., and Loter, A., *J. Org. Chem.*, **21**, 1276 (1956).
240. Hull, R., *J. Chem. Soc.*, 2746 (1958).
241. Whitehead, C. W., and Traverso, J. J., *J. Am. Chem. Soc.*, **82**, 3971 (1960).
242. Kissman, H. M., and Weiss, M. J., *J. Org. Chem.*, **21**, 1053 (1956).
243. Hampton, A., Biesele, J. J., Moore, A. E., and Brown, G. B., *J. Am. Chem. Soc.*, **78**, 5695 (1956).
244. Fischer, E., and Helferich, B., *Chem. Ber.*, **47**, 210 (1914).
245. Gulland, J. M., Holiday, E. R., and Macrae, T. F., *J. Chem. Soc.*, 1639 (1934).
246. Gulland, J. M., and Story, L. F., *J. Chem. Soc.*, 259 (1938).
247. Fischer, E., *Chem. Ber.*, **47**, 1377 (1914).
248. Levene, P. A., and Sobotka, H., *J. Biol. Chem.*, **65**, 469 (1925).
249. Hilbert, G. E., and Johnson, T. B., *J. Am. Chem. Soc.*, **52**, 4489 (1930).
250. Hilbert, G. E., and Jansen, E. F., *J. Am. Chem. Soc.*, **58**, 60 (1936).
251. Howard, G. A., Lythgoe, B., and Todd, A. R., *J. Chem. Soc.*, 1052 (1947).
252. Davoll, J., Lythgoe, B., and Todd, A. R., *J. Chem. Soc.*, **967**, 1685 (1948).
253. Davoll, J., and Lowy, B. A., *J. Am. Chem. Soc.*, **73**, 1650 (1951).
254. Viscontini, M., and Huwyler, S., *Helv. Chim. Acta*, **43**, 782 (1960).
255. Reist, E. J., Spencer, R. R., and Baker, B. R., *J. Org. Chem.*, **23**, 1958 (1958).
256. Reist, E. J., Goodman, L., and Baker, B. R., *J. Am. Chem. Soc.*, **80**, 5775 (1958).
257. Baker, B. R., and Hewson, K., *J. Org. Chem.*, **22**, 959 (1957).
258. Baker, B. R., and Hewson, K., *J. Org. Chem.*, **22**, 966 (1957).
259. Reist, E. J., Spencer, R. R., and Baker, B. R., *J. Org. Chem.*, **23**, 1753 (1958).
260. Reist, E. J., Spencer, R. R., and Baker, B. R., *J. Org. Chem.*, **23**, 1757 (1958).

261. Reist, E. J., Goodman, L., Spencer, R. R., and Baker, B. R., *J. Am. Chem. Soc.*, **80**, 3962 (1958).
262. Gordon, M. P., Intrieri, O. M., and Brown, G. B., *J. Am. Chem. Soc.*, **80**, 5161 (1958).
263. Kissman, H. M., and Baker, B. R., *J. Am. Chem. Soc.*, **79**, 5534 (1957).
264. Kissman, H. M., and Weiss, M. J., *J. Am. Chem. Soc.*, **80**, 5559 (1958).
265. Wolfrom, M. L., McWain, P., Shafizadeh, F., and Thompson, A., *J. Am. Chem. Soc.*, **81**, 6080 (1959).
266. Wolfrom, M. L., McWain, P., and Thompson, A., *J. Am. Chem. Soc.*, **82**, 4353 (1960).
267. Zorbach, W. W., and Durr, G. J., *Abstr.* 138*th Am. Chem. Soc. Meeting*, 2D (1960).
268. McEvoy, F. J., Weiss, M. J., and Baker, B. R., *J. Am. Chem. Soc.*, **82**, 205 (1960).
269. McEvoy, F. J., Baker, B. R., and Weiss, M. J., *J. Am. Chem. Soc.*, **82**, 209 (1960).
270. Reist, E. J., and Baker, B. R., *J. Org. Chem.*, **23**, 1083 (1958) ; Baker, B. R., Schaub, R. E., and Kissman, H. M., *J. Am. Chem. Soc.*, **77**, 5911 (1955).
271. Wolfrom, M. L., Foster, A. B., McWain, P., von Bebenburg, W., and Thompson, A., *Abstr.* 137*th Am. Chem. Soc. Meeting*, 3D (1960).
272. Davoll, J., and Lowy, B. A., *J. Am. Chem. Soc.*, **74**, 1563 (1952).
273. Johnson, J. A., and Thomas, H. J., *J. Am. Chem. Soc.*, **78**, 3863 (1956).
274. Schaeffer, H. J., and Thomas, H. J., *J. Am. Chem. Soc.*, **80**, 4896 (1958).
275. Davoll, J., and Kerridge, K. A., *J. Chem. Soc.*, 2589 (1961).
276. Davoll, J., *J. Chem. Soc.*, 1593 (1958).
277. Montgomery, J. A., and Hewson, K., *J. Am. Chem. Soc.*, **79**, 4559 (1957).
278. Brown, G. B., and Weliky, V. S., *J. Org. Chem.*, **23**, 125 (1958).
279. Schaeffer, H. J., and Thomas, H. J., *J. Am. Chem. Soc.*, **80**, 3738 (1958).
280. Montgomery, J. A., and Hewson, K., *J. Am. Chem. Soc.*, **82**, 463 (1960).
281. Blackburn, G. M., and Johnson, A. W., *J. Chem. Soc.*, 4347 (1960).
282. Baker, B. R., Joseph, J. P., Schaub, R. E., and Williams, J. H., *J. Org. Chem.*, **19**, 1786 (1954). See also, Howard, G. A., *J. Chem. Soc.*, 1045 (1950).
283. Wright, R. S., Tener, G. M., and Khorana, H. G., *J. Am. Chem. Soc.*, **80**, 2004 (1958).
284. Fox, J. J., Yung, N., Davoll, J., and Brown, G. B., *J. Am. Chem. Soc.*, **78**, 2117 (1956).
285. Kissman, H. M., and Weiss, M. J., *J. Am. Chem. Soc.*, **80**, 2575 (1958).
286. Duschinsky, R., Pleven, E., Malbica, J., and Heidelberger, C., *Abstr.* 132*nd Am. Chem. Soc. Meeting*, 19C (1957).
287. Ikehara, M., *Chem. and Pharm. Bull. (Tokyo)*, **8**, 308 (1960).
288. Funakoshi, R., Irie, M., and Ukita, C., *Chem. and Pharm. Bull. (Tokyo)*, **9**, 406 (1961).
289. Hall, R. H., *J. Am. Chem. Soc.*, **80**, 1145 (1958).
290. Handschumacher, R. E., *J. Biol. Chem.*, **235**, 764 (1960).
291. Prystas, M., Gut, J., and Sorm, F., *Chem. and Ind. (London)*, 947 (9161).
292. Pliml, J., and Sorm, F., *Chem. Ind. (London)*, 655 (1962).
293. Blumbergs, P., and Stevens, C. L., *Abstr.* 139*th Am. Chem. Soc. Meeting*, 30N (1961).
294. Fox, J. J., Yung, N., Wempen, I., and Doerr, I. L., *J. Am. Chem. Soc.*, **79**, 5060 (1957).
295. Fox, J. J., Yung, N., and Praag, D. V., *Federation Proc.*, **16**, 182 (1957).

296. Fox, J. J., and Praag, D. V., *J. Org. Chem.*, **26**, 526 (1961).
297. Ness, R. K., and Fletcher, H. G., *J. Am. Chem. Soc.*, **81**, 4752 (1959); **82**, 3434 (1960).
298. Hoffer, M., Duschinsky, R., Fox, J. J., and Yung, N., *J. Am. Chem. Soc.*, **81**, 4112 (1959).
299. Hoffer, M., *Chem. Ber.*, **93**, 2777 (1960).
300. Fox, J. J., Yung, N. C., Wempen, I., and Hoffer, M., *J. Am. Chem. Soc.*, **83**, 4066 (1961)
301. Venner, H., *Chem. Ber.*, **93**, 140 (1960).
302. Pedersen, C., and Fletcher, H. G., *J. Am. Chem. Soc.*, **82**, 5210 (1960).
303. Robins, R. K., and Lewis, L. R., *Abstr. 138th Am. Chem. Soc. Meeting*, 16P (1960).
304. Robins, R. K., Godefroi, E. F., Taylor, E. C., Lewis, L. R., and Jackson, A., *J. Am. Chem. Soc.*, **83**, 2574 (1961).
305. Schramm, G., Grötsch, H., and Pollmann, W., *Angew. Chem.*, **73**, 619 (1961).
306. Kenner, G. W., Taylor, C. W., and Todd, A. R., *J. Chem. Soc.*, 1620 (1949) and earlier papers by Todd and co-workers.
307. Ikehara, M., Ohtsuka, E., Kitagawa, S., Yagi, K., and Tonomura, Y., *J. Am. Chem. Soc.*, **83**, 2679 (1961).
308. Howard, G. A., McLean, A. C., Newbold, G. T., Spring, F. S., and Todd, A. R., *J. Chem. Soc.*, 232 (1949).
309. Baddiley, J., Buchanan, J. G., and Osborne, G. O., *J. Chem. Soc.*, 1651 (1958).
310. Baddiley, J., Buchanan, J. G., and Osborne, G. O., *J. Chem. Soc.*, 3606 (1958).
311. Baddiley, J., Buchanan, J. G., Hardy, F. E., and Stewart, J., *J. Chem. Soc.*, 2893 (1959).
312. Bauer, H., *Biochim. et Biophys. Acta*, **30**, 219 (1958); *J. Org. Chem.*, **27**, 167 (1962).
313. Baddiley, J., Buchanan, J. G., Hayes, D. H., and Smith, P. A., *J. Chem. Soc.*, 3743 (1958).
314. Baddiley, J., Buchanan, J. G., Hodges, R., and Prescott, J. F., *J. Chem. Soc.*, 4769 (1957).
315. Ralph, R. K.. and Shaw, G., *J. Chem. Soc.*, 1877 (1956).
316. Shaw, G., Warrener, R. N., Maguire, M. H., and Ralph, R. K., *J. Chem. Soc.*, 2294 (1958).
317. Shaw, G., Warrener, R. N., Butler, D. N., and Ralph, R. K., *J. Chem. Soc.*, 1648 (1959).
318. Shaw, G., and Wilson, D. V., *Proc. Chem. Soc.*, 381 (1961) ; *J. Chem. Soc.*, 2937 (1962).
319. Shaw, G., and Wilson, D. V., *Proc. Chem. Soc.*, 115 (1962).
320. Goodman, I., *Federation Proc.*, **15**, 264 (1956).
321. Hoffer, M., U.S. 2, 949, 449; Aug. 16, 1960 [*Chem. Abstr.*, **55**, 586 (1961)].
322. Davoll, J., and Evans, D. D., *J. Chem. Soc.*, 5041 (1960).
323. Michelson, A. M., and Todd, A. R., *J. Chem. Soc.*, 816 (1955).
324. Brown, D. M., Todd, A. R., and Varadarajan, S., *J. Chem. Soc.*, 2388 (1956).
325. Fox, J. J., Yung, N., and Bendich, A., *J. Am. Chem. Soc.*, **79**, 2775 (1957).
326. Yung, N. C., Burchenal, J. H., Fecher, R., Duschinsky, R., and Fox, J. J., *J. Am. Chem. Soc.*, **83**, 4060 (1961).
327. Fox, J. J., Codington, J. F., Yung, N. C., Kaplan, L., and Lampen, J. O., *J. Am. Chem. Soc.*, **80**, 5155 (1958).

328. Yung, N. C., and Fox, J. J., *J. Am. Chem. Soc.*, **83**, 3060 (1961).
329. Fecher, R., Codington, J. F., and Fox, J. J., *J. Amer. Chem. Soc.*, **83**, 1889 (1961).
330. Codington, J. F., Fecher, R., and Fox, J. J., *J. Am. Chem. Soc.*, **82**, 2794 (1960).
330. Codington, J. F., Fecher, R., and Fox, J. J., *J. Am. Chem. Soc.*, **83**, 2794 (1960).
331. Codington, J. F., Fecher, R., and Fox, J. J., *J. Org. Chem.*, **27**, 163 (1962).
332. Reist, E. J., Osiecki, J. H., Goodman, L., and Baker, B. R., *J. Am. Chem. Soc.*, **83**, 2208 (1961).
333. Letters, R., and Michelson, A. M., *J. Chem. Soc.*, 1410 (1961).
334. Brown, D. M., Parihar, D. B., and Todd, A. R., *J. Chem. Soc.*, 4242 (1958).
335. Walwick, E. R., Roberts, W. K., and Dekker, C. A., *Proc. Chem. Soc.*, 84 (1959).
336. Brown, D. M., Parihar, D. B., Reese, C. B., and Todd, A. R., *J. Chem. Soc.*, 3035 (1958).
337. Codington, J. F., Doerr, I., Praag, D. V., Bendich, A., and Fox, J. J., *J. Am. Chem. Soc.*, **83**, 5030 (1961).
338. Shaw, G., and Warrener, R. N., *J. Chem. Soc.*, 50 (1959).
339. McCasland, G. E., Clark, R. K., and Carter, H. E., *J. Am. Chem. Soc.*, **71**, 637 (1949).
340. Winstein, S., Goodman, L., and Boschan, R., *J. Am. Chem. Soc.*, **72**, 2311 (1950).
341. Baker, B. R., and Schaub, R. E., *J. Am. Chem. Soc.*, **77**, 2396 (1955).
342. Baker, B. R., and Schaub, R. E., *J. Am. Chem. Soc.*, **77**, 5900 (1955).
343. Lee, W. W., Benitez, A., Goodman, L., and Baker, B. R., *J. Am. Chem. Soc.*, **82**, 2648 (1960).
344. Davoll, J., Lythgoe, B., and Trippett, S., *J. Chem. Soc.*, 2230 (1951).
345. Anderson, C. D., Goodman, L., and Baker, B. R., *J. Am. Chem. Soc.*, **81**, 3967 (1959).
346. Benitez, A., Crews, O. P., Goodman, L., and Baker, B. R., *J. Org. Chem.*, **25**, 1946 (1960).
347. Lee, W. W., Benitez, A., Anderson, C. D., Goodman, L., and Baker, B. R., *J. Am. Chem. Soc.*, **83**, 1906 (1961).
348. Anderson, C. D., Lee, W. W., Goodman, L., and Baker, B. R., *J. Am. Chem. Soc.*, **83**, 1900 (1961).
349. Todd, A. R., and Ulbricht, T. L. V., *J. Chem. Soc.*, 3275 (1960).
350. Fox, J. J., Wempen, I., Hampton, A., and Doerr, I. L., *J. Am. Chem. Soc.*, **80**, 1669 (1958).
351. Moravek, J., and Nejedly, Z., *Chem. and Ind. (London)*, 530 (1960).
352. Goodman, I., *Federation Proc.*, **18**, 933 (1959).
353. Robins, R. K., *J. Am. Chem. Soc.*, **82**, 2654 (1960).
354. Fox, J. J., Praag, D. V., Wempen, I., Doerr, I. L., Cheong, L., Knoll, J. E., Eidinoff, M. L., Bendich, A., and Brown, G. B., *J. Am. Chem. Soc.*, **81**, 178 (1959).
355. Wempen, I., Duschinsky, R., Kaplan, L., and Fox, J. J., *J. Am. Chem. Soc.*, **83**, 4755 (1961).
356. Sorm, F., Smrt, J., and Cerneckij, V., *Experientia*, **17**, 64 (1961).
357. Sorm, F., Chernetskii, V. P., Hladik, S., Vesely, J., and Smrt, J., *Doklady Akad. Nauk. S.S.S.R.*, **137**, 1393 (1961).

358. Fox, J. J., and Praag, D. V., *J. Am. Chem. Soc.*, **82**, 486 (1960).
359. Cline, R. E., Fink, R. M., and Fink, K., *J. Am. Chem. Soc.*, **81**, 2521 (1959).
360. Burckhalter, J. H., Seiwald, R. J., and Scarborough, H. C., *J. Am. Chem. Soc.*, **82**, 991 (1960).
361. Ulbricht, T. L. V., *Tetrahedron*, **6**, 225 (1959).
362. Shaw, E., *J. Am. Chem. Soc.*, **80**, 3899 (1958).
363. Shaw, E., *J. Am. Chem. Soc.*, **81**, 6021 (1959).
364. Shaw, E., *J. Am. Chem. Soc.*, **83**, 4770 (1961).
365. Leonard, N. J., and Deyrup, J. A., *J. Am. Chem. Soc.*, **84**, 2148 (1962).
366. Leonard, N. J., and Laursen, R. A., unpublished work.
367. Brookes, P., and Lawley, P. D., *J. Chem. Soc.*, 1348 (1962).
368. Hogenkamp, H. P. C., Ladd, J. N., and Barker, H. A., *J. Biol. Chem.*, **237**, 1950 (1962).
369. Marmur, J., and Cordes, S., *Symposium on Informational Macromolecules*, Rutger's University, Sept. 1962.

Chapter 3

CHEMISTRY OF NUCLEOTIDES

The term *nucleotide* was introduced in 1908 by Levene and Mandel[1] to denote the products isolated from acidic digests of thymus nucleic acid. Until recently, the phosphate esters of nucleosides were often characterised by naming the source material as in the use of the terms " yeast adenylic acid " and " muscle adenylic acid " to describe two distinct isomers of the nucleotide. Such terminology is now somewhat meaningless and, when known, the position of the phosphate is generally defined as in " adenosine-2' phosphate ". With respect to monophosphate esters of the naturally occurring ribonucleosides, three isomers can occur (2', 3' or 5' esters) and in the deoxyribose series both 3' phosphates and 5' phosphates are possible and have been isolated.

ISOLATION

Partly as the result of controversies raised by Berzelius over the presence of creatine in boiled and unboiled beef, the first nucleotide, inosinic acid (Greek = muscle fibre) was isolated from beef extract by Liebig[2] in 1847. Since then, many mononucleotides, usually the 5' phosphates, (though adenosine-3' phosphate is present in the venom of tiger snakes and related species[3]) have been isolated by direct extraction of tissue or organism,[4-9] in which they are generally present in small amounts as metabolic intermediates. However, the main sources of mononucleotides are the polymeric derivatives, the nucleic acids. Mild alkaline degradation[10, 11] of ribonucleic acid yields a mixture of the 2' and 3' phosphates of the constituent nucleosides which can be separated readily by ion exchange chromatography.[12] For the isolation of the analogous 5' esters, enzymic hydrolysis must be employed, usually with snake venom phosphodiesterase.[13, 14] Similar enzymic treatment of deoxyribonucleic acid after a preliminary treatment with deoxyribonuclease, gives the deoxynucleoside-5' phosphates.[15-17] Again, purified snake venom diesterase is superior to the crude intestinal phosphatase preparations with which the deoxynucleotides were first obtained, using arsenate to inhibit the monoesterases present.[18, 19] Recent work has shown that the analogous deoxynucleoside-3' phosphates can also be obtained from deoxyribonucleic acid by digestion with an enzyme produced by *Staphylococcus aureus*.[20] Deoxyribonucleic acid is relatively stable to alkali; mild acidic hydrolysis liberates small amounts of the 3' and 5' phosphates of the pyrimidine deoxynucleosides together with pyrimidine deoxynucleoside-3',5' diphosphates

Uridine-2' phosphate   Cytidine-3' phosphate   Adenosine-5' phosphate

Inosine-5' phosphate   Guanosine-5' phosphate   Xanthosine-3' phosphate

Thymidine-3' phosphate   5-Hydroxymethyl-   Deoxyadenosine-5'
                                deoxycytidine-5' phosphate   phosphate

Nucleotides

and oligonucleotides.[21-24]   The extreme sensitivity of the 2'-deoxy-glycosyl-purine linkage to acid results in complete degradation of all the purine deoxynucleoside components to the free base.

Since the basic structure of nucleic acids involves a 3'-5' phosphate diester linkage between nucleosides it is clear that nucleotides derived from all the nucleosides reported present in nucleic acids can be, and generally have been, isolated.

STRUCTURE

As the nucleotides (except pseudouridylic acid) can all be hydrolysed to the free base by acidic hydrolysis under suitable conditions and to the nucleoside by chemical or enzymic dephosphorylation, only those structural problems concerned with the location of the phosphate residue will be considered.

NUCLEOSIDE-5' PHOSPHATES

Mild acidic hydrolysis of the inosinic acid isolated from meat liberates a ribose phosphate that on oxidation with nitric acid yields D-ribonic acid-5 phosphate rather than a phosphate ester of *ribo*trihydroxyglutaric acid, and inosinic acid is therefore inosine-5' phosphate.[25, 26] The structure of the liberated ribose-5' phosphate was fully confirmed by synthesis of the ester from methyl 2,3-*O*-isopropylideneribofuranoside.[27, 28] Since so-called muscle adenylic acid is readily deaminated to inosine-5' phosphate by enzyme preparations from muscle (adenosine-5' phosphate deaminase) the phosphate component is likewise located at the primary 5' hydroxyl group.[29] More general methods for the identification of 5' phosphates include the use of nucleotidases that are specific for nucleoside-5' phosphates,[30] demonstration of the presence of an unsubstituted 2',3'-*cis* glycol structure by periodate oxidation[31, 32] or formation of boric acid complexes[33] (in the ribose series), and comparison with synthetic nucleotides. In the case of the deoxynucleoside-5' phosphates, their behaviour on ion exchange chromatography compared with that of the corresponding ribonucleotides was also of value.[34] Preliminary reduction of the base in pyrimidine nucleotides facilitates glycosyl cleavage.[35] Confirmation of the structure of the uridylic acid moiety of uridine diphosphate glucose was obtained by treating the coenzyme with hydrazine hydrate to liberate ribose-5 phosphate by destruction of the pyrimidine.[36]

Application of the above mentioned general methods has demonstrated the location of the ester linkage in all the major nucleoside-5' phosphates and many of the minor nucleotides, whether derived from ribonucleic acids, deoxyribonucleic acids or the many naturally occurring nucleotide mixed anhydrides. Further details of geometry and bond lengths have been provided for calcium thymidine-5' phosphate[37] and adenosine-5' phosphate[38] by X-ray analysis.

NUCLEOSIDE-2' AND -3' PHOSPHATES

For many years it was considered that mild alkaline hydrolysis of ribonucleic acids gave rise to a mixture of the 3' phosphates only of adenosine, cytidine, guanosine, and uridine. This misconception existed mainly because of the inadequate methods of classical organic chemistry as applied to the identification and characterisation of nucleotides. Most of the earlier work on the location of the phosphate residue by Levene and his co-workers is ambiguous in that the nucleotides used were possibly mixtures of the 2′ and 3′ isomers. In addition, the isolation of an optically inactive ribitol phosphate by reduction of

the ribose phosphate obtained from guanylic acid (via the deaminated derivative, xanthylic acid)[39] loses significance when conditions that permit phosphate migration are used. Nevertheless, this early work did show that the 2′ or 3′ sugar hydroxyl group of the nucleoside was esterified by phosphate. Thus deamination of adenylic acid yielded an inosinic acid that on hydrolysis gave hypoxanthine and a ribose phosphate which was not ribose-5 phosphate,[40] and phosphorylation of 5′-O-trityluridine gave a uridylic acid that was identical (using the methods then available) with that obtained from ribonucleic acid.[41]

However, in 1949 Cohn isolated two isomeric adenylic acids from alkaline digests of yeast ribonucleic acid, by the application of ion exchange chromatography.[42, 43] Subsequently, the presence of similar pairs of isomeric nucleotides derived from the other nucleosides was demonstrated.[44–46] In each case the less acidic isomer (with respect to ion exchange chromatography) was termed " a " and the other " b "; although quite stable in alkali, the isomers were rapidly interconverted to an equilibrium mixture under acidic conditions.[47, 48] Both adenylic acids a and b were dephosphorylated to adenosine[49] and both were stable to periodate oxidation.[50] A mixture of the two isomers was obtained on phosphorylation of 5'-O-trityladenosine,[47] and either isomer yielded the same nucleoside cyclic phosphate[51] that on alkaline or acidic hydrolysis gave a mixture of the a and b phosphates.[51, 52] Analogous properties were shown by the cytidylic acid isomers and deamination of cytidylic acid b yielded uridylic acid b.[53] Enzymic dephosphorylation of the nucleotides by a specific b nucleotidase suggested that all the b isomers were structurally similar and hence that the a isomers likewise formed a distinct series.[54] It was clear therefore that the isomers were 2' and 3' phosphates although at this point further identification could not be established.

Ribitol-2 phosphate (optically active)

Very short treatment of the a and b adenylic and guanylic acids with a sulphonic acid resin in the acid form (to minimise phosphate migration) followed by ion exchange chromatography of the resultant ribose phosphates, in each case yielded a higher proportion of ribose-2 phosphate from the a isomers and a greater proportion of ribose-3 phosphate from the b compounds. Whereas ribose-3 phosphate gave optically inactive ribitol-3 phosphate on reduction, an optically active compound was obtained from the ribose-2 phosphate. Confirmation of the structures assigned to the ribose phosphates was obtained by periodate oxidation of the derived methyl glycosides.[55, 56]

More conclusive evidence relating adenylic acid a to adenosine-2′ phosphate and the b isomer to adenosine-3′ phosphate was provided by the unambiguous synthesis of adenosine-2′ phosphate.[57] Partial acetylation of 5′-O-acetyladenosine gave a diacetyladenosine that on toluenesulphonylation followed by methanolysis gave a methyl O-

Ts = $CH_3C_6H_4SO_2$

toluene-p-sulphonylriboside. This was methylated and the sulphonyl group removed by reductive fission with sodium amalgam. Acidic hydrolysis then yielded a mixture of methylated sugars, the dimethylribose fraction being essentially 3,5-di-O-methylribose. Similarly, deacetylation of the intermediate toluene-p-sulphonyl-di-O-acetyladenosine followed by methylation, reduction and acidic hydrolysis gave 3-O-methylribose and 3,5-di-O-methylribose. The original diacetyl derivative was therefore 3′,5′-di-O-acetyladenosine. Treatment of this with O-benzyl phosphorous O-diphenyl phosphoric anhydride and oxidation of the resultant nucleoside phosphite followed by removal of protecting groups gave adenylic acid a uncontaminated by the b isomer, thus precluding phosphate migration during the synthesis. Adenylic acid a is therefore adenosine-2' phosphate.[57]

Physical methods were also used to identify the a and b isomers of adenylic and cytidylic acids. High precision density measurements of aqueous solutions of the nucleotides showed that in each case the b isomer has a higher solution density (because of electrostriction) indicating a greater separation of charge in the dipolar ions. It is also known that the field effect of a negatively charged group tends to increase the pK of an ammonium group, with a greater shift the smaller the distance between the charged groups. Measurements of the dissociation constants of the adenine and cytosine amino groups again indicated that the a isomers were 2' phosphates and that the b series were 3' phosphates.[58]

Compound	pK $(NH_2{}^-)$	pK (secondary phosphoryl)
Adenosine	3·5	—
Adenylic acid a	3·81	6·17
Adenylic acid b	3·74	5·92
Cytidine	4·2	—
Cytidylic acid a	4·44	6·19
Cytidylic acid b	4·31	6·04

Variations in the ultraviolet absorption spectra of the cytidylic acids in the pH range 12–14 (largely due to ionisation of the sugar 2' hydroxyl group) also indicate an $a = 2'$ and $b = 3'$ relationship.[59] This was further confirmed by a comparison of the infrared[60, 61] and ultraviolet absorption spectra, and optical rotations of the 2', 3', and 5' isomers of cytidylic acid with those of synthetic deoxycytidine-3' and -5' phosphates.[61]

Chemical proof of the structures of the a and b isomers of cytidylic acid was obtained by fission of the nucleotides with hydrazine hydrate to give 3-amino-pyrazole and low yields of ribose -2 or -3 phosphate from the a or b isomer respectively. The same treatment converted uridylic acid b into pyrazolone and ribose-3 phosphate.[62] In an alternate approach, the dihydrouridylic acids obtained by rhodium catalysed hydrogenation[35, 63] of either the cytidylic or uridylic nucleotides were cleaved with dilute alkali to the N-ribosyl phosphates of β-ureido-propionic acid. These were hydrolysed to the ribose phosphates without appreciable migration of the phosphate group by the action of dilute acid at room temperature. Again, the a and b nucleotides were correlated with 2' and 3' phosphates respectively.[35]

Further chemical evidence for the structure of the pyrimidine nucleotides was provided by an unambiguous synthesis of uridine-2′ phosphate from 3′,5′-di-O-acetyluridine, the structure of the latter being proven by its conversion into 3-β-D-arabinofuranosyluracil via the 2′-O-toluene-p-sulphonyl- and O²,2′-cyclonucleoside derivatives.[64]

Ts = $CH_3C_6H_4SO_2$

Full confirmation of the structures of adenosine-3′ phosphate[65] and cytidine-3′ phosphate[66] has been afforded by X-ray crystallographic analyses.

The structures of the deoxynucleoside-3′ phosphates isolated from enzymic digests of deoxyribonucleic acid were readily demonstrated by the resistance shown by the nucleotides to 5′-nucleotidase, and bv direct comparison with synthetic compounds.[67]

NUCLEOSIDE CYCLIC PHOSPHATES

Intermediate products from the action of ribonuclease on ribonucleic acids include the pyrimidine nucleoside-2′,3′ cyclic phosphates, that on further treatment with ribonuclease yield the 3′-phosphates exclusively.[68, 69] Degradation of ribonucleic acid with barium carbonate,[68] or better, with potassium t-butoxide,[70] gives purine and pyrimidine nucleoside-2′,3′ cyclic phosphates. These are also obtained by heating a solution of the nucleic acid in formamide with ammonia.[71] The compounds were shown to have 2′,3′ cyclic phosphate structures by their titrimetric and paper chromatographic and electrophoretic behaviour, by acidic or alkaline hydrolysis to mixtures of the 2′ and 3′ phosphates, and by comparison with synthetic specimens.[52, 53]

These cyclic phosphates were of considerable importance in the elucidation of the mechanism of phosphate migration and of the chemical and enzymic (ribonuclease) degradation of ribonucleic acid.[69]

Despite prognostications denying the possible formation of ribonucleoside-3',5' cyclic phosphates, adenosine-3',5' cyclic phosphate has been isolated recently from a barium hydroxide digest of adenosine-5' triphosphate.[72] The cyclic phosphate arises by intramolecular phosphorylation and it is identical with an adenine nucleotide formed from adenosine-5' triphosphate by particulate preparations from dog liver, heart, skeletal muscle, or brain.[73] Tracer studies have shown that the enzymic synthesis involves attack at the α phosphorus atom by the 3'-hydroxyl group, with release of inorganic pyrophosphate.[239] Biologically the nucleotide stimulates the conversion of inactive glycogen-phosphorylase into the active form in liver preparations and functions as an intermediate agent in the adrenocorticotropic hormone-induced stimulation of adrenal phosphorylase, and also stimulates the production of steroid hormones by the adrenal cortex.[74, 75]

Molecular weight determinations by equilibrium sedimentation in the ultracentrifuge established the mononucleotide nature of the compound. The presence of diesterified phosphate, indicated by titration with alkali and by the resistance of the ester to attack by phosphomonoesterases was in accord with the electrophoretic, ion exchange and paper chromatographic characteristics. The nucleotide was not oxidised by periodate and was deaminated to the inosine analogue (also obtained from inosine-5' triphosphate by treatment with barium hydroxide). Although resistant to intestinal and spleen phosphodiesterases and to ribonuclease, the compound was slowly hydrolysed to adenosine and adenosine-3' phosphate by high concentrations of snake venom. The purified diesterase gave a mixture of adenosine-3' and -5' phosphates, and a partially purified enzyme from heart effected rapid hydrolysis to adenosine-5' phosphate only. Hydrolysis with an acidic ion exchange resin or with hydrochloric acid gave adenine and an equilibrium mixture of ribose-2 and -3 phosphates, as significant cleavage of the glycosyl linkage in this nucleoside cyclic phosphate (in contrast with other adenylic acids) occurs only under conditions that are conducive to phosphate migration. Treatment of the nucleotide

with liquid anhydrous hydrofluoric acid gave ribose, while methylation followed by reaction with hydrofluoric acid yielded a methyl ribose (different from 3-O-methylribose and 5-O-methylribose) with the properties of 2-O-methylribose.[76] Alkaline hydrolysis with sodium hydroxide gave adenine and a small amount of adenosine. However, hydrolysis with dilute barium hydroxide gave a mixture of adenosine-3' and -5' phosphate in the ratio 5 : 1, but no -2' phosphate.[73, 76] Molecular models also indicated a -3',5' cyclic structure rather than the isomeric -2',5' form.[76] Retention of the β-configuration was further confirmed by synthesis of adenosine-3',5' cyclic phosphate (and of other ribo- and deoxyribonucleoside-3',5' cyclic phosphates) from the nucleoside-5' phosphate.[76–78]

Vigorous treatment of thymidine-3',5' cyclic phosphate with aqueous sodium hydroxide gave a mixture of thymidine-3' phosphate ($\sim$ 80%) and thymidine-5' phosphate ($\sim$ 20%). Hydrolysis with snake venom diesterase was slow, but again both the isomeric nucleotides were obtained. In contrast with thymidine-5′ phosphate the glycosyl linkage in thymidine-3′,5′ cyclic phosphate was rapidly cleaved on acidic hydrolysis. A small hypsochromic shift of the ultraviolet absorption maximum was also noted.[77]

Whereas presence of the 6-membered phosphate ring stabilises purine-glycosyl linkages towards acidic hydrolysis, in uridine-3′,5′ cyclic phosphate and the corresponding thymidine derivative (but *not* cytidine-3′,5′ cyclic phosphate) the glycosyl linkage is rendered particularly unstable. Considerable general degradation, including glycosyl-bond cleavage, occurs on alkaline hydrolysis of ribonucleoside-3′,5′

cyclic phosphates, especially purine derivatives, in sodium hydroxide (this is not the case with thymidine-3′,5′ cyclic phosphate and possibly other 2′-deoxy derivatives), but in barium hydroxide the products are the nucleoside-3′ and -5′ phosphates in the ratio 5 : 1. Small amounts of what are possibly xylofuranosyl derivatives are also formed in the barium ion catalysed hydrolysis of pyrimidine ribo- and deoxyribo-nucleoside-3′,5′ cyclic phosphates, perhaps the consequence of nucleophilic attack at C3′ by the pyrimidine 2-carbonyl group.[78]

NUCLEOSIDE-2′ (OR 3′),5′ DIPHOSPHATES

Adenosine-3′,5′ diphosphate has been isolated from enzymic hydrolysates of coenzyme A and " active sulphate "; it is a cofactor in the bioluminescence of *Renilla reniformis* (sea pansy).[242]   The isomeric -2′,5′ derivative occurs in nicotinamide adenine dinucleotide phosphate. A more convenient source of such compounds again lies in the ribo-nucleic acids, particularly degraded specimens of relatively short chain length.   Enzymic hydrolysis with snake venom (or the purified di-esterase) gives nucleoside-3′,5′ diphosphates arising from the terminal nucleoside bearing a 3′ phosphate.   Under conditions that permit phosphate migration, mixtures of the -2′,5′ and -3′,5′ diphosphates are

obtained.[79]   Similarly, alkaline degradation of any polyribonucleotide possessing a terminal -5′ phosphate gives rise to the mixed -2′,5′ and -3′,5′ diphosphates of this terminal nucleoside.   Monoesterases that are specific for the hydrolysis of 2′ or 3′ phosphates have been particularly useful for structural studies of this type of nucleotide.

The related -3′,5′ diphosphates of thymidine, 2′-deoxycytidine[22, 80–83] and 5-methyl-2′-deoxycytidine have been isolated from acidic hydro-lysates of deoxynucleic acid by ion exchange chromatography.[22] Catalytic hydrogenation of thymidine-3′,5′ diphosphate followed by mild acidic hydrolysis yielded dihydrothymine and a sugar diphosphate with reducing properties, in confirmation of the assigned structure.[80]

SYNTHESIS OF NUCLEOTIDES

While in principle nucleotides could be synthesised by any of the methods described for the synthesis of nucleosides, the sugar moiety being replaced by a suitably protected sugar phosphate, this approach[241] would seldom be superior to methods involving phosphorylation of a preformed nucleoside. In general, the successful synthesis of nucleotides results from the application of a good phosphorylating agent to nucleosides in which functional groups, other than the sugar hydroxyl at which esterification is desired, have been blocked, although selective phosphorylation of the free nucleoside can be achieved occasionally. In view of the instability of certain nucleotides it is essential that protecting groups, both of the nucleoside and of the phosphorylating agent, be removable under relatively mild conditions. For this reason most of the older methods of phosphorylation are of limited value and in any case they generally give a rather complex mixture of products.

RIBONUCLEOSIDE-5' PHOSPHATES

The first synthetic nucleotide was prepared in 1914 by Emil Fischer by phosphorylation of glucosyltheophylline with phosphoryl chloride in aqueous barium hydroxide.[84] A crystalline phosphate ester was obtained that on hydrolysis gave a glucose phosphate; the precise location of the phosphate is unknown.

The same reagent was later used by Levene and Tipson for the (partial) synthesis of nucleotides derived from naturally occurring nucleosides. Treatment of 2',3'-O-isopropylideneuridine with phosphoryl chloride in pyridine followed by acidic hydrolysis to remove the isopropylidene residue gave uridine-5' phosphate.[85] The -5' phosphates of inosine[86] and adenosine[87] were likewise prepared from the respective isopropylidene derivatives, low yields being obtained, particularly of adenylic acid. Subsequent application of the method to 2',3'-O-benzylidenecytidine (erroneously described as a -3',5' derivative) gave cytidine-5' phosphate,[88] and 2',3'-O-isopropylideneguanosine gave guanosine-5' phosphate,[89] contaminated with pyrophosphate and triphosphate derivatives.[90]

Direct phosphorylation of unprotected nucleosides with phosphoryl chloride in pyridine[91-93] gives all three monophosphates (-2', -3' or -5'), the molar proportions depending to some extent on the presence or absence of water.[94] Again, yields are unsatisfactory.

Difficulties associated with the polyfunctional nature of phosphoryl chloride can be avoided by the use of dialkyl (or diaryl) phosphorochloridates such as dibenzyl[95] and diphenyl[96] phosphorochloridates.

For the phosphorylation of nucleoside derivatives the former reagent is preferable because of the ease with which benzyl groups can be removed by a variety of methods including hydrogenolysis, acidic or alkaline hydrolysis, and anionic fission.[97] Treatment of 2',3'-O-isopropylidene-adenosine with dibenzyl phosphorochloridate gave the 5'-dibenzyl phosphate from which benzyl groups were removed by catalytic hydrogenolysis. Cleavage of the isopropylidene residue by the action of dilute acid then gave a good yield of adenosine-5' phosphate.[98] In an alternate procedure, mild acidic hydrolysis of 2',3'-O-isopropylidene-adenosine-5' dibenzyl phosphate gave adenosine-5' benzyl phosphate from which the free nucleotide was obtained by hydrogenolysis.[98]

Phosphorylation of the 2',3'-O-isopropylidene derivatives of uridine, cytidine,[89] and 9-β-D-ribofuranosylpurine[99] with dibenzyl phosphoro-

chloridate followed by removal of protecting groups gave the corresponding -5' phosphates. Guanosine derivatives proved somewhat resistant to this type of reagent. A more successful approach lay in the capacity of tetra-alkyl and tetra-aryl pyrophosphates to act as phosphorylating agents by virtue of their anhydride nature.[100, 101] Thus treatment of 2',3'-O-isopropylideneguanosine with tetra-p-nitrophenyl pyrophosphate (prepared in situ by the action of di-p-tolylcarbodiimide on di-p-nitrophenyl phosphoric acid) gave 2',3'-O-isopropylideneguanosine-5' di-p-nitrophenyl phosphate, the reagent being sufficiently powerful to render base catalysis unnecessary. Mild alkaline hydrolysis removed one p-nitrophenol residue; hydrolysis of the second required somewhat vigorous alkaline conditions resulting in some coincident dephosphorylation. Treatment of the mono-aryl nucleotide with snake venom (diesterase) was more effective, the 5'-monoesterase also present in the venom being inactive against the resultant nucleotide owing to the presence of the 2',3'-O-isopropylidene blocking group. This group was then removed in the usual manner giving guanosine-5' phosphate in good overall yield.[90]

The same reagent has been used for the phosphorylation of 9-β-D-2',3'-O-isopropylideneribofuranosyl derivatives of 6-chloropurine, 6-mercaptopurine and 2-amino-6-mercaptopurine,[102] and for the synthesis of 3-β-D-ribofuranosyl-4-azauracil-5' phosphate[103] and 2'-deoxy-uridine-5' phosphate.[104]

Another phosphorylating reagent related to the phosphorochloridates is O-benzyl phosphorous O-diphenyl phosphoric anhydride, readily prepared from diphenyl phosphorochloridate and monobenzyl phosphite.[105] Alcohols react with this reagent by nucleophilic attack at the less acidic component of the anhydride to give the alkyl benzyl phosphite, which can then be chlorinated[106] with N-chlorosuccinimide to the alkyl benzyl phosphorochloridate. Hydrolysis to the alkyl benzyl phosphate followed by hydrogenolysis gives the alkyl phosphate. The reagent has been applied to a number of protected nucleosides, both as a method of nucleotide synthesis and as a route to active nucleotide intermediates. Thus treatment of 2',3'-O-isopropylideneuridine with O-benzyl phosphorous O-diphenyl phosphoric anhydride in the presence of tertiary base gave the protected nucleoside phosphite which was oxidised to the phosphorochloridate. Mild basic hydrolysis gave 2',3'-O-isopropylideneuridine-5' benzyl phosphate from which the free nucleotide was obtained by removal of protecting groups in the usual way.[105]

Since the phosphite mixed anhydride reagent is a more powerful reagent than dibenzyl phosphorochloridate, it is of value for the phosphorylation of nucleoside derivatives that are resistant to the phosphorochloridate, and has been so used for the synthesis of 6-dimethyl-amino-9-β-D-ribofuranosylpurine-5' phosphate[107] among other nucleotides.

Perhaps the most convenient synthesis of pyrimidine ribonucleoside-5' phosphates is that employing one of the oldest of phosphorylating agents, " polyphosphoric acid ".[108] Treatment of 2',3'-O-isopropylidene-cytidine (or -uridine)[109] or the analogous 2',3'-O-benzylidene derivative[110] followed by acidic hydrolysis to degrade polyphosphates and to remove the protecting group gives the nucleotide which can be readily isolated in good yield.[110] The nature of the conditions employed for

Tr = Triphenylmethyl

phosphorylation preclude the application of this method to the less stable purine ribonucleosides or to the deoxynucleosides.

Another approach to nucleoside-5' phosphates utilises the reaction of silver dibenzyl phosphate with 5'-iodo-5'-deoxy-2',3'-O-isopropylideneuridine followed by removal of protecting groups.[111] The formation of cyclonucleoside derivatives limits this method to the uracil type of natural nucleotides, but the same procedure has been used for the synthesis of 7-β-D-ribofuranosyltheophylline-5' phosphate and 7-β-D-glucopyranosyltheophylline-6' phosphate,[112, 113]

While condensation of the nucleoside with acetone[85] or benzaldehyde[88] has generally been used for blocking the 2' and 3' hydroxyl groups, the 2',3'-di-O-acetylnucleosides[114] are occasionally of value. These are obtained by acetylation of the 5'-O-tritylnucleoside followed by mild acidic treatment to remove the trityl group. Other acyl groups such as benzoyl can also be used. A 2,3-carbonyl derivative has been employed in puromycin studies,[115] and for the synthesis of α-D-ribose-1 phosphate[116] and the α- and β-anomers of adenosine,[117] but has not so far been applied to the protection of nucleosides for subsequent phosphorylation.

As previously indicated, the chemical synthesis of nucleotides from the free base and a sugar phosphate has not been extensively explored. However, the biochemical synthesis of nucleoside-5' phosphates by this method is occasionally convenient, particularly in the case of nucleotides derived from " unnatural " bases which in the general chemical route would require prior synthesis of the nucleoside. Orotidine-5' phosphate and uridine-5′ phosphate are readily isolated from cultures of azauracil-inhibited *Escherichia coli*, the nucleotides accumulating as the result of a metabolic block.[118] A more controlled approach employs the actual substrates and purified enzyme responsible for the synthesis.[119] Thus interaction[120] of 6-mercaptopurine with 5-phosphoribosyl-1 pyrophosphate (α-D-ribofuranose-5 phosphate-1 pyrophosphate)[121] in the presence of a pyrophosphorylase from beef liver gives 9-β-D-ribofuranosyl-6-mercaptopurine-5′ phosphate. A similar enzyme present

in hog-liver extracts catalyses the synthesis of the corresponding nucleoside-5′ phosphates from 5-phosphoribosyl-1 pyrophosphate and 8-azaguanine, 2,6-diaminopurine, 6-mercaptopurine, and guanine analogues of the pyrazole-[3,4-*d*]-pyrimidine series, as well as adenine and hypoxanthine.[122] Partially purified yeast enzymes have also been used for the analogous synthesis of 5-fluorouridine-5′ phosphate from 5-fluoro-orotic acid, decarboxylation occurring at some stage,[123] presumably of 5-fluoro-orotidine-5′ phosphate. As is often the case with pyrophosphorylases, optimal enzymic activity is obtained with equimolar ratios of magnesium ion and 5-phosphoribosyl-1 pyrophosphate. The actual substrate is possibly the magnesium complex of the pyrophosphate.[123]

Finally, adenylosuccinic acid (an immediate precursor of adenosine-5' phosphate in the biosynthesis of this nucleotide) has been prepared by a different type of enzymic synthesis involving the condensation of adenosine-5' phosphate and fumaric acid, catalysed by yeast adenylosuccinase.[124]

RIBONUCLEOSIDE-2' AND -3' PHOSPHATES

Very small yields of what were presumably mixtures of 2' and 3' phosphates were obtained by direct phosphorylation of free nucleosides with phosphoryl chloride in aqueous baryta.[93, 125] A reinvestigation with adenosine, using modern techniques, has shown that there is indeed complete specificity for the 2' and 3' hydroxyl groups under these conditions, no 5' phosphate being obtained.[94]

Phosphorylation of 5'-O-trityl nucleosides[89, 126–128] gives mixtures of the 2' and 3' phosphates after removal of protecting groups.[47] In view of the ready migration of phosphate in these positions, the question of preferential phosphorylation at either the 2' or 3' hydroxyl group remains unanswered.

Earlier claims[89, 129] to unambiguous syntheses of nucleoside-2' and -3' phosphates were based on erroneous proofs of the structure of benzylideneguanosine[130, 131] and have been shown to be incorrect.[50] However, adenosine-2' phosphate and uridine-2' phosphate have both been synthesised by unambiguous routes involving phosphorylation of the 3',5'-di-O-acetyl nucleoside with O-benzyl phosphorous O-diphenyl phosphoric anhydride to give the phosphite, followed by oxidation and hydrolysis.[57, 64] Unambiguous syntheses of -3' phosphates lie in the reaction of dihydropyran with uridine-3',5' cyclic phosphate to give the 2'-O-tetrahydropyranyl derivative.[132]

Addition of dibenzyl phosphoric acid to the epoxide 7-β-(4,6-benzylidene-2,3-anhydro-D-allopyranosyl)-theophylline gives 7-β-D-glucopyranosyltheophylline-3' phosphate.[133] This type of reaction has not been applied to the synthesis of pentosyl (arabinose and xylose) nucleoside-3' phosphates, although the necessary 2',3'-anhydronucleosides are now available.

RIBONUCLEOSIDE-2′,3′ CYCLIC PHOSPHATES

Phosphorylation of glucosyltheophylline with phosphoryl chloride in pyridine gave a cyclic phosphate,[84] possibly the -4′,6′ cyclic phosphate.[134]

The naturally occurring nucleoside-2′,3′ cyclic phosphates are readily obtained by treatment of the nucleoside-2′ (or -3′) phosphate (or a mixture of the -2′ and -3′ phosphates) with any of a number of anhydride reagents including trifluoroacetic anhydride,[51] tetraphenyl pyrophosphate, and diphenyl phosphorochloridate (or better, diethyl phosphorochloridate since subsequent polymerisation does not occur).[134, 135] An intermediate nucleotide mixed anhydride is formed, with subsequent rapid intramolecular phosphorylation.

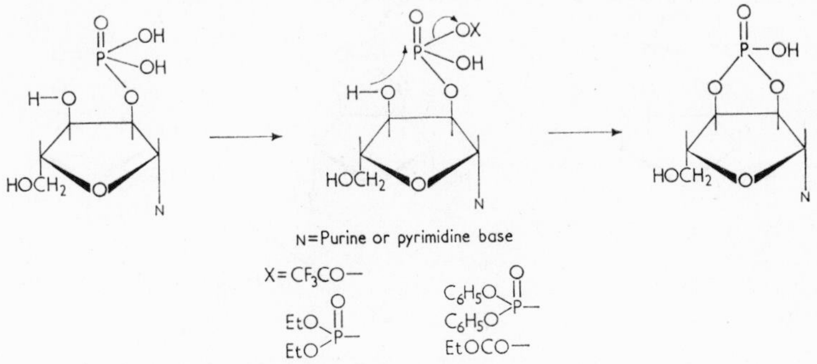

N = Purine or pyrimidine base

X = CF₃CO—

EtO—P(=O)— (EtO)
EtO

C₆H₅O—P(=O)— (C₆H₅O)

EtOCO—

In a related approach the nucleotide is treated with ethyl chloroformate and base in aqueous solution; a quantitative yield of the nucleoside-2′,3′ cyclic phosphate is thus obtained.[136] Intramolecular reaction rather than aqueous hydrolysis of the intermediate nucleotide-ethyl carbonate anhydride occurs because of the proximity and favourable conformation of the neighbouring hydroxyl group. The location of this hydroxyl group also accounts for the rapidity of the reaction; in contrast, the ethyl carbonate anhydrides of the nucleoside-5′ phosphates (also prepared in aqueous solution) are stable enough to permit isolation.[137]

Nucleoside-2′,3′ cyclic phosphates have also been obtained by the action of carbodi-imides on nucleoside-2′ (or -3′) phosphates.[138] In wet pyridine a mixture of the cyclic phosphate and the -2′ and -3′ phosphoryl ureas was obtained, the phosphoryl ureas resulting from further reaction of the cyclic phosphate monoanion with dicyclohexyl-carbodi-imide. This can be avoided by the use of ammonium[139] or trialkylammonium[140] salts of the nucleotides in anhydrous solution. In the presence of the stronger bases, addition of a proton to the carbodi-imide is greatly reduced so that reaction with the cyclic phos-

N = Purine or pyrimidine base

phate, which is also considerably less nucleophilic than the nucleotide di-anion, is negligible. Similar results can be obtained by using a less basic carbodi-imide.[140, 141] As in the mixed anhydride route, the location and configuration of the neighbouring hydroxyl group is of importance in the formation of cyclic phosphates from the initial pseudourea adduct despite the poor nucleophilic character of sugar hydroxyl groups.

Riboflavin-4',5' cyclic phosphate has been prepared by treating riboflavin with a pyridine solution of phosphoryl chloride to which one molar equivalent of water was added.[142] It is likely that the effective phosphorylating agent is a metaphosphate derivative formed by the action of base on phosphorodichloridic acid.[143] The cyclic phosphate has also been obtained by the action of carbodi-imides on riboflavin-5' phosphate,[141] and more conveniently by treatment of the nucleotide with ethyl chloroformate and tri-n-butylamine in aqueous solution.[137]

NUCLEOSIDE-3',5' CYCLIC PHOSPHATES

The action of aqueous barium hydroxide on a nucleoside-5' triphosphate is complex and gives rise to a number of products[144]

N = Purine or pyrimidine base

including the nucleoside-3',5' cyclic phosphate.[76] Both ribo- and deoxyribonucleoside-3',5' cyclic phosphates can be prepared more directly by heating a mixture of the tri-n-butylammonium nucleoside-5' phosphate and dicyclohexylcarbodi-imide in pyridine.[76–78] A nucleoside monomeric metaphosphate intermediate derived from the initially formed imidoyl phosphate, or from a P^1,P^2-dinucleoside-5' pyrophosphate by further reaction with excess of the carbodi-imide, is possibly involved,[143] though intramolecular phosphorylation to give the 3',5' cyclic phosphate also occurs on heating anhydrous pyridine solutions of the P^1,P^2-dinucleoside-5' pyrophosphate.[76–78] Thymidine-3',5' cyclic phosphate is formed at room temperature on treatment of thymidine-5' phosphate with dicyclohexylcarbodi-imide in very dilute pyridine solution.[77] Good yields of the ribonucleoside-3',5' cyclic phosphates have been obtained by the action of dicyclohexylcarbodi-imide on the 4-morpholine-N,N'-dicyclohexylcarboxamidinium salt of the ribonucleoside-5' phosphate (or the N-benzoyl nucleotide in the case of cytidine and guanosine derivatives).[78]

NUCLEOSIDE-3' (OR 2'),5' DIPHOSPHATES

Direct phosphorylation of thymidine (or deoxycytidine) with excess of dibenzyl phosphorochloridate followed by hydrogenolysis of the benzyl groups gives the deoxynucleoside-3',5' diphosphate,[22] together with some -5' phosphate but no 3' phosphate, indicating preferential phosphorylation at the 5' hydroxyl group.[145] The pyrimidine base can exert considerable influence on the relative reactivity of sugar hydroxyl groups since application of the same procedure to 4-azathymidine (prepared enzymically by a transglycosylation reaction between thymidine and 4-azathymine) gave a crude product that was separated into a 36% yield of the -3' phosphate, 18·5% of the 5' phosphate and 24% of the -3',5' diphosphate.[146]

An analogous phosphorylation of adenosine gave a mixture of the nucleoside-2',5' and -3',5' diphosphates. In this case anionic fission (lithium chloride) and alkaline hydrolysis were used in addition to hydrogenolysis for the removal of benzyl groups.[147] The isomeric diphosphates can be separated by ion exchange chromatography using concave gradient elution, and characterised by chemical or enzymic hydrolysis.[148] Adenosine-2',3',5' trisphosphate was isolated from the same reaction mixture; deamination gave inosine-2',3',5' trisphosphate.[148] Direct phosphorylation of adenosine with 2-cyanoethyl phosphate and dicyclohexylcarbodi-imide has also been described.[237]

In an alternative synthesis of the mixed -2',5' and -3',5' diphosphates of adenosine, adenosine-2',3' cyclic phosphate was treated with O-

benzylphosphorous O-diphenylphosphoric anhydride giving adenosine-(2',3'-cyclic phosphate)-5'-benzyl phosphite together with polymeric material. The phosphite was chlorinated and the product subjected to mild basic hydrolysis to give adenosine-(2',3'-cyclic phosphate)-5'-benzyl phosphate. Alkaline hydrolysis followed by hydrogenolysis (or the reversed procedures) yielded the mixed diphosphates via adenosine-2' (or -3') phosphate 5'-benzyl phosphate (or via the 2',3'-cyclic phosphate 5'-phosphate).[149] Adenosine-2'(3'),5' diphosphate has also been obtained by phosphorylation of adenosine-2',3' cyclic phosphate with dibenzyl phosphorochloridate (followed by hydrogenolysis) or with a mixture of cyanoethyl phosphate and dicyclohexylcarbodi-imide (followed by treatment with alkali).[150] The last method has also been applied to the synthesis of guanosine-2′(3′),5′ diphosphate from guanosine-2′,3′ cyclic phosphate.[137]

The pyrimidine ribonucleoside-2′,5′ and -3′,5′ diphosphates are conveniently prepared by direct treatment of the nucleoside with polyphosphoric acid. As initially described[109] the reaction produces considerable amounts of the O^2,2′-cyclonucleoside-3′,5′ diphosphates (and hence arabinosyl derivatives) from uridine and cytidine.[151] This can be avoided by suitable modification of the reaction conditions.[110]

Mixtures of nucleoside-2′,5′ and -3′,5′ diphosphates are readily converted into the homogeneous nucleoside-3′,5′ diphosphate by specific enzymic opening of a -2′,3′ cyclic phosphate intermediate. Thus treatment of adenosine-2′(3′),5′ diphosphate with ethyl chloroformate and base in aqueous solution gives adenosine-(2′,3′ cyclic phosphate)-5′ phosphate ethyl carbonate anhydride quantitatively. This, on digestion with rattlesnake venom or better, takadiastase ribonuclease T2, (to cleave the cyclic phosphate to -3′ phosphate) followed by alkaline hydrolysis of the 5′-phospho-carbonate anhydride linkage (conditions under which migration of 2′- or 3′-phosphate groups does not occur) gives adenosine-3′,5′ diphosphate exclusively. Similarly, with the analogous pyrimidine compounds, hydrolysis of the nucleoside-(2′,3′ cyclic phosphate)-5′ phosphate ethyl carbonate anhydride with pancreatic ribonuclease followed by alkaline treatment gives the pure uridine-3′,5′ (or cytidine-3′,5′) diphosphate uncontaminated by the isomeric 2′,5′ diphosphate.[152] Other enzymes can be used in a similar fashion for the synthesis of pure nucleoside-2′,5′ diphosphates.

(+ isomeric 3',5' diphosphate)

DEOXYNUCLEOSIDE-3' AND -5' PHOSPHATES

Phosphorylation of 5'-O-tritylthymidine with dibenzyl phosphorochloridate followed by mild acidic hydrolysis gave thymidine-3' benzyl phosphate from which thymidine-3' phosphate was obtained by hydrogenolysis of the benzyl group. For the synthesis of the isomeric -5′ phosphate, 3′-O-acetyl-5′-O-tritylthymidine was detritylated to give 3′-O-acetylthymidine which on phosphorylation and then alkaline treatment of the product yielded thymidine-5′ benzyl phosphate and this was converted into thymidine-5′ phosphate in the usual way.[153] An analogous series of reactions gave the deoxycytidine mononucleotides, N^6,3′-O-diacetyl-2′-deoxycytidine being used for synthesis of the -5′ phosphate.[154]

Thymidine-5′ phosphate has also been prepared by treating 3′-O-acetyl-5′-iodo-5′-deoxythymidine with silver dibenzyl phosphate; protecting groups were removed from the product in the usual way.[155]

The purine deoxyribonucleotides were synthesised by methods essentially similar to those used for the pyrimidine compounds. Partial acetylation of 2′-deoxyadenosine (or better, partial deacetylation of 3′,5′-di-O-acetyl-2′-deoxyadenosine) gave a mixture of acetates from which the two monoacetates were separated by counter-current distribution. Comparison of these with an authentic specimen of 3′-O-acetyldeoxyadenosine prepared by the more laborious route involving acetylation of 5′-O-trityl-2′-deoxyadenosine followed by hydrogenolytic removal of the trityl group (instability of the glycosyl linkage in purine deoxynucleosides limits the use of acidic hydrolysis) identified the monoacetate obtained in smaller yield as 3′-O-acetyldeoxyadenosine and hence the other was 5′-O-acetyldeoxyadenosine. Phosphorylation of 3′-O-acetyldeoxyadenosine with dibenzyl phosphorochloridate gave the dibenzyl phosphate from which the acetyl group and one benzyl group were removed by treatment with methanolic ammonia to give 2′-deoxyadenosine-5′ benzyl phosphate. Hydrogenolysis in a buffered (pH 7) aqueous solution (to avoid cleavage of the glycosyl linkage) gave deoxyadenosine-5′ phosphate. Phosphorylation of 5′-O-acetyldeoxyadenosine with dibenzyl phosphorochloridate was unsatisfactory, but treatment of the acetate with a more powerful reagent, O-benzyl phosphorous O-diphenyl phosphoric anhydride, gave the 3′-benzyl phosphite. Conversion into the benzyl phosphate followed by removal of protecting groups gave deoxyadenosine-3′ phosphate.[156]

For the synthesis of the corresponding deoxyguanosine phosphates the isomeric monoacetates were likewise prepared by partial deacetylation of 3′,5′-di-O-acetyl-2′-deoxyguanosine, or by partial acetylation of deoxyguanosine. Orientation of each deoxyguanosine monoacetate was achieved by a direct comparison of the monoacetyl deoxyribose liberated on mild acidic hydrolysis of the acylated nucleoside with those produced by a similar treatment of 3′-O-acetyldeoxyadenosine and 5′-O-acetyldeoxyadenosine. Each monoacetyl (3′ or 5′) deoxyguanosine was then phosphorylated with O-benzyl phosphorous

Tr=Triphenylmethyl

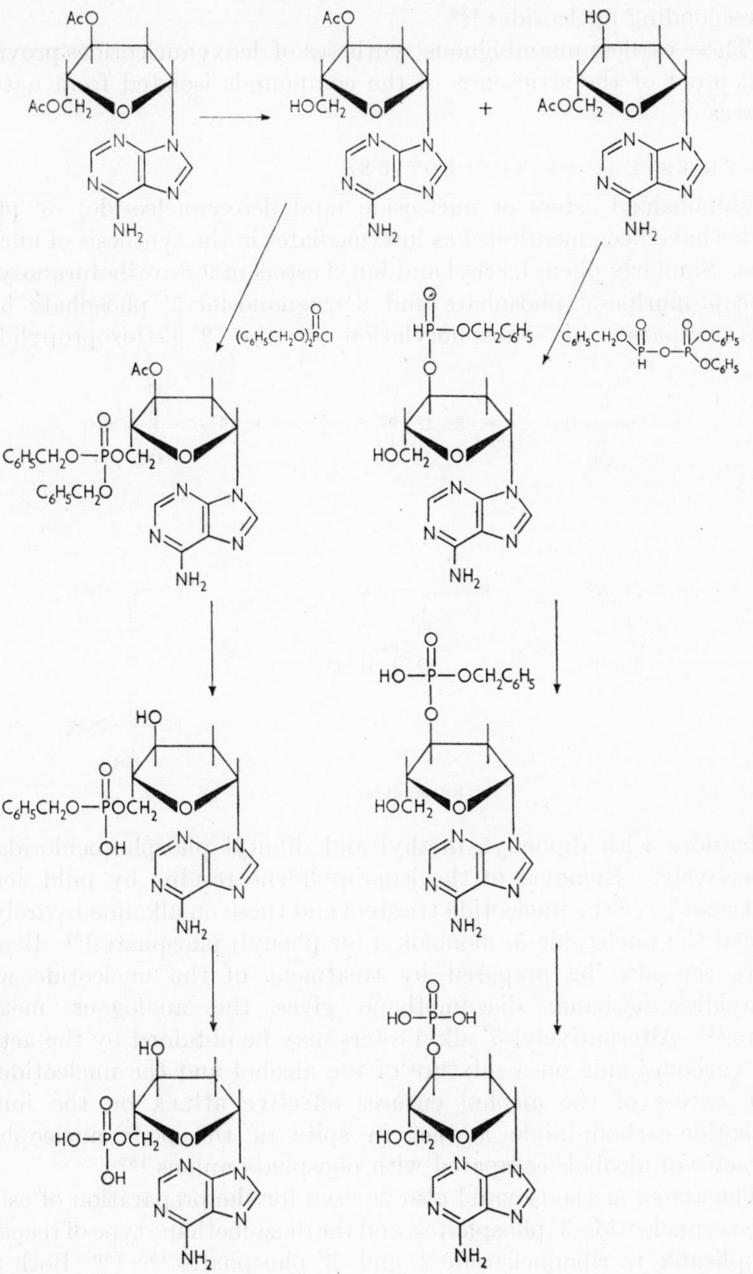

AcO

AcOCH₂

NH₂

→

HO

HOCH₂

NH₂

+

HO

AcOCH₂

NH₂

(C₆H₅CH₂O)₂PCl

$$HP \overset{O}{-} OCH_2C_6H_5$$

C₆H₅CH₂O—P—O—P OC₆H₅ / H / OC₆H₅

AcO

C₆H₅CH₂O—P—OCH₂ / C₆H₅CH₂O / O

NH₂

HOCH₂

O═P—OCH₂C₆H₅ / O

NH₂

$$HO-P \overset{O}{-} OCH_2C_6H_5$$

HO

C₆H₅CH₂O—P—OCH₂ / OH / O

NH₂

HOCH₂

HO—P—O / OH / O

NH₂

HO

HO—P—OCH₂ / OH / O

NH₂

HOCH₂

O

NH₂

O-diphenyl phosphoric anhydride and the products converted into the corresponding nucleotides.[156]

These earliest unambiguous syntheses of deoxynucleotides provided final proof of the structures of the compounds isolated from natural sources.

ALKYL ESTERS OF NUCLEOTIDES

Monobenzyl esters of nucleoside (and deoxynucleoside) -5' phosphates have been mentioned as intermediates in the synthesis of nucleotides. Similarly phenyl, ethyl and butyl esters of 9-β-D-ribofuranosyl-6-mercaptopurine-5' phosphate and 8-azaguanosine-5' phosphate have been prepared by phosphorylation of the 2',3'-O-isopropylidene

R = nucleoside -5'

nucleosides with diphenyl, diethyl and dibutyl phosphorochloridates respectively. Removal of the isopropylidene residue by mild acidic treatment gave the nucleotide triesters and these on alkaline hydrolysis yielded the nucleoside-5' monoalkyl (or phenyl) phosphate.[157] Benzyl esters can also be prepared by treatment of the nucleotide with phenyldiazomethane; diazomethane gives the analogous methyl esters.[158] Alternatively, 5' alkyl esters may be obtained by the action of a carbodi-imide on a mixture of the alcohol and the nucleotide; a large excess of the alcohol ensures effective attack on the initial nucleotide-carbodi-imide adduct in spite of the poor nucleophilic character of alcohols compared with phosphate anions.[159]

The above methods could also be used for the preparation of esters of deoxynucleoside-3' phosphates, and the diazomethane type of reaction is applicable to ribonucleoside-2' and -3' phosphates.[158, 160] Both the base-catalysed[138, 161] and acid-catalysed esterification (the latter is preferable)[162, 163] of primary alcohols by nucleoside-2',3' cyclic phosphates (or the nucleotide-ureas obtained by the use of dicyclohexyl-carbodi-imide on the mononucleotide in wet pyridine) give mixtures of the nucleoside-2' and -3' alkyl phosphates. These are also conveniently obtained by treating the diphenyl phosphate anhydride of the nucleoside-2',3' cyclic phosphate with excess of an alcohol.[164]

N=Purine or pyrimidine base

OTHER PHOSPHORYLATING AGENTS

As stated in the introductory paragraph of this section, the synthesis of nucleotides is largely concerned with the treatment of a blocked nucleoside with a satisfactory phosphorylating agent. In addition to the reagents previously mentioned, phenyl phosphorodichloridate has also been used, with somewhat limited success.[92, 165] Phosphorylation of 5'-O-tritylthymidine with the analogous p-nitrophenyl phosphorodichloridate gives somewhat better yields of the 3' phosphate than does the relatively mild reagent dibenzyl phosphorochloridate. Since alkaline treatment of thymidine-3' p-nitrophenyl phosphate gives rise to both the 3' phosphate and the 5' phosphate (via an intermediate -3',5' cyclic phosphate) the *p*-nitrophenyl residue was hydrolysed with alkali prior to removal of the trityl group.[166] The synthesis of riboflavin-5' phosphite (oxidation with potassium permanganate gives the phosphate) by treatment of riboflavin with 2-chloro-5,6-benzo-1,3,2-dioxaphosphorin-4-one in phenol suggests a reagent of possible value in nucleotide work.[167] Riboflavin has also been converted into the -5' phosphite by treatment with diphenyl chlorophosphite in phenol.[168] Other phosphorylating agents that have not been applied to nucleotides but which may be useful, include phosphorodimorpholidic bromide,[169] (phos-

phorodimorpholidic chloride has been used for phosphorylation of 2',3'-isopropylidene-N^1-methyluridine;[170] protecting groups were removed by mild acidic treatment), and hydrobenzoin cyclic phosphate.[171] Acid catalysed alcoholysis of the latter reagent using trifluoracetic acid gives alkyl 1,2-diphenyl-2-hydroxyethyl-1 phosphates from which the alkyl phosphate is obtained by catalytic hydrogenolysis. Similar alcoholyses in the presence of hydrogen chloride give the alkyl phosphate directly.[171] Alcoholysis of catechol cyclic phosphate has proved effective for the preparation of a number of polyol phosphates including riboflavin-5' phosphate.[172, 173]

Dichlorophosphoric anhydride[174, 175] appears to be an excellent phosphorylating agent.[174] Treatment of 2',3'-isopropylideneguanosine with excess of this reagent gave phosphorodichloridic acid and the nucleoside-5′ phosphorodichloridate; mild hydrolysis of the latter gave a high yield of guanosine-5′ phosphate. Adenosine-5′ phosphate was prepared similarly.[174]

Di-(β-cyanoethyl) phosphorochloridate has been used for the synthesis of nucleotides in good yield. Mild treatment of the intermediate triester with aqueous barium hydroxide eliminates two mols of acrylonitrile to give the monoester.[176] Other methods of phosphorylation that await full development include the use of enol phosphates,[177, 178] guanidino phosphates[179] and, under oxidising conditions, quinol phosphates.[180]

In the main the reagents and methods so far described fall into a general class wherein phosphorylation is effected either by formation of a phosphorylium cation by ionisation, or by nucleophilic attack at a phosphorus atom with simultaneous expulsion of a stable anion.[143] Recently, a number of methods of phosphorylation have been developed, that fall into a second general class wherein the effective phosphorylating agent is probably a monomeric metaphosphate derivative. Ethyl metaphosphate (polymeric) was introduced[181] as a phosphorylating agent in 1910, but has not been extensively applied to the phosphorylation of carbohydrate derivatives.[182] However, it is likely that a metaphosphate derivative is the true phosphorylating agent, rather than phosphorodichloridic acid, when pyridine solutions of phosphoryl chloride plus one equivalent of water are employed.[143] This method has been used for syntheses of riboflavin-5′ phosphate[142] and 5-fluoro-2′-deoxyuridine-5′ phosphate[183] and is quite effective. Even more powerful methods of phosphorylation lie in the use of esters of monomeric metaphosphate.[143] These are readily obtained by treatment of a monoesterified phosphate with the chloride of a very strong acid (such as toluene-p-sulphonyl chloride)[184] to give an intermediate mixed anhydride which then yields the strong acid anion and the alkyl (aryl) monomeric metaphosphate.[143] Alternatively, treatment of the phosphate monoester with excess of dicyclohexylcarbodi-imide in pyridine[185, 186] gives initially the P^1,P^2-diester of pyrophosphoric and this reacts further with the carbodi-imide to yield the pseudourea pyrophosphate which then breaks down to liberate a monomeric metaphosphate ester.[143] Under the conditions generally employed (large excess of dicyclohexylcarbodi-imide), direct formation of "monomeric metaphosphate" from the imidoyl phosphate intermediate may also be expected, as would further reaction with pyridine to give zwitterionic phospho-pyridinium derivatives (base-metaphosphate complexes) active as phosphorylating agents. A desirable, but not entirely mandatory, absence of strong base (such as tri-n-butylamine) is explicable in terms of competition between the base and carbodi-imide for protons, and the greatly reduced nucleophilic character of P^1,P^2-dialkyl (or aryl) pyrophosphates compared with monoesterified phosphate. Experimental evidence supporting the concepts expressed above is provided to some extent by a number of attempts to prepare P^1,P^1-diesters of pyrophosphoric acid (that is an anhydride of phosphoric acid with a very much stronger acid). Although these were doubtless formed, addition of water always resulted in the isolation of metaphosphate.[187]

The powerful nature of this approach to nucleotides has been demonstrated by the phosphorylation in high yield of nucleoside secondary hydroxyl groups that are normally rather resistant to phosphorylation by milder reagents. Thus treatment of 5'-O-tritylthymidine with monobenzyl phosphate and dicyclohexylcarbodi-imide in anhydrous pyridine followed by removal of protecting groups gave thymidine-3' phosphate.[185, 186] A more satisfactory reagent is the metaphosphate derived from β-cyanoethyl phosphate. Fully esterified pyrophosphate products are cleaved by addition of water to the pyridine solution and the β-cyanoethyl group is readily removed by treatment with alkali; in general high yields are obtained. In this way thymidine-3' phosphate, thymidine-5' phosphate, and guanosine-5' phosphate have been prepared by the action of dicyclohexylcarbodi-imide and β-cyanoethyl phosphate on the protected nucleoside.[185, 186] The method has also been used for the synthesis of 6-thioguanosine-5' phosphate, 6-thioinosine-5' phosphate,[188, 189] and 8-azaguanosine-5' phosphate.[189] In addition, the reagent is effective for the phosphorylation of di(deoxynucleoside) phosphates and has been used for the preparation of 5'-phosphoryl-thymidylyl-3':5'-thymidine-3' phosphate from thymidylyl-3':5'-thymidine, and of thymidylyl-3':5'-thymidine-3' phosphate from 5'-O-tritylthymidylyl-3':5'-thymidine.[186]

Nucleoside phosphites are readily obtained in good yield by treating the protected nucleoside with phosphorous acid (equivalent to a monoalkyl phosphate with respect to dissociations) and di-p-tolyl-carbodi-imide in anhydrous pyridine.[190] Oxidation of purine nucleoside phosphites with potassium permanganate gives the nucleotide; this is not possible in the case of pyrimidine compounds owing to destruction of the heterocyclic ring. It is of interest that when the procedure was applied directly to unprotected deoxynucleosides, thymidine gave mainly the -3' phosphite (43% of the -3' and 24% of the -5' compound) but with deoxyadenosine more -5' (42%) than -3' (29%) phosphite was obtained. In accord with the postulate that phosphorylation with phosphate monoesters and carbodi-imides is due to formation of "monomeric metaphosphate", monobenzyl phosphite (equivalent to

a dialkyl phosphate which cannot form "metaphosphate") and di-*p*-tolylcarbodi-imide proved very poor for "phosphitylation". The reaction mechanism presumably involves formation of "monomeric metaphosphite" (HPO_2) in a manner analogous to that obtaining when monoalkyl phosphates and carbodi-imides are used in approximately stoichiometric conditions.[190]

It may be noted that a mixture of di-*p*-tolylcarbodi-imide and phosphoric acid in pyridine does not act as an effective phosphorylating

Tr = Triphenylmethyl

agent, presumably because the metaphosphate retains an anionic dissociation.[190] However, ^{32}P labelled nucleoside-5′ phosphates have been obtained in low yield by treating tri-n-butylammonium ^{32}P inorganic phosphate with dicyclohexylcarbodi-imide and a somewhat overwhelming 285 molar excess of the 2′,3′-isopropylidene nucleoside.[191] Considerably more effective phosphorylation with phosphoric acid, dicyclohexylcarbodi-imide and a stoichiometric amount of nucleoside can be achieved simply by using the mono(methyl-tri-n-octylammonium) salt of phosphoric acid.[137] The long chain fatty amine presumably prevents dissociation to a large extent and the phosphoric acid acts as a monoalkyl phosphate.

Direct esterification of alcohols by the imidoyl phosphate intermediates from trichloracetonitrile,[192, 193] and cyanuric chloride[194] has been claimed. Relatively vigorous conditions are required and in contrast with carbodi-imides the reagents do not react with diesterified phosphates, carboxylic acids or water. Treatment of $2',3'-O$-isopropylideneadenosine with phenyl phosphoric acid and trichloracetonitrile in pyridine yielded the -5' phenyl phosphate.[192, 193] Trichloracetonitrile and phosphoric acid has been used with success for the synthesis of farnesyl phosphate and pyrophosphate.[195]

Finally, phosphoramidates have proved of value as phosphorylating agents for anions, and in particular for the synthesis of pyrophosphates. To some extent they can be regarded as "base-metaphosphate complexes".[143] Undoubtedly, suitable phosphoramidates will also prove to be effective phosphorylating agents for alcohols. Indeed, the acid catalysed reaction between adenosine-5' phosphoromorpholidate and methanol yields adenosine-5' methyl phosphate.[196, 197] Recent studies on phosphorylation reactions with diesters of imidazolylphosphoric acid and monoesters of di-imidazolylphosphinic acid have shown that treatment of $2',3'-O$-isopropylideneadenosine with di-imidazolylphenylphosphinic acid gives $2',3'-O$-isopropylideneadenosine-5' phenyl phosphate.[198]

NUCLEOTIDE ANALOGUES

Alkyl and aryl phosphonate analogues of adenosine-5' phosphate and uridine-5' phosphate have been obtained by the action of benzyl ethyl (or phenyl) phosphonochloridate on the $2',3'-O$-isopropylidene nucleoside followed by removal of the isopropylidene and benzyl groups.[199]

Phosphonate analogues containing a nucleoside carbon–phosphorus bond are more difficult to prepare. However, 9-(5'-deoxy-5'-diethyl phosphonate-β-D-ribofuranosyl)-6-amino-2-methylthiopurine was obtained from 5-deoxy-D-ribose-5 diethyl phosphonate by application of the method for synthesis of purine nucleosides involving Schiff base formation with 2-methylthio-4,6-diaminopyrimidine.[200, 201] A Michaelis–Arbuzov reaction of $2',3'$-isopropylidene-5'-deoxy-5'-iodo-uridine with triethyl phosphite followed by removal of the isopropylidene residue gave the diethyl ester of 5'-deoxyuridine-5' phosphonate.[202]

Diethyl thionophosphate and alkyl (or aryl) dimethyl phosphoramidate derivatives of adenosine have been prepared by use of the appropriate phosphorylating agents.[203]

Treatment of adenosine with chlorosulphonic acid ($ClSO_3H$) gave the nucleoside tris-sulphate; similarly, adenosine-5′ sulphate was obtained from 2′,3′-O-isopropylidene adenosine.[204, 240] Related methods have been used for the synthesis of sulphate esters of cytidine.[238] In contrast with the phosphate, cytidine-5′ sulphate is readily hydrolysed by acid.

The -2′, -3′, -4′ and -6′ phosphates of 9-β-D-glucopyranosyladenine (and the -4′,6′ cyclic phosphate) were obtained by phosphorylation of suitable derivatives of the glucosyl.[205] No isomerisation of the -2′, -3′ or -4′ phosphates occurred under conditions that brought about inter-conversion of ribonucleoside-2′ and -3′ phosphates. (A glucosyladenine phosphate has been isolated from cotton plant leaves.[206] The structure is not yet known.)

An analogue of adenosine-5′ triphosphate, adenylyl-5′ methylene diphosphonic acid, has been described.[207] Other analogues include phosphates and polyphosphates derived from 6-deoxyuridine, 9-β-D-ribofuranosyl-6-dimethylaminopurine, and 9-β-D-ribofuranosyl-6-methylaminopurine.[165, 208] Mono-, pyro- and triphosphate derivatives of 9-hydroxyalkyl-6-aminopurines (4'-hydroxybutyl, 3'-hydroxypropyl and 2'-hydroxyethyl) have also been prepared, using "polyphosphoric" acid for synthesis of the monophosphates.[208, 209]

PROPERTIES OF NUCLEOTIDES

The orthodox methods of classical organic chemistry are of little value for the characterisation of nucleotides (and can indeed be misleading) and have been replaced by techniques such as paper chromatography, infrared and ultraviolet spectroscopy, and X-ray examination (powder diffraction patterns). As nucleoside esters of phosphoric acid, the nucleotides possess many of the properties described for the nucleosides, including N-oxide formation (by the adenine nucleotides),[210, 211] cyclisation of suitable derivatives to cyclonucleoside phosphates,[164] and halogenation[212-215] and reduction of the ring system of pyrimidine nucleotides.[35, 63] Uridine-5' phosphate is readily converted into 5-bromouridine-5' phosphate by the action of N-bromosuccinimide,[212] but more convenient general methods for halogenation of the uridine nucleotides have been developed. Chlorination is rapidly effected by brief treatment of a solution of uridine-2' (3' or 5') phosphate in acetic acid with chlorine at room temperature. Some saturation of the 4,5 double bond also occurs, but such intermediates are converted into 5-chlorouridine-2' (-3' or -5') phosphate on heating.[214, 215] Treatment of the free nucleotide with aqueous dioxan bromide (that is, a solution of bromine in aqueous dioxan) yields the 5-bromo derivative at room temperature. More rapid conversion occurs in the presence of small amounts of nitric acid. For the preparation of 5-iodouridine-2' (-3' or -5') phosphate, the nucleotide is treated with iodine and dilute nitric acid in dioxan. Both the dioxan and nitric acid are essential for rapid iodination and the reaction possibly involves intermediate formation of iodine nitrate from dioxan iodide and the nitric acid, since any acidic catalysis necessary would be provided by the nucleotide itself.[214, 215] The methods have also been applied to the halogenation of deoxyuridine and its derivatives. Treatment of uridine-5' phosphate with bromine water in pyridine gives 5-hydroxyuridine-5' phosphate.[216]

Further evidence for hydrogen bonding between the pyrimidine and sugar rings is provided by the photochemical behaviour at 2537 Å of the various pyrimidine nucleotides.[217, 218] Irradiation of aqueous solutions of nucleotides with X-rays causes a complex series of reactions involving attack by free radicals formed by the initial splitting of water molecules.[219] Ammonia is liberated, as are unstable phosphate

3. CHEMISTRY OF NUCLEOTIDES

esters,[220] and cleavage of the glycosyl linkage of adenylic and guanylic acids yields the free base;[219, 221] 2,4-diamino-5-formamido-6-hydroxy-pyrimidine has also been identified after irradiation of solutions of guanosine and guanylic acid with 15 MeV electrons.[221]

The phosphate residue causes slight modification of physical properties such as ultraviolet absorption and dissociation constants of the bases; more profound effects are evidenced in such properties as optical rotation and infrared absorption spectra, as may be expected. The influence of the phosphate group on the stability of the glycosyl linkage in nucleotides towards acidic hydrolysis has been observed repeatedly. This effect is dependent on the location and number of phosphates[222]; the -3',5' cyclic phosphate grouping has a very marked effect,[77, 78] and the glycosyl linkage in 2',3'-O-isopropylidene-9-β-D-ribofuranosylpurine-5' phosphate is more stable than it is in the corresponding 5'-dibenzyl ester.[223]

That interaction between the neighbouring hydroxyl and phosphoryl groups takes place is shown by the fact that (like sugar phosphates)[224] the mononucleotides are abnormally strong acids compared with the monoalkyl phosphates. The precise geometry of the hydroxyl groups (maintained by the sugar ring system) is of importance, as shown by pK values of the glycerol phosphates. Effects of interaction, presumably hydrogen bonding, with a *cis* vicinal hydroxyl group are also evident in a comparison of corresponding ribonucleoside- and deoxy-ribonucleoside-3' phosphates. From their behaviour on anion exchange columns the former are considerably stronger acids and the two (e.g. cytidine-3' phosphate and deoxycytidine-3' phosphate) can be separated

TABLE I. Phosphoryl Dissociation Constants

Compound	pK_1	pK_2
Adenylic acid	∼0·9	6·1
Cytidylic acid	∼0·8	6·3
Guanylic acid	∼0·7	6·1
Uridylic acid	∼1·0	6·4
Methyl phosphate	1·54	6·31
Propyl phosphate	1·88	6·67
Phosphoric acid	1·97	6·82
Dimethyl phosphate	1·29	—
Dipropyl phosphate	1·59	—
α-Glycerol phosphate	1·40	6·44
β-Glycerol phosphate	1·37	6·34
Glucose-6 phosphate	0·94	6·11
Glucose-3 phosphate	0·84	5·67
Phosphoramidic acid	−0·9	2·8

readily.   In contrast, corresponding ribonucleoside- and deoxyribo-
nucleoside-5' phosphates display closely similar characteristics.[67, 154]

The influence of zwitterion formation (most pronounced in phosphoramidic acid itself) is also indicated in the values of the primary
phosphoryl dissociations for the mononucleotides. To a large extent the
increase in acidic strength is determined by the closeness of the charged
groups.   With respect to anion exchange chromatography, basic
ionisations (and possibly other factors such as molecular size and shape)
as well as acidic pK values determine the relative distribution coefficients of the nucleotides at different pHs.[44] Nucleotide diesters
(including cyclic phosphates) are stronger acids than the free nucleotides at pHs such that the secondary dissociation is suppressed; however, at pH 7 adenosine-2',3' cyclic phosphate is eluted from ECTEOLA
prior to the 2' (or 3') phosphate.[136]

Alkaline or neutral[225] hydrolysis of the ribonucleotides (catalysed
by metal ions) gives the corresponding nucleoside and inorganic phosphate.   Liberation of phosphate by acidic hydrolysis (pH $\sim$ 1) is
probably mainly preceded by glycosyl fission to give the sugar phosphate,* which is then degraded.[226]   Since pyrimidine glycosyls are
considerably more stable than the purine compounds, liberation of
inorganic phosphate by acidic hydrolysis is much less rapid in the case
of cytidylic and uridylic acids than with adenylic and guanylic acids
(and the 4,5-dihydropyrimidine nucleotides).   At pH 4, however, a
different mechanism occurs, involving direct P–O fission in the absence
of glycosyl cleavage, and without appreciable phosphate migration.[148]
Hydrolysis in ammonium formate buffer at this pH has proved useful
for determining the location of the phosphate groups in adenosine-2',5'
diphosphate and adenosine-3',5' diphosphate. Thus the -2',5' isomer
yielded adenosine, adenosine-2' phosphate, adenosine-5' phosphate and
only traces of adenosine-3' phosphate. The structures of these synthetic
diphosphates were confirmed by the use of a monoesterase specific for
the -3' phosphate in adenosine-3',5' diphosphate.

Enzymic dephosphorylation of the nucleotides can be effected by
non-specific monoesterases (such as that from prostate) or by monoesterases specific for a particularly located phosphate group (e.g. snake
venom 5'-nucleotidase). Specificity may be even more pronounced;
the deoxynucleoside-3' phosphates are resistant to 3'-ribonucleotidase
(and are also relatively stable in the presence of ceric hydroxide).[67]

Although the nucleoside-5' phosphates and their esters show no

* The more rapid release of phosphate from ribose-2 or -3 phosphate (ester linkage α
or β to a latent aldehydo group) compared with ribose-5 phosphate results in considerable
dephosphorylation of purine nucleotide derivatives containing 2' or 3' phosphate linkages
(e.g. RNA) under standard conditions for determination of acid-labile phosphate
(polyphosphate type). This is not always taken into consideration.

tendency to isomerise, the ribonucleoside-2' and -3' phosphates are readily interconverted to an equilibrium mixture in acidic solution. This acid catalysed migration proceeds via an intermediate 2',3' cyclic phosphate[47] and is analogous to the interconversion of glycerol-α and -β phosphates to an equilibrium mixture.[227-229]

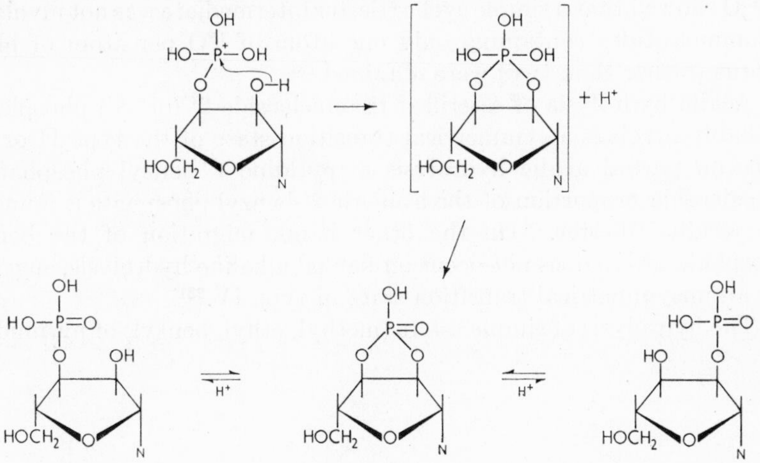

N = Purine or pyrimidine base

In alkaline solution the isomeric mononucleotides, like the glycerol monophosphates, are not interconverted. However, alkaline treatment of alkyl esters of the ribonucleoside-2' (or 3') phosphates gives a mixture of the isomeric mononucleotides, as does acidic hydrolysis.[52, 158] Again

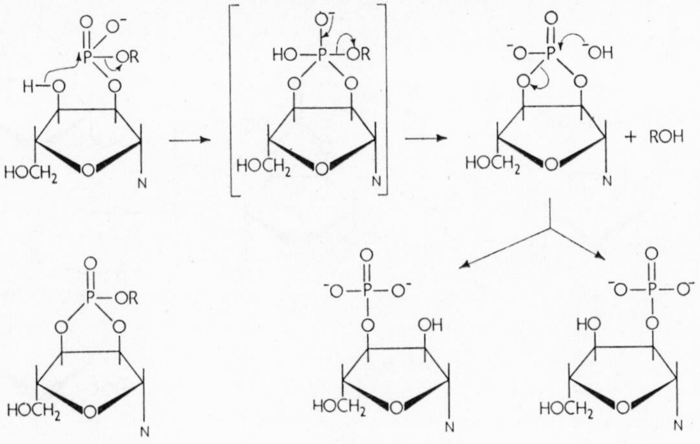

N = Purine or pyrimidine base

the process is considered to involve attack by the vicinal hydroxyl group at the P atom (catalysed by hydroxyl or hydrogen ions) with simultaneous removal of the alkyl group as an alkoxy anion, possibly via a pentacovalent transition complex, to give a cyclic phosphate intermediate.[52, 158, 230] Alkaline hydrolysis of yeast ribonucleic acid in $H_2^{18}O$ showed that a simple cyclic triester intermediate was not involved. Mononucleotides containing only one atom of ^{18}O per atom of phosphorus (rather than two) were obtained.[230]

Acidic hydrolysis of esterified ribonucleoside-2' (or -3') phosphates probably involves a symmetrical transition state of the type II or III since on partial acidic hydrolysis of cytidine-3' benzyl phosphate a considerable proportion of the isomeric 2'-benzyl phosphate is found in the residual diester. On the other hand, migration of the benzyl phosphate group does not occur on partial alkaline hydrolysis, suggesting an unsymmetrical transition state of type IV.[231]

The hydrolysis of simple esters (methyl, ethyl, benzyl) of pyrimidine

N = Purine or pyrimidine base

nucleoside-3′ phosphates with pancreatic ribonuclease occurs by unidirectional cleavage of an intermediate -2′,3′ cyclic phosphate to give the -3′ phosphate only.[158] The purine compounds are unaffected by this enzyme but are converted into the free nucleotide by other specific diesterases.[232] Related enzymes have been isolated that have no action on esters of the nucleotides but will open a preformed -2′,3′ cyclic phosphate to give the -2′ phosphate exclusively.[233] The first stage of pancreatic ribonuclease hydrolysis is reversible, and the enzyme catalyses transesterification of pyrimidine nucleoside-2′,3′ cyclic phosphates with suitable primary alcohols (including nucleosides and nucleoside-2′,3′ cyclic phosphates) to give the pyrimidine nucleoside-3′ alkyl phosphate.[161, 234] A similar reversibility is evident in the replacement of the benzyl group in cytidine-3′ (or adenosine-3′) benzyl phosphate by methyl or ethyl groups catalysed by spleen phosphodiesterase. Hydrolysis by the spleen enzyme does not proceed via a -2′,3′ cyclic phosphate (such synthetic intermediates are converted into -2′ phosphates), but again the reaction is direct transesterification rather than synthesis. The imidazole nucleus of a histidine residue in the enzyme is possibly responsible for the phosphate transfer.[235]

The dimethyl or dibenzyl ester of uridine-3′ phosphate (and

presumably of other ribonucleoside-2' and -3' phosphates) is unstable over the whole pH range, decomposing to a mixture of the monoesters of uridine-2' and -3' phosphate together with traces of the -2',3' cyclic phosphate.[160] In contrast, diesters of nucleoside-5' phosphates show the normal behaviour of triesterified phosphate, and it is clear that in the former cases the vicinal hydroxyl group is involved in formation of a cyclic intermediate.

Studies on the synthesis of pantetheine-2',4' cyclic phosphate from pantolactone-2 diphenyl phosphate demonstrated the formation of a six membered ring system by transesterification.[236] Similar cyclic phosphates have been identified as intermediates in the hydrolysis of

esters of deoxynucleoside-3' phosphates and would presumably occur with ribonucleoside derivatives suitably blocked at the more favourable 2' position. Thus, alkaline treatment of thymidine-3' p-nitrophenyl phosphate gave a mixture of thymidine-3' and -5' phosphates via the 3',5' cyclic phosphate formed by transphosphorylation.[166]

Esters of the ribo- (and deoxyribo-) nucleoside-5' phosphates show the normal properties associated with di- or tri-esterified phosphate. Mild acidic or alkaline hydrolysis of a nucleoside-5' dibenzyl phosphate gives the -5' monobenzyl ester which is somewhat resistant to further hydrolysis. Specific diesterases, such as that present in snake venom, readily hydrolyse monoesters of nucleoside-5' phosphates to the free nucleotide.[145]

REFERENCES

1. Levene, P. A., and Mandel, H., *Chem. Ber.*, **41**, 1905 (1908).
2. Liebig, J. von, *Ann.*, **62**, 257 (1847).
3. Doery, H. M., *Nature*, **177**, 381 (1956); **180**, 799 (1957).
4. Embden, G., and Zimmermann, M., *Z. physiol. Chem.*, **167**, 137 (1927).
5. Schmitz, H., Hurlbert, R. B., and Potter, V. R., *J. Biol. Chem.*, **209**, 41 (1954).
6. Smith, E. E. B., and Mills, G. T., *Biochim. et Biophys. Acta*, **13**, 386 (1954).
7. Segal, H. L., *Biochim. et Biophys. Acta*, **21**, 194 (1956).
8. Osawa, S., Allfrey, V. G., and Mirsky, A. E., *J. Gen. Physiol.*, **40**, 491 (1957).
9. Potter, R. L., Schlesinger, S., Buettner-Janusch, V., and Thompson, L., *J. Biol. Chem.*, **226**, 381 (1957).
10. Levene, P. A., *J. Biol. Chem.*, **33**, 425 (1918); **40**, 415 (1919).
11. Chargaff, E., Magasanik, B., Vischer, E., Green, C., Doniger, R., and Elson, D., *J. Biol. Chem.*, **186**, 51 (1950).
12. Cohn, W. E., *J. Am. Chem. Soc.*, **71**, 2275 (1949); **72**, 1471, 2811 (1950).
13. Cohn, W. E., and Volkin, E., *Nature*, **167**, 483 (1951).
14. Cohn, W. E., and Volkin, E., *Arch. Biochem. Biophys.*, **35**, 465 (1952).
15. Volkin, E., Khym, J. X., and Cohn, W. E., *J. Am. Chem. Soc.*, **73**, 1533 (1951).
16. Hurst, R. O., Little, J. A., and Butler, G. C., *J. Biol. Chem.*, **188**, 705 (1951).
17. Sinsheimer, R. L., and Koerner, J. F., *J. Biol. Chem.*, **198**, 293 (1952).
18. Klein, W., *Z. physiol. Chem.*, **218**, 164 (1933).
19. Klein, W., and Thannhauser, S. J., *Z. physiol. Chem.*, **218**, 173 (1933); **224**, 252 (1934); **231**, 96 (1935).
20. Cunningham, L., *J. Am. Chem. Soc.*, **80**, 2546 (1958).
21. Levene, P. A., and Mandel, H., *Chem. Ber.*, **41**, 1905 (1908).
22. Dekker, C. A., Michelson, A. M., and Todd, A. R., *J. Chem. Soc.*, 947 (1953).
23. Cohn, W. E., and Volkin, E., *Biochim. et Biophys. Acta*, **24**, 359 (1957).
24. Shapiro, H. S., and Chargaff, E., *Biochim. et Biophys. Acta*, **23**, 451 (1957).
25. Levene, P. A., and Jacobs, W. A., *Chem. Ber.*, **44**, 746 (1911).
26. Levene, P. A., and Mori, T., *J. Biol. Chem.*, **81**, 215 (1929).
27. Levene, P. A., and Stiller, E. T., *J. Biol. Chem.*, **104**, 299 (1934).
28. Michelson, A. M., and Todd, A. R., *J. Chem. Soc.*, 2476 (1949).
29. Schmidt, G., *Z. physiol. Chem.*, **179**, 243 (1928).
30. Carter, C. E., *J. Am. Chem. Soc.*, **73**, 1537 (1951).
31. Lythgoe, B., and Todd, A. R., *J. Chem. Soc.*, 592 (1944).
32. Paladini, A. C., and Leloir, L. F., *Biochem. J.*, **51**, 426 (1952).
33. Klimek, R., and Parnas, J. K., *Biochem. Z.*, **292**, 356 (1937).
34. Volkin, E., Khym, J. X., and Cohn, W. E., *J. Am. Chem. Soc.*, **73**, 1533 (1951).
35. Cohn, W. E., and Doherty, D. G., *J. Am. Chem. Soc.*, **78**, 2863 (1956).
36. Caputto, R., Leloir, L. F., Cardini, C. E., and Paladini, A. C., *J. Biol. Chem.*, **184**, 333 (1950).
37. Horn, P., Luzzati, V., and Trueblood, K. N., *Nature*, **183**, 880 (1959).
38. Kraut, J., and Jensen, L. H., *Nature*, **186**, 798 (1960).
39. Levene, P. A., and Harris, S. A., *J. Biol. Chem.*, **95**, 755 (1932); **98**, 9 (1932).
40. Levene, P. A., and Harris, S. A., *J. Biol. Chem.*, **101**, 419 (1933).

41. Bredereck, H., and Berger, E., *Chem. Ber.*, **73**, 1124 (1940).
42. Carter, C. E., and Cohn, W. E., *Federation Proc.*, **8**, 190 (1949).
43. Cohn, W. E., *Science*, **109**, 377 (1949).
44. Cohn, W. E., *J. Am. Chem. Soc.*, **72**, 1471, 2811 (1950).
45. Cohn, W. E., *J. Cellular Comp. Physiol.*, **38**, (S1) 21 (1951).
46. Loring, H. S., Luthy, N. G., Bortner, H. W., and Levy, L. W., *J. Am. Chem. Soc.*, **72**, 2811 (1950).
47. Brown, D. M., and Todd, A. R., *J. Chem. Soc.*, 44 (1952).
48. Cohn, W. E., *J. Am. Chem. Soc.*, **72**, 1471 (1950).
49. Carter, C. E., *J. Am. Chem. Soc.*, **72**, 1466 (1950).
50. Brown, D. M., Haynes, L. J., and Todd, A. R., *J. Chem. Soc.*, 3299 (1950).
51. Brown, D. M., Magrath, D. I., and Todd, A. R., *J. Chem. Soc.*, 2708 (1952).
52. Brown, D. M., and Todd, A. R., *J. Chem. Soc.*, 52 (1952).
53. Brown, D. M., Dekker, C. A., and Todd, A. R., *J. Chem. Soc.*, 2715 (1952).
54. Shuster, L., and Kaplan, N. O., *J. Biol. Chem.*, **201**, 535 (1953).
55. Khym, J. X., and Cohn, W. E., *J. Am. Chem. Soc.*, **76**, 1818, (1954).
56. Khym, J. X., Doherty, D. G., and Cohn, W. E., *J. Am. Chem. Soc.*, **76**, 5523 (1954).
57. Brown, D. M., Fasman, G. D., Magrath, D. I., and Todd, A. R., *J. Chem. Soc.*, 1448 (1954).
58. Cavalieri, L. F., *J. Am. Chem. Soc.*, **75**, 5268 (1953).
59. Fox, J. J., Cavalieri, L. F., and Chang, N., *J. Am. Chem. Soc.*, **75**, 4315 (1953).
60. Harris, R. J. C., Orr, S. F. D., Roe, E. M. F., and Thomas, J. F., *J. Chem. Soc.*, 489 (1953).
61. Michelson, A. M., and Todd, A. R., *J. Chem. Soc.*, 34 (1954).
62. Baron, F., and Brown, D. M., *J. Chem. Soc.*, 2855 (1955).
63. Green, M., and Cohen, S. S., *J. Biol. Chem.*, **225**, 397 (1957); **228**, 601 (1958).
64. Brown, D. M., Todd, A. R., and Varadarajan, S., *J. Chem. Soc.*, 2388 (1956).
65. Brown, D. M., Fasman, G. D., Magrath, D. I., Todd, A. R., Cochran, W., and Woolfson, M. M., *Nature*, **172**, 1184 (1953).
66. Alver, E., and Furberg, S., *Acta Chem. Scand.*, **11**, 188 (1957).
67. Cunningham, L., *J. Am. Chem. Soc.*, **80**, 2546 (1958).
68. Markham, R., and Smith, J. D., *Biochem. J.*, **52**, 552 (1952).
69. Brown, D. M., and Todd, A. R., *J. Chem. Soc.*, 52 (1952).
70. Lipkin, D., and Talbert, P. T., *Chem. and Ind.* (*London*), 143 (1955).
71. Tanaka, K., *J. Biochem.* (*Japan*), **47**, 398 (1960).
72. Cook, W. H., Lipkin, D., and Markham, R., *J. Am. Chem. Soc.*, **79**, 3607 (1957).
73. Rall, T. W., and Sutherland, E. W., *J. Biol. Chem.*, **232**, 1065 (1958); Sutherland, E. W., and Rall, T. W., *J. Biol. Chem.*, **232**, 1077 (1958).
74. Haynes, R. C., Koritz, S. B., and Peron, F. G., *J. Biol. Chem.*, **234**, 1421 (1959).
75. Peron, F. G., *J. Biol. Chem.*, **236**, 1764 (1961).
76. Lipkin, D., Cook, W. H., and Markham, R., *J. Am. Chem. Soc.*, **81**, 6198 (1959).
77. Tener, G. M., Khorana, H. G., Markham, R., and Pol, E. H., *J. Am. Chem. Soc.*, **80**, 6223 (1958).
78. Smith, M., Drummond, G. I., and Khorana, H. G., *J. Am. Chem. Soc.*, **83**, 698 (1961).
79. Cohn, W. E., and Volkin, E., *Nature*, **167**, 483 (1951); *J. Biol. Chem.*, **203**, 319 (1953).

80. Levene, P. A., and Jacobs, W. A., *J. Biol. Chem.*, **12,** 411 (1912).
81. Levene, P. A., *J. Biol. Chem.*, **126,** 63 (1938).
82. Thannhauser, S. J., and Ottenstein, B., *Z. physiol. Chem.*, **114,** 39 (1921).
83. Thannhauser, S. J., and Blanco, G., *Z. physiol. Chem.*, **161,** 116 (1926).
84. Fischer, E., *Chem. Ber.*, **47,** 3193 (1914).
85. Levene, P. A., and Tipson, R. S., *J. Biol. Chem.*, **106,** 113 (1934).
86. Levene, P. A. and Tipson, R. S., *J. Biol. Chem.*, **111,** 313 (1935).
87. Levene, P. A., and Tipson, R. S., *J. Biol. Chem.*, **121,** 131 (1937).
88. Gulland, J. M., and Smith, H., *J. Chem. Soc.*, 1527 (1948).
89. Michelson, A. M., and Todd, A. R., *J. Chem. Soc.*, 2476 (1949).
90. Chambers, R. W., Moffat, J. G., and Khorana, H. G., *J. Am. Chem. Soc.*, **79,** 3747 (1957).
91. Jachimowicz, T., *Biochem. Z.*, **292,** 356 (1937).
92. Gulland, J. M., and Hobday, G. I., *J. Chem. Soc.*, 746 (1940).
93. Barker, G. R., and Gulland, J. M., *J. Chem. Soc.*, 231 (1942).
94. Barker, G. R., and Foll, G. E., *J. Chem. Soc.*, 3798 (1957).
95. Atherton, F. R., Openshaw, H. T., and Todd, A. R., *J. Chem. Soc.*, 382 (1945).
96. Brigl, P., and Müller, H., *Chem. Ber.*, **72,** 2121 (1939).
97. Clark, V. M., and Todd, A. R., *J. Chem. Soc.*, 2030 (1950).
98. Baddiley, J., and Todd, A. R., *J. Chem. Soc.*, 648 (1947).
99. Magrath, D. I., and Brown, G. B., *J. Am. Chem. Soc.*, **79,** 3252 (1957).
100. Atherton, F. R., and Todd, A. R., *J. Chem. Soc.*, 674 (1947).
101. Mason, H. S., and Todd, A. R., *J. Chem. Soc.*, 2267 (1951).
102. Hampton, A., and Maguire, M. H., *J. Am. Chem. Soc.*, **83,** 150 (1961).
103. Smrt, J., Beránek, J., and Šorm, F., *Collection Czechoslov. Chem. Communs.*, **25,** 130 (1960).
104. Smrt, J., and Šorm, F., *Collection Czechoslov. Chem. Communs.*, **25,** 553 (1960).
105. Corby, N. S., Kenner, G. W., and Todd, A. R., *J. Chem. Soc.*, 3669 (1952).
106. Kenner, G. W., Todd, A. R., and Weymouth, F. J., *J. Chem. Soc.*, 3675 (1952).
107. Andrews, K. J. M., and Barber, W. E., *J. Chem. Soc.*, 2768 (1958).
108. Church, A. H., *Proc. Roy. Soc.*, **13,** 520 (1864).
109. Hall, R. H., and Khorana, H. G., *J. Am. Chem. Soc.*, **77,** 1871 (1955).
110. Michelson, A. M., *J. Chem. Soc.*, 1957 (1958).
111. Davoll, J., in Anand, N., Clark, V. M., Hall, R., and Todd, A. R., *J. Chem. Soc.*, 3665 (1952).
112. Kanazawa, T., Tamura, H., and Sato, T., *Nippon Kagaku Zasshi*, **79,** 393 (1958).
113. Kanazawa, T., Tamura, H., Nozoe, Y., and Sato, T., *Nippon Kagaku Zasshi*, **79,** 698 (1958).
114. Bredereck, H., Berger, E., and Ehrenberg, J., *Chem. Ber.*, **73,** 269 (1940).
115. Baker, B. R., and Joseph, J. P., *J. Am. Chem. Soc.* **77,** 15 (1955).
116. Tener, G. M., Wright, R. S., and Khorana, H. G., *J. Am. Chem. Soc.*, **79,** 441 (1957).
117. Wright, R. S., Tener, G. M., and Khorana, H. G., *J. Am. Chem. Soc.*, **80,** 2004 (1958).
118. Handschumacher, R. E., *Nature*, **182,** 1090 (1958).
119. Lieberman, I., Kornberg, A., and Simms, E. S., *J. Biol. Chem.*, **215,** 403 (1955).

120. Lukens, L. N., and Herrington, K. A., *Biochim. et Biophys. Acta*, **24,** 432 (1957).
121. Tener, G. M., and Khorana, H. G., *J. Am. Chem. Soc.*, **80,** 1999 (1958).
122. Way, J. L., and Parks, R. E., *J. Biol. Chem.*, **231,** 467 (1958).
123. Dahl, J. L., Way, J. L., and Parks, R. E., *J. Biol. Chem.*, **234,** 2998 (1959).
124. Carter, C. E., and Cohen, L. H., *J. Biol. Chem.*, **222,** 17 (1956).
125. Gulland, J. M., and Hobday, G. I., *J. Chem. Soc.*, 746 (1940).
126. Bredereck, H., *Z. physiol. Chem.*, **224,** 79 (1934).
127. Bredereck, H., and Berger, E., *Chem. Ber.*, **73,** 1124 (1940).
128. Barker, G. R., *J. Chem. Soc.*, 3396 (1954).
129. Gulland, J. M., and Smith, H., *J. Chem. Soc.*, 338 (1947); 1527, 1532 (1948).
130. Bredereck, H., and Berger, E., *Chem. Ber.*, **73,** 1124 (1940).
131. Gulland, J. M., and Overend, W. G., *J. Chem. Soc.*, 1380 (1948).
132. Smith, M., and Khorana, H. G., *J. Am. Chem. Soc.*, **81,** 2911 (1959).
133. Harvey, W. E., Michalski, J. J., and Todd, A. R., *J. Chem. Soc.*, 2271 (1951).
134. Forrest, H. S., Mason, H. S., and Todd, A. R., *J. Chem. Soc.*, 2530 (1952).
135. Michelson, A. M., *Chem. and Ind. (London)*, 70 (1958).
136. Michelson, A. M., *J. Chem. Soc.*, 3655, (1959).
137. Michelson, A. M., unpublished work.
138. Dekker, C. A., and Khorana, H. G., *J. Am. Chem. Soc.*, **76,** 3522 (1954).
139. Shugar, D., and Wierzchowski, K. L., *Bull. acad. polon. sci. Ser. sci. biol.*, **6,** 283 (1958).
140. Smith, M., Moffatt, J. G., and Khorana, H. G., *J. Am. Chem. Soc.*, **80,** 6204 (1958).
141. Tanaka, T., *Yakugaku Zasshi*, **78,** 627 (1958).
142. Forrest, H. S., and Todd, A. R., *J. Chem. Soc.*, 3295 (1950).
143. Todd, A., *Proc. Natl. Acad. Sci. U.S.A.*, **45,** 1389 (1959).
144. Lipkin, D., Markham, R., and Cook, W. H., *J. Am. Chem. Soc.*, **81,** 6075 (1959).
145. Michelson, A. M., *Tetrahedron*, **2,** 333 (1958).
146. Hall, R. H., and Haselkorn, R., *J. Am. Chem. Soc.*, **80,** 1138 (1958).
147. Cramer, F., Kenner, G. W., Hughes, N. A., and Todd, A., *J. Chem. Soc.*, 3297 (1957).
148. Baddiley, J., Buchanan, J. G., and Letters, R., *J. Chem. Soc.*, 1000 (1958).
149. Michelson, A. M., *J. Chem. Soc.*, 2055 (1958).
150. Michelson, A. M., in press.
151. Walwick, E. R., Roberts, W. K., and Dekker, C. A., *Proc. Chem. Soc.*, 84 (1959).
152. Michelson, A. M., *Biochem. et Biophys. Acta*, **50,** 605 (1961).
153. Michelson, A. M., and Todd, A. R., *J. Chem. Soc.*, 951 (1953).
154. Michelson, A. M., and Todd, A. R., *J. Chem. Soc.*, 34 (1954).
155. Michelson, A. M., and Todd, A. R., *J. Chem. Soc.*, 816 (1955).
156. Hayes, D. H., Michelson, A. M., and Todd, A. R., *J. Chem. Soc.*, 808 (1955).
157. Montgomery, J. A., Thomas, H. J., and Schaeffer, H. J., *J. Org. Chem.*, **26,** 1929 (1961).
158. Brown, D. M., and Todd, A. R., *J. Chem. Soc.*, 2040 (1953).
159. Smith, M., Moffat, J. G., and Khorana, H. G., *J. Am. Chem. Soc.*, **80,** 6204 (1958).
160. Brown, D. M., Magrath, D. I., and Todd, A. R., *J. Chem. Soc.*, 4396 (1955).
161. Barker, G. R., Montague, M. D., Moss, R. J., and Parsons, M. A., *J. Chem. Soc.*, 3786 (1957).

162. Tener, G. M., and Khorana, H. G., *J. Am. Chem. Soc.*, **77,** 5349 (1955).
163. Tanaka, T., *Yakugaku Zasshi*, **78,** 627 (1958).
164. Michelson, A. M., *J. Chem. Soc.*, 1371 (1959).
165. Ikehara, M., Ohtsuka, E., and Ishikawa, F., *Chem. and Pharm. Bull.* (*Tokyo*), **9,** 173 (1961).
166. Turner, A. F., and Khorana, H. G., *J. Am. Chem. Soc.*, **81,** 4651 (1959).
167. Tanaka, T., *Yakugaku Zasshi*, **79,** 437 (1959).
168. Tanaka, T., *Yakugaku Zasshi*, **79,** 721 (1959).
169. Montgomery, H. A. C., and Turnbull, J. H., *Proc. Chem. Soc.*, 178 (1957).
170. Kochetkov, N. K., Budowsky, E. I., and Shibaev, V. N., *Biochim. et Biophys. Acta*, **53,** 415 (1961).
171. Ukita, T., Nagasawa, K., and Irie, M., *J. Am. Chem. Soc.*, **80,** 1373 (1958).
172. Nagasawa, K., *Chem. and Pharm. Bull.* (*Tokyo*), **7,** 397 (1959).
173. Ukita, T., and Nagasawa, K., *Chem. and Pharm. Bull.* (*Tokyo*), **7,** 401, 466 (1959).
174. Grunze, H., and Koransky, W., *Angew. Chem.*, **71,** 407 (1959).
175. Crofts, P. C., Downie, I. M., and Heslop, R. B., *J. Chem. Soc.*, 3673 (1960).
176. Witzel, H., Mirbach, H., and Dimroth, K., *Angew. Chem.*, **72,** 751 (1960).
177. Cramer, F., and Gärtner, K. G., *Chem. Ber.*, **91,** 704 (1958).
178. Wasserman, H. H., and Cohen, D., *J. Am. Chem. Soc.*, **82,** 4435 (1960).
179. Morton, R. K., *Biochem. J.*, **70,** 150 (1958).
180. Clark, V. M., Kirby, G. W., and Todd, A. R., *Nature*, **181,** 1650 (1958).
181. Langheld, K., *Chem. Ber.*, **43,** 1857 (1910); **44,** 2076 (1911).
182. Schramm, G., Grötsch, H., and Pollmann, W., *Angew. Chem.*, **73,** 619 (1961).
183. Farkas, W. G., Iacono, L. C., and Duschinsky, R., *Abstracts IV International Congress of Biochemistry, Vienna*, 6 (1958).
184. Khorana, H. G., Tener, G. M., Moffatt, J. G., and Pol, E. H., *Chem. and Ind.* (*London*), 1523 (1956).
185. Gilham, P. T., and Tener, G. M., *Chem. and Ind.* (*London*), 542 (1959).
186. Tener, G. M., *J. Am. Chem. Soc.*, **83,** 159 (1961).
187. Brown, D. M., and Hamer, N. K., *J. Chem. Soc.*, 1155 (1960).
188. Roy, J. K., Kvam, D. C., Dahl, J. L., and Parks, R. E., *J. Biol. Chem.*, **236,** 1158 (1961).
189. Montgomery, J. A., and Thomas, H. J., *J. Org. Chem.*, **26,** 1926 (1961).
190. Schofield, J. A., and Todd, A., *J. Chem. Soc.*, 2316 (1961).
191. Strauss, D. B., and Goldwasser, E., *Biochim. et Biophys. Acta*, **47,** 186 (1961).
192. Cramer, F. D., and Weimann, G., *Chem. and Ind.* (*London*), 46 (1960).
193. Cramer, F., and Baldauf, H. J., *Angew. Chem.*, **72,** 627 (1960).
194. Wittmann, R., and Cramer, F., *Angew. Chem.*, **73,** 220 (1961).
195. Cramer, F., and Bohm, W., *Angew. Chem.*, **71,** 775 (1959).
196. Chambers, R. W., and Khorana, H. G., *J. Am. Chem. Soc.*, **80,** 3749 (1958).
197. Chambers, R. W., and Moffatt, J. G., *J. Am. Chem. Soc.*, **80,** 3752 (1958).
198. Cramer, F., and Schaller, H., *Chem. Ber.*, **94,** 1634 (1961).
199. Anand, N., and Todd, A. R., *J. Chem. Soc.*, 1867 (1951).
200. Wolff, M. E., and Burger, A., *J. Am. Pharm. Assoc.*, **48,** 56, (1959).
201. Parikh, J. R., Wolff, M. E., and Burger, A., *J. Am. Chem. Soc.*, **79,** 2778 (1957).
202. Bannister, B., and Kagan, F., *J. Amer. Chem. Soc.*, **82,** 3363 (1960).
203. Wolff, M. E., and Burger, A., *J. Am. Chem. Soc.*, **79,** 1970 (1957).
204. Huber, G., *Chem. Ber.*, **89,** 2853 (1956).
205. Barker, G. R., and Foll, G. E., *J. Chem. Soc.*, 3794 (1957).

206. Plaisted, P. H., and Reggio, R. B., *Nature*, **193**, 685 (1962).
207. Flesher, J. W., Oester, Y. T., and Myers, T. C., *Nature*, **185**, 772 (1960).
208. Ikehara, M., Ohtsuka, E., Kitagawa, S., Yagi, K., and Tonomura, Y., *J. Am. Chem. Soc.*, **83**, 2679 (1961).
209. Ikehara, M., and Ohtsuka, E., *Chem. and Pharm. Bull.* (*Tokyo*), **9**, 27 (1961).
210. Stevens, M. A., Smith, H. W., and Brown, G. B., *J. Am. Chem. Soc.*, **81**, 1734 (1959).
211. Cramer, F., and Randerath, K., *Angew. Chem.*, **70**, 571 (1958).
212. Michelson, A. M., *J. Chem. Soc.*, 1957 (1958).
213. Moore, A. M., and Anderson, S. M., *Can. J. Chem.*, **37**, 590 (1959).
214. Letters, R., and Michelson, A. M., *J. Chem. Soc.*, **71** (1962).
215. Michelson, A. M., Dondon, J., and Grunberg-Manago, M., *Biochim. et Biophys. Acta*, **55**, 529 (1962).
216. Ueda, T., *Chem. and Pharm. Bull.* (*Tokyo*), **8**, 455 (1960).
217. Shugar, D., and Wierzchowski, K. L., *Biochim. et Biophys. Acta*, **23**, 657 (1957); **25**, 355 (1957).
218. Shugar, D., and Wierzchowski, K. L., *J. Polymer Sci.*, **31**, 269 (1958).
219. Scholes, G., and Weiss, J., *Biochem. J.*, **53**, 567 (1953).
220. Daniels, M., Scholes, G., and Weiss, J., *J. Chem. Soc.*, 3771 (1956).
221. Hems, G., *Nature*, **181**, 1721 (1958).
222. Shapiro, H. S., and Chargaff, E., *Biochim. et Biophys. Acta*, **26**, 596 (1957); **39**, 62 (1960).
223. Magrath, D. I., and Brown, G. B., *J. Am. Chem. Soc.*, **79**, 3252 (1957).
224. Kumler, W. D., and Eiler, J. J., *J. Am. Chem. Soc.*, **65**, 2355 (1943).
225. Levene, P. A., and Jacobs, W. A., *Chem. Ber.*, **42**, 335, 2469, 2474 (1909); **44**, 1027 (1911); *Biochem. Z.*, **28**, 127 (1910).
226. Bacher, J. E., and Allen, F. W., *J. Biol. Chem.*, **182**, 701 (1950).
227. Bailly, M. C., *Compt. rend.*, **208**, 443 (1939).
228. Verkade, P. E., Stoppelenburg, J. C., and Cohen, W. D., *Rec. trav. chim.*, **59**, 886 (1940).
229. Chargaff, E., *J. Biol. Chem.*, **145**, 455 (1942).
230. Lipkin, D., Talbert, P. T., and Cohn, M., *J. Am. Chem. Soc.*, **76**, 2871 (1954).
231. Brown, D. M., Magrath, D. I., Neilson, A. H., and Todd, A. R., *Nature*, **177**, 1124 (1956).
232. Brown, D. M., Heppel, L. A., and Hilmoe, R. J., *J. Chem. Soc.*, 40 (1954).
233. Davis, F. F., and Allen, F. W., *Biochim. et Biophys. Acta*, **21**, 14 (1956).
234. Heppel, L. A., and Whitfield, P. R., *Biochem. J.*, **60**, 1 (1955).
235. Baddiley, J., Buchanan, J. G., and Letters, R., *J. Chem. Soc.*, 2812 (1956).
236. Baddiley, J., and Thain, E. M., *J. Chem. Soc.*, 903 (1953).
237. Fogarty, L. M., and Rees, W. R., *Nature*, **193**, 1180 (1962).
238. Arnold, J., and Price, T. D., *J. Am. Chem. Soc.*, **84**, 1406 (1962).
239. Rall, T. W., and Sutherland, E. W., *J. Biol. Chem.*, **237**, 1228 (1962).
240. Egami, F., and Takahashi, N., *Bull. Chem. Soc.* (*Japan*), **28**, 666 (1955).
241. Ukita, T., and Hayatsu, H., *J. Am. Chem. Soc.*, **84**, 1879 (1962).
242. Cormier, M. J., *J. Biol. Chem.*, **237**, 2032 (1962).

Chapter 4

NUCLEOTIDE ANHYDRIDES

For some considerable time the known nucleotide coenzymes formed a relatively small group of derivatives of adenosine-5' pyrophosphate that included the oxidation-reduction cofactors flavin adenine dinucleotide and di- and triphosphopyridine nucleotides in addition to adenosine-5' triphosphate. More recently, knowledge of the biological significance of a large number of nucleotide derivatives, collectively known somewhat loosely as nucleotide coenzymes, has expanded rapidly and the biochemistry of such compounds is now quite extensive. Apart from amplifying the function of cofactors of biological transphosphorylation and electron transport, these developments have demonstrated the role of mixed anhydride intermediates in the transfer of sugars, carboxylic acids, amino acids, sulphate and nucleotides. Although some of these nucleotide compounds may well function as coenzymes in complex multi-enzyme systems where regeneration can occur, in the main they are more accurately described as " active intermediates " or, when purified enzyme preparations are used, as substrates. Chemically, the group is best defined simply as nucleotide mixed anhydrides, that is, anhydrides of a nucleoside-5' phosphate and another acid which may be pyrophosphoric acid, phosphoric acid and mono-esters thereof, carboxylic acids, amino acids and peptides, or sulphuric acid. As yet, no biological function has been ascribed to symmetrical dinucleoside pyrophosphates, nor have naturally occurring diesters of triphosphoric acid been observed.

Adenosine-5' Triphosphate and Other Nucleoside-5' Polyphosphates

Perhaps the most important compound in present day terrestrial* living processes (if any component of necessarily multicomponent systems can be singled out) is adenosine-5' triphosphate. First isolated in 1929 from muscle extracts,[1, 2] adenosine-5' triphosphate is involved in a vast number of metabolic reactions at all levels of organisation and is a key intermediate in the transfer of energy in living organisms whether derived by oxidation, fermentation, or by photochemical means.

Hydrolysis of adenosine-5' triphosphate (ATP) with dilute alkali gives adenosine-5' phosphate and inorganic pyrophosphate; acidic

* In the cosmological sense.

hydrolysis rapidly liberates two of the three phosphates as inorganic phosphate with the production of adenine and ribose-5 phosphate.[3] Deamination of ATP with nitrous acid yields an analogous inosine-5' triphosphate,[4] indicating lack of substitution at the 6-amino group. Esterification of a 2' or 3' sugar hydroxyl group is excluded since ATP gives positive Klimek–Parnas and Boeseken tests for a *cis*-1,2 glycol grouping[4, 5] and, more specifically, consumes one molar equivalent of periodate.[6] Titrimetric evidence[4, 7] shows the presence of three primary and one secondary phosphate dissociations, and ATP therefore has the structure shown.[4]

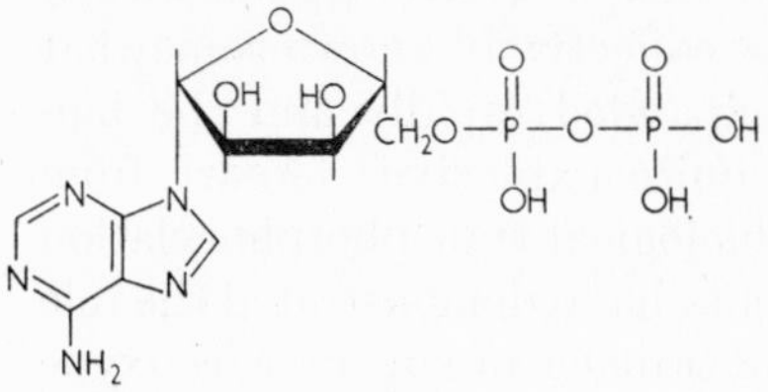

ADP 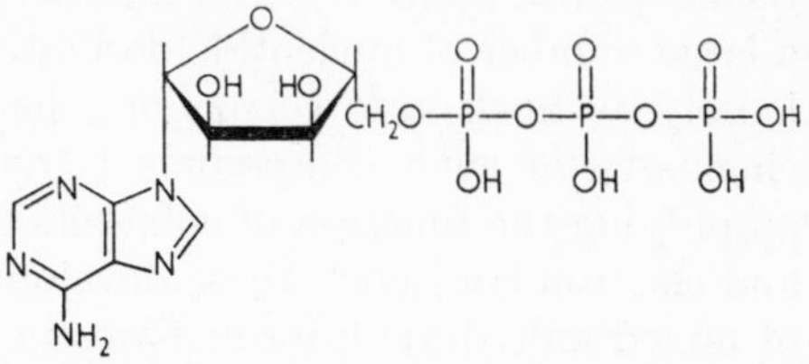   ATP

Enzymic removal of one phosphate group from ATP gives adenosine-5' pyrophosphate (ADP),[8] the structure of which is confirmed by titration and by the ratio of " acid-labile " to " acid-stable " phosphate. Adenosine-5' tetraphosphate has been isolated from several sources.[9–11] It does not substitute for ATP in phosphorylation reactions and the biological significance, if any, of both the tetraphosphate and the pentaphosphate (which has also been detected[12] in commercial preparations of ATP) is unknown.

As in the case of the adenine nucleotides, the 5'-phosphates, 5'-pyrophosphates and 5'-triphosphates of cytidine, guanosine and uridine are of widespread occurrence.[13–16] They are metabolic intermediates in the biosynthesis of ribonucleic acids. The triphosphates are also of importance in the biosynthesis of a variety of diesterified pyrophosphate derivatives, in addition to replacing ATP as a phosphorylating agent or coenzyme in several specific enzymic reactions.[17–21] Polyphosphates of the deoxynucleosides have also been isolated[22–25] and again, while the triphosphates are immediate precursors of deoxynucleic acid, a second major function probably lies in the biosynthesis of intermediates such as thymidine-5' pyrophosphate glucose and deoxycytidine-5' pyrophosphate choline. The structures of all these nucleoside polyphosphates were determined by methods analogous to those used for ATP and have been confirmed by synthesis.

Rotatory dispersion studies indicate that in aqueous solution the polyphosphate chain of adenosine-5' triphosphate may be folded back to give bonding between the β- and γ-phosphates and the adenine amino group.[26]   Although calcium and magnesium ions at pH 7 have no influence on the optical symmetry of the molecule, the effect of zinc ions suggests a conformation stabilised by zinc chelation between the terminal phosphate and the 6-substituent in purine and pyrimidine pyrophosphates and triphosphates, but not in the -5' monophosphates.[27] Spectral titration curves in the presence and absence of magnesium ions possibly show that in solution nucleoside-5' triphosphates are partly in a curled conformation with Mg^{++} chelated between the pyrophosphate structure and the heterocyclic base.   Small shifts to lower apparent pK values in the presence of Mg^{++} were noted for the triphosphates (approximately 0·3 units drop), but not with the nucleosides.[28]   However, nuclear magnetic resonance spectra suggest that a chelate conformation is unlikely and that the metal–ATP complex is extended in solution.[29]   The results also indicate that in magnesium and calcium complexes the β- and γ-phosphate groups are involved.[30]

Determination of the stability constants of a number of metal complexes with nucleotides shows that stability is in the order manganous > cobalt > magnesium > calcium > strontium > barium,[31, 32] and that triphosphate > pyrophosphate > mononucleotide.[31]   The secondary phosphoryl dissociation is of considerable importance in these complexes since the stability constant of the magnesium complex of flavin adenine dinucleotide[31] is much smaller than that of adenosine-5' pyrophosphate, and the zinc complex of nicotinamide adenine nucleotide is likewise less stable than the zinc–ADP complex.[33]   The shape of the complex is determined by the size of the cation,[34] and since magnesium ion is a cofactor for many enzymic reactions of ATP, with an optimum ratio of one, it is likely that the complex is the actual substrate,[35] in which case inhibition of enzymic reaction could occur by the action of chelating agents, or by the presence of other cations leading to formation of complexes that are sterically different from those required by the enzyme.[34]   Formation of such metal ion complexes can also have a profound effect on the stability of the anhydride linkage.   ATP is most stable in slightly alkaline conditions ($\sim$ pH 10), degradation being more rapid in neutral and acidic solutions[36] when ionisation of the secondary acid group of the terminal phosphate is negligible.   Since ADP is somewhat more stable than the triphosphate, it can be obtained by hydrolysis of ATP under controlled conditions.[37]

Nucleophilic attack by orthophosphate on ATP to give ADP and inorganic pyrophosphate in very low yield (up to 0·2%) is also catalysed by bivalent metal ions[38] with an optimum at pH 9·0.   Calcium and manganous ions are particularly effective, the latter also catalysing non-enzymic transphosphorylation from ATP to carboxylic acids (as indicated by hydroxamate formation).[39] Berylium ions are particularly effective in this reaction and it is likely that the mechanism involves nucleophilic attack by acetate ion (pH optimum is 5·2) on the ATP–metal chelate.[40] Ligand formation would be expected to increase the electrophilic character of the phosphorus atoms and also reduce electrostatic shielding.

Intramolecular phosphorylation occurs on treatment of ATP with aqueous barium hydroxide. Among the many products of hydrolysis are adenosine-3',5' cyclic phosphate and adenosine-2' (or 3'),5' diphosphates, as well as the -2', -3', and -5' phosphates of adenosine.[41, 42] Adenine, adenosine, and adenosine-5' pyrophosphate are also present.

Two types of reaction explain the formation of most of the observed products.[42] Intermolecular nucleophilic attack by hydroxide ions or water molecules at the phosphorus atoms, particularly the β- and γ-, gives the classical type of hydrolytic products; intramolecular reaction, in which the 3'-hydroxyl group of the ribose residue of adenosine-5' triphosphate attacks the phosphorus atoms, gives rise to a range of phosphorylated products and intermediates including adenosine-3',5' cyclic phosphate. The presence of -2' phosphorylated derivatives is best accounted for by hydrolysis of a -2',3' cyclic phosphate intermediate. This would be obtained readily from a 3' pyrophosphate formed either directly by attack of the 3'-hydroxyl group at the β-phosphorus atom, or perhaps more likely by nucleophilic attack of a -3' phosphate group (phosphorylation of the 3'-hydroxyl by the γ-phosphate group) at the β-phosphorus atom of the 5'-pyrophosphate residue in adenosine-3' phosphate 5' pyrophosphate. Adenosine is probably formed by attack of hydroxide ion at the 5' carbon atom of adenosine-5' triphosphate with carbon–oxygen bond cleavage and displacement of inorganic triphosphate, rather than by hydrolysis of nucleoside monophosphates (P—O cleavage) since these are stable under the conditions used.[42]

Apart from neutralisation of negative charges on the oxygen atoms of the triphosphate chain thus increasing the positive electrical potential on the phosphorus atoms (i.e. increase in electrophilic character leading to more rapid nucleophilic attack) the catalytic effect of barium ion complex formation may also involve the sugar hydroxyl groups,[43] the nucleophilic character of which would be increased by co-ordination with barium (as well as by high pH conditions).

Other di- and polyvalent metal ions also show catalytic effects, and varying degrees of control over the nature of the reaction products from mild degradation of ATP (and other nucleoside-5' triphosphates).

A = Adenine

In particular, may be mentioned hydrolysis to adenosine-5' phosphate catalysed by calcium or lanthanum ions, and the almost quantitative conversion of adenosine-5' triphosphate into adenosine-5' pyrophosphate by the action of zinc oxide slurry. The effects seem to be a function of the ionic size and may well result from the position of the metal ion on the triphosphate chain at the moment that a nucleophilic species (water molecule, alcoholic hydroxyl group, hydroxide ions or anions of phosphates and other acids) combines with the nucleotide–metal ion complex to give the activated complex of the transition state.[44] It is likely that full elaboration of this work will assist considerably in elucidation of the role or roles played by metal ions in so many of the enzymic reactions of organic phosphates.

Phosphorus magnetic resonance of adenosine-5' triphosphate has been examined at high resolution, and the α-, β-, and γ-phosphorus peaks unequivocally identified.[45] The chemical shift of each phosphorus atom was determined as a function of pH; the difference in shift of the absorption peak of the β-phosphorus atom compared with the α- and γ-phosphorus atoms correlates with the difference in reactivity of the β-phosphorus atom in enzymic reactions.

NICOTINAMIDE ADENINE DINUCLEOTIDES

First discovered in dialysates of yeast juice by Harden and Young[46] in 1905 as a thermostable factor essential for fermentation, cozymase (coenzyme I, diphosphopyridine nucleotide, DPN, and now nicotinamide adenine dinucleotide, NAD[47]) was not isolated in pure form till many years later.[48] Isolation of the closely related coenzyme II (triphosphopyridine nucleotide, TPN, nicotinamide adenine dinucleotide phosphate, NADP) from vast quantities of horse blood[49] was likewise attended with considerable difficulty owing to lack of suitable methods. Both factors function in enzyme systems involved in oxidation–reduction processes by virtue of the redox properties of the pyridine moiety.

Acidic hydrolysis[50, 51] of NAD gives adenine, nicotinamide, pentose and phosphoric acid in the molar ratio 1 : 1 : 2 : 2, the same results being obtained with NADP except that a third phosphate group is liberated.[49] From the mixture of products obtained by mild acidic hydrolysis of NAD, ribose-5 phosphate was isolated in a yield sufficient to indicate that both pentoses were D-ribose.[52] Deamination of the adenine residue with nitrous acid yields the corresponding hypoxanthine compounds[53] without degradation, and complete deamination of NAD to hypoxanthine nicotinic acid dinucleotide (and of nicotinamide nucleotide to the nicotinic acid derivative) is readily effected by treatment with nitrous anhydride.[54] Treatment of NAD with alkali liberates nicotinamide and adenosine-5' pyrophosphate,[55] probably by phosphate elimination from ADP ribose (or a degradation product). While the coenzymes are unstable in alkali but relatively stable towards acid, the dihydro-compounds (readily obtained by reduction with sodium hyposulphite) are relatively stable in alkali but quite unstable towards acids. Catalytic hydrogenation of NAD and NADP gives hexahydro derivatives which, unlike the dihydro compounds, are not reoxidised by the action of flavoprotein. The changes in ultraviolet absorption spectra that accompany " reversible reduction " and complete hydrogenation, together with the changes in pH-stability properties, are typical of quaternary pyridinium derivatives such as trigonelline and nicotinamide methiodide, both of which, unlike nicotinamide itself, readily form dihydro derivatives on treatment with sodium hyposulphite.[56, 57] That the coenzymes are quaternary pyridinium phosphates is further demonstrated by titration of NAD (a monobasic acid)[58] and dihydro-NAD (dibasic),[59] the results indicating both the presence of a zwitterion and a diesterified pyrophosphate linkage. Enzymic hydrolysis of NAD to nicotinamide nucleoside (N^1-β-D-ribofuranosylnicotinamide),[60] and comparisons of the redox behaviour and spectroscopic and pH-stability properties of synthetic glycosyl derivatives of nicotinamide[61] with those of NAD and NADP, establish the structure of NAD as P^1-adenosine-5' P^2-nicotinamide nucleoside-5' pyrophosphate. More recent work has shown the reduced form of NAD to have a 4-hydro structure.[62]

Enzymic studies have fully confirmed the structure assigned to

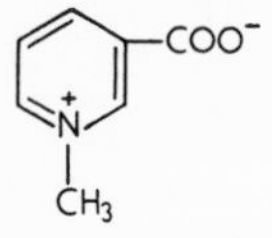

Trigonelline

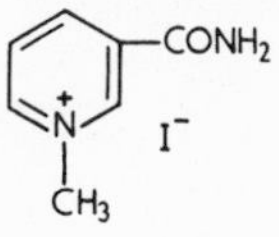

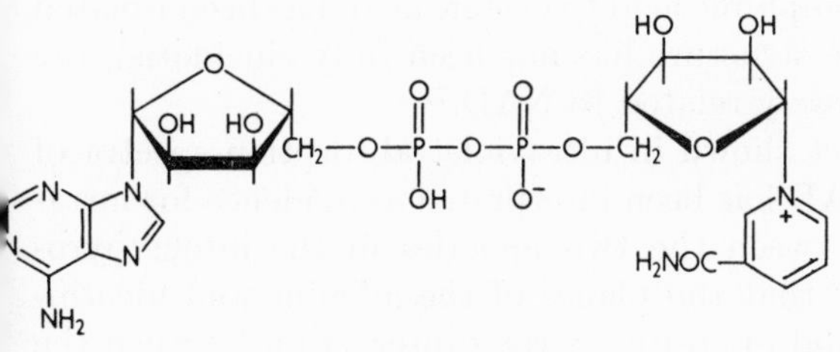

NAD

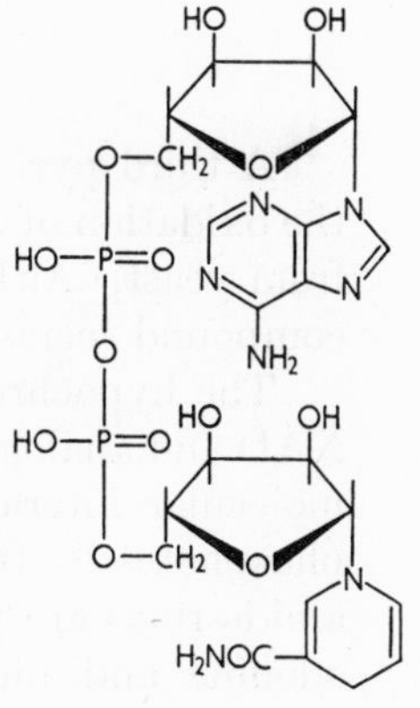

Reduced NAD

F*

NAD. Treatment with pyrophosphatase yields nicotinamide mono-nucleotide and adenosine-5' phosphate,[63, 64] and the coenzyme has been synthesised from ATP and nicotinamide mononucleotide by a reversible enzymic pyrophosphorolysis.[65]

Until 1950, the location of the third phosphate residue in NADP was unknown. Treatment of NAD with phosphoryl chloride gives some NADP,[66] and the two coenzymes are readily interconvertible by enzymic reactions.[67-69] Hydrolysis of NADP with pyrophosphatase gives nicotinamide mononucleotide and an adenosine diphosphate (not a pyrophosphate) that on hydrolysis with a 5'-nucleotidase yields adenosine-2' phosphate. The third phosphate in NADP therefore esterifies the 2'-hydroxyl group of the adenosine moiety.[70]

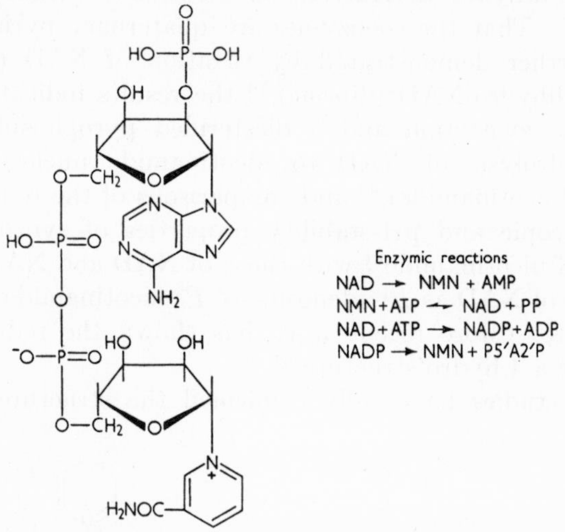

Enzymic reactions

NAD → NMN + AMP
NMN + ATP ⇌ NAD + PP
NAD + ATP → NADP + ADP
NADP → NMN + P5'A2'P

NADP

A third pyridine nucleotide cofactor (coenzyme III), necessary for the oxidation of cysteine sulphinic acid to cysteic acid, has been isolated from yeast. Although the structure has not been fully elucidated, the compound seems to be closely related to NAD.[71]

The hypochromic effect shown in ultraviolet absorption spectra of NAD and analogues of NAD has been interpreted as evidence for intra-molecular interactions between the two moieties in the intact pyro-phosphates.[72] It is likely that the planes of the adenine and nicotin-amide rings are parallel and opposite. Strong interaction between the adenine and nicotinamide residues also occurs in reduced NAD.[73] The effect is possibly a result of hydrogen bonding, though direct interaction between the ring systems (even in the reduced form) cannot be excluded.

FLAVIN ADENINE DINUCLEOTIDE

While the pyridine nucleotide coenzymes are active in biological oxidations by virtue of their reduction, the resulting dihydro-compounds are not autoxidisable. Re-oxidation to NAD and NADP normally occurs by the action of a flavoprotein, the prosthetic group of which is usually the coenzyme, flavin adenine dinucleotide (FAD).

Isolated[74] in 1938 from yeast (and from liver and kidney), the pure coenzyme was found to be a dibasic acid that on mild alkaline hydrolysis

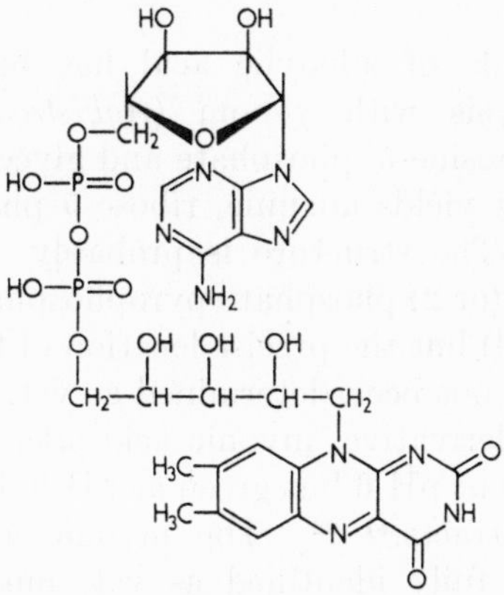

FAD

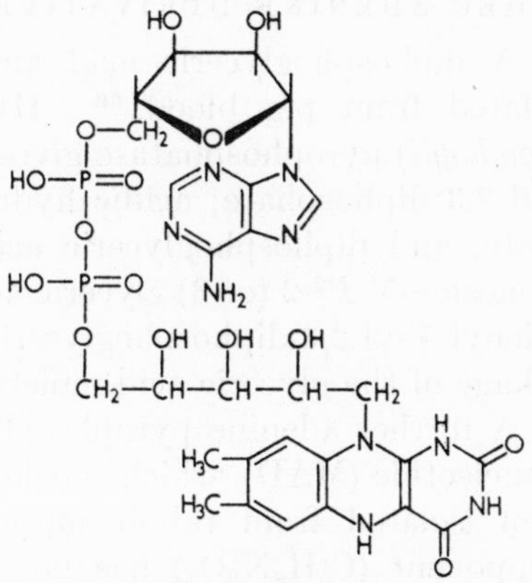

Dihydro FAD

Riboflavin + ATP → FMN + ADP
FMN + ATP ⇌ FAD + PP
Enzymic reactions

gave adenosine-5′ phosphate (and riboflavin-4,5-cyclic phosphate[75]) while treatment with acid yielded riboflavin-5′ phosphate.[76] The 6-amino group of the adenine moiety of FAD can be replaced by hydroxyl on treatment with nitrous acid, and alkaline photolysis of FAD produces lumiflavin at the same rate as from riboflavin. Flavin adenine dinucleotide is therefore P^1-adenosine-5′ P^2-riboflavin-5′ pyrophosphate, a structure that has been confirmed by chemical synthesis. The coenzyme is synthesised enzymically by phosphorylation of riboflavin[77] with ATP, followed by a reversible pyrophosphorolysis[78] with ATP.

Reversible reduction of FAD with sodium hyposulphite gives a dihydro (leuco) compound that is autoxidisable. Biochemically, the coenzyme (redox potential ~ -0.19 volt) functions mainly in electron transport between the nicotinamide coenzymes (redox potential ~ -0.28 volt) and the respiratory cytochrome systems (redox potential ~ 0 to $+0.29$ volt), although in some cases the flavin enzymes act directly, for example, oxidation of D-amino acids.

As with the pyridine nucleotide coenzymes, interaction occurs between the adenine and riboflavin ring systems of FAD (shown by the marked quenching of fluorescence of the riboflavin moiety)[79] restricting the pyrophosphate to a definite conformation under normal conditions. It is perhaps not surprising, in view of the relationship between nucleic acids and proteins, that this conformation should involve stacking of the planes of the bases, in much the same manner as in polynucleotides.

OTHER ADENINE DERIVATIVES

A diphosphoglyceric acid anhydride of adenylic acid has been isolated from pig blood. [80] Hydrolysis with venom (*Agkistrodon Blomhoffii*) pyrophosphatase gives adenosine-5' phosphate and glyceric acid-2,3 diphosphate; acidic hydrolysis yields adenine, ribose-5 phosphate, and diphosphoglyceric acid. The structure is probably P^1-adenosine-5' P^2-2 (or 3) glyceric acid 3 (or 2) phosphate pyrophosphate (adenyl-5'-yl 2,3-diphosphoglyceric acid) but the precise location of the linkage of the glyceric acid moiety has not been determined as yet.

A further adenine pyrophosphate derivative, myonic acid adenine dinucleotide (MAD), which is colourless at pH 6 but green at pH 9, has been isolated from rabbit muscle extracts.[81, 82] The myonic acid component ($C_9H_6N_2O_3$) has not been fully identified as yet, but is probably a 1-carboxy-3-hydroxy derivative of 2,6- or 2,7-naphthyridine. Enzymic hydrolysis of the pyrophosphate gives adenosine-5' phosphate and ribosylmyonic acid phosphate; alkaline hydrolysis (barium hydroxide) gives myonic acid, whereas on acidic hydrolysis ribosyl-myonic acid phosphate and a small amount of ribosylmyonic acid are formed.[82]

COENZYME A

A further nucleotide derivative of a vitamin was discovered in liver, and brain extracts, when studies of the enzymic acetylation of sulphanilamide[83] and of choline[84] indicated that a cofactor was required. This cofactor was soon shown to contain pantothenic acid and to be very widely distributed, yeast being a particularly good source. Coenzyme A, as the factor was named, is now known to participate in a large number of biochemical reactions involved in the metabolism of citrate, pyruvate, succinate, fatty acids, isoprene and steroids.

Hydrolysis of coenzyme A using a combination of enzymes yielded adenosine and pantothenic acid in equimolar proportions. Acidic hydrolysis gave adenine, β-alanine, three phosphate residues, and a sulphur compound,[85] later identified as 2-mercaptoethylamine.[86, 87] A derivative of pantothenic acid containing 2-mercaptoethylamine had been isolated earlier, and identified as the *Lactobacillus bulgaricus* factor, pantetheine,[88] and some evidence for the presence of this compound in enzymic digests of coenzyme A was obtained by growth tests.[89] It was also found that pantetheine could be converted into coenzyme A by the action of adenosine-5′ triphosphate and a pigeon liver extract.[90] Further evidence for the structure of the coenzyme was obtained by the isolation of adenosine-5′ phosphate and pantothenic · acid-4 phosphate from the mixture of products obtained by mild acidic hydrolysis,[91] the structure of the latter compound being fully established by comparison with synthetic pantothenic acid-2 phosphate, -4 phosphate, -2,4 diphosphate and -2,4 cyclic phosphate.[92, 93]

HOCH$_2$C—CH—CONHCH$_2$CH$_2$COOH (with CH$_3$, OH, CH$_3$ substituents)

HOCH$_2$C—CH—CONHCH$_2$CH$_2$CONHCH$_2$CH$_2$SH (with CH$_3$, OH, CH$_3$ substituents)

HO—P(=O)(OH)—O—CH$_2$—C—CH—CONHCH$_2$CH$_2$CONHCH$_2$CH$_2$SH (with CH$_3$, OH, CH$_3$ substituents)

Coenzyme A

Hydrolysis of coenzyme A with potato pyrophosphatase indicated the presence of a pyrophosphate linkage.[94] Treatment with alkali readily cleaved the molecule to give pantetheine-2,4 cyclic phosphate (and pantothenic acid-2,4 cyclic phosphate),[95] behaviour analogous to that of flavin adenine dinucleotide and uridine diphosphate glucose. The third phosphate group was removed from the intact coenzyme by the action of a monophosphatase specific for -3′ phosphates;[96, 97] confirmation of esterification of the 2′ or 3′ hydroxyl group in the adenosine moiety by this monophosphate was afforded by periodate titration.[98] Hydrolysis of the pyrophosphate linkage by means of a purified pyrophosphatase yielded pantetheine-4 phosphate, the structure of which was established by synthesis[99] of the compound, and adenosine-3′,5′ diphosphate rather than the isomeric-2′,5′ diphosphate (shown by the action of a specific 3′-nucleotidase).[96, 97] Coenzyme A therefore has the structure shown. Final proof of this structure has been provided by chemical synthesis of the coenzyme, and by enzymic synthesis (via 3′-dephospho coenzyme A). Two biochemical routes from pantothenic acid have been described.[100–102]

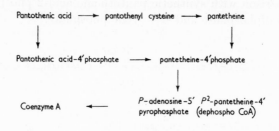

The active intermediate in the transfer of acetate is the thiol acetate of coenzyme A,[103] this " active acetate " being formed enzymically by the action of acetyl phosphate[104] or adenylyl acetate[105] on the coenzyme. Thiol esters, particularly those of 2-mercaptoethylamine[106–108] and pantetheine,[109–111] are quite active chemical acylating agents. The influence of the sulphur atom is also found in proton release from the α-position. This occurs more readily in thiol esters than in the corresponding oxygen compounds.[112] Enzymic S-phosphorylation of coenzyme A by guanosine-5' triphosphate in yeast and in heart muscle[113] (but by adenosine-5' triphosphate in other tissues[114]) provides an alternate pathway for the activation of succinic acid. Chemical phosphorylation of coenzyme A with phosphorus oxychloride to give presumably the thiol phosphate has been claimed,[115] but degradation of the anhydride, or formation of a -2',3' cyclic phosphate derivative, appears more likely.

URIDINE-5' PYROPHOSPHATE DERIVATIVES

As a result of various studies of galactose metabolism in yeast, Leloir and his collaborators isolated and identified (in 1950) the first nucleotide cofactor containing a base other than adenine.[116] This was uridine diphosphate glucose, cofactor for the transformation of α-D-galactose-1 phosphate into α-D-glucose-1 phosphate in galactose-adapted yeast. Subsequently, a large number of uridine diphosphate compounds have been isolated and shown to be of considerable significance with respect to sugar metabolism, the biosynthesis of polysaccharides, and cell wall synthesis in micro-organisms.

URIDINE DIPHOSPHATE GLUCOSE

Mild acidic hydrolysis of uridine diphosphate glucose (UDPG) yielded glucose and uridine-5 pyrophosphate; more vigorous hydrolysis liberated glucose, inorganic phosphate and uridine-5' phosphate. The nucleotide was further characterised by hydrazinolysis to give ribose-5 phosphate. Treatment of UDPG with ammonia gave uridine-5' phosphate and glucose-1,2 cyclic phosphate, alkaline hydrolysis of the latter yielding a mixture of glucose-1 phosphate (25%) and glucose-2 phosphate (75%). Acidic hydrolysis of the glucose cyclic phosphate gave glucose-2 phosphate; under the conditions employed the less stable glucose-1 phosphate also formed was dephosphorylated.[117] The instability towards acid and negative reducing properties of the glucose moiety in UDPG indicated the presence of glucose-1 phosphate, and the cofactor was therefore formulated as P^1-uridine-5' P^2-glucose-1 pyrophosphate.[116, 117] Further evidence defining the configuration and ring structure of the glucose was obtained by cleavage of the anhydride with pyrophosphatase to give α-D-glucose-1 phosphate, by enzymic synthesis of UDPG from uridine-5' triphosphate and α-D-glucose-1 phosphate,[118, 119] and by chemical synthesis.

The role of UDPG in the enzymic conversion of galactose into glucose involves anion exchange with galactose-1 phosphate to give uridine diphosphate galactose,[120] with subsequent inversion at C4 of the hexose via an intermediate 4-keto derivative.[121–123] While protein-

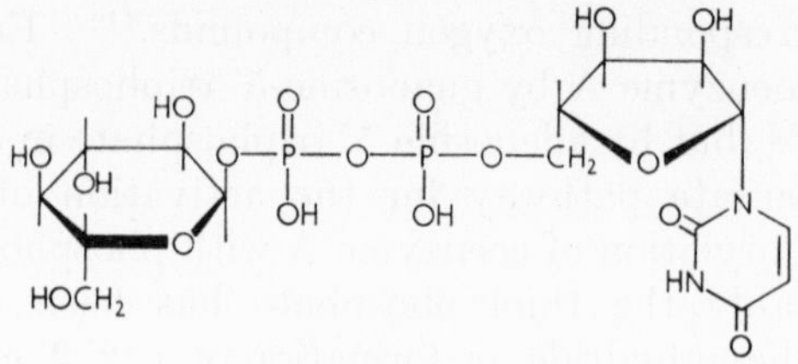

UDP glucose

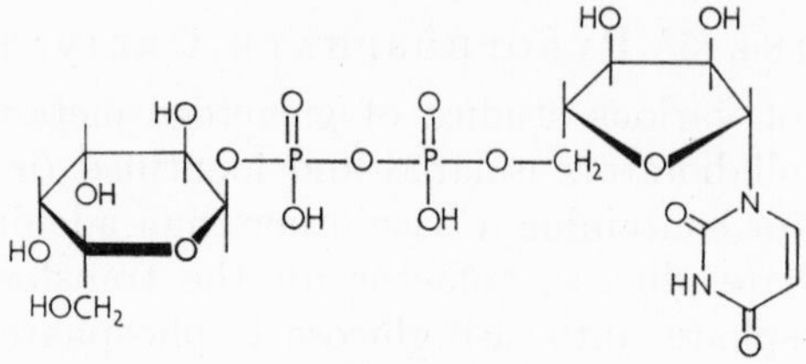

UDP galactose

$$\alpha\text{-D-Glucose-1 phosphate} + \text{UTP} \rightleftharpoons \text{UDPG} + \text{PP}$$

$$\alpha\text{-D-Galactose-1 phosphate} + \text{UTP} \rightleftharpoons \text{UDPGal} + \text{PP}$$

$$\text{UDPG} + \alpha\text{-D-Galactose-1 phosphate} \underset{\text{uridylyl transferase}}{\rightleftharpoons} \text{UDPGal} + \alpha\text{-D-Glucose-1 phosphate}$$

$$\text{UDPG} \underset{\text{galactowaldenase}}{\rightleftharpoons} \text{UDPGal}$$

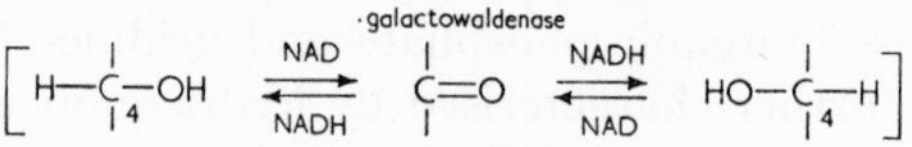

Enzymic reactions

bound nicotinamide adenine dinucleotide functions in this oxidation–reduction reaction, attempts to trap the reduced form of the nicotinamide coenzyme or to introduce tritium into the hexose by the use of NAD (or the reduced form) labelled with tritium in the *para* position have been unsuccessful.[124, 125]

The chemistry of uridine diphosphate galactose (UDPGal) is analogous to that of UDPG. A second pathway for the enzymic conversion of α-D-galactose-1 phosphate into UDPGal by pyrophosphorolysis of uridine-5′ triphosphate has been found in galactose adapted *Saccharomyces fragilis*,[126] in green plants,[127] and in mammalian tissues.[128] Presumably this second route[128] accounts for the galactose metabolism that can occur in cases of galactosaemia (a congenital deficiency of the enzyme galactose-1 phosphate uridylyl transferase[129] leading to an accumulation of ingested galactose as galactose-1 phosphate, with somewhat disastrous physiological effects).

The widespread distribution of UDPG, and the presence of uridine diphosphate galactose (and galactowaldenase, the enzyme catalysing the UDPGal ⇋ UDPG interconversion) in certain yeasts not adapted to galactose[130] suggested that these compounds possessed biological functions other than the interconversion of galactose and glucose. Brewer's yeast was shown to contain an enzyme that catalysed the synthesis of trehalose phosphate from UDPG and glucose-6 phosphate,[131, 132] and two routes to sucrose involving UDPG have been demonstrated.[133, 134]

UDPG + Glucose-6 phosphate → UDP + Trehalose-6 phosphate
UDPG + D-Fructose-6 phosphate → UDP + Sucrose phosphate
UDPG + D-Fructose → UDP + Sucrose
UDPGal + D-glucose → UDP + Lactose
UDPGal + α-D-Glucose-1   phosphate → UDP + Lactose-1   phosphate.

Similar syntheses of lactose and of lactose-1 phosphate from uridine diphosphate galactose and D-glucose or α-D-glucose-1 phosphate have been demonstrated, using preparations of bovine mammary tissue.[135, 136] In addition to functioning in disaccharide biosynthesis, UDPG is involved as an active glucose donor in the synthesis of polysaccharides such as cellulose,[137] starch,[138, 139] and glycogen.[140–143] In each case an oligosaccharide primer or acceptor is required. (Recently it has been found that synthetic adenosine diphosphate glucose is some ten times more effective than UDPG for enzymic transfer of glucose to starch or oligosaccharides. Various other nucleoside diphosphate sugars were inactive).[144] Direct glucosidation of 5-hydroxymethylcytosine residues in T2 bacteriophage deoxynucleic acid by uridine diphosphate glucose

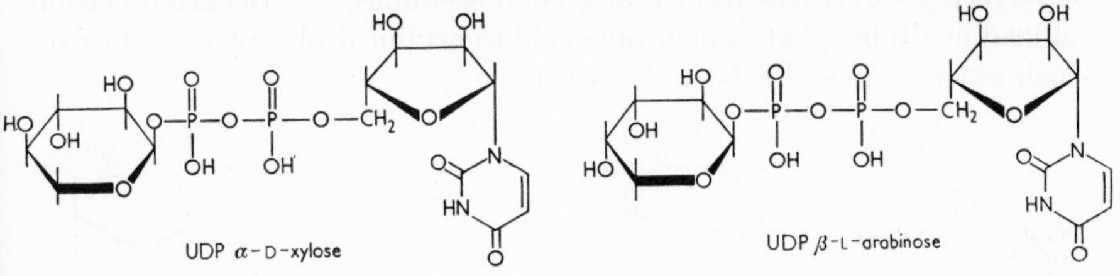

UDP α-D-xylose

UDP β-L-arabinose

UDP-glucuronic acid
↓
UTP + α-D-xylose-1 phosphate ⟶ UDP xylose + PP
UTP + β-L-arabinose-1 phosphate ⟶ UDP arabinose + PP
UDP xylose   ⟩⟶ hemicellulose
UDP arabinose ⟩

Enzymic reactions

has also been demonstrated,[145] and the enzymic synthesis of psychosine (galactosyl sphingosine) involves transfer of galactose to sphingosine from uridine diphosphate galactose with liberation of uridine-5' pyrophosphate.[146]

Uridine diphosphate α-D-xylose and uridine diphosphate β-L-arabinose have been isolated from mung bean seedlings;[147] the two compounds are interconvertible by enzymic epimerisation at C4, and are presumably precursors of plant polysaccharides. A rhamnose analogue, uridine diphosphate rhamnose, has been identified in extracts from two noncapsulated variants of pneuococcus type II.[148]

Uridine diphosphate dihydroxyacetone has been isolated from *Diplococcus pneumoniae* (Type II, Strain R19). Acidic hydrolysis yielded uridine-5' phosphate; treatment with venom pyrophosphatase (containing 5'-nucleotidase) gave uridine, inorganic phosphate and dihydroxyacetone phosphate.[149]

URIDINE DIPHOSPHATE GLUCURONIC ACID

Uridine diphosphate glucuronic acid acts as a glucuronyl donor in the enzymic synthesis of ester, and aliphatic and steroid ether, glucuronides,[150] and also transfers the glucuronic acid moiety to amino acids forming *N*-glucosyluronic derivatives.[151] The mixed anhydride has been isolated from animal,[152, 153] plant[154] and micro-organism[155] sources and is formed enzymically by oxidation of uridine diphosphate glucose with nicotinamide adenine dinucleotide.[156] A single dehydrogenase enzyme is probably involved; no aldehyde intermediate has been detected. An alternate synthesis of uridine diphosphate glucuronic acid from glucuronic acid 1 phosphate and uridine-5' triphosphate is catalysed by extracts from mung bean seedlings.[157] Decarboxylation of uridine diphosphate glucuronic acid to uridine diphosphate xylose by such extracts has also been described.[158]

UDP glucuronic acid   UDP galacturonic acid

UTP + Glucuronic acid 1-phosphate ⇌ UDP glucuronic acid + PP
UDPG ⟶ UDP glucuronic acid
UDP glucuronic acid + ROH ⟶ R-O-glucuronate + UDP

Enzymic reactions

Whereas types II and III pneumococci contain uridine diphosphate glucuronic acid, this is replaced by the galacturonic acid analogue[159] in type I, presumably reflecting the function of these pyrophosphate derivatives in the biosynthesis of specific capsular polysaccharides. Enzymic synthesis of type III pneumococcal polysaccharide, a β-linked polymer of cellobiuronic acid (glucose-4-β-1-glucuronic acid), from uridine diphosphate glucose and uridine diphosphate glucuronic acid has been demonstrated[160, 161] using a cell free extract of *Diplococcus pneumoniae* type III. In like manner, extracts of type I pneumococci catalyse the synthesis of a serologically reactive polymer from uridine diphosphate galacturonic acid.[162] The polygalacturonic acid formed possibly constitutes the backbone of type I capsular polysaccharide.

URIDINE DIPHOSPHATE N-ACETYLGLUCOSAMINE

A contaminant of uridine diphosphate glucose preparations from yeast was separated,[163, 164] and identified as a 2-amino-2-deoxy sugar derivative of uridine-5′ pyrophosphate.[163] Mild acidic hydrolysis liberated the nucleoside pyrophosphate and N-acetyl-D-glucosamine; treatment with alkali gave uridine-5′ phosphate and N-acetylglucosamine-1 phosphate, in contrast with the behaviour of uridine diphosphate glucose. Enzymic synthesis[165] of the anhydride from α-D-N-acetylglucosamine-1 phosphate and uridine-5′ triphosphate established the structure as P^1-uridine-5′ P^2-α-D-N-acetylglucosamine-1 pyrophosphate. The compound is widely distributed and can be equilibrated with uridine diphosphate N-acetylgalactosamine[166] by the action of the appropriate waldenase enzyme.[167]

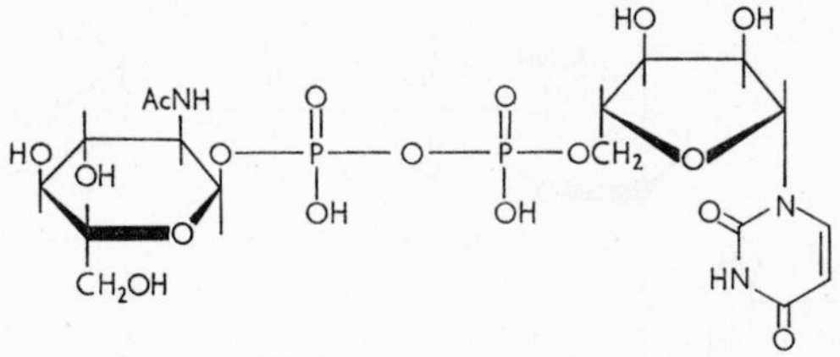

UDP N–acetylglucosamine

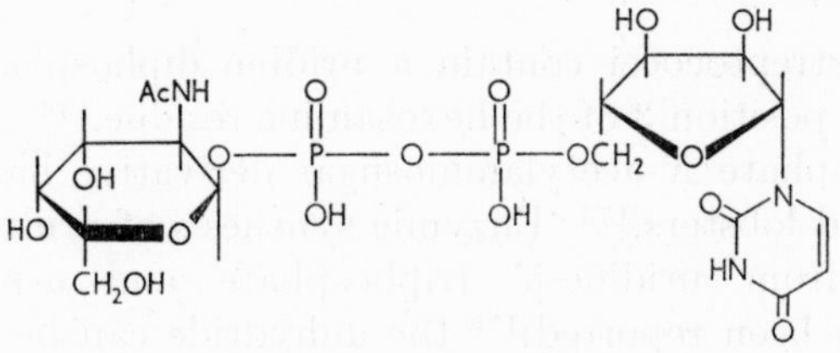

UDP N– acetylgalactosamine

Like other sugar derivatives of uridine-5′ pyrophosphate, uridine diphosphate N-acetylglucosamine participates in the biosynthesis of polymeric material. Tracer studies have demonstrated the enzymic formation of hyaluronic acid from uridine diphosphate N-acetylglucosamine and uridine diphosphate glucuronic acid.[168, 169] Uridine diphosphate N-acetylglucosamine also acts as a glycosyl donor in the synthesis of chitin using extracts of *Neurospora crassa* in the presence of a primer.[170]

Other aminosugar nucleotides include uridine diphosphate N-acetylglucosamine-6 phosphate and uridine diphosphate N-acetylgalactosamine-4 sulphate, both of which have been isolated from hen oviduct.[171] The former derivative is probably a degradation product of uridine diphosphate N-acetylglucosamine-6-phospho-1-β-D-galactose, also isolated from the oviduct of laying hens.[172] Hydrolysis with dilute acetic acid gave equivalent amounts of uridine-5′ pyrophosphate, galactose and N-acetylglucosamine-6 phosphate; treatment with ammonia (at 100°) yielded β-D-galactose-1 phosphate and uridine diphosphate N-acetylglucosamine. (The D-configuration of the galactose was determined by biological means.) Hydrolysis of the compound with purified venom pyrophosphatase gave uridine-5′ phosphate and N-acetylglucosamine-(1 phosphate)-6-phospho-β-1-galactose. The latter compound was further degraded to N-acetylglucosamine-1,6 diphosphate and galactose by the action of dilute acetic acid;[172] alternatively, dephosphorylation with monophosphatase yielded N-acetylglucosamine-6-phospho-1-galactose which on alkaline treatment gave galactose-1 phosphate.[173]

Group A streptococci contain a uridine diphosphate hexosamine substituted at position 3 of the hexosamine residue.[174] An unidentified uridine diphosphate N-acetylaminosugar derivative has been isolated from crabs and lobsters.[175] Enzymic synthesis of uridine diphosphate glucosamine from uridine-5′ triphosphate and α-D-glucosamine-1 phosphate has been reported;[176] the anhydride can be converted into uridine diphosphate galactosamine by liver extracts.[177]

URIDINE-5' PYROPHOSPHATE SUGAR PEPTIDES

A number of nucleotide derivatives containing sugar peptides, that are precursors of peptides present in bacterial cell walls, have been isolated in recent years. These compounds, normally present in the cell in small amounts, are more readily obtained by imposing a suitable metabolic block on the biochemical activities leading to cell wall synthesis.

Accumulation of acid-labile phosphate esters in penicillin-inhibited

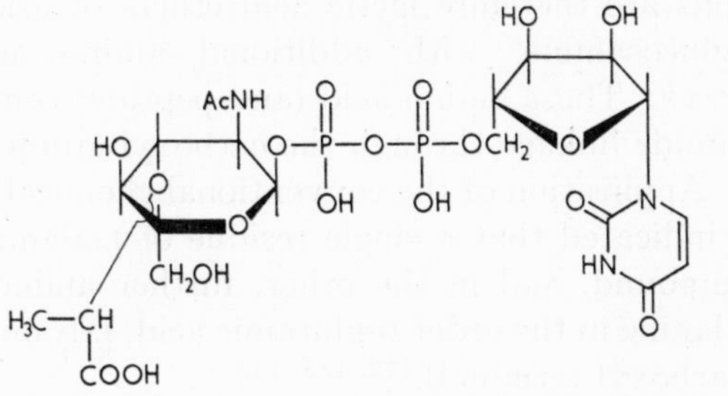

UDP N-acetylmuramic acid

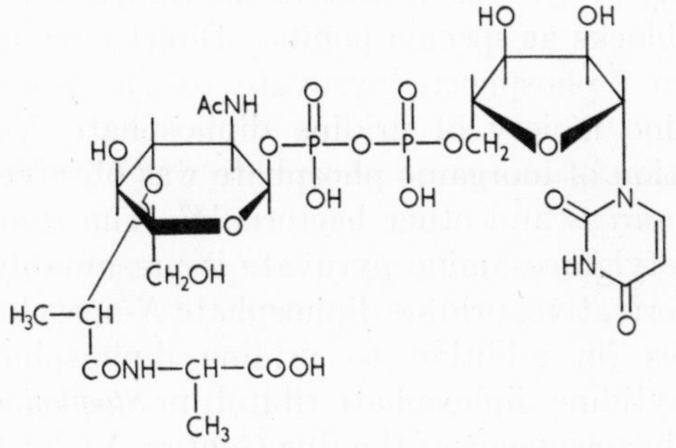

UDP N-acetylglucosamine-3'-lactyl-L-alanine

UDP N-acetylglucosamine-3'-lactyl-L-ala-D-glu-L-lys-D-ala-D-ala COOH

ala = Alanine
glu = Glutamic
lys = Lysine

Staphylococcus aureus was first observed in 1949.[178] Fractionation of crude preparations of these esters yielded three uracil derivatives which on mild acidic treatment liberated uridine-5' pyrophosphate, further hydrolysis giving uridine-5' phosphate. Amino acids were also identified among the hydrolysis products of two of the compounds, while electrometric titrations of the third derivative, before and after hydrolysis, indicated a P^1, P^2 diesterified pyrophosphate structure which was confirmed by cleavage with pyrophosphatase.[179] A second major component, with which reducing properties were associated only after liberation from the pyrophosphate, and which was common to all three uridine derivatives, was subsequently identified as N-acetylmuramic acid,[180] the structure of muramic acid (a constituent of bacterial spores and cell walls)[181, 182] having been established as 3-O-1'-carboxyethyl-2-amino-2-deoxyglucose.[183, 184]

The compounds are therefore lactic acid ethers of uridine diphosphate N-acetylglucosamine, with additional amino acid residues present in two cases. These amino acid (and peptide) components are attached by an amide linkage through the carboxyl group of the lactic acid component. Application of the conventional chemical methods for peptide analysis indicated that a single residue of L-alanine was combined in one compound, and in the other, further amino acids were linked to this L-alanine in the order D-glutamic acid, L-lysine, D-alanine, and D-alanine (carboxyl terminal).[179, 185, 186]

To some extent, confirmation of the structure of the pentapeptide derivative of uridine diphosphate N-acetylmuramic acid has been obtained by a study of the biosynthesis of the compound, including the use of metabolic blocks at specific points. Direct enzymic transfer of enolpyruvate from 2-phosphoenolpyruvate to the 3 position of the N-acetylglucosamine moiety of uridine diphosphate N-acetylglucosamine with liberation of inorganic phosphate was observed in extracts of *Staphylococcus aureus* and other bacteria.[187] The resultant uridine diphosphate N-acetylglucosamine pyruvate is presumably a precursor of the lactic acid derivative, uridine diphosphate N-acetylmuramic acid, which accumulates (in addition to uridine diphosphate N-acetylglucosamine and cytidine diphosphate ribitol) in *Staphylococcus aureus* inhibited by certain specimens of the dye Gentian Violet.[188] Penicillin inhibition leads to accumulation of UDP-N-acetylmuramic acid-L-alanine while UDP-N-acetylmuramic acid-L-alanine-D-glutamic acid has been isolated from *S. aureus* grown in a lysine deficient medium.[189] The use of oxamycin, a competitive antagonist for D-alanine incorporation, gives rise to accumulated UDP-N-acetylmuramic acid–L-alanine–D-glutamic–L-lysine[190] while penicillin treatment inhibits transfer of the N-acetylmuramic acid–pentapeptide moiety of UDP-N-acetylmuramic acid–L-alanine–D-glutamic–L-lysine–D-alanine–D-alanine to the cell wall, in which alanine, lysine, glutamic acid and muramic acid occur in much the same ratio and configuration.[191] The presence of D-amino acids doubtless affords the bacterial cell wall a measure of protection against digestion by many proteolytic enzymes.[185, 186]

Accumulation of these intermediates is a result of the inhibition of specific enzymic steps, a number of which have been characterised and the enzymes partially purified. Single amino acids are added to the lactic acid derivative of uridine diphosphate N-acetylglucosamine in a stepwise fashion up to the tripeptide derivative, which is then converted directly into the pentapeptide by the addition of the dipeptide D-alanyl-D-alanine, cofactors in each case being adenosine-5′ triphosphate and manganese ions.[192] Although oxamycin has no effect on this last enzymic

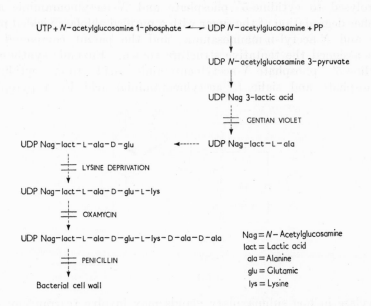

reaction, both the enzymic conversion of L-alanine into D-alanine and synthesis of the D-alanine dipeptide are inhibited.[193]

A hexapeptide derivative in which the ϵ-amino group of the lysine residue is acylated by L-alanine has been found recently in penicillin-treated *Streptococcus faecalis*.[474]

Related peptide derivatives in which lysine is replaced by a,ϵ-diaminopimelic acid have been isolated from strains of *Escherichia coli*.[194, 195] Several uridine diphosphate sugar peptides containing aspartic acid and glycine in addition to alanine, glutamic acid and lysine, have been found in *Staphylococcus aureus* strain 209P.[196] These are possibly the result of differences in the composition of the bacterial cell wall or they may be precursors subsequent to the pentapeptide derivative previously described.

NEURAMINIC ACID AND OTHER DERIVATIVES

Nucleotide-linked neuraminic acid peptides have been observed[197] in colominic acid fractions prepared from culture filtrates of *Escherichia coli* $K_{235}L + O$. These compounds are possibly precursors of colominic acid, a polysaccharide that contains N-acetylneuraminic acid.[198] Cytidine-5′ phosphate-N-acetylneuraminic acid has been isolated from the same organism.[199] The nucleotide derivative is resistant to 5′-nucleotidase but is extremely unstable in acidic solutions, being rapidly hydrolysed to cytidine-5′ phosphate and N-acetylneuraminic acid. Further degradation of the sugar with a purified aldolase yielded pyruvate and N-acetyl-D-mannosamine, and the parent compound has been assigned the tentative structure shown. Enzymic synthesis of cytidine-5′ phosphate-N-acetylneuraminic acid from cytidine-5′ triphosphate and sialic (N-acetylneuraminic) acid by a pyrophos-

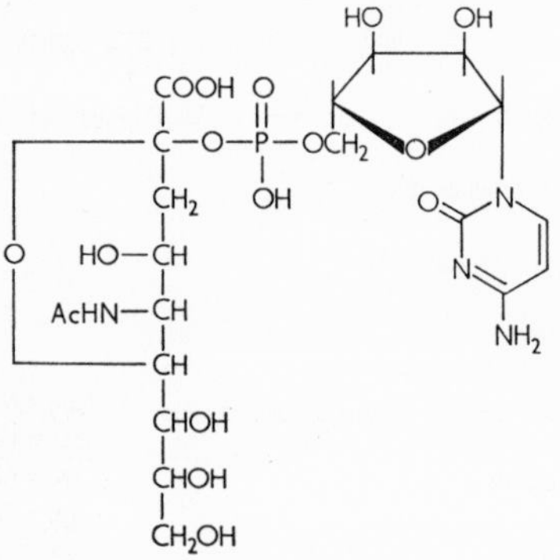

phorylase in hog submaxillary glands may involve rearrangement of an intermediate cytidine-5′ phosphate-carboxylate anhydride.[470]

Two compounds containing uridine-5′ pyrophosphate, N-acetylglucosamine, galactose, and N-acetylneuraminic acid have been isolated from goat colostrum. They are possibly involved in the biosynthesis of glycoproteins and glycolipids.[200] Both UDP N-acetylglucosamine (4 ← 1) galactose (i.e. UDP N-acetyl-lactosamine) and UDP N-acetyl-lactosamine fucoside have been isolated from human milk.[471] Ethanolic extracts of *Aerobacter cloacae* contain a glucosamine–muramic-adenylic–amino acid complex.[201]

CYTIDINE-5′ PYROPHOSPHATE DERIVATIVES

Derivatives of cytidine-5′ phosphate participate in the biosynthesis of phospholipids and are also involved in the formation of teichoic (wall) acids in various bacteria.

Arising from the observation that cytidine-5′ triphosphate was required for the enzymic incorporation of choline phosphate into lecithin, the " activated " forms of choline phosphate and ethanolamine phosphate were found to be P^1-cytidine-5' P^2-choline pyrophosphate and P^1-cytidine-5' P^2-ethanolamine pyrophosphate respectively.[202] The structures of these compounds were readily confirmed by chemical synthesis, and by enzymic synthesis from cytidine-5' triphosphate and choline (or ethanolamine) phosphate.[203]

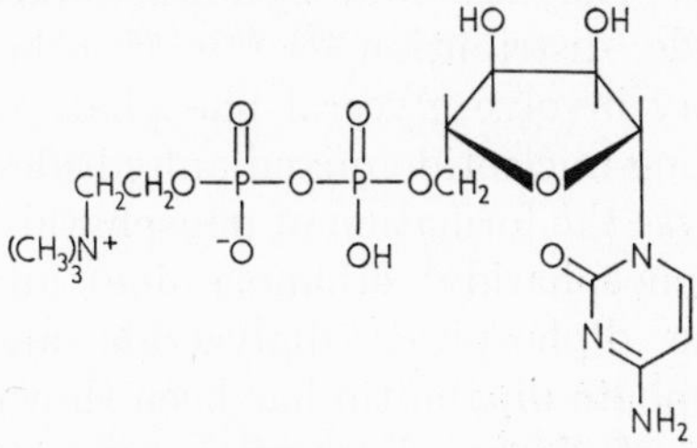

CDP choline

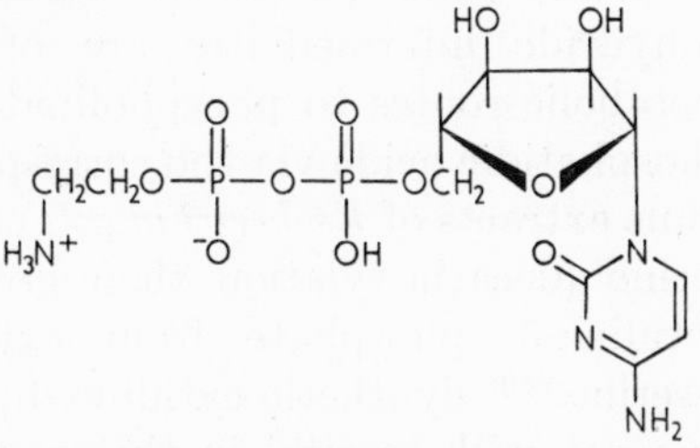

CDP ethanolamine

In the presence of the appropriate transferase enzymes the mixed anhydrides react with α,β-diglycerides to give lecithin or phosphatidyl-ethanolamine, with liberation of cytidine-5' phosphate.[204] An analogous enzymic reaction of cytidine diphosphate choline with N-acetyl-DL-*threo-trans*-sphingosin gives a sphingomyelin.[205] Relatively small amounts of the cytidine intermediates are necessary, as rephosphoryla-

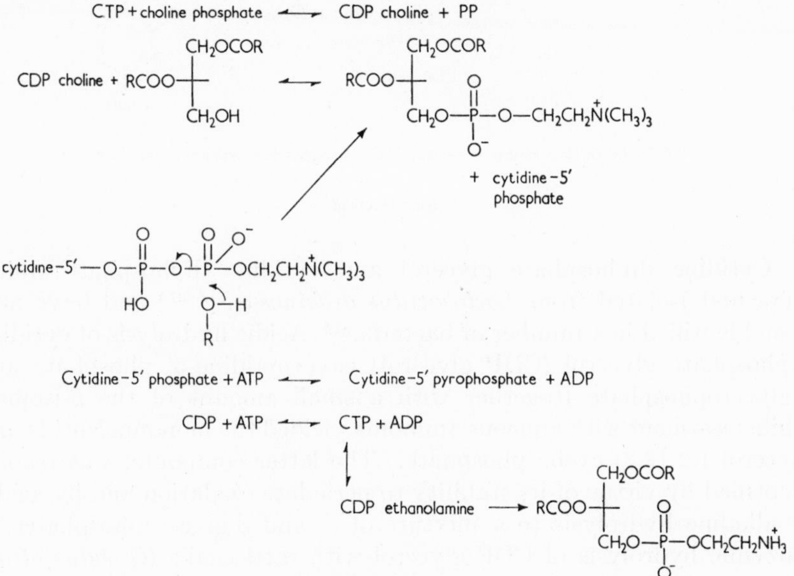

Enzymic reactions

tion of cytidine-5' phosphate to cytidine-5' triphosphate by the action of adenosine-5' triphosphate and phosphokinases[206] occurs, with subsequent regeneration of the required cytidine diphosphate choline (or ethanolamine). As in the case of many biochemical reactions of this nature, activation of the choline phosphate transferase enzyme systems requires magnesium (or manganese) ions,[203] presumably for complex formation with the substrates.

While these particular transferase enzymes and cytidine mixed anhydride intermediates are of wide distribution,[202, 207, 208] other metabolic routes to phospholipids may involve glycerol phosphate or phosphatidic acids via the corresponding nucleotide mixed anhydrides. Thus extracts of *Escherichia coli* catalyse the formation of phosphatidyl serine (decarboxylation then gives phosphatidyl ethanolamine) and cytidine-5' phosphate from cytidine diphosphate diglyceride and L-serine.[209] Synthetic cytidine diphosphate dipalmitin has been shown to react with inositol in the presence of chicken liver microsomes to yield inositol monophosphatide and cytidine-5' phosphate.[210] Cytidine diphosphate inositol (isolated from slices of duck pancreas incubated with inositol-2-[³H]) may also take part in phosphatide biosynthesis.[211]

CDP diglyceride + inositol ⟶ inositol monophosphatide + cytidine-5' phosphate

Enzymic reactions

Cytidine diphosphate glycerol and cytidine diphosphate ribitol were first isolated from *Lactobacillus arabinosus*,[212-214] and have now been identified in a number of bacteria.[215] Acidic hydrolysis of cytidine diphosphate glycerol (CDP glycerol) gave cytidine-5' phosphate and α-glycerophosphate (together with a small amount of the β-isomer) while treatment with aqueous ammonia yielded the mononucleotide and glycerol-1,2 (2,3) cyclic phosphate. The latter compound was readily identified by virtue of its stability to periodate oxidation and by acidic or alkaline hydrolysis to a mixture of α- and β-glycerophosphates.[216] Enzymic hydrolysis of CDP glycerol with rattlesnake (*Crotalus atrox*) venom, which contains a pyrophosphatase and a 5'-nucleotidase, yielded cytidine, inorganic phosphate and glycerophosphate. Periodate oxidation of the glycerophosphate gave glycolaldehyde phosphate, thus defining the position of the phosphate as α; the configuration of the α-glycerophosphate was determined by enzymic oxidation with nicotinamide adenine dinucleotide and glycerophosphate dehydrogenase to give dihydroxyacetone phosphate. Since the enzyme is specific for L-α-glycerophosphate, the structure of cytidine diphosphate glycerol was fully established as P^1-cytidine-5' P^2-L-glycerol-α pyrophosphate.[217] Final confirmation was afforded by synthesis of the mixed anhydride by chemical methods and by the reversible enzymic pyrophosphorolysis reaction with cytidine-5' triphosphate and L-α-glycerophosphate.[218]

CH₂OH ... CDP glycerol ... snake venom ... + HO ... + H₃PO₄ ... monoesterase ... IO₄⁻ ... α-L-Glycerophosphate dehydrogenase + NAD ... + Cytidine-5' phosphate ... H⁺ ... NH₃

Analogous degradative methods were applied to cytidine diphosphate ribitol.[219] Treatment with ammonia yielded cytidine-5' phosphate and ribitol-1,2(4,5) cyclic phosphate; mild acidic hydrolysis gave the nucleoside-5' phosphate, ribitol-1(5) phosphate, and other ribitol phosphates resulting from acid-catalysed phosphate migration. Further treatment with acid gave inorganic phosphate and 1,4-anhydroribitol, no ribitol being formed under the conditions employed.[220] Enzymic hydrolysis of cytidine diphosphate ribitol with snake venom gave cytidine, inorganic phosphate, and a ribitol phosphate which could be degraded enzymically (prostate monoesterase) to ribitol and orthophosphate. Periodate oxidation of the ribitol phosphate gave glycolaldehyde phosphate, indicating esterification of a primary hydroxyl group. The configuration of the compound was determined by means of specific enzymes.[217] Periodate oxidation of the ribitol-1,2 (4,5) cyclic phosphate previously mentioned, followed by further oxidation of the product with bromine water, gave glyceric acid-2,3 cyclic phosphate from which a mixture of the -2 and -3 phosphates of glyceric acid was obtained by acidic hydrolysis. These were completely utilised as substrates in a glycolytic enzyme system from rabbit muscle specific

for the D-glyceric acid configuration, and hence cytidine diphosphate ribitol is P^1-cytidine-5' P^2-D-ribitol-5 pyrophosphate. Synthesis of cytidine diphosphate ribitol from cytidine-5' phosphate and D-ribose-5 phosphate (with subsequent reduction of the cytidine diphosphate ribose) provided final confirmation of this structure.

Enzymic synthesis of cytidine diphosphate glycerol and cytidine diphosphate ribitol from cytidine-5' triphosphate and L-α-glycerol phosphate or D-ribitol phosphate respectively, has been reported.[218] The anhydrides are almost certainly involved in the biosynthesis of teichoic acids that have been isolated from a number of bacterial cells. In addition to ribitol (or glycerol) residues these polymers also contain alanine, glucose, or glucosamine components, the actual composition of the teichoic acid being characteristic of the organism to a considerable extent.[221, 222] Rather large quantities of a cytidine diphosphate derivative, probably cytidine diphosphate ribitol, accumulate when *Staphylococcus aureus* is cultured in the presence of penicillin[223] (cf. effect of Gentian Violet, p. 172).

Other cytidine diphosphate derivatives that are connected with the biosynthesis of cell wall polysaccharides have been reported. Cytidine diphosphate tyvelose (3,6-dideoxy-D-mannose) has been isolated from strains of *Salmonella enteritidis*; related mutant (lack of UDP galactose-4-epimerase) strains of *Salmonella typhimurium* contain CDP abequose (3,6-dideoxy-D-galactose). In each case the dideoxy sugar corresponds to that present in the cell wall of the wild type strain.[224]

GUANOSINE-5' PYROPHOSPHATE DERIVATIVES

In recent years, a variety of P^1-guanosine-5' P^2-sugar-1 pyrophosphates have been isolated and identified. Guanosine diphosphate mannose[225] occurs in yeast (which contains a mannan), and guanosine diphosphate fucose has been isolated from an *Aerobacter aerogenes* strain[226] that produces a polysaccharide containing L-fucose, and from sheep milk.[227] Glucose and fructose analogues have been found in *Eremothecium ashbyii*,[228] and guanosine diphosphate colitose (3,6-dideoxy-L-galactose) has been isolated from *Escherichia coli*.[229] Guanosine diphosphate glucose is also present in bovine mammary glands; enzymic synthesis from guanosine-5' triphosphate and α-D-glucose-1 phosphate has been described.[472] A guanosine diphosphate aldoheptose has been isolated from yeast; the heptose was identified as D-*glycero*-D-*manno*heptose.[230] Both guanosine diphosphate D-mannose and guanosine diphosphate L-galactose have been identified in extracts from the red alga *Porphyra perforata* J. G. Agardh.[231] The galactose released on mild acidic hydrolysis was identified as L- by its resistance to oxidation by a specific D-galactose dehydrogenase. (It may be noted that uridine diphosphate galactose from the same alga contained D-galactose only.) Reduction of the free hexose with sodium borohydride gave the glycitol; cleavage of the anhydride with pyrophosphatase gave guanosine-5' phosphate and the sugar phosphate.[231] Structures of the different anhydrides were in general determined by the usual hydrolytic methods. Further definition of P^1-guanosine-5' P^2-mannose-1 pyrophosphate as an α-D-mannose derivative is indicated by virtue of the relative stability of the anhydride towards ammonia, and by enzymic synthesis from guanosine-5′ triphosphate and α-D-mannose-1 phosphate.[232]

Enzymic conversion of guanosine diphosphate α-D-mannose into guanosine diphosphate L-fucose[233] occurs via an intermediate guanosine diphosphate 4-keto-6-deoxymannose.[230, 234, 235] Catalytic (rhodium/H_2) reduction of this intermediate followed by acidic hydrolysis gave a mixture of 6-deoxy-D-talose and 6-deoxy-D-mannose. A second intermediate, GDP 4-keto-6-deoxy-L-galactose, is probably formed enzymically by ene-diol inversions, and this is finally reduced to GDP-L-fucose.[235]

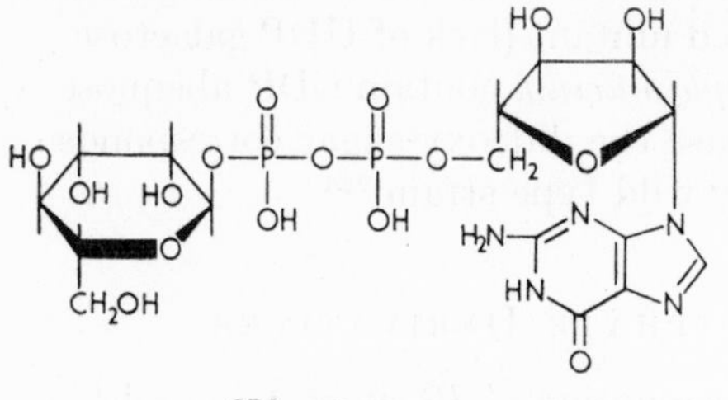

GDP α-D-mannose

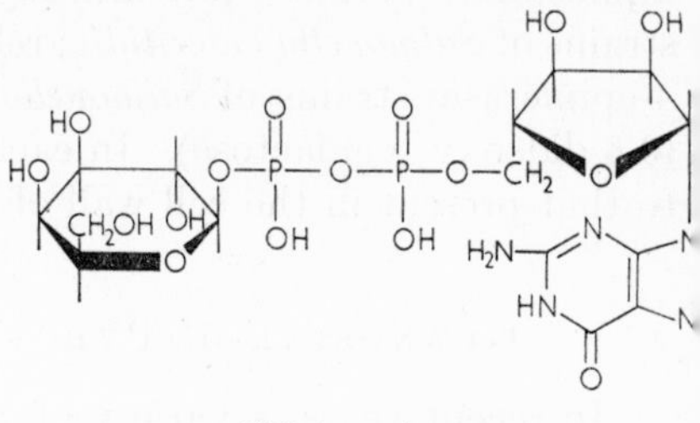

GDP β-L-galactose

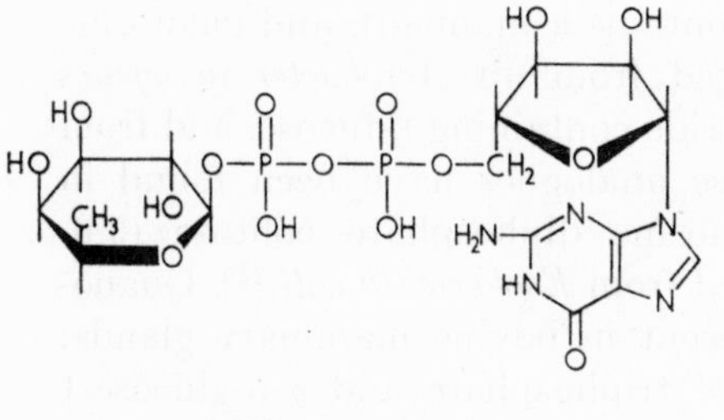

GDP β-L-fucose

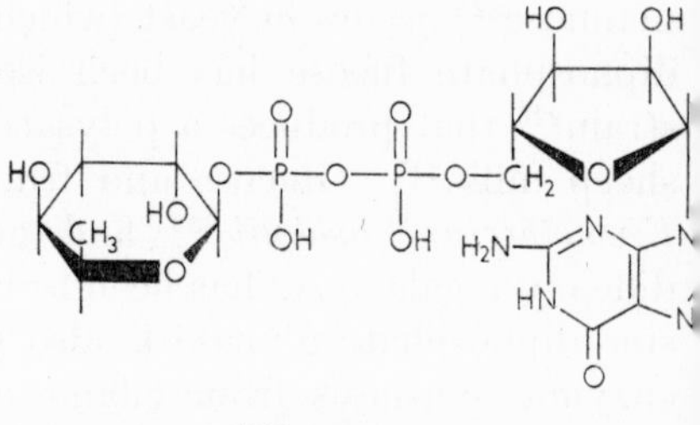

GDP β-colitose

Guanosine diphosphate mannose is also converted into guanosine diphosphate rhamnose and guanosine diphosphate 6-deoxytalose by crude extracts of a soil bacterium.[236] Both D-rhamnose and D-6-deoxy-talose are present in a polysaccharide isolated from the same organism, and in this case (in contrast with thymidine diphosphate L-rhamnose) the hexose in the anhydride is probably of D configuration. [Compare CDP abequose (3,6-dideoxy-D-galactose) and GDP colitose (3,6-dideoxy-L-galactose), UDP D-galactose and GDP L-galactose].

DEOXYNUCLEOTIDE DERIVATIVES

Deoxycytidine diphosphate choline (analogous to cytidine diphosphate choline) has been isolated from sea urchin eggs.[237] It has also been identified, together with deoxycytidine diphosphate ethanolamine,

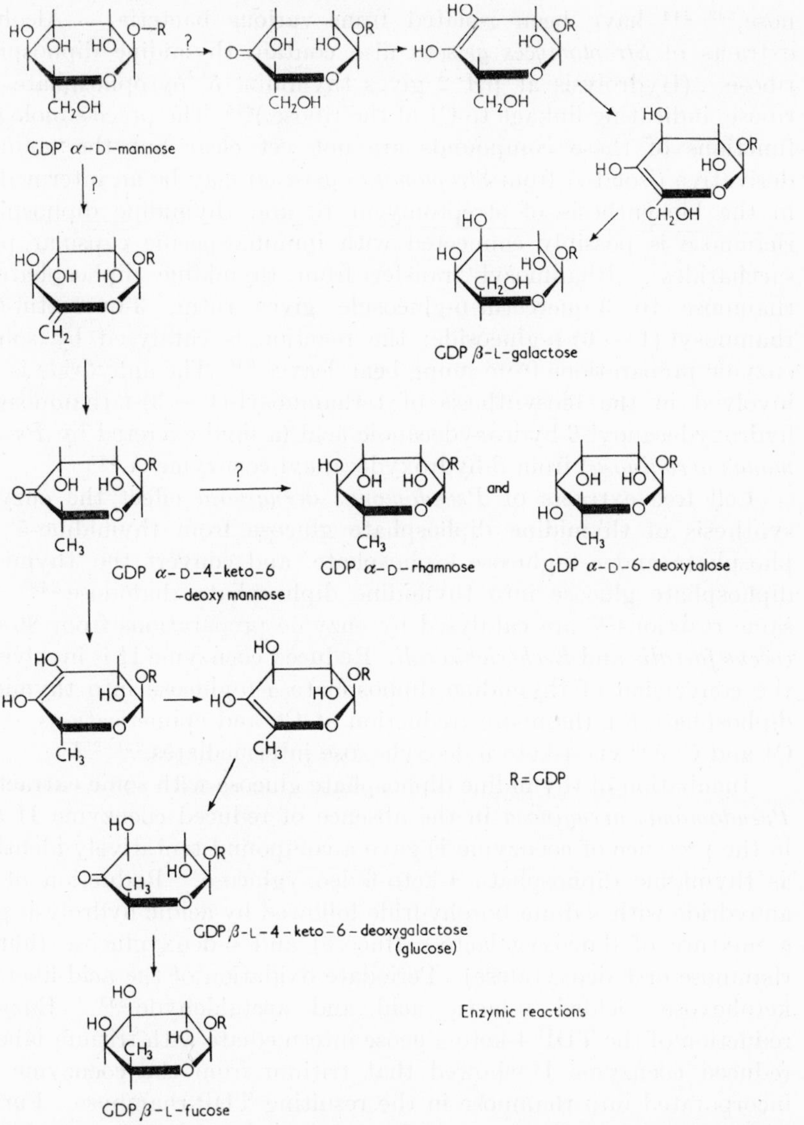

GDP α-D-mannose

GDP β-L-galactose

GDP α-D-4-keto-6 -deoxy mannose

GDP α-D-rhamnose

and

GDP α-D-6-deoxytalose

R = GDP

GDP β-L-4-keto-6-deoxygalactose
(glucose)

Enzymic reactions

GDP β-L-fucose

in extracts of calf thymus.[238]   Whereas deoxycytidine diphosphate
choline is fully as active as the ribose compound in enzymic systems
catalysing the synthesis of lecithin, deoxycytidine diphosphate
ethanolamine is much less active than cytidine diphosphate ethanolamine in the enzymic synthesis of phosphatidylethanolamine.[239]

Thymidine diphosphate sugar compounds[240] such as thymidine
diphosphate rhamnose,[241–244] and thymidine diphosphate man-

nose,[243, 244] have been isolated from various bacteria.   Alcoholic extracts of *Streptomyces griseus* also contain thymidine diphosphate ribose. (Hydrolysis at pH 2 gives thymidine-5′ pyrophosphate and ribose, indicating linkage to C1 of the ribose.)[245] The precise biological functions of these compounds are not yet clear but the mannose derivative (isolated from *Streptomyces griseus*) may be an intermediate in the biosynthesis of streptomycin B, and thymidine diphosphate rhamnose is possibly connected with immunospecific capsular polysaccharides. Rhamnosyl transfer from thymidine diphosphate L-rhamnose to 3-quercetin-D-glucoside gives rutin, 3-quercetin-O-L-rhamnosyl-(1 → 6)-D-glucoside; the reaction is catalysed by soluble enzyme preparations from mung bean leaves.[246] The anhydride is also involved in the biosynthesis of L-rhamnosyl-(1 → 3)-L-rhamnosyl-β-hydroxydecanoyl-β-hydroxydecanoic acid (a lipid excreted by *Pseudomonas aeruginosa*) from β-hydroxydecanoyl coenzyme A.[247]

Cell free extracts of *Pseudomonas aeruginosa* effect the enzymic synthesis of thymidine diphosphate glucose from thymidine-5′ triphosphate and α-D-glucose-1 phosphate, and convert the thymidine diphosphate glucose into thymidine diphosphate rhamnose.[248] The same reactions[249] are catalysed by enzyme preparations from *Streptococcus faecalis* and *Escherichia coli*. Reduced coenzyme II is involved in the conversion of thymidine diphosphate α-D-glucose into thymidine diphosphate β-L-rhamnose (reduction at C6 and epimerisations at C3, C4 and C5)[250] via 4-keto-6-deoxyhexose intermediates.[251-253]

Incubation of thymidine diphosphate glucose with sonic extracts of *Pseudomonas aeruginosa* in the absence of reduced coenzyme II (but in the presence of coenzyme I) gave a compound tentatively identified as thymidine diphosphate 4-keto-6-deoxyglucose. Reduction of the anhydride with sodium borohydride followed by acidic hydrolysis gave a mixture of 6-deoxygalactose (fucose) and 6-deoxyglucose (but no rhamnose or 6-deoxytalose). Periodate oxidation of the acid-liberated ketohexose yielded D-lactic acid and acetaldehyde.[253] Enzymic reduction of the TDP 4-keto glucose intermediate with tritium-labelled reduced coenzyme II showed that tritium from the coenzyme was incorporated into rhamnose in the resulting TDP-rhamnose. Further work using tritiated water as solvent suggested that epimerisations at C3 and C5 occurred by keto-enol transformations.[254] Rigorous identification of TDP α-D-4-keto-6-deoxyglucose as an intermediate in the enzymic synthesis of TDP L-rhamnose from TDP-D-glucose by sonic extracts of *Escherichia coli* strains has been achieved.[255] Hydrolysis of the isolated intermediate with pyrophosphatase gave thymidine-5′ phosphate and 4-keto-6-deoxyglucose-1 phosphate. (Coincident with cleavage of the anhydride there is a marked drop in absorption at

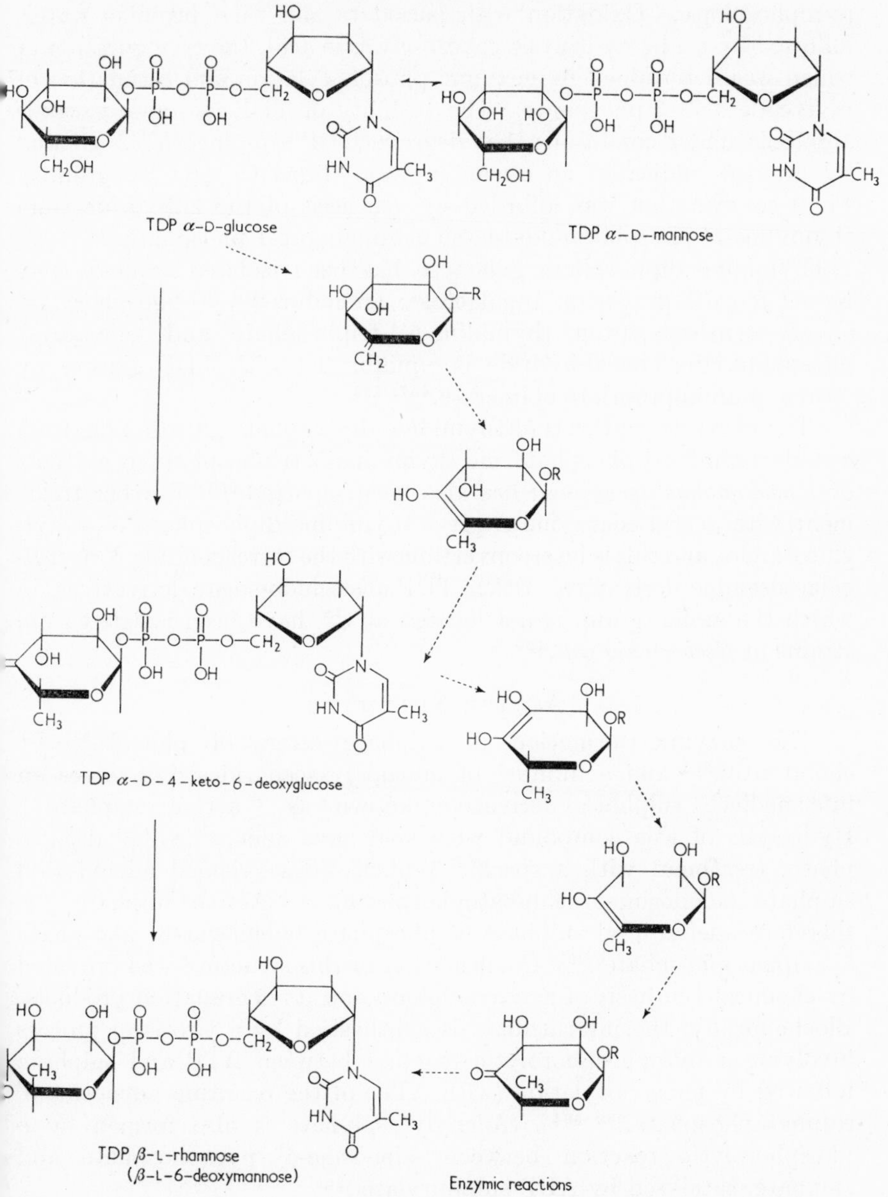

TDP α-D-glucose

TDP α-D-mannose

TDP α-D-4-keto-6-deoxyglucose

TDP β-L-rhamnose
(β-L-6-deoxymannose)

Enzymic reactions

320 mμ and shift of an absorption maximum from 320 mμ to 333 mμ. Absorption in this region is characteristic of the 4-keto sugar.)

An enzyme preparation from *Streptomyces griseus* interconverts TDP α-D-glucose and TDP mannose.[244] The structure of the latter nucleotide has been established as P^1-thymidine-5′ P^2-α-D-mannose-1 pyrophosphate. Oxidation with periodate and then bromine water, followed by acidic hydrolysis gave D-glyceric acid, the configuration of which was determined by enzymic phosphorylation and estimation of D-glyceric acid 3-phosphate. The stability of TDP mannose towards ammonia under conditions that degrade UDP a-D-glucose (cis C1 and C2 groups), indicated an a-configuration (trans C1 and C2 groups). Final confirmation was afforded by synthesis of the anhydride from thymidine-5' phosphoramidate and a-D-mannose-1 phosphate.[244]

Thymidine diphosphate galactose has been isolated from Streptococcus faecalis grown on D-galactose; an induced pyrophosphorylase effects synthesis from thymidine-5' triphosphate and galactose-1 phosphate.[467] The anhydride is equilibrated with TDP glucose by means of an appropriate epimerase.[467, 468]

The enzymic synthesis of thymidine diphosphate glucosamine from a-D-glucosamine-1 phosphate and thymidine-5' triphosphate by extracts of Pseudomonas aeruginosa has also been reported.[256] Further treatment with acetyl coenzyme A gives thymidine diphosphate N-acetylglucosamine and this is interconvertible with the corresponding N-acetylgalactosamine derivative. Other TDP acetamido-sugar derivatives, in which the amino group is not located at C2, have been isolated from strains of Escherichia coli.[469]

ACTIVE SULPHATE

The enzymic formation of sulphate esters of phenols,[257, 258] chondroitin,[259] and a number of mucopolysaccharides[260] involves an intermediate sulphate derivative known as " active sulphate ". Hydrolysis of this compound with acid gave adenosine-3',5' diphosphate; treatment with a specific 3'-nucleotidase yielded adenyl-5'-yl sulphate (adenosine-5' sulphatophosphate). " Active sulphate " is therefore adenyl-5'-yl sulphate 3' phosphate (adenosine-3' phosphate 5'-sulphatophosphate).[261] Confirmation of this structure was provided by chemical synthesis of active sulphate and its degradation products. Biochemically, the intermediate is synthesised by a two step process involving a pyrophosphorolytic reaction between ATP and sulphate followed by phosphorylation (with ATP) of the resulting adenosine-5' sulphatophosphate.[262-264] (Adenylyl sulphate is also formed by a phosphorolytic reaction between adenosine-5' pyrophosphate and sulphate, catalysed by ADP sulphurylase.)[264]

Extracts of yeast catalyse the reduction of " active sulphate " by dihydro NADP to adenosine-3',5' diphosphate and sulphite.[265-268] Similarly, adenylyl sulphate is converted into adenosine-5' phosphate and sulphite by extracts of Desulphovibrio desulphuricans.[269]

$$\text{APS} + 2\,\epsilon \leftrightarrows \text{AMP} + \text{SO}_3^{--}$$

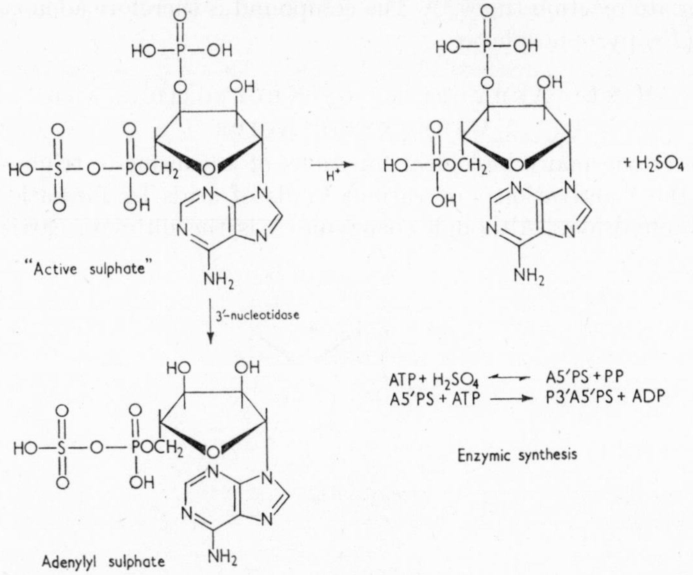

"Active sulphate"

3'-nucleotidase

Adenylyl sulphate

$ATP + H_2SO_4 \longleftarrow A5'PS + PP$
$A5'PS + ATP \longrightarrow P3'A5'PS + ADP$

Enzymic synthesis

Reversal of this reaction probably accounts for the formation of adenylyl sulphate as an intermediate[270, 271] in the oxidation of thiosulphate by *Thiobacillus thioparus*.

Selenate analogues of the anhydrides have been identified.[272] Isolation from salmon liver of a succinyladenosine-5' sulphatophosphate linked to serine and glutamic acid has been reported.[273]

ADENOSINE-3',5' PYROPHOSPHATE

This internal anhydride has been isolated from a red alga *Porphyra perforata* J. G. Agardh. Electrophoresis indicated two primary

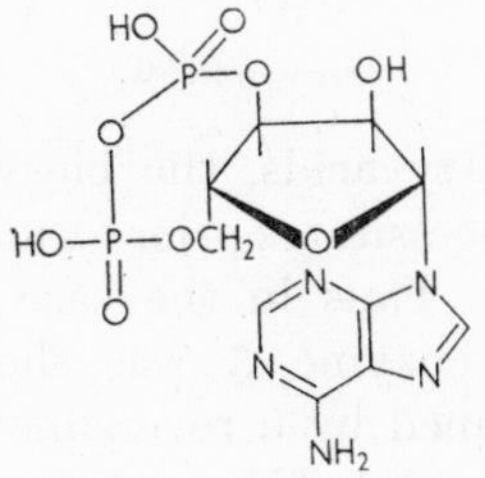

phosphoryl dissociations; acidic hydrolysis or treatment with a pyrophosphatase yielded adenosine-3',5' diphosphate. Further degradation of the diphosphate by the action of a non-specific phosphatase gave a mixture of adenosine-3' phosphate and adenosine-5' phosphate using appropriate reaction times.[231] The compound is therefore adenosine-3'-(P^1),5'(P^2) pyrophosphate.

MIXED ANHYDRIDES OF NUCLEOTIDES AND CARBOXYLIC ACIDS

One of the many biological functions of adenosine-5' triphosphate lies in the " activation " of various kinds of acids by formation of a mixed anhydride. Although coenzyme A is the ultimate carrier and

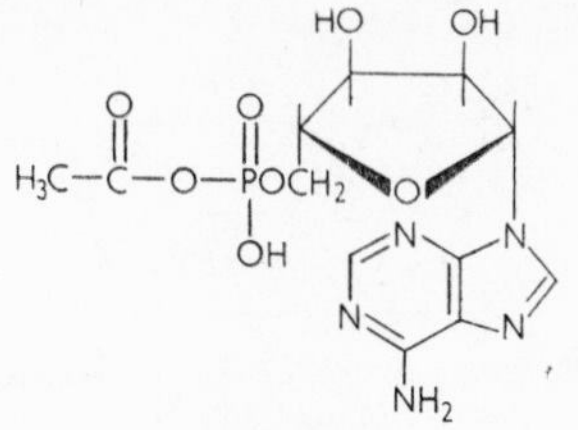

Adenylyl acetate

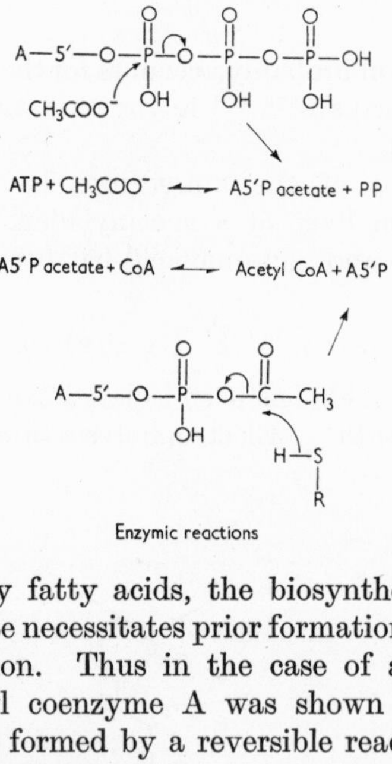

$$ATP + CH_3COO^- \longleftarrow A5'P \text{ acetate} + PP$$

$$A5'P \text{ acetate} + CoA \longleftarrow \text{Acetyl CoA} + A5'P$$

Enzymic reactions

" activator " of many fatty acids, the biosynthesis of an S-acyl coenzyme A intermediate necessitates prior formation of an acyl anhydride suitable for S-acylation. Thus in the case of acetate, the enzymic formation of S-acetyl coenzyme A was shown to involve adenylyl acetate, and this was formed by a reversible reaction between adenosine-5' triphosphate and acetate.[274]

Although the intermediate adenylyl acetate could not be isolated from this enzymic sequence (presumably because it is strongly bound to the enzyme), acethydroxamic acid was formed from ATP, acetate and hydroxylamine in the absence of coenzyme A, the formation of hydroxamic acids being indicative of acyl anhydrides. With this enzymic system, synthetic adenylyl acetate was converted into adenosine-5′ triphosphate in the presence of pyrophosphate, and to S-acetyl coenzyme A in the presence of coenzyme A. The reaction mechanism was fully established by tracer studies which showed that (1) exchange of inorganic pyrophosphate (^{32}P) with ATP requires acetate, (2) exchange of adenosine-5′ phosphate (^{14}C) with ATP is dependent on the presence of acetate and coenzyme A, and (3) acetate (^{14}C) exchange with S-acetyl coenzyme A requires both adenosine-5′ phosphate and inorganic pyrophosphate.[275] Moreover, in the enzymic formation of S-acetyl coenzyme A from acetate (^{18}O), coenzyme A, and adenosine-5′ triphosphate, ^{18}O is transferred from the acetate to the adenosine-5′ phosphate produced.[276]

Butyryl adenylate is likewise an intermediate in the conversion of butyrate into butyryl coenzyme A;[277] biochemical carboxylation with adenosine-5′ triphosphate and carbon dioxide then gives 2-ethylmalonyl coenzyme A.[278] Similarly, both adenylyl benzoate and S-benzoyl coenzyme A are intermediates in the enzymic synthesis of hippuric acid.[279, 280]

Benzoate + ATP $\leftrightarrows$ A5′P—O.CO.C_6H_5 + PP
A5′P—O—CO.C_6H_5 + Coenzyme A—SH $\leftrightarrows$
Coenzyme A—S—COC$_6$H$_5$ + A5′P
Coenzyme A—S.CO.C_6H_5 + NH_2CH_2COOH →
$C_6H_5CO.NH.CH_2COOH$ + Coenzyme A—SH
(Coenzyme A—SH = thiol form of Coenzyme A)

An analogous reaction sequence occurs in the biosynthesis of phenylacetylglutamine from phenylacetic acid, ATP and L-glutamine,[281] but in the case of pantothenic acid (a precursor of coenzyme A), reversible pyrophosphorolysis of ATP by nucleophilic attack of pantoic acid yields adenylyl pantoate which then acylates the amino group of β-alanine directly, and coenzyme A is not required.[282]

On the basis of hydroxamic acid formation and exchange of inorganic pyrophosphate with ATP, a number of other acyl adenylates have been postulated as enzyme bound intermediates.[283–287]

Amino-acyl adenylates play a significant role in the polymerisation or incorporation of amino acids into proteins.[288] Like the acyl adenylates, these intermediates are formed by a reversible enzymic pyrophosphorolysis of ATP, and are either firmly bound to the enzyme or have a short physiological life.[289, 290] Examination of purified activating enzymes suggests that there is a specific enzyme for each of the naturally occurring amino acids. Use of purified enzymes has also enabled isolation of several amino-acyl adenylates for comparison with synthetic anhydrides.[291–293] Biochemically, the amino acid is transferred from the mixed anhydride (which acts as a simple acylating agent) to the 2'- or 3'-hydroxyl group of the terminal nucleoside in a specific carrier " soluble RNA ", with subsequent incorporation into protein.[288, 294, 295] The significance of nucleotide sequence in these transfer ribonucleic acids has been demonstrated by the inhibition of enzymic amino-acylation (leucine) on treatment of soluble RNA (from *Escherichia coli*) with nitrous acid to the extent that only one nucleotide is de-

aminated per polynucleotide chain.[296] Although the enzyme systems are quite specific for the L-amino acids, a number of trytophan analogues (5-fluoro-, 6-fluoro-, 7-aza-tryptophan) have been activated in the ATP–pyrophosphate exchange reaction and are incorporated into protein, presumably blocking growth by erroneous protein biosynthesis. Other tryptophan analogues (5-methyl-, 6-methyl-) are not activated, and inhibit growth immediately.[297]

Evidence that amino-acyl adenylates can act directly in the biological synthesis of isolated peptide bonds is provided by the synthesis of carnosine from β-alanyl adenylate and histidine, using soluble enzyme preparations from chicken and rabbit skeletal muscle.[298]

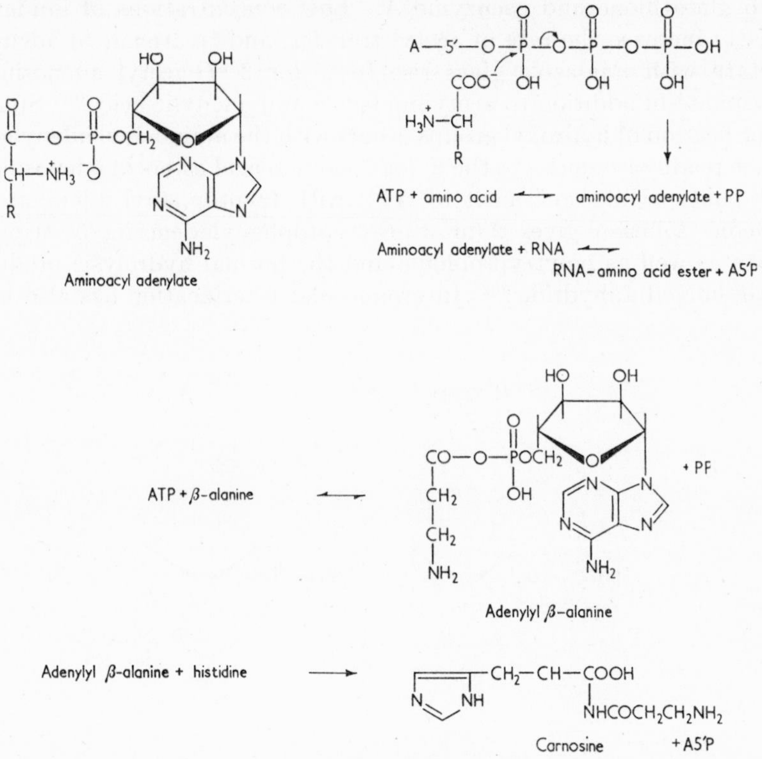

$$ATP + \text{amino acid} \rightleftharpoons \text{aminoacyl adenylate} + PP$$

Aminoacyl adenylate

$$\text{Aminoacyl adenylate} + RNA \rightleftharpoons RNA-\text{amino acid ester} + A5'P$$

$$ATP + \beta\text{-alanine} \rightleftharpoons$$

Adenylyl β-alanine

$+ PF$

$$\text{Adenylyl } \beta\text{-alanine} + \text{histidine} \longrightarrow$$

Carnosine $+ A5'P$

Enzymic reactions

PROPERTIES OF ACYL AND AMINO-ACYL ADENYLATES

Unlike adenosine-5′ phosphate, acetyl adenylate is unaffected by 5′-nucleotidase or by adenosine-5′ phosphate deaminase. The mixed anhydride shows greatest stability at slightly acid pH, but is rapidly cleaved at pH 2 (or less) at 100° while at pH 10 (or greater) rapid hydrolysis[299] occurs even at 0°. The α-amino-acyl adenylates exhibit similar instability, but at pH 7·2 are markedly less stable than benzoyl adenylate; β-alanyl adenylate is intermediate in behaviour. Stability towards neutral hydrolysis is increased when the amino group is protected, as in the benzyloxycarbonylamino-acyl adenylates.[300] All the compounds on treatment with hydroxylamine yield hydroxamic acids. As mixed anhydrides, they are active acylating agents in a number of non-enzymic reactions. Thus the reaction of adenylyl acetate with glycine, leucine, cystine, or glycylglycine gives the corresponding N-acetyl compounds and adenylic acid, while S-acetylation occurs with glutathione and coenzyme A. Low concentrations of imidazole greatly increase the rate of acetyl transfer, and treatment of adenylyl acetate with imidazole gives rise to 2' (or 3')-O-acetyl adenosine-5' phosphate in addition to acetylimidazole and adenylic acid.[301] Similar esterification of hydroxyl groups occurs with the amino-acyl adenylates. These readily isomerise to the 2' (or 3') amino acid esters of adenosine-5' phosphate, while treatment of ATP with tryptophanyl adenylate in aqueous solution gives 2'(or 3')-O-tryptophanyladenosine-5' triphosphate as well as polytryptophane and the normal hydrolysis products of the mixed anhydride.[302] Intermolecular esterification has also been

demonstrated in the reaction of tryptophanyl adenylate with (^{14}C) adenosine-5' phosphate to give labelled 2'(or 3')-O-tryptophanyl-adenosine-5' phosphate.[300] Under suitable conditions, such amino acid esters readily give hydroxamic acids on treatment with hydroxylamine. The amino-acyl adenylates react rapidly with ammonia to form the amino acid amide, and with amino acids to yield peptides,[300] analogous to the behaviour of acetyl adenylate[301] and of phosphate anhydrides of amino acids.[303, 304] Transfer of the amino-acyl moiety to proteins (including activating enzymes) can also occur in a non-enzymic manner.[300, 305] Non-enzymic transfer to ribonucleic acid gives amino acid derivatives which contain a variety of linkages with considerably different stabilities.[300] Some of these are undoubtedly due to acylation of the 6-amino group of cytosine residues; esterification of ribose hydroxyl groups, and anion exchange by nucleophilic attack of a terminal monoesterified phosphate (to give an

$$
\text{amino-acyl—O—}\overset{\displaystyle O}{\overset{\displaystyle \|}{\underset{\displaystyle \underset{\textstyle OH}{|}}{P}}}\text{—O—RNA}
$$

mixed anhydride + AMP) provide other possibilities.

OTHER ANHYDRIDES AND RELATED COMPOUNDS

In the main, attention has been focused on acyl and aminoacyl anhydrides of adenosine-5′ phosphate because of the biological significance of the adenylic acid derivatives. However, identification of an aspartic acid derivative of uridine-5′ phosphate in Ehrlich ascites cells has been reported,[306] as has the presence of aspartic, glutamic, arginine and alanine derivatives of uridine-5′ pyrophosphate in yeast (*Torulopsis utilis*) extracts.[307] Glutamic and aspartic acid derivatives of adenosine-5′ pyrophosphate have been isolated from liver, and from lactating mammary glands.[308] In connection with such compounds, it is of interest that a nucleoside-5′ triphosphate dependent peptide activation that is coupled with a proteolytic process (since no amino acids or peptides were added to the dialysed crude protein fraction) has been found in baker's yeast. Stoichiometrically, one mol of hydroxamate (from the activated peptide) is formed per mol of inorganic phosphate liberated. The same enzyme fraction catalyses the exchange of radioactive phosphate with each of the four major ribonucleoside-5′ triphosphates.[309]

An unstable derivative of guanosine-3′ phosphate has been isolated from an alcoholic extract of brewer's yeast;[310] it is possibly guanosine-2′,3′ cyclic phosphate. This has been isolated from *Chromobacterium violaceum* and may arise from an unknown precursor.[311]

Various nucleotide–peptide compounds (somewhat ill-defined at the moment) have been described, ranging from protein-bound nucleotides[312] to nucleic acid-bound peptides[313–315] and amino acids.[316] Nucleotide- and oligonucleotide-bound carboxyl-activated (both anhydride- and ester-linked)[465] peptides have been isolated from baker's yeast and from *Saccharomyces cerevisiae*.[317–321] Such compounds include a tetrapeptide anhydride of uridine-5′ phosphate, containing two arginines and two alanines.[322] This has been identified as arginyl-alanylarginylalanyl-5′ uridylate.[323] Other, as yet unidentified, peptide anhydrides of uridine-5′ phosphate have been isolated from brewer's yeast. In addition, several amino acid and peptide anhydrides of the dinucleotide adenylyl-5':3'-uridine-5' phosphate have been isolated and partially characterised.[324, 325] One of these is the alanyl derivative of the dinucleotide. Treatment with ribonuclease gave adenosine and alanyl uridine-3',5' diphosphate while hydrolysis with venom diesterase gave adenosine-5' phosphate and uridyl-5'-yl alanine.[324, 325] The general properties of the compound and its degradation products indicate the structure shown; confirmation is afforded by a synthesis of the anhydride from the dinucleotide and free amino acid by treatment with dicyclohexylcarbodi-imide.[466]

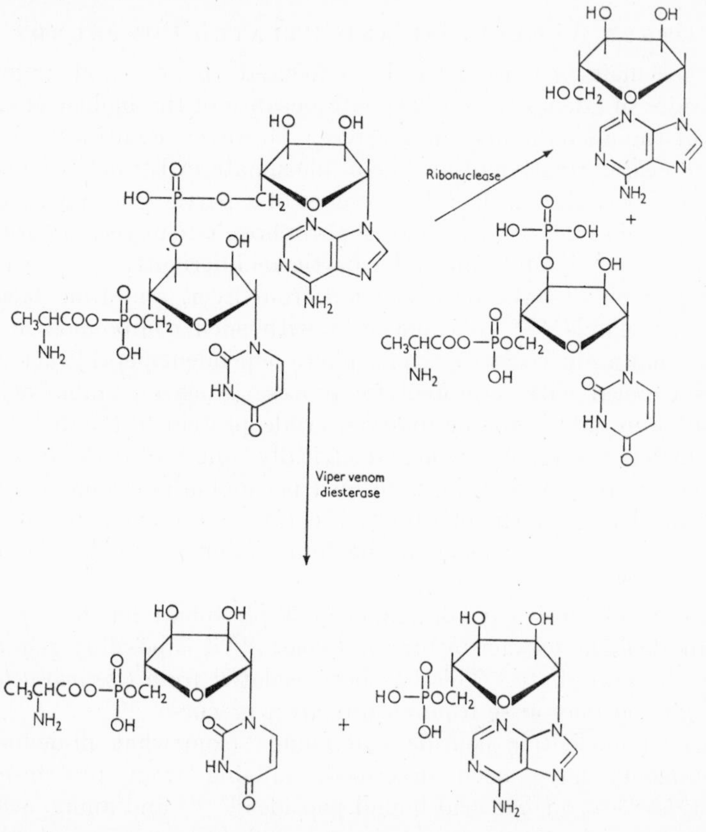

Ribonuclease

Viper venom diesterase

The presence of nucleotide–peptide derivatives, some of which are carboxyl-activated, in extracts of bacteria,[326, 327] mushrooms, rabbit tissues,[326] and mammalian liver[328–330] has been reported. Protein-free extracts from guinea pig liver contain a number of carboxyl-activated oligonucleotide-peptides.[331, 332] These derivatives contain adenine, guanine, cytosine, uracil, and thymine in addition to the peptide components and their formation has been observed both *in vivo* and

in vitro.[333]   Sulphur containing peptide–nucleotide and -polydeoxy-
nucleotide compounds occur in extracts of chlorella, and yeast.[334–336]
Nucleotide-bound   peptides   isolated   from   *Streptococcus   faecalis*
apparently possess a polyadenylic acid structure which is esterified at
a ribose (presumably terminal) hydroxyl group by the amino acid
residue.[337]

A cytidylic acid–peptide complex has been isolated from *Polyporus
squamosus*.[338] Acidic hydrolysis yielded cytidine-2' and -3' phosphates;
a phosphoramidate linkage is not excluded.   A similar substance was
also detected in acidic extracts of the mycelium of a strain of *Penicillium
urticae*.   A phosphoramidate linkage is also possible in the alkali-stable
nucleotide-amino acid complexes present in alkaline digests of ribonucleic acid.[339, 340]   It is perhaps pertinent to mention here that
adenosine-5' phosphoramidate is the primary product of ammonia

$$A\overline{T}P + NH_3 \;\longleftarrow\; \text{Adenosine-5' phosphoramidate} + \text{inorganic pyrophosphate}$$

Enzymic reaction

activating enzymes in various organisms, being formed from ATP by
the usual pyrophosphorolytic reaction.[341]

A nucleotide–peptide isolated from bovine liver is probably a
derivative of adenosine-(3' phosphate)-5' pyrophosphate.[342]   Enzymic
removal of the 3' phosphate group (by a specific 3'-nucleotidase) leaves
the nucleotide–peptide linkage intact, and the product reacts with
periodate.   Since the compound is relatively stable to both acids and
alkalis and does not give a hydroxamic acid with hydroxylamine, an
anhydride or phosphoramidate structure of any kind is unlikely.   The
peptide contains glycine, β-alanine, glutamic acid (NH_2 terminal),
cysteic acid, taurine, and an unidentified ninhydrin positive component.   If this last is a hydroxy amino acid, a possible structure for
the nucleotide peptide would involve ester linkage between the β
phosphate of adenosine-(3' phosphate)-5' pyrophosphate and the
peptide (via the unidentified component), that is, a P^1,P^2-dialkyl
pyrophosphate.[342]

As yet, the precise biological significance of most of these compounds is obscure, but nucleotide–peptides have been observed as products from the breakdown of serum albumin added to a liver mitochondrial fraction.[343] It may be that they are catabolic intermediates[344] rather than *de novo* precursors of nucleoproteins, proteins, or nucleic acids. In growing yeast the amounts of the nucleotide–peptide derivatives are low relative to the free nucleotides present, and it is considered improbable that they play a general role in protein synthesis.[345] Such a function has been postulated[346] with particular reference to yeast.

Synthesis of Nucleotide Anhydrides

Essentially, the synthesis of nucleotide coenzymes involves the union of a nucleotide (or protected nucleotide) with another acid to form an anhydride. The main approaches that have been used are adaptation and modification of old organic chemical techniques, the use of carbodi-imides and related reagents, and the phosphoramidate method. More recently, a simple, rapid, and effective method involving controlled nucleophilic displacement of one component of a nucleotide anhydride by a third acid (an anion exchange procedure analogous to the enzymic synthesis of nucleotide coenzymes) has been developed and found to be of wide applicability. Other approaches, such as esterification of a preformed pyrophosphate, have occasionally been examined, but generally with rather small success.

CLASSICAL METHOD

The first synthesis of a nucleotide coenzyme (adenosine-5' pyrophosphate) was achieved in 1947 by Baddiley and Todd,[347] who employed the classical method of preparing mixed anhydrides, treatment of the salt of an acid with an acid chloride. Mild acidic hydrolysis of 2',3'-O-isopropylidene adenosine-5' dibenzyl phosphate yielded adenosine-5' benzyl phosphate, the silver salt of which was treated with dibenzyl phosphorochloridate to give adenosine-5' tribenzyl pyrophosphate. Benzyl groups were then removed by catalytic hydrogenolysis and the resulting adenosine-5' pyrophosphate isolated as its acridinium complex. Extension of this method, making use of a quaternisation procedure[348] with N-methylmorpholine to remove one benzyl group from the fully esterified adenosine-5' pyrophosphate, yielded adenosine-5' triphosphate by further treatment of the silver salt of the pyrophosphate with dibenzyl phosphorochloridate followed by hydrogenolysis of benzyl groups.[349] When phenolic solvents were used partial debenzylation of the unstable fully esterified polyphosphates occurred, and to a large extent the preliminary removal of a benzyl group by quaternisation was then unnecessary. Because of this *in situ* phenolic debenzylation of the benzylated adenosine-5' tri-

A = Adenine

phosphate intermediate, disproportionation reactions were restricted, with consequent improvement in the yield of final product.

In an alternate synthesis of adenosine-5' triphosphate, the disilver salt of adenosine-5' phosphate was treated directly with excess of dibenzyl phosphorochloridate, followed by hydrogenolysis of the product.[350] The resulting triphosphate was identical with natural ATP and no evidence was obtained for the expected isomeric form, the absence of which was presumably due to formation of the cyclic trimetaphosphate (or a benzylated intermediate) followed by ring opening. Alternatively, partial debenzylation may have occurred during the initial condensation to give a diesterified pyrophosphate followed by further reaction with dibenzyl phosphorochloridate.

Since this early work, the introduction of a number of techniques has greatly facilitated the development of newer and more convenient methods of synthesis. Nevertheless, in spite of considerable inherent disadvantages the classical approach has had a fair degree of success, particularly when benzyl phosphorous diphenyl phosphoric anhydride was introduced as a mixed anhydride reagent for the synthesis of nucleoside benzyl phosphites.[351] As with dibenzyl phosphite these derivatives can be oxidised to the phosphorochloridate by the action of N-chlorosuccinimide.[352]

Treatment of 2′,3′-O-isopropylideneuridine-5′ benzyl phosphorochloridate with triethylammonium dibenzyl phosphate gave a product from which benzyl groups were removed by nucleophilic displacement with lithium chloride (or by treatment with phenol) followed by catalytic hydrogenolysis of remaining benzyl esters. Removal of the isopropylidene residue by mild acidic hydrolysis yielded uridine-5′ pyrophosphate.[352] In a similar fashion, the reaction of 2′,3′-O-isopropylideneuridine-5′ benzyl phosphorochloridate with triethylammonium tribenzyl pyrophosphate followed by removal of protecting groups gave uridine-5′ triphosphate.[353]

Since tetra-esters of pyrophosphates are particularly susceptible to a wide variety of exchange reactions by anionic attack,[354] yields in this type of reaction were considerably improved by treating the phosphorochloridate with the salt of a monoesterified phosphate to produce a tri-esterified pyrophosphate intermediate that, being ionised, was much more resistant to nucleophilic attack. Thus adenosine-5′, uridine-5′, and thymidine-5′ pyrophosphates were readily obtained in

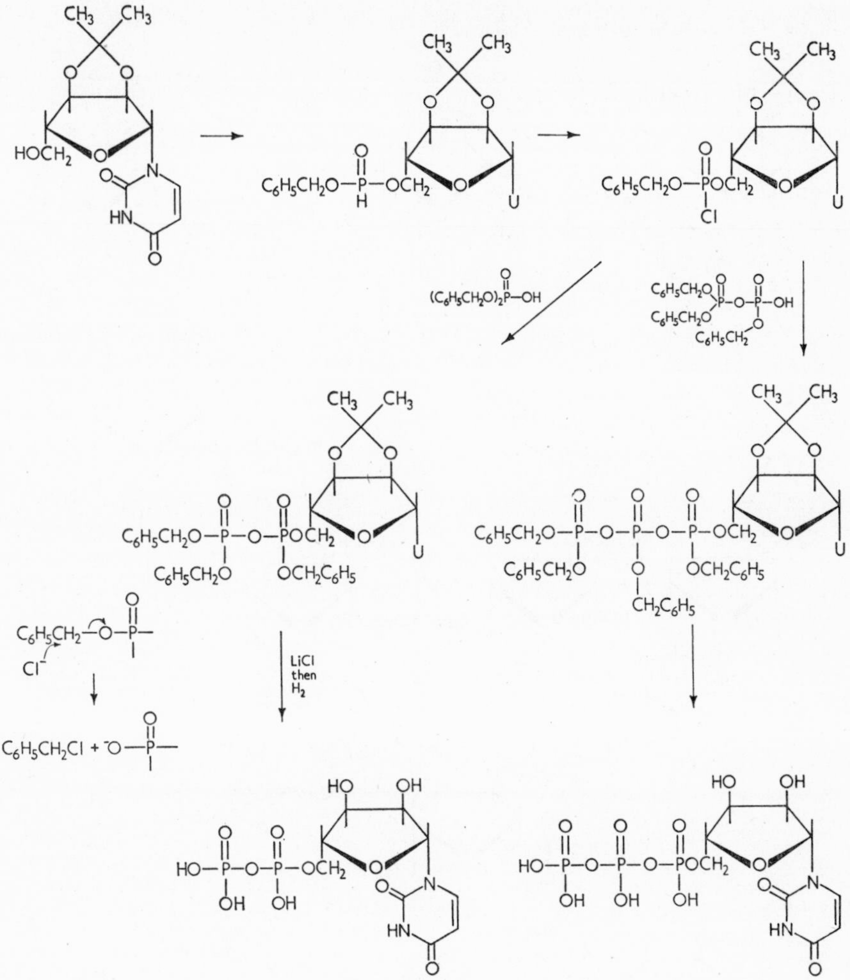

CH₃ CH₃

HOCH₂

$C_6H_5CH_2O-P-OCH_2$ ... U

$C_6H_5CH_2O-POCH_2$ ... U
Cl

$(C_6H_5CH_2O)_2P-OH$

$C_6H_5CH_2O$
$C_6H_5CH_2O$—P—O—P—OH
$C_6H_5CH_2$

$C_6H_5CH_2O-P-O-POCH_2$ ... U
$C_6H_5CH_2O$ $OCH_2C_6H_5$

$C_6H_5CH_2O-P-O-P-O-P-OCH_2$ ... U
$C_6H_5CH_2O$ $OCH_2C_6H_5$
$CH_2C_6H_5$

$C_6H_5CH_2-O-P-$
Cl

$C_6H_5CH_2Cl + O-P-$

LiCl
then
H₂

HO OH

$HO-P-O-P-OCH_2$ ... U
OH OH

HO OH

$HO-P-O-P-O-POCH_2$ ... U
OH OH OH

U = Uracil

very high yield when the tri-n-octylammonium nucleotide was treated with dibenzyl phosphorochloridate, followed by hydrogenolytic removal of benzyl groups from the product.[355] The method has also been used for the synthesis of 4-azauridine-5' pyrophosphate,[356] N^1-methyluridine-5' pyrophosphate,[357] and other nucleoside-5' pyrophosphates.[358] For solubility reasons, the methyl-tri-n-octylammonium salts of guanine and cytosine nucleotides are particularly useful in this type of reaction.[358] A similar treatment of uridine-2'(3'),5' diphosphate with dibenzyl phosphorochloridate followed by hydrogenolysis

N = Nucleoside-5' (ribo- or deoxyribo-)

Tr = Triphenylmethyl
T = Thymine

of the product yielded uridine-2',3' cyclic phosphate-5' pyrophosphate.[355]

The alternative approach, synthesis of the protected nucleoside-5' benzyl phosphorochloridate which is then condensed with benzyl dihydrogen phosphate, has been used for the preparation of thymidine-5' pyrophosphate. The reaction sequence was extended to the synthesis of thymidine-5' triphosphate by use of dibenzyl pyrophosphate.[359]

The first synthesis of a diesterified pyrophosphate coenzyme, that of flavin adenine dinucleotide, was also achieved by application of the

phosphorochloridate method. Apart from the usual technical difficulties, the problem was further complicated in this case by the presence of a vicinal hydroxyl group that could attack an intermediate esterified pyrophosphate (a mixed anhydride) to give riboflavin-4',5' cyclic phosphate.[360] Nevertheless, Christie, Kenner and Todd were able to prepare FAD by treating the monothallous salt of riboflavin-5' phosphate with 2',3'-O-isopropylideneadenosine-5' benzyl phosphorochloridate in phenol solution. Phenolic debenzylation of the product, followed by mild acidic hydrolysis to remove the isopropylidene residue, gave a complex mixture containing some 6% of the coenzyme from which pure FAD was isolated by chromatographic methods.[361]

    To some extent the rather low yield resulted from the hydrolytic conditions necessary for removal of protecting groups. Since uridine diphosphate glucose (UDPG) is less stable than FAD, ether benzyl groups (readily removed by hydrogenolysis) were used rather than the isopropylidene residue for nucleoside hydroxyl group protection. Solubility difficulties with respect to the α-D-glucose-1 phosphate moiety

Oct₃N = Tri-n-octylamine

    were circumvented by use of salts with long chain amines. Benzylation of 5'-O-trityluridine followed by removal of the trityl group gave 2',3'-di-O-benzyluridine which with O-benzyl phosphorous O-diphenyl phosphoric anhydride yielded 2',3'-di-O-benzyluridine-5' benzyl phosphite. Treatment of the phosphorochloridate with mono-(tri-n-octylammonium)-α-D-glucose-1 phosphate in benzene solution gave a product from which the pyrophosphate benzyl and ether benzyls were removed by catalytic hydrogenolysis to yield UDPG.[362] In a similar fashion, using α-D-galactose-1 phosphate, the first synthesis of uridine diphosphate galactose was achieved.[362]

A nucleoside phosphorochloridate intermediate has also been used to prepare mixed anhydrides of 2',3'-O-isopropylideneadenosine-5' benzyl phosphate and benzyloxycarbonyl amino acids (leucine and glycine).[363, 364] Reaction of the same intermediate with carboxyl-protected amino acids gave phosphoramidate derivatives from which

Z = Benzyloxycarbonyl

monoesterified phosphoramidates were obtained by hydrogenolytic removal of the benzyl group.

The undesirability of fully esterified pyrophosphate intermediates was demonstrated in the synthesis of P^1-adenosine-5' P^2-uridine-5' pyrophosphate from 2',3'-O-isopropylideneadenosine-5' benzyl phosphorochloridate and 2',3'-O-isopropylideneuridine-5' benzyl phosphate, or alternatively from the adenosine benzyl phosphate and the uridine phosphorochloridate. After removal of benzyl groups (by treatment with ammonium thiocyanate) and isopropylidene residues (by acidic hydrolysis), in both cases some symmetrical dinucleoside pyrophosphate was obtained.[365]

Although chloridates have been extensively employed for pyrophosphate synthesis, other nucleotide anhydrides, such as those with diphenyl phosphoric, toluene-p-sulphonic, or trifluoracetic acid may be used, subject to the limitation imposed by exchange reactions. Thus

N = Nucleoside–5′

treatment of a nucleoside-5' phosphate with trifluoracetic anhydride gives the P^1,P^2-dinucleoside-5' pyrophosphate, the intermediate mixed anhydride not being obtained.[366] However, nicotinamide adenine dinucleotide has been synthesised (together with the two symmetrical pyrophosphates) in low yield, by treating a mixture of adenosine-5' phosphate and nicotinamide nucleotide with trifluoracetic anhydride.[367] In the same way, flavin adenine dinucleotide and guanine, cytosine, uracil, and nicotinamide analogues were obtained from mixtures of riboflavin-5' phosphate and the nucleoside-5' phosphate.[368] To some

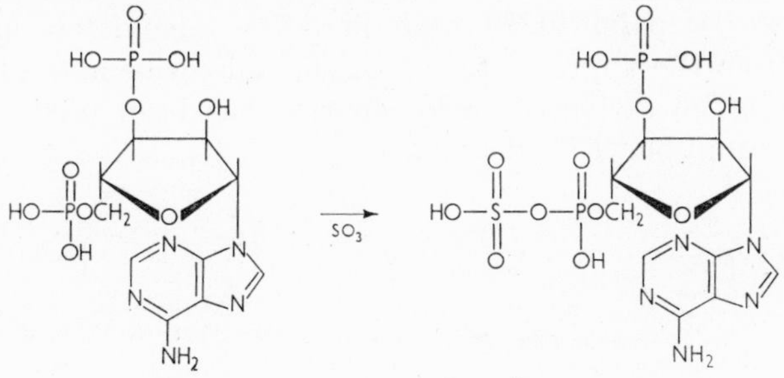

"Active sulphate"

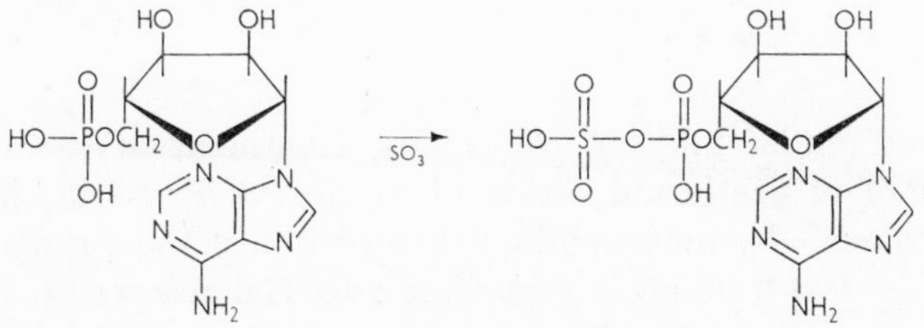

Adenylyl sulphate

extent trifluoracetic anhydride is a degradative reagent, being effective for the cleavage, as well as synthesis, of pyrophosphate linkages.[367]

Both adenyl-5'-yl sulphate (adenosine-5' sulphatophosphate) and adenosine-3' phosphate 5'-sulphatophosphate (" active sulphate ") have been obtained by treatment of the appropriate nucleotide with pyridine–sulphur trioxide in aqueous sodium bicarbonate.[369, 370] Treatment of adenosine-5' pyrophosphate with pyridine–sulphur trioxide gives adenosine-5' pyrophosphoryl sulphate in extremely low yield.[371]

ACYL ADENYLATES

Anhydrides of nucleoside-5' phosphates with carbonic acid esters have been prepared by the action of an alkyl chloroformate on the nucleotide in aqueous or anhydrous solution.[358] They are resistant to attack by rattlesnake venom. Under certain conditions the carbonate anhydride can be formed.[372]

A simple and effective method for the synthesis of mixed anhydrides of nucleoside-5' phosphates and carboxylic acids lies in the reaction of a nucleotide with the carboxylic acid anhydride. Thus treatment of riboflavin-5' phosphate with acetic anhydride in aqueous pyridine yielded acetyl riboflavin-5' phosphate, and from adenosine-5' phosphate the corresponding adenylyl acetate was obtained.[373, 374] In an analogous manner benzoyl,[375] propionyl,[376] butyryl,[377] hexanoyl,[378, 417] octanoyl,[378, 417] palmityl,[379] and lipoyl[380] adenylates have been prepared from the appropriate carboxylic anhydride and adenosine-5' phosphate. The carboxylic acid chloride has been used to prepare acetyl[374] and hippuryl[375] adenylates.

+ RCOO⁻

However, under limiting conditions, treatment of the nucleotide with 0·5 mol of acetic anhydride gives rise to P^1,P^2-di-adenosine-5' pyrophosphate[381] by nucleophilic displacement of the stronger acetate anion (pK ∼ 4·8) from an intermediate adenylyl acetate by adenosine-5' phosphate (pK ∼ 6·0). The degradative effective of trifluoroacetic anhydride has been mentioned previously; P^1,P^2-di-adenosine-5' pyrophosphate is also cleaved by acetic anhydride (by virtue of the additive properties of the carbonyl group), but is resistant to nucleophilic attack by acetate ion since this would involve liberation of a less stable anion.

Biochemical interest in fatty acid activation and transport has led mainly to the synthesis of acyl adenylates. The same methods are presumably applicable to the other nucleoside-5' phosphates.

CARBODI-IMIDES AND RELATED REAGENTS

Since the classical approach was of somewhat limited application, each coenzyme presenting a set of problems peculiar to its synthesis, more effective if less elegant methods were desirable. Earlier work had shown that carboxylic acid anhydrides could be obtained by treating the

aliphatic acid with substituted carbodi-imides.[382] The introduction of
this type of reagent, particularly dicyclohexylcarbodi-imide, to the
formation of pyrophosphates from phosphoric acid and its esters provided a relatively simple method for the synthesis of nucleotide
anhydrides.[383] Although some disadvantages are inherent in the method,
such as the lack of reproducibility of reported yields in certain cases[384]
and the formation of all three possible anhydrides from a given pair of
acids when the anions are comparable nucleophiles, the carbodi-imides
and related reagents have been successfully employed for the synthesis

$$C_6H_{11}-N=C=N-C_6H_{11} \quad + \quad \begin{array}{c} C_6H_5CH_2O \\ C_6H_5CH_2O \end{array}\!\!\!\!\overset{\displaystyle O}{\underset{}{P}}\!\!-OH$$

$$\downarrow$$

$$C_6H_{11}-\overset{+}{N}H=C=N-C_6H_{11}$$
$$\overset{O^-}{\underset{}{\big|}}\!\!-\overset{\displaystyle O}{\underset{}{P}}\!\!\overset{OCH_2C_6H_5}{\underset{OCH_2C_6H_5}{\big<}} \quad\longrightarrow\quad C_6H_{11}-NH-\overset{}{C}=N-C_6H_{11}$$
$$\overset{O}{\underset{}{\big|}}\overset{\displaystyle O}{\underset{}{P}}\!\!\overset{OCH_2C_6H_5}{\underset{OCH_2C_6H_5}{\big<}}$$

$$\begin{array}{c} C_6H_5CH_2O \\ C_6H_5CH_2O \end{array}\!\!\!\!\overset{\displaystyle O}{\underset{}{P}}\!\!-OH$$

$$C_6H_{11}-NH-\overset{}{C}=NH-C_6H_{11}$$
$$\overset{O}{\underset{}{\big|}}\overset{\displaystyle O}{\underset{}{P}}\!\!\overset{OCH_2C_6H_5}{\underset{OCH_2C_6H_5}{\big<}}$$
$$\begin{array}{c} C_6H_5CH_2O \\ C_6H_5CH_2O \end{array}\!\!\!\!\overset{\displaystyle O}{\underset{}{P}}\!\!-O$$

$$\downarrow$$

$$\begin{array}{c} C_6H_5CH_2O \\ C_6H_5CH_2O \end{array}\!\!\!\!\overset{\displaystyle O}{\underset{}{P}}\!\!-O-\overset{\displaystyle O}{\underset{}{P}}\!\!\overset{OCH_2C_6H_5}{\underset{OCH_2C_6H_5}{\big<}} \quad + \quad C_6H_{11}NHCONHC_6H_{11}$$

of a large number of nucleotide derivatives. When the coenzyme or
anhydride contains a *cis* hydroxyl group adjacent to the pyrophosphate
linkage (e.g. flavin adenine dinucleotide, uridine diphosphate glucose)
yields are very low because of cyclic phosphate formation.[385, 386]
However, reasonable yields can be obtained in general by using appropriate reaction conditions.

Treatment of dibenzyl phosphoric acid with dicyclohexylcarbodi-
imide in anhydrous media rapidly gave tetrabenzyl pyrophosphate, with
concomitant formation of dicyclohexylurea.[383]

Various analogous pyrophosphates, including P^1,P^2-diphenyl pyrophosphate, were prepared with the same reagent, and it was found that
while use of anhydrous media led to superior yields, the presence of

water did not interfere too seriously with the reaction provided an excess of the carbodi-imide was used.[383] Application to nucleotides showed that P^1,P^2-diuridine-5′ pyrophosphate could be obtained from pyridinium uridine-5′ phosphate and dicyclohexylcarbodi-imide in pyridine.[366] Nucleoside-5′ polyphosphates were synthesised in similar fashion by condensation of phosphoric acid with the mononucleotides, though in this case the procedure gave complex mixtures, the composition of which could be controlled to some extent by variation of the ratio of reactants and experimental conditions. Again, anhydrous media were not essential, but when water was present (for solubility reasons) a massive excess of the carbodi-imide was necessary, and it was found preferable to use anhydrous pyridine solutions of the tri-n-butylammonium nucleotides.[387] The generality of the method was demonstrated by the synthesis of pyrophosphates and triphosphates

N = Nucleoside-5′

(separated by ion exchange chromatography) of all the major natural nucleosides, as well as of analogues such as 8-azaguanosine.[388]

As applied to the synthesis of certain unsymmetrical diesterified pyrophosphates, the method has proved quite successful. Thus the reaction of dicyclohexylcarbodi-imide with a mixture of N-D-ribofuranosylnicotinamide-5′ phosphate and adenosine-5′ phosphate in aqueous pyridine yielded nicotinamide adenine dinucleotide (NAD) as the major product, with rather less diadenosine-5′ pyrophosphate and very little of the P^1,P^2-di(nicotinamide nucleoside-5′) pyrophosphate.[389] Ion exchange chromatography gave crude NAD consisting mainly of the active β-form, together with some of the α-anomer. The β-form was reduced by a yeast alcohol-dehydrogenase system to the alkali-stable dihydro derivative and the unchanged quaternary α-isomer destroyed by treatment with alkali. Re-oxidation of the unaffected dihydro compound gave the pure β-form of nicotinamide adenine dinucleotide identical with the natural coenzyme. A similar process, replacing adenosine-5′ phosphate by a mixture of the -2′,5′ and -3′,5′ diphosphates of adenosine gave nicotinamide adenine di-

nucleotide-2′ phosphate (NADP, coenzyme II) together with the isomeric unnatural form containing a -3′ phosphate group in the adenosine
moiety.[389]

The action of dicyclohexylcarbodi-imide on a mixture of choline
phosphate and cytidine-5′ phosphate gave cytidine diphosphate choline
in low yield, together with P^1,P^2-dicytidine pyrophosphate, but not
P^1,P^2-dicholine pyrophosphate.[390]   As in the case of nicotinamide
nucleotide, it is likely that because of the dipolar character of choline

phosphate the anion is a weaker nucleophile than cytidine-5' phosphate (or adenosine-5' phosphate), and hence the initial addition of phosphate to the carbodi-imide occurs preferentially by the pyrimidine (or purine) nucleotide, followed by a less specific nucleophilic attack on the adduct by either of the two anions.[391]

Analogous adenosine, guanosine, and uridine diphosphate cholines,[390] as well as intermediates involved in lipid metabolism such

as cytidine diphosphate ethanolamine[390] and cytidine diphosphate diglycerides,[392] (CDP dipalmitin and CDP dilaurin) have been prepared by the same method. For the synthesis of cytidine diphosphate glycerol, protection of the glycerol residue was necessary to avoid cyclisation. Pyrophosphate formation from cytidine-5' phosphate and 1,2-O-isopropylidene-L-glycerol-3 phosphate by the action of dicyclohexylcarbodi-imide followed by removal of the isopropylidene residue gave cytidine diphosphate glycerol.[393]

In the case of cytidine diphosphate ribitol, polyol protection was unnecessary as the synthetic route exploited pyrophosphate formation from cytidine-5' phosphate and D-ribofuranose-5 phosphate (using approximately 10^2 molar excess of dicyclohexylcarbodi-imide) followed by reduction of the resultant cytidine diphosphate ribose with sodium borohydride.[394]

Other applications of dicyclohexylcarbodi-imide include the synthesis of adenosine-5' sulphatophosphate[395] (sulphate esterification of sugar hydroxyl groups further complicates the mixture), and luciferyl and oxyluciferyl adenylates (intermediates in the glow of fireflies).[396] Treatment of a mixture of dehydroepiandrosterone phosphate and adenosine-5' pyrophosphate with the reagent gave a P^1-adenosine-5' P^3-steroid triphosphate derivative.[397, 398]

AMINO ACYL ADENYLATES

Mixed anhydrides of amino acids and adenosine-5' phosphate (and presumably of other nucleoside and deoxynucleoside-5' phosphates) can be prepared by treating a mixture of the nucleotide and free amino acid with dicyclohexylcarbodi-imide in aqueous pyridine.[399] Considerably higher yields are obtained by use of N-benzyloxycarbonyl amino acids, followed by removal of the protecting group from the product by hydrogenation.[400, 401] An alternative procedure uses benzylmercaptoformyl amino acids, the free acyl adenylate being obtained by perbenzoic acid oxidation of the protected intermediate.[402]

Since the nucleophilic characters of benzyloxycarbonylamino acids and nucleotides are greatly dissimilar, fairly high yields of the mixed anhydrides are obtained, with negligible formation of the dinucleoside pyrophosphate. Presumably the amino acid (i.e. the stronger nucleophile) forms the initial adduct which is then attacked by nucleotide anion to give the anhydride.[403] Attack by carboxylate would give the benzyloxycarbonylamino acid anhydride which would then react rapidly with nucleotide (or any dinucleoside-5' pyrophosphate) to yield likewise the mixed anhydride.

Direct extension of the method to the synthesis of mixed anhydrides of peptides and nucleotides is not entirely satisfactory, but dicyclohexylcarbodi-imide has been used for the preparation in low yield of leucylglycyl adenylate,[404] glycyl-L-leucyl adenylate,[405] glycylglycyl adenylate,[405] and L-arginyl-L-alanyl-L-arginyl-L-alanyl uridyl-5'-ate[406] from the nucleotide and appropriate peptide.

Fatty acid anhydrides of adenosine-5' phosphate have also been obtained by means of this reagent. In view of the reaction conditions employed it is likely that the initial step involves *in situ* formation of the di-acyl anhydride, which then reacts with the nucleotide.[407, 418]

$$R\!-\!\underset{\underset{NHZ}{|}}{CH}COOH \; + \; HO\!-\!\underset{\underset{OH}{\|}}{\overset{O}{P}}OCH_2 \qquad \xrightarrow{\;R'-N=C=N-R'\;} \qquad R\!-\!\underset{\underset{NHZ}{|}}{CH}COO\!-\!\underset{\underset{OH}{\|}}{\overset{O}{P}}OCH_2$$

$$Z = \text{Benzyloxycarbonyl}$$
$$N = \text{Nucleoside-5'}$$

$$\underset{R\!-\!\underset{\underset{O^-}{|}}{\overset{+}{C}H}\!-\!NH_3}{COO\!-\!\overset{O}{\underset{}{P}}OCH_2}$$

$$R\!-\!\underset{\underset{NHZ}{|}}{CH}\!-\!COOH \; + \; R'N=C=NR' \longrightarrow \underset{\underset{\underset{\underset{NHZ}{|}}{R}}{OCO\,CH}}{R'NH\!-\!C\!=\!NR'}$$

$$N\!-\!O\!-\!\underset{\underset{OH}{\|}}{\overset{O}{P}}\!-\!O\!-\!\underset{\underset{NHZ}{|}}{CO}CHR$$

$$N\!-\!O\!-\!\overset{O}{\underset{OH}{P}}\!-\!OH$$

$$R\!-\!\underset{\underset{NHZ}{|}}{CH}CO\!-\!O\!-\!\underset{\underset{NHZ}{|}}{CO}CH\!-\!R$$

RELATED REAGENTS

Other carbodi-imides examined, including di-p-tolylcarbodi-imide, have generally proved less satisfactory than dicyclohexylcarbodi-imide; acyl ureas are occasionally obtained. As indicated in the mechanism sequence,[391] the reaction of an acid with a carbodi-imide is dependent on the basicity of the carbodi-imide and the nucleophilicity of the acid. The presence and nature of bases in the reaction medium is also of some consequence with respect to competition between the carbodi-imide and such bases for protons. To some extent, the nature of the solvent will also influence the rate of reaction.

Except in special instances where the two acids possess grossly disparate nucleophilic character, carbodi-imides have proved to be non-specific for the synthesis of unsymmetrical pyrophosphate esters. Attempts to remedy this by isolation of the intermediate phosphate adduct, so that nucleophilic attack by a specific second anion could

$$RN{=}C{=}NR' + H^+ \ \longleftrightarrow \ R'\overset{+}{H}N{=}C{=}NR'$$

$$R'\overset{+}{HN}{=}\overset{\cdot\cdot}{C}{=}NR' \longrightarrow R'HN{-}\underset{\underset{OX}{|}}{C}{=}NR'$$

$$R'HN{-}\underset{\underset{OX}{|}}{C}{=}NR' + H^+ \longleftrightarrow R'HN{-}\underset{\underset{OX}{|}}{C}{=}\overset{+}{N}HR'$$

$$R'HN{-}C{\overset{\cdot\cdot}{=}}\overset{+}{N}HR' \longrightarrow \ \begin{array}{c} R'HN{-}CO{-}NHR' \\ + \\ XOZ \end{array}$$

$$R'HN{-}C{=}NR' \longrightarrow R'HN{-}\underset{\underset{COR}{|}}{\overset{\overset{O}{\|}}{C}}{-}NR'$$

XO^- and ZO^- = Phosphate or carboxylate anions

hen occur have not met with success. However, in the course of these attempts a number of reagents related to carbodi-imides have been leveloped. These show a varying performance compared with dicyclo-hexylcarbodi-imide, depending on the substrates used.

Like the initial phosphate adduct from carbodi-imides, imidoyl phosphates undergo phosphorolysis. Reaction of N-s-alkyl (or N-

phenyl) benzimidoyl chlorides with salts of dibenzyl phosphate yielded the benzimidoyl phosphate which on treatment with diphenyl or dibenzyl phosphate yielded the corresponding pyrophosphate.[408] Although dialkyl phosphates reacted readily with ketene imines (such as diphenylketene-*p*-tolylimine) to give tetra-alkyl pyrophosphates, the intermediate imidoyl phosphate could not be isolated.[408]

In an alternative approach to imidoyl phosphates, anion exchange during Beckmann re-arrangement of an oxime *p*-nitrobenzenesulphonate in the presence of tetra-n-butylammonium 2′,3′-*O*-isopropylidene-uridine-5′ benzyl phosphate gave an imidoyl phosphate intermediate and this on treatment with dibenzyl phosphate in benzene gave uridine-5′ pyrophosphate after removal of protecting groups.[409] However, in a polar solvent such as nitromethane the major product was P^1,P^2-di-uridine-5′ pyrophosphate as a result of exchange reactions.

Treatment of adenosine-5' phosphate with cyclopentanone oxime p-nitrobenzenesulphonate and benzyl phosphate in dimethylformamide gave P^1-benzyl P^2-adenosine-5' pyrophosphate (from which ADP was obtained by hydrogenolysis) together with the two symmetrical pyrophosphates. The same reagent with adenosine-5' phosphate and excess of phosphoric acid yielded adenosine-5' triphosphate.[409]

Cyanamide and dialkylcyanamides have also been used as reagents

for pyrophosphate synthesis.[365] Thus P^1-adenosine-5' P^2-uridine-5' pyrophosphate was prepared by the action of dimethylcyanamide on a mixture of the two nucleotides; as with carbodi-imides all three possible pyrophosphates were formed. Similarly, when cytidine-5' phosphate was heated with benzyl phosphate in aqueous dimethylcyanamide and the product debenzylated, cytidine-5' pyrophosphate was obtained.[365]

Other reagents such as trichloracetonitrile[410, 464] and cyanuric chloride[411] have also been examined.

PHOSPHORAMIDATES

Apart from low specificity when applied to the synthesis of pyrophosphate anhydrides, the carbodi-imide method is of limited value for the synthesis of coenzymes such as flavin adenine dinucleotide, uridine diphosphate glucose, or coenzyme A owing to cyclisation and other undesirable reactions. However, relatively efficient syntheses of a number of coenzymes of this type (including those mentioned) have been achieved, using nucleoside-5' phosphoramidates.

Whereas the di-anion of phosphoramidic acid[412] is quite stable, the monoprotonated anion is readily hydrolysed to orthophosphoric acid, the electrophilic character of the phosphorus atom being greatly increased by the adjacent positive nitrogen. Reaction of phosphate anion with a phosphoramidate zwitterion gives the pyrophosphate linkage,[413, 414] but with such simple derivatives, reactivity is rather low. However, the N-substituted phosphoramidates are more reactive, and indeed N-phosphoryl derivatives of imidazole can be used for phosphorylation of amines and alcoholic hydroxyl groups, as well as anions.[415, 416] Since pyrophosphate formation is obtained in the presence of bases, the phosphoramidate nitrogen is presumably sufficiently basic to compete for protons.

Treatment of adenosine-5' phosphate with triethylammonium phosphoramidate gave a mixture of adenosine-5' pyrophosphate, the triphosphate, and higher adenosine-5' polyphosphates, in addition to unreacted nucleotide.[414] In a more controlled approach, the reaction of benzyl hydrogen phosphoramidate with uridine-5' phosphate gave P^1-benzyl P^2-uridine-5' pyrophosphate; the same reagent with pyridinium adenosine-5' phosphate gave adenosine-5' pyrophosphate after removal of the benzyl group from the product.[413] Further reaction of adenosine-5' pyrophosphate with benzyl hydrogen N-cyclohexylphosphoramidate gave the nucleoside triphosphate monobenzyl ester, from which adenosine-5' triphosphate was obtained in high yield. In this case, small amounts of higher adenosine polyphosphates were also produced.[413] The same approach (using benzyl hydrogen phosphoramidate) has been used for the synthesis of guanosine-5' pyrophosphate,[419] and the 5'-pyrophosphates and 5'-triphosphates of 5-hydroxymethyl-2'-deoxycytidine and its 5-glucosidic derivative, from the corresponding nucleoside-5' phosphates.[420]

Nucleoside-5' phosphoramidates are of greater general utility than the alkyl derivatives so far described. Initially, adenosine-5' phosphoramidate was prepared by reaction between 2',3'-di-O-acetyl-adenosine and phenyl phosphorodichloridate to give the nucleoside-5' phenyl phosphorochloridate; this on treatment with ammonia gave the

$$
\begin{array}{c}
\text{H}_3\overset{+}{\text{N}}-\overset{\overset{\displaystyle O}{\|}}{\text{P}}-\text{O}^- \\
\text{OH}
\end{array}
\quad\cdots\quad
A-O-\overset{\overset{\displaystyle O}{\|}}{\underset{OH}{P}}-O-\overset{\overset{\displaystyle O}{\|}}{\underset{OH}{P}}-O^- \quad NH_4^+
$$

$$
\begin{array}{c}
\text{H}_3\overset{+}{\text{N}}-\overset{\overset{\displaystyle O}{\|}}{\text{P}}-\text{O}^- \\
\text{OH}
\end{array}
\quad\cdots\quad
A-O-\overset{\overset{\displaystyle O}{\|}}{\underset{OH}{P}}-O-\overset{\overset{\displaystyle O}{\|}}{\underset{OH}{P}}-O-\overset{\overset{\displaystyle O}{\|}}{\underset{OH}{P}}-O^- \quad NH_4^+
$$

$$
\begin{array}{c}
\text{H}_3\overset{+}{\text{N}}-\overset{\overset{\displaystyle O}{\|}}{\text{P}}-\text{O}^- \\
\text{OCH}_2\text{C}_6\text{H}_5
\end{array}
\quad\cdots\quad
A-O-\overset{O}{\underset{OH}{P}}-O-\overset{O}{\underset{O^- NH_4^+}{P}}-OCH_2C_6H_5 \quad\longrightarrow\quad A-O-\overset{O}{\underset{OH}{P}}-O-\overset{O}{\underset{OH}{P}}-OH
$$

$$
\begin{array}{c}
\text{C}_6\text{H}_{11}\overset{+}{\text{NH}}_2-\overset{\overset{\displaystyle O}{\|}}{\text{P}}-\text{O}^- \\
\text{OCH}_2\text{C}_6\text{H}_5
\end{array}
\quad\cdots\quad
A-O-\overset{O}{\underset{OH}{P}}-O-\overset{O}{\underset{OH}{P}}-O-\overset{O}{\underset{O^- C_6H_{11}\overset{+}{N}H_3}{P}}-OCH_2C_6H_5
$$

$$
A-O-\overset{O}{\underset{OH}{P}}-O-\overset{O}{\underset{OH}{P}}-O-\overset{O}{\underset{OH}{P}}-OH
$$

A = Adenosine–5'

phosphoramidate, from which protecting groups were removed by alkaline hydrolysis.[414]

More conveniently, the nucleoside-5' phosphoramidates can be obtained directly as dicyclohexylguanidinium (or ammonium) salts from the nucleotide and ammonia by the action of dicyclohexylcarbodimide. In this way, the 5'-phosphoramidates of adenosine, cytidine, guanosine and uridine have been prepared. The generally more reactive N-substituted phosphoramidates (such as the nucleoside-5′ phosphoromorpholidates and phosphoroimidazoles) are obtained by use of the appropriate base.[421]

The method has been used for syntheses of nucleoside-5′ pyrophosphates (by treating the nucleoside-5′ phosphoramidate with phenyl phosphoric acid, phosphoric acid,[414, 422] or dioxan diphosphoric acid),[423, 424] and for diesterified pyrophosphates such as uridine diphosphate α-D-glucose,[425] (and of the β-D-glucose analogue),[426]

N = Nucleoside − 5′

N^1-methyluridine diphosphate glucose,[427] uridine diphosphate glucuronic acid,[428] and (in low yield) guanosine diphosphate mannose,[429] and guanosine diphosphate glucose[430] from the appropriate nucleoside phosphoramidate (or N-substituted phosphoramidate) and sugar phosphate. Similarly, the reaction of dicyclohexylguanidinium adenosine-5′ phosphoramidate with riboflavin-5′ phosphate gave flavin adenine dinucleotide.[425] Unsubstituted nucleoside-5′ phosphoramidates have also been applied to the synthesis of nucleoside-5′ triphosphates by reaction with inorganic pyrophosphate.[431, 432]

Improved yields of nucleoside-5′ pyrophosphates were obtained by

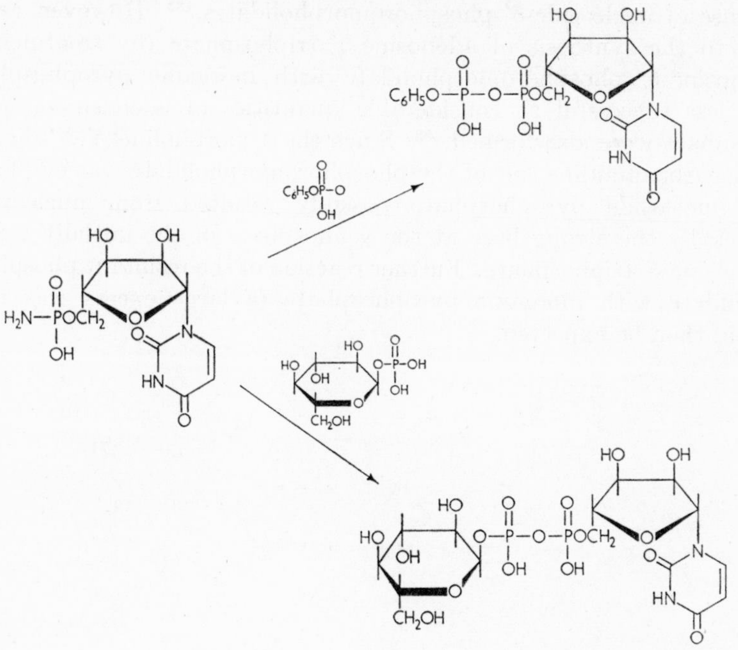

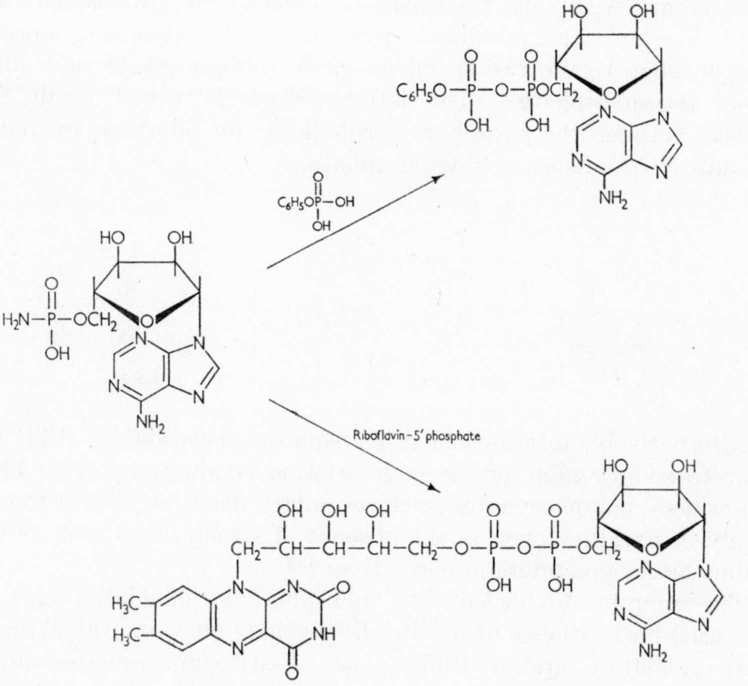
Riboflavin-5′ phosphate

the use of nucleoside-5′ phosphoromorpholidates.[433] However, extension to the synthesis of adenosine-5′ triphosphate (by treatment of adenosine-5′ phosphoromorpholidate with inorganic pyrophosphate) was less successful as considerable quantities of adenosine-5′ pyrophosphate were also formed.[433] Since the 4-morpholine N,N'-dicyclohexylcarboxamidine salt of the phosphoromorpholidate was employed, the nucleoside pyrophosphate possibly resulted from nucleophilic attack by the strong base at the γ phosphate of the initially formed adenosine-5′ triphosphate. Further reaction of the resultant phosphoroguanidate with inorganic pyrophosphate (a large excess was used) would then be expected.

In accord with this, treatment of adenosine-5′ triphosphate with morpholine and the guanidine in pyridine (in the absence of inorganic pyrophosphate) gave rise to adenosine-5′ pyrophosphate and adenosine-5′ tetraphosphate. The latter anhydride would result from reaction between the phosphoromorpholidate (or phosphoroguanidate) and unreacted adenosine-5′ triphosphate.

Alternatively, intermolecular transphosphorylation by ATP may occur to some extent under such reaction conditions. With higher adenosine-5′ polyphosphates, such secondary reactions appear to occur readily in pyridine, even in the absence of strong bases such as morpholine or the guanidinium derivatives.[358]

The appropriate nucleoside-5′ phosphoromorpholidates have also been used for syntheses of uridine diphosphate glucose, uridine diphosphate galactose, uridine diphosphate N-acetylglucosamine, uridine diphosphate glucuronic acid, cytidine diphosphate glycerol, and guanosine diphosphate mannose in satisfactory yields,[434] and for the preparation of cytidine diphosphate diglyceride in rather low yield.[435]

The capacity of the method was demonstrated by syntheses of

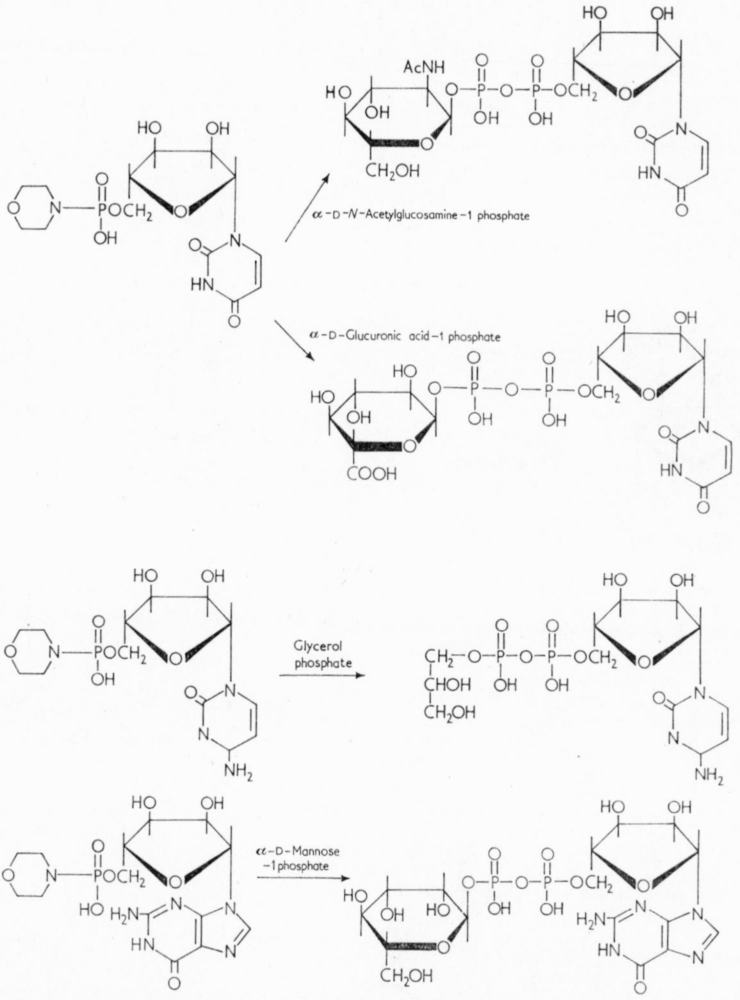

α-D-N-Acetylglucosamine-1 phosphate

α-D-Glucuronic acid-1 phosphate

Glycerol phosphate

α-D-Mannose -1 phosphate

3'-dephospho-coenzyme A and coenzyme A. Reaction between DL-pantetheine-4' phosphate and adenosine-5' phosphoromorpholidate gave dephospho-coenzyme A (containing a racemic pantetheine moiety). Similarly, treatment of D-pantetheine-4' phosphate with adenosine-(2',3' cyclic phosphate)-5' phosphoromorpholidate, obtained by the action of morpholine and dicyclohexylcarbodi-imide on

Coenzyme A

iso Coenzyme A

adenosine-2'(3'),5' diphosphate, gave a product that on treatment with dilute acid to open the cyclic phosphate group yielded a mixture of coenzyme A and iso-coenzyme A (possessing a -2' phosphate in the adenosine moiety instead of the -3' phosphate). A somewhat laborious separation of the two isomers on cellulose ion exchange columns gave coenzyme A in approximately 15% yield.[436]

Other applications include the synthesis of P^1-adenosine-5' P^2-dehydroepiandrosterone pyrophosphate, P^1-adenosine-5' P^2-5-pregnenolone pyrophosphate, and P^1-adenosine-5' P^2-17a-hydroxy-5-pregnenolone pyrophosphate from dicyclohexylguanidinium adenosine-5' phosphoramidate and a ten molar excess of the steroid phosphate.[397, 398] Syntheses of P^1-adenosine-5' P^2-DL-cobinamide pyrophosphate and the corresponding guanosine derivative have also been described.[476]

ANION EXCHANGE

Anion exchange reactions using fully esterified anhydride intermediates have not been generally successful when applied to the synthesis of pyrophosphate coenzymes owing to the high reactivity of all the intermediates. This results in further exchange reactions to give the most stable anhydride, usually a symmetrical pyrophosphate, while formation of cyclic phosphate occurs when a suitably located unprotected hydroxyl group is present. Thus treatment of 2',3'-O-isopropylideneuridine-5' benzyl phosphate with tetraphenyl pyrophosphate gave P^1,P^2-di(uridine-5') pyrophosphate after removal of protecting groups, the intermediate P^1-diphenyl P^2-benzyl P^2-uridine-5' pyrophosphate having undergone further reaction.[366] However, when an unprotected ionisable phosphoryl group is present in the anhydride the ease of nucleophilic attack is considerably reduced, and under suitable conditions quantitative yields of P^1-diphenyl P^2-nucleoside-5' pyrophosphates are obtained by treatment of nucleoside-5' phosphates with tetraphenyl pyrophosphate.[355]

Although such triesterified pyrophosphate derivatives are relatively stable in dioxan (in the presence of hindered tertiary bases such as tri-n-butylamine), when dissolved in pyridine they are rapidly attacked by a wide variety of anions of acids weaker than diphenyl phosphoric acid. Since diphenyl phosphoric acid is a considerably stronger acid than are the nucleotides, displacement of the more stable anion by a nucleophile such as phosphoric acid or glucose-1 phosphate results in the formation of a new nucleotide anhydride. This, particularly when two or more dissociating groups are present in the molecule, is then resistant to further nucleophilic displacement. Unlike the previously mentioned synthesis of pyrophosphate coenzymes by the action of trifluoroacetic anhydride on a mixture of the component phosphates (p. 203), this approach allows a considerable measure of control and selectivity to be exerted, with consequent high yields of the desired product. Essentially, the nucleotide moiety is converted into the diphenyl nucleoside pyrophosphate by treatment with diphenyl phosphorochloridate and tri-n-butylamine in dioxan. Addition of a solution of the second component in pyridine then gives the final anhydride, reaction occurring rapidly at room temperature.[437]

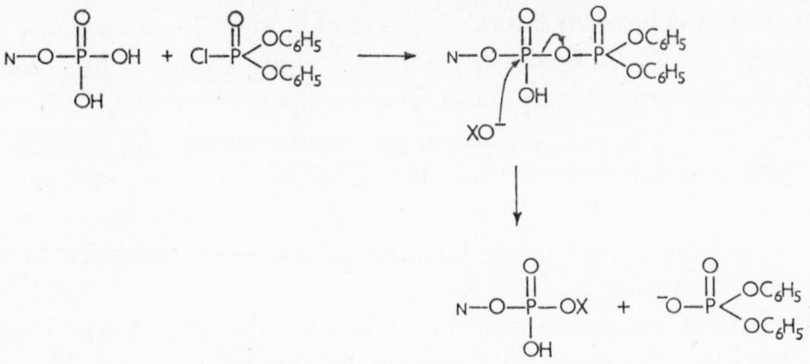

N = nucleoside-5'

⁻OX = phosphates, inorganic sulphate or carboxylates

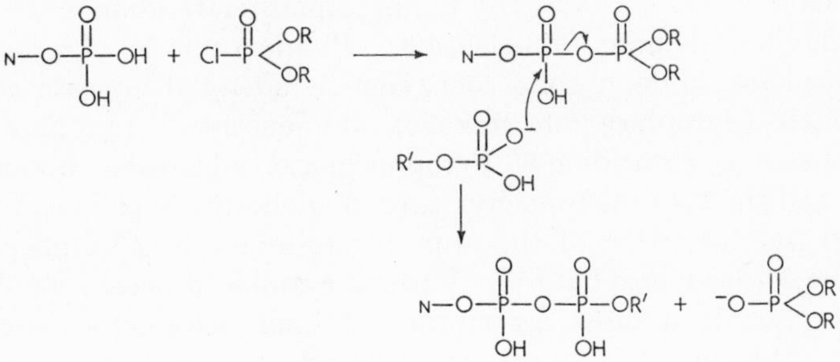

R = alkyl or aryl

R' = alkyl, aryl, phosphate or polyphosphate

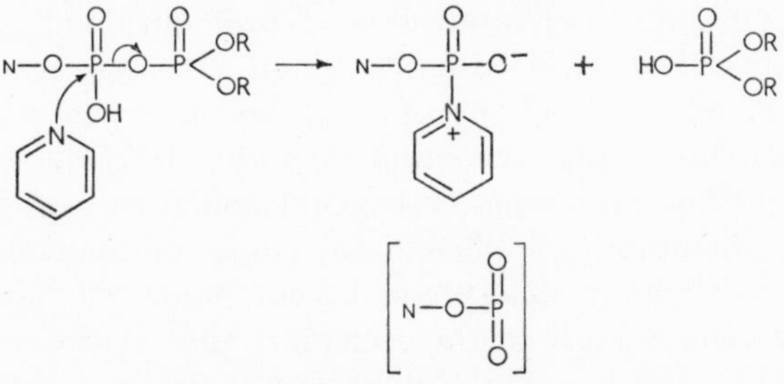

The method is general, simple in operation, gives extremely high yields (thus simplifying purification procedures), and avoids the necessity for protecting groups, or the preparation and purification of elaborate intermediates such as nucleoside-5' phosphoromorpholidates. Although represented as rear displacement of diphenyl phosphate anion by attack of the nucleophile at the nucleotide phosphorus atom,

H*

an alternate mechanism involving a nucleoside-5' monomeric metaphosphate (or more likely the pyridinium complex) may be considered. Similar results would be expected from both mechanisms. Unlike other procedures, no solubility problems are encountered. In general, tri-n-octylammonium salts of the mononucleotides are used, except that in the case of cytosine derivatives the methyl-tri-n-octylammonium salt of the nucleotide is preferable because of greater solubility in dioxan and dimethylformamide.

The scope of the reaction is indicated by the wide range of nucleotide anhydrides prepared. Treatment of the appropriate P^1-diphenyl P^2-nucleoside-5' pyrophosphate with α-D-glucose-1 phosphate gave uridine diphosphate glucose, adenosine diphosphate glucose, guanosine diphosphate glucose, cytidine diphosphate glucose, deoxycytidine diphosphate glucose,[438] and thymidine diphosphate glucose.[255] Similarly, flavin adenine dinucleotide, P^1-adenosine-5' P^2-glycerol-2 pyrophosphate, 3'-dephospho coenzyme A, adenylyl glyceric acid-2,3 diphosphate (pyrophosphate linkage), di-adenosine-5' pyrophosphate, P^1-adenosine-5' P^2-uridine-5' pyrophosphate, adenosine diphosphate phenol, and the 2,4-dinitrophenyl ester of adenosine-5' phosphate, were obtained by the action of the appropriate anion on P^1-diphenyl P^2-adenosine-5' pyrophosphate.[438] Various cytidine diphosphate derivatives of possible interest for studies of lipid metabolism, including cytidine diphosphate inositol, CDP-serine, -ethanolamine, -methylaminoethanol, -dimethylaminoethanol, and -choline were readily prepared in good yield by this approach.[439] Displacement of diphenyl phosphate from the appropriate nucleoside diphenyl pyrophosphate by phosphoric acid gave the 5'-pyrophosphates of cytidine, adenosine, guanosine, thymidine, 5-chlorouridine, 5-bromouridine, and 5-iodouridine,[440] in excellent yield. Similar anion exchange reactions with P^1-diphenyl P^2-adenosine-5' pyrophosphate using inorganic pyrophosphoric, triphosphoric, trimetaphosphoric, tetrametaphosphoric, polyphosphoric,[439] phosphorous or hypophosphorous acid yielded the corresponding adenosine polyphosphates (some of them unstable).[358] Displacement of diphenyl phosphate by inorganic sulphate was also possible despite the low pK of the secondary dissociation of sulphuric acid, and in this way adenylyl sulphate and uridylyl sulphate were readily prepared.

Treatment of P^1-diphenyl P^2-uridine-5' pyrophosphate with α-D-glucuronic acid-1 phosphate gave an excellent yield (86% of isolated pure material) of uridine diphosphate glucuronic acid.[441] It may be noted that in this case as with the glyceric acid-2,3 diphosphate anhydride, two kinds of anion are present in the displacing molecule, glucuronic acid-1 phosphate. Since the carboxyl group has a pK of

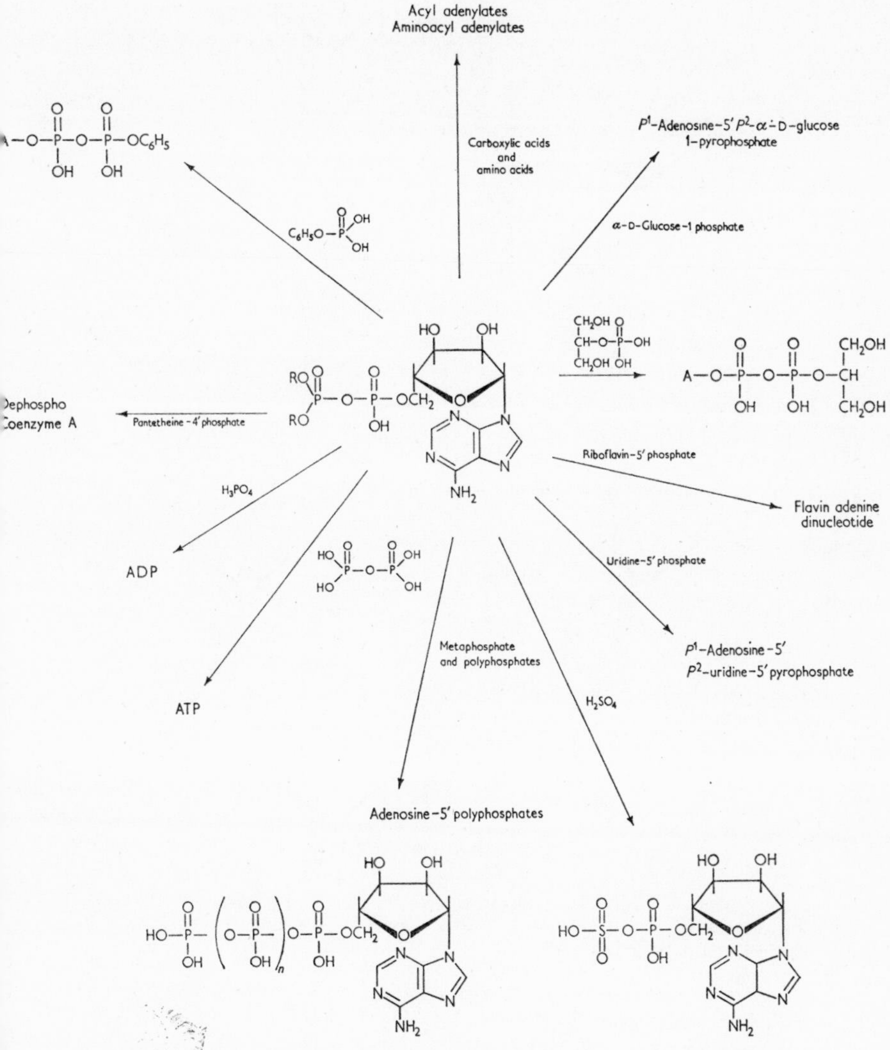

Acyl adenylates
Aminoacyl adenylates

P^1-Adenosine-5' P^2-α-D-glucose
1-pyrophosphate

Carboxylic acids
and
amino acids

α-D-Glucose-1 phosphate

C_6H_5O-P OH OH

A$-O-P-O-P-OC_6H_5$

Dephospho
Coenzyme A

Pantetheine - 4' phosphate

Riboflavin-5' phosphate

Flavin adenine
dinucleotide

H_3PO_4

ADP

$HO-P-O-P-OH$

Uridine-5' phosphate

P^1-Adenosine-5'
P^2-uridine-5' pyrophosphate

ATP

Metaphosphate
and polyphosphates

H_2SO_4

Adenosine-5' polyphosphates

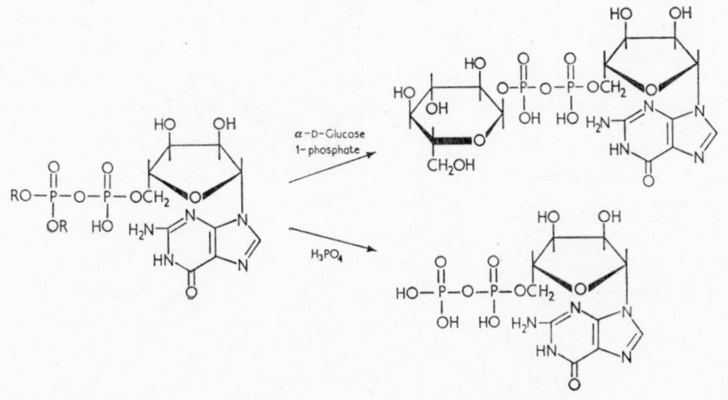

α-D-Glucose
1-phosphate

H_3PO_4

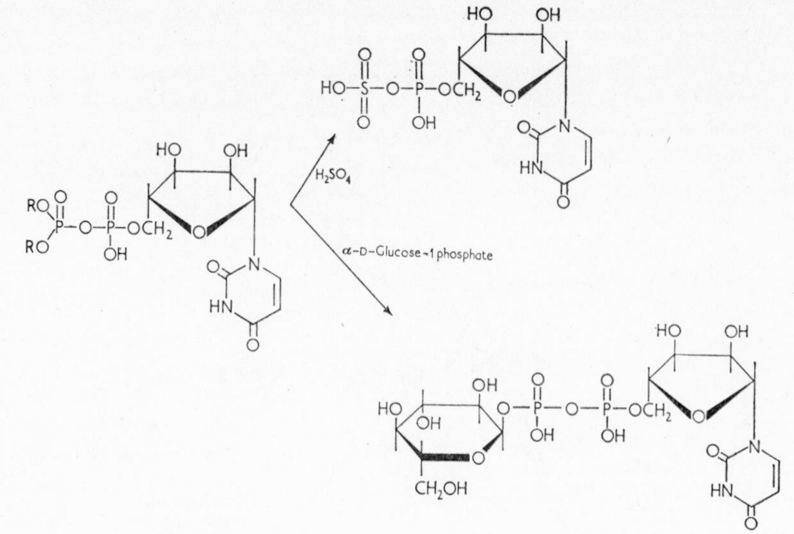
H_2SO_4
α-D-Glucose-1 phosphate

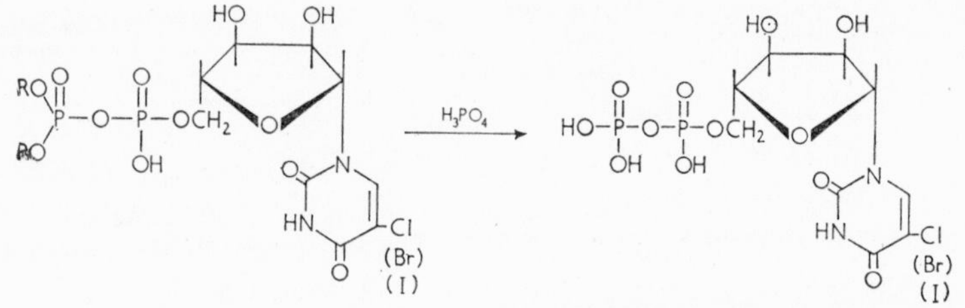
H_3PO_4

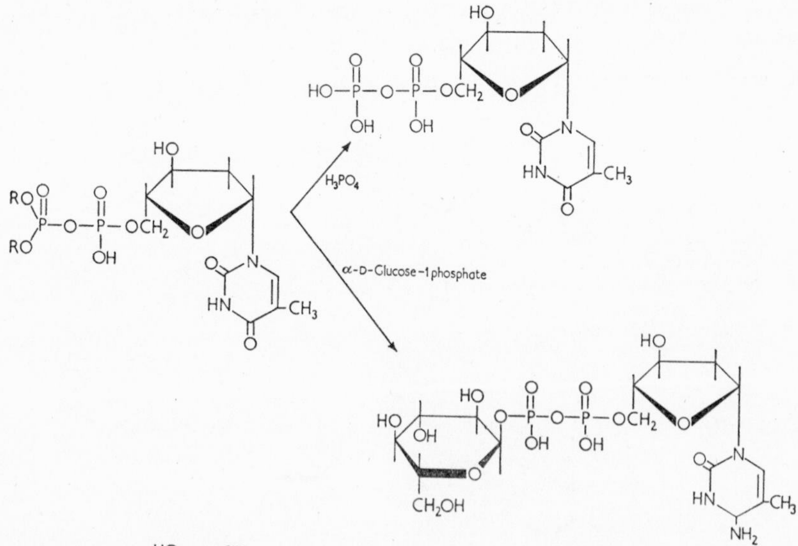
H_3PO_4
α-D-Glucose-1 phosphate

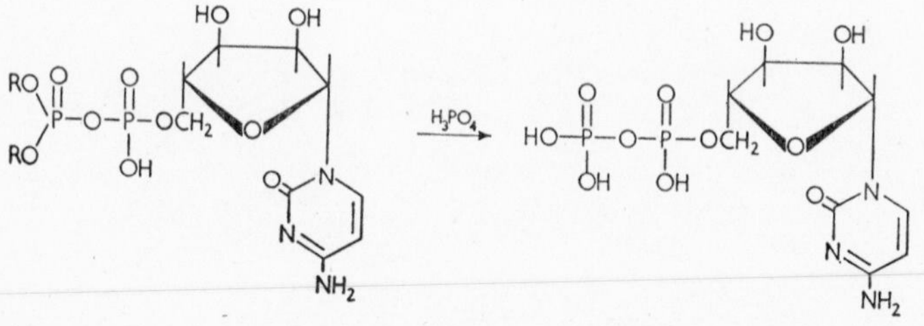
H_3PO_4

about 4 and the phosphate group a pK of about 6, it is clear that any intermediate carboxyl anhydride that might be formed would itself be subject to attack by the phosphate group (with displacement of the more stable anion) so that only the more stable product, P^1-uridine-5′ P^2-α-D-glucuronic acid-1 pyrophosphate, would result from the reaction. Nevertheless, the same approach can be used for the synthesis of acyl or amino-acyl anhydrides of nucleotides by anion exchange between the intermediate triesterified pyrophosphate and carboxylic acids or carbobenzyloxyamino acids and peptides. Since such compounds are none too stable in pyridine, the yields are comparatively low (approximately 40 to 50%). However, nucleotide-carboxylate anhydrides are relatively stable in dioxan solution as hindered tertiary base (tri-n-butylamine) salts, and virtually quantitative yields are obtained by the ethyl carbonate mixed anhydride method.[439]

The utility of the general approach has been fully demonstrated by the synthesis of coenzyme A and related derivatives in very high yield.[442] Treatment of adenosine-2'(3'),5' diphosphate with diphenyl phosphorochloridate gave P^1-adenosine-(2',3'-cyclic phosphate)-5' P^2-diphenyl pyrophosphate quantitatively. Further treatment of this anhydride with inorganic orthophosphate in pyridine then gave adenosine-(2',3'-cyclic phosphate)-5' pyrophosphate in 90% yield. Since chemical hydrolysis of the 2',3'-cyclic phosphate moiety in such compounds gives rise to a mixture of the 2' and 3' phosphates, specific cleavage was effected by the use of takadiastase ribonuclease T2 to yield adenosine-(3'-phosphate)-5' pyrophosphate, uncontaminated by the isomeric 2' phosphate derivative. In a similar fashion, the takadiastase enzyme being replaced by pancreatic ribonuclease, uridine-(3'-phosphate)-5' pyrophosphate was prepared from a mixture of uridine-2',5' and -3',5' diphosphates.

Treatment of P^1-adenosine-(2',3'-cyclic phosphate)-5' P^2-diphenyl pyrophosphate with pantethine-4',4' bis phosphate gave the -2',3' cyclic phosphate form of oxidised coenzyme A. This was incubated with ribonuclease T2 (to give the -3' phosphate exclusively), converted into the thiol form and then purified by chromatography to give coenzyme A in 63% overall yield. Biochemical estimation showed that the material was completely active. Alkaline hydrolysis or digestion with rattlesnake venom gave adenosine-3',5' diphosphate as the only nucleotide derivative, with no trace of the -2',5' biphosphate.[442]

Acidic hydrolysis of the intermediate cyclic phosphate form of coenzyme A yielded a mixture of coenzyme A and iso-coenzyme A. However, specific enzymic opening of the cyclic phosphate to the -2' phosphate (iso-coenzyme A) was obtained by means of a purified enzyme from calf brain.[358] It is likely that spleen diesterase would also prove effective on this type of compound, to give the -2' phosphate exclusively.

Similar procedures have been used for the synthesis of " active sulphate " (adenyl-5'-yl sulphate-3' phosphate).[358]

Such is the mildness of the method, that oligoribonucleotides containing a terminal -5' pyrophosphate residue were readily prepared by the action of dibenzyl phosphorochloridate on the oligonucleotide (carrying a terminal -5' phosphate) followed by nucleophilic displacement of dibenzyl phosphate from the product with inorganic phosphate. However, in this case, better yields were obtained by hydrogenolysis of the intermediate oligonucleotide pyrophosphate triester.[358]   A

Coenzyme A

similar procedure would doubtless be effective in the somewhat simpler case of oligodeoxynucleotides.

Although rigorously anhydrous conditions are not essential, a considerable decrease in yield occurs when wet pyridine (5% water) is used for the anion exchange reaction, presumably owing to pyridine catalysed hydrolysis of the intermediate nucleotide diphenyl phosphate anhydride to free nucleotide. Diphenyl phosphorochloridate has been used extensively to prepare the intermediate anhydride but, within certain limitations, this may contain any esterified phosphoric acid that is stronger than both the nucleotide and the attacking anion, the efficiency of anion exchange being dependent on this difference in acidic strengths to a large extent. Thus treatment of the nucleotide in dioxan with diethyl phosphorochloridate likewise gives a suitable anhydride intermediate which, while less reactive than the diphenyl derivative, readily undergoes controlled anionic nucleophilic displacement in pyridine to give excellent yields of the nucleotide coenzymes and related compounds. However, methanesulphonyl derivatives are

not satisfactory, owing to quantitative conversion of the nucleotide into P^1,P^2-dinucleoside-5' pyrophosphate even in dioxan and in the absence of base catalysis.[438]

The relative stability of pyrophosphates containing two or more dissociating groups has been mentioned previously. Nevertheless, under suitably vigorous conditions nucleophilic attack of inorganic pyrophosphate on P^1,P^2-di(adenosine-5') pyrophosphate in pyridine solution gives rise to a mixture of adenosine-5' phosphate, adenosine-5' pyrophosphate, and adenosine-5' triphosphate (and possibly adenosine-5' tetraphosphate).[445] Similar anion exchange mechanisms can be postulated for the slow conversion of acid salts of ribo- and deoxyribo-nucleoside-5' pyrophosphates in the solid state into mixtures of nucleoside-5' triphosphate and nucleoside-5' phosphate.[443]

As may be expected, diphenyl phosphate anhydrides of nucleoside-5' phosphates readily yield phosphoramidate derivatives quantitatively on treatment with a mixture of pyridine and a primary or secondary amine, such as ammonia, cyclohexylamine, hydrazine, morpholine, piperidine, or n-, s-, iso-, and t-butylamines. In common with the anion exchange reactions, preferential nucleophilic attack at the nucleotide phosphorus atom occurs with liberation of the stronger (more stable) anion and formation of nucleoside-5' phosphoramidates.[437, 438]

N = Nucleoside-5'

In general, formation of the nucleoside diphenyl pyrophosphate is preferable to the alternate procedure involving nucleophilic displacement of diphenyl phosphate from an anhydride of the non-nucleotide moiety of the coenzyme. However, in certain cases (in the absence of a proximal hydroxyl group) this can be employed with advantage. Thus

P^1-oestrone P^2-adenosine-5' pyrophosphate has been obtained in high yield (90% isolated pure material) by treatment of the steroid phosphate with diphenyl phosphorochloridate, followed by displacement of diphenyl phosphate from the resultant anhydride with adenosine-5' phosphate.[444] A variety of other P^1-steroid P^2-adenosine-5' pyrophosphates, and steroid polyphosphates have been synthesised by the same approach. Direct comparison with other general methods for pyrophosphate synthesis (including the phosphoromorpholidate approach) showed that the anion exchange method was " incomparablement plus selective ".[444] In many cases the product could be isolated directly from the reaction mixture in a pure condition without laborious purification procedures. Indeed, crystalline oestrone phosphoromorpholidate was obtained directly when P^1-oestrone P^2-diphenyl pyrophosphate was treated with morpholine. The approach appears to be generally superior to the dicyclohexylcarbodi-imide method for the synthesis of phosphoramidates and substituted phosphoramidates.

A further variation lies in the synthesis of aminoacyl nucleotides in very high yield by the action of ethyl chloroformate on a carbobenzyloxyamino acid to give the ethyl carbonate anhydride, followed by reaction with a nucleoside-5' phosphate. The stronger additive properties of the amino-acyl carbonyl group ensure specific formation of the amino-acyl nucleotide, rather than the relatively stable ethyl carbonate-nucleotide anhydride.[437, 439] This method has also been applied to the synthesis (in good yield) of amino-acyl and peptide anhydrides of oligonucleotides carrying a terminal 5'-phosphate group.[445]

The anion exchange method for the synthesis of nucleotide anhydrides offers a number of advantages compared with the earlier approaches. Apart from wider applicability, the method is markedly superior for the synthesis of coenzyme A, nucleoside-5' triphosphates (70 to 80% compared with the 20 to 40% yield by the phosphoramidate method), nucleoside-5' phosphoropiperidates (quantitative compared with 40% obtained by the dicyclohexylcarbodi-imide method), and 2,4-dinitrophenyl esters of nucleoside-5' phosphates (80 to 90% compared with 25 to 30% by the phosphoromorpholidate method). Extravagant excess of one or other of the components is seldom necessary (yields of 90%, using an 0·2 molar excess of the attacking anion have been reported);[444] this is of some importance when relatively rare substances are involved. Use of a slight excess of the P^1-nucleoside-5' P^2-diphenyl pyrophosphate is advantageous for the synthesis of anhydrides containing a radioactive-labelled sugar phosphate.

Tri-esters of pyrophosphoric acid have also been applied to the synthesis of model compounds.[446]

$+ CO_2 + EtOH$

OTHER METHODS

Uridine-5′ pyrophosphate was first synthesised by the reaction of 2′,3′-O-isopropylidene-5′-iodo-5′-deoxyuridine with silver tribenzyl pyrophosphate, followed by removal of protecting groups from the product.[447] However, the scope of this type of reaction is limited by cyclonucleoside formation, and to some extent the instability of fully esterified intermediates results in low yields.

The synthesis of adenosine-5′ polyphosphates from adenosine-5′ phosphate and phosphoric acid using benzene sulphonic acid as catalyst has been reported.[448] A 60% yield of polyphosphates composed of some 10% ADP, 30% ATP, 25% adenosine-5′ tetraphosphate, 15% adenosine-5′ pentaphosphate and 20% of higher polyphosphates was obtained.

In model systems of oxidative phosphorylation, adenosine-5′

pyrophosphate has been successfully prepared by the oxidation of quinol phosphates.[449]   Bromine oxidation of a mixture of tetra-n-butylammonium adenosine-5' phosphate and 2,3-dimethyl naphtha-1,4-quinol monophosphate under rigorously anhydrous conditions gave ADP in rather low yield. The anhydride was similarly obtained by oxidation of the naphtha-1,4-quinol ester of 2',3'-O-isopropylidene-adenosine-5' phosphate in the presence of inorganic phosphate.[449] During isolation the isopropylidene protecting group was lost from the initially formed product. The reaction mechanisms involved in this type of

oxidative phosphorylation have not been fully elucidated, but it is possible that monomeric metaphosphates (or related derivatives) are involved. The quinol ester of the nucleotide[449, 450] was obtained from 2,3-dimethyl-1,4-naphthaquinone and 2',3'-O-isopropylideneadenosine-5' benzyl phosphite (in the presence of potassium t-butoxide) with subsequent removal of the benzyl group from the product by anionic fission with sodium thiocyanate.[449]

The oxidation of phosphorohydrazidates with iodine has been employed for the synthesis of pyrophosphates (both symmetrical and unsymmetrical) and for the phosphorylation of alcoholic hydroxyl groups.[451]

Carbamoyl phosphates (prepared from the phosphate and isocyanates) react with bases in aqueous solution by transfer of the carbamoyl moiety, but in pyridine-methyl cyanide they slowly react with phosphate anions to give pyrophosphate derivatives.[452] This procedure,

A' = 2',3'-Isopropylideneadenosine-5'

A = Adenosine-5'

$$(RO)_2PONHNH_2 + 2I_2 \xrightarrow{H_2O} (RO)_2POOH + N_2 + 4HI$$

analogous to the trifluoracetic anhydride and anion exchange approaches, has not been applied to nucleotides but would presumably lead to mixtures of all the possible pyrophosphates since transfer of carbamic acid from one phosphate to another could be expected to occur much more rapidly than pyrophosphate formation. The ethyl carbonate anhydrides of nucleoside-5' phosphates, readily prepared by treating the nucleotide with ethyl chloroformate in aqueous solution, were not effective in this type of reaction.[358]

In a modification of the phosphoramidate approach,[453, 454] imidazolium adenosine-5' imidazol-1-yl phosphonate was prepared[454, 455] from adenosine-5' phosphate and 1,1'-carbonyldi-imidazole.[456, 457] Treatment of the nucleoside-5' phosphoroimidazole with phosphoric acid gave a low yield of adenosine-5′ pyrophosphate. Nucleophilic attack by adenosine-5′ phosphate or uridine-5′ phosphate yielded the respective di-nucleoside-5′ pyrophosphates and conversion into adenosine-5′ phosphoramidate was effected by the action of ammonia.[454] Phos-

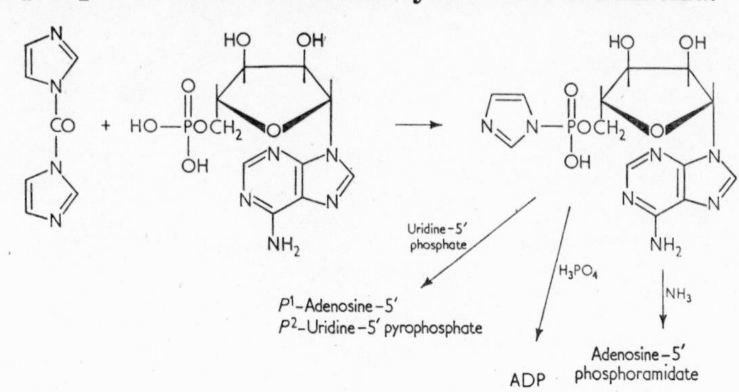

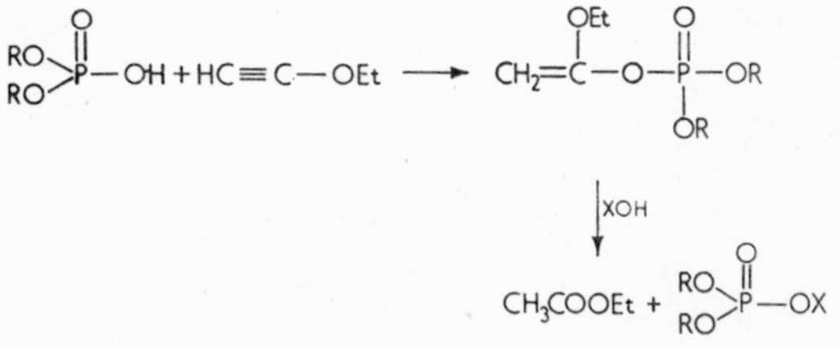

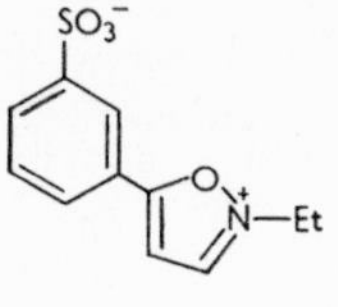

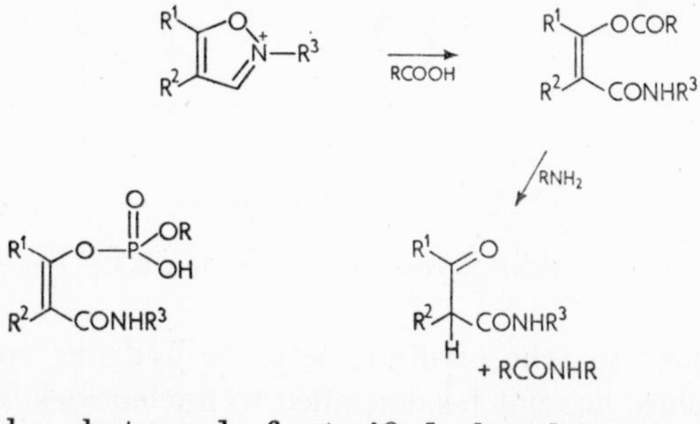

Uridine-5′ phosphate

H_3PO_4

P^1-Adenosine-5′
P^2-Uridine-5′ pyrophosphate

ADP

NH_3

Adenosine-5′ phosphoramidate

phorylation of orthophosphate and of esterified phosphates by mono- and di-esters of imidazolylphosphonic acid[415, 416, 453, 458] and mono- esters of di-imidazolyl phosphinic acid has been examined in detail,[453, 458] and the synthesis of a variety of diesterified and mono- esterified pyrophosphates described.[453, 458] Treatment of thymidine-5′ phosphate with di-imidazolyl phosphinic acid gave P^1,P^3-dithymidine- 5′ triphosphate.[458]

The action of ethoxyacetylene on phosphate derivatives (catalysed by mercuric ion) gives 1-alkoxy-vinyl esters which are active as phos- phorylating agents for amines and alcoholic and acidic hydroxyl groups. The approach may provide a useful method for the synthesis of nucleotides and nucleotide anhydrides.[459]

A reagent that has been found useful for the synthesis of peptides,[460] N-ethyl-5-phenylisoxazolium-3'-sulphonate, may be equally valuable for pyrophosphate synthesis. The initial intermediate would be an enol phosphate derivative.

An interesting approach has been used for the synthesis of cytidine diphosphate ethanolamine by the action of ethyleneimine on cytidine-5'

pyrophosphoric acid.[461] The carbodi-imide method gives a lower yield and many contaminating products that are difficult to remove. Methylation of CDP ethanolamine with methyl iodide yields cytidine diphosphate choline.

Uridine diphosphate glucuronic acid has been obtained by the direct catalytic (platinum) oxidation of uridine diphosphate glucose.[428, 462]

Treatment of ATP with ethylene oxide gives P^1-2-hydroxyethyl P^3-(N^1-hydroxyethyl)-adenosine-5' triphosphate.[463] This, on mild alkaline hydrolysis, is converted into 6-(2-hydroxyethylamino)-9-β-D-ribofuranosylpurine-5' pyrophosphate.[358]

238   NUCLEOSIDES AND NUCLEOTIDES

1. Lohmann, K., *Naturwiss.*,**17,** 624 (1929).
2. Fiske, C. H., and Subbarow, Y., *Science,* **70,** 381 (1929).
3. Lohmann, K., *Biochem. Z.,* **233,** 460 (1931).
4. Lohmann, K., *Biochem. Z.,* **254,** 381 (1932).
5. Barrenscheen, H. K., and Jachimowicz, T., *Biochem. Z.,* **292,** 350 (1937).
6. Lythgoe, B., and Todd, A. R., *Nature,* **155,** 695 (1945).
7. Makino, K., *Biochem. Z.,* **278,** 161 (1935).
8. Lohmann, K., *Biochem. Z.,* **282,** 104, 120 (1935).
9. Marrian, D. H., *Biochim. et Biophys. Acta,* **13,** 278 (1954).
10. Liebecq, C., *Bull. Soc. Chim. Biol.,* **43,** 331 (1961).
11. Lieberman, I., *J. Am. Chem. Soc.,* **77,** 3373 (1955).
12. Sacks, J., *Biochim. et Biophys. Acta,* **16,** 436 (1955).
13. Schmitz, H., Hurlbert, R. B., and Potter, V. R., *J. Biol. Chem.,* **209,** 41 (1954).
14. Schmitz, H., Potter, V. R., Hurlbert, R. B., and White, D. M., *Cancer Research,* **14,** 66 (1954).
15. Bergkvist, R., and Deutsch, A., *Acta Chem. Scand.,* **8,** 1889 (1954).
16. Smith, E. E. B., and Mills, G. T., *Biochim. et Biophys. Acta,* **13,** 386 (1954).
17. Lieberman, I., *J. Biol. Chem.,* **223,** 327 (1956).
18. Sanadi, D. R., Gibson, D. M., Ayengar, P., and Jacob, M., *J. Biol. Chem.,* **218,** 505 (1956).
19. Keller, E. B., and Zamecnik, P. C., *J. Biol. Chem.,* **221,** 45 (1956).
20. Brown, G. M., *J. Am. Chem. Soc.,* **80,** 3161 (1958).
21. Kurahashi, K., Pennington, R. T., and Utter, M. F., *J. Biol. Chem.,* **226,** 1059 (1957).
22. Potter, R. L., and Schlesinger, S., *J. Am. Chem. Soc.,* **77,** 6714 (1955).
23. Potter, R. L., Schlesinger, S., Buettner-Janusch, V., and Thompson, L., *J. Biol. Chem.,* **226,** 381 (1957).
24. Daoust, R., and Cantero, A., *Proc. Am. Assoc. Cancer Res.,* **1,** 10 (1954).
25. Le Page, G. A., *J. Biol. Chem.,* **226,** 135 (1957).
26. Levedahl, B. H., and James, T. W., *Biochim. et Biophys. Acta,* **21,** 298 (1956).
27. McCormick, W. G., and Levedahl, B. H., *Biochim. et Biophys. Acta,* **34,** 303 (1959).
28. Hotta, K., Brahms, J., and Morales, M., *J. Am. Chem. Soc.,* **83,** 997 (1961).
29. Hammes, G. G., Maciel, G. E., and Waugh, J. S., *J. Am. Chem. Soc.,* **83,** 2394 (1961).
30. Cohn, M., and Hughes, T. R., *J. Biol. Chem.,* **237,** 176 (1962).
31. Walaas, E., *Acta Chem. Scand.,* **12,** 528 (1958).
32. Nanninga, L. B., *Biochim. et Biophys. Acta,* **54,** 330 (1961).
33. Weitzel, G., and Spehr, T., *Z. physiol. Chem.,* **313,** 212 (1958).
34. Melchior, N. C., *J. Biol. Chem.,* **208,** 615 (1954).
35. Hers, H. G., *Biochim. et Biophys. Acta,* **8,** 424 (1952).
36. Hock, A., and Huber, G., *Biochem. Z.,* **328,** 44 (1956).
37. Bielschowsky, M., *Biochem. J.,* **47,** 105 (1950).
38. Lowenstein, J. M., *Biochem. J.,* **70,** 222 (1958); **75,** 269 (1960).
39. Lowenstein, J. M., *Biochim. et Biophys. Acta,* **28,** 206 (1958).
40. Lowenstein, J. M., and Schatz, M. N., *J. Biol. Chem.,* **236,** 305 (1961).
41. Cook, W. H., Lipkin, D., and Markham, R., *J. Am. Chem. Soc.,* **79,** 3607 (1957).

42. Lipkin, D., Markham, R., and Cook, W. H., J. Am. Chem. Soc., **81**, 6075 (1959).
43. Brintzinger, H., Helv. Chim. Acta, **44**, 1199 (1961).
44. Cook, W. H., and Lipkin, D., unpublished work.
45. Cohn, M., and Hughes, T. R., J. Biol. Chem., **235**, 3250 (1960).
46. Harden, A., and Young, W. J., Proc. Chem. Soc., **21**, 189 (1905).
47. Dixon, M., Nature, **188**, 464 (1960).
48. von Euler, H., and Schlenk, F., Svensk, Kem. Tidskr., **48**, 135 (1936).
49. Warburg, O., Christian, W., and Griese, A., Biochem. Z., **282**, 157 (1935).
50. von Euler, H., and Myrbäck, K., Z. physiol. Chem., **233**, 95 (1935); **198**, 236 (1931).
51. von Euler, H., Albers, H., and Schlenk, F., Z. physiol. Chem., **240**, 113 (1936); **237**, 1 (1935).
52. Schlenk, F., J. Biol. Chem., **146**, 619 (1942).
53. Schlenk, F., Hellstrom, H., and von Euler, H., Chem. Ber., **71**, 1471 (1938).
54. Atkinson, M. R., and Morton, R. K., Nature, **188**, 58 (1960).
55. Vestin, R., Schlenk, F., and von Euler, H., Chem. Ber., **70**, 1369 (1937).
56. Warburg, O., and Christian, W., Biochem. Z., **285**, 297 (1936).
57. Karrer, P., Schwarzenbach, G., Benz, F., and Solmssen, U., Helv. Chim. Acta, **19**, 811 (1936).
58. von Euler, H., and Schlenk, F., Z. physiol. Chem., **246**, 64 (1937).
59. Ohlmeyer, P., Biochem. Z., **297**, 66 (1938).
60. Schlenk, F., Arch. Biochem., **3**, 93 (1943).
61. Karrer, P., Ringier, B. H., Buchi, J., Fritzsche, H., and Solmssen, U., Helv. Chim. Acta, **20**, 55 (1937).
62. Pullman, M. E., San Pietro, A., and Colowick, S. P., J. Biol. Chem., **206**, 129 (1954).
63. Heiwinkel, H., Svensk Vet. Akad. Arkiv Kemi, **13A**, 19 (1939).
64. Kornberg, A., and Pricer, W. E., J. Biol. Chem., **182**, 763 (1950).
65. Kornberg, A., J. Biol. Chem., **182**, 779 (1950).
66. Schlenk, F., Naturwiss., **25**, 668 (1937).
67. von Euler, H., and Bauer, E., Chem. Ber., **71**, 411 (1938).
68. von Euler, H., and Adler, E., Z. physiol. Chem., **252**, 41 (1938).
69. Kornberg, A., J. Biol. Chem., **182**, 805 (1950).
70. Kornberg, A., and Pricer, W. E., J. Biol. Chem., **186**, 557 (1950).
71. Singer, T. P. and Kearney, E. B., Biochim. et Biophys. Acta, **11**, 290 (1953); Advances in Enzymol., **15**, 79 (1954).
72. Siegel, J. M., Montgomery, G. A., and Bock, R. M., Arch. Biochem. Biophys., **82**, 288 (1959).
73. Weber, G., J. chim. phys., **55**, 878 (1958).
74. Warburg, O., and Christian, W., Biochem. Z., **298**, 150 (1938).
75. Forrest, H. S., and Todd, A. R., J. Chem. Soc., 3295 (1950).
76. Abraham, E. P., Biochem. J., **33**, 543 (1939).
77. Kearney, E. B., and England, S., Arch. Biochem. Biophys., **32**, 222 (1951).
78. Schrecker, A. W., and Kornberg, A., J. Biol. Chem., **182**, 795 (1950).
79. Weber, G., Biochem. J., **47**, 114 (1950).
80. Hashimoto, T., and Yoshikawa, H., Biochem. Biophys. Research Communs., **5**, 71 (1961).
81. Mosley, W. H., and Caputto, R., J. Am. Chem., Soc., **80**, 4746 (1958).
82. de Caputto, D. P., Mosley, W. H., Poyer, J. L., and Caputto, R., J. Biol. Chem., **236**, 2727 (1961).
83. Lipmann, F., J. Biol. Chem., **160**, 173 (1945).

84. Lipmann, F., and Kaplan, N. O., *J. Biol. Chem.*, **162,** 743 (1946).
85. de Vries, W. H., Govier, W. M., Evans, J. S., Gregory, J. D., Novelli, G. D., Soodak, M., and Lipmann, F., *J. Am. Chem. Soc.*, **72,** 4838 (1950).
86. Baddiley, J., and Thain, E. M., *J. Chem. Soc.*, 2253 (1951).
87. Gregory, J. D., Novelli, G. D., and Lipmann, F., *J. Am. Chem. Soc.*, **74,** 854 (1952).
88. Brown, G. M., and Snell, E. E., *J. Am. Chem. Soc.*, **75,** 1691 (1953).
89. Brown, G. M., and Snell, E. E., *J. Biol. Chem.*, **198,** 375 (1952).
90. McRorie, R. A., and Williams, W. L., *J. Bacteriol.*, **61,** 737 (1951).
91. Baddiley, J., and Thain, E. M., *J. Chem. Soc.*, 2253, 3421 (1951); 3783 (1952).
92. Baddiley, J., and Thain, E. M., *J. Chem. Soc.*, 246, 3421 (1951).
93. King, T. E., and Strong, F. M., *J. Biol. Chem.*, **189,** 315 (1951).
94. Novelli, G. D., Kaplan, N. O., and Lipmann, F., *Federation Proc.*, **9,** 209 (1950).
95. Baddiley, J., and Thain, E. M., *J. Chem. Soc.*, 3783 (1952); 903 (1953).
96. Wang, T. P., Shuster, L., and Kaplan, N. O., *J. Am. Chem. Soc.*, **74,** 3204 (1952).
97. Wang, T. P., and Kaplan, N. O., *J. Biol. Chem.*, **206,** 311 (1954).
98. Baddiley, J., and Thain, E. M., *J. Chem. Soc.*, 3421 (1951).
99. Baddiley, J., and Thain, E. M., *J. Chem. Soc.*, 1610 (1953).
100. Hoagland, M. B., and Novelli, G. D., *J. Biol. Chem.*, **207,** 767 (1954).
101. Levintow, L., and Novelli, G. D., *J. Biol. Chem.*, **207,** 761 (1954).
102. Brown, G. M., *J. Biol. Chem.*, **234,** 370 (1959).
103. Lynen, F., Reichert, E., and Rueff, L., *Ann.*, **574,** 1 (1951).
104. Wang, T. P., Shuster, L., and Kaplan, N. O., *J. Am. Chem. Soc.*, **74,** 3204 (1952).
105. Berg, P., *J. Biol. Chem.*, **222,** 991, 1015, 1025 (1956).
106. Baddiley, J., and Thain, E. M., *J. Chem. Soc.*, 3425 (1951).
107. Kuhn, R., and Quadbeck, G., *Chem. Ber.*, **84,** 844 (1951).
108. Wieland, T., and Bokelmann, E., *Ann.*, **576,** 20 (1952).
109. Baddiley, J., and Thain, E. M., *Science*, **117,** 439 (1953).
110. King, T. E., Stewart, C. J., and Cheldelin, V. H., *Science*, **117,** 439 (1953).
111. Schwyzer, R., *Helv. Chim. Acta*, **35,** 1903 (1952).
112. Lynen, F., *Federation Proc.*, **12,** 683 (1953).
113. Sanadi, D. R., Gibson, D. M., and Ayengar, P., *Biochim. et Biophys. Acta*, **14,** 434 (1954).
114. Kaufman, S., and Alivisatos, S. G. A., *J. Biol. Chem.*, **216,** 141 (1955).
115. Feuer, G., and Wollmann, M., *Acta Physiol. Acad. Sci. Hung.*, **10,** 1 (1956).
116. Caputto, R., Leloir, L. F., Cardini, C. E., and Paladini, A. C., *J. Biol. Chem.*, **184,** 333 (1950).
117. Paladini, A. C., and Leloir, L. F., *Biochem. J.*, **51,** 426 (1952).
118. Trucco, R. E., *Arch. Biochem. Biophys.*, **34,** 482 (1951).
119. Munch-Petersen, A., Kalckar, H. M., Cutolo, E., and Smith, E. E. B., *Nature*, **172,** 1036 (1953).
120. Leloir, L. F., *Arch. Biochem. Biophys.*, **33,** 186 (1951).
121. Anderson, L., Landel, A. M., and Diedrich, D. F., *Biochim. et Biophys. Acta*, **22,** 573 (1956).
122. Kowalsky, A., and Koshland, D. E., *Biochim. et Biophys. Acta*, **22,** 575 (1956).
123. Kalckar, H. M., and Maxwell, E. S., *Biochim. et Biophys. Acta*, **22,** 588 (1956).

124. Maxwell, E. S., *J. Am. Chem. Soc.*, **78**, 1074 (1956); *J. Biol. Chem.*, **229**, 139 (1957).
125. Maxwell, E. S., and Robichon-Szulmajster, H., *J. Biol. Chem.*, **235**, 308 (1960).
126. Kalckar, H. M., Braganca, B., and Munch-Petersen, A., *Nature*, **172**, 1038 (1953).
127. Neufeld, E. F., Ginsburg, V., Putman, E. W., Fanshier, D., and Hassid, W. Z., *Arch. Biochem. Biophys.*, **69**, 602 (1957).
128. Isselbacher, K. J., *J. Biol. Chem.*, **232**, 429 (1958).
129. Kalckar, H. M., Anderson, E. P., and Isselbacher, K. J., *Biochim. et Biophys. Acta*, **20**, 262 (1956).
130. Mills, G. T., Smith, E. E. B., and Lochhead, A. C., *Biochim. et Biophys. Acta*, **25**, 521 (1957).
131. Leloir, L. F., and Cabib, E. J., *J. Am. Chem. Soc.*, **75**, 5445 (1953).
132. Cabib, E., and Leloir, L. F., *J. Biol. Chem.*, **231**, 259 (1958).
133. Leloir, L. F., and Cardini, C. E., *J. Am. Chem. Soc.*, **75**, 6084 (1953).
134. Cardini, C. E., and Leloir, L. F., *J. Biol. Chem.*, **214**, 157 (1955).
135. Gander, J. E., Petersen, W. E., and Boyer, P. D., *Arch. Biochem. Biophys.*, **69**, 85 (1957).
136. Watkins, W. M., and Hassid, W. Z., *Biochem. Biophys. Research Communs.*, **5**, 260 (1961).
137. Glaser, L., *Biochim. et Biophys. Acta*, **25**, 436 (1957).
138. de Fekete, M. A. R., Leloir, L. F., and Cardini, C. E., *Nature*, **187**, 918 (1960).
139. Leloir, L. F., de Fekete, M. A. R., and Cardini, C. E., *J. Biol. Chem.*, **236**, 636 (1961).
140. Leloir, L. F., Olavarria, J. M., Goldemberg, S. H., and Carminatti, H., *Arch. Biochem. Biophys.*, **81**, 508 (1959).
141. Leloir, L. F., and Cardini, C. E., *J. Am. Chem. Soc.*, **79**, 6340 (1957).
142. Leloir, L. F., and Goldemberg, S. H., *J. Biol. Chem.*, **235**, 919 (1960).
143. Algranati, I. D., and Cabib, E., *Biochem. et Biophys. Acta*, **43**, 141 (1960).
144. Recondo, E., and Leloir, L. F., *Biochem. Biophys. Research Communs.*, **6**, 85 (1961).
145. Kornberg, A., Zimmerman, S. B., Kornberg, S. R., and Josse, J., *Proc. Natl. Acad. Sci. U.S.A.*, **45**, 772 (1959).
146. Cleland, W. W., and Kennedy, E. P., *J. Biol. Chem.*, **235**, 45 (1960).
147. Ginsburgh, V., Stumpf, P. K., and Hassid, W. Z., *J. Biol. Chem.*, **223**, 977 (1956).
148. Smith, E. E. B., Galloway, B., and Mills, G. T., *Biochim. et Biophys. Acta*, **33**, 276 (1959). See also reference 473.
149. Smith, E. E. B., Galloway, B., and Mills, G. T., *Biochem. Biophys. Research Communs.*, **5**, 148 (1961).
150. Dutton, G. J., *Biochem. J.*, **64**, 693 (1956).
151. Axelrod, J., Inscoe, J. K., and Tomkins, G. M., *J. Biol. Chem.*, **232**, 835 (1958).
152. Dutton, G. J., and Storey, I. D. E., *Biochem., J.*, **57**, 275 (1954).
153. Smith, E. E. B., and Mills, G. T., *Biochim. et Biophys. Acta*, **13**, 386 (1954).
154. Solms, J., and Hassid, W. Z., *J. Biol. Chem.*, **228**, 357 (1957).
155. Smith, E. E. B., Mills, G. T., and Harper, E. M., *J. Gen. Microbiol.*, **16**, 426 (1957).
156. Strominger, J. L., Maxwell, E. S.. Axelrod, J., and Kalckar, H. M., *J. Biol. Chem.*, **224**, 79 (1957).

242   NUCLEOSIDES AND NUCLEOTIDES

157. Feingold, D. S., Neufeld, E. F., and Hassid, W. Z., *Arch. Biochem. Biophys.*, 78, 401 (1958).
158. Feingold, D. S., Neufeld, E. F., and Hassid, W. Z., *J. Biol. Chem.*, 235, 910 (1960).
159. Smith, E. E. B., Mills., G. T., and Harper, E. M., *Biochim. et Biophys. Acta*, 23, 662 (1957).
160. Smith, E. E. B., Mills, G. T., Bernheimer, H. P., and Austrian, R., *J. Biol. Chem.*, 235, 1876 (1960).
161. Smith, E. E. B., Mills, G. T., and Bernheimer, H. P., *J. Biol. Chem.*, 236, 2179 (1961).
162. Smith, E. E. B., Galloway, B., and Mills, G. T., *Biochem. Biophys. Research Communs.*, 4, 420 (1961).
163. Cabib, E., Leloir, L. F., and Cardini, C. E., *J. Biol. Chem.*, 203, 1055 (1953).
164. Kurtz, E., and Binkley, S. B., *Biochim. et Biophys. Acta*, 46, 595 (1961).
165. Maley, F., Maley, G. F., and Lardy, H. A., *J. Am. Chem. Soc.*, 78, 5303 (1956).
166. Pontis, H. G., *J. Biol. Chem.*, 216, 195 (1955).
167. Glaser, L., *Biochim. et Biophys. Acta*, 31, 575 (1959); *J. Biol. Chem.*, 234, 2801 (1959).
168. Glaser, L., and Brown, D. H., *Proc. Natl. Acad. Sci. U.S.A.*, 41, 253 (1955).
169. Markovitz, A., Cifonelli, J. A., and Dorfman, A., *J. Biol. Chem.*, 234, 2343 (1959).
170. Glaser, L., and Brown, D. H., *J. Biol. Chem.*, 228, 729 (1957).
171. Strominger, J. L., *Biochim. et Biophys. Acta*, 17, 283 (1955); *J. Biol. Chem.*, 237, 1388 (1962).
172. Suzuki, S., *Biochim. et Biophys. Acta*, 50, 395 (1961); *J. Biol. Chem.*, 237, 1393 (1962).
173. Gabriel, O., and Ashwell, G., *Biochem. Biophys. Research Communs.*, 6, 89 (1961); *J. Biol. Chem.*, 237, 1400 (1962).
174. Cifonelli, J. A., and Dorfman, A., *J. Biol. Chem.*, 228, 547 (1957).
175. Kent, P. W., and Lunt, M. R., *Biochim. et Biophys. Acta*, 28, 657 (1958).
176. Maley, F., Maley, G. F., and Lardy, H. A., *J. Am. Chem. Soc.*, 78, 5303 (1956).
177. Maley, F., and Maley, G. F., *Biochim. et Biophys. Acta*, 31, 577 (1959).
178. Park, J. T., and Johnson, M. J., *J. Biol. Chem.*, 179, 585 (1949).
179. Park, J. T., *J. Biol. Chem.*, 194, 877, 885, 897 (1952).
180. Park, J. T., and Strominger, J. L., *Science*, 125, 99 (1957).
181. Strange, R. E., and Powell, J. F., *Biochem. J.*, 58, 80 (1954).
182. Cummins, C. S., and Harris, H., *J. Gen. Microbiol.*, 14, 583 (1956).
183. Strange, R. E., *Biochem. J.*, 64, 23P (1956).
184. Kent, L. H., *Biochem. J.*, 67, 5P (1957).
185. Strominger, J. L., *Compt. rend. Lab. Carlsberg*, 31, 181 (1959).
186. Strominger, J. L., and Threnn, R. H., *Biochim. et Biophys. Acta*, 33, 280 (1959).
187. Strominger, J. L., *Biochim. et Biophys. Acta*, 30, 645 (1958).
188. Strominger, J. L., *J. Biol. Chem.*, 234, 1520 (1959).
189. Strominger, J. L. Threnn, R. H., *Biochim. et Biophys. Acta*, 36, 83 (1959).
190. Strominger, J. L., Threnn, R. H., and Scott, S. S., *J. Am. Chem. Soc.*, 81, 3803 (1959).
191. Strominger, J. L., Park, J. T., and Thompson, R. E., *J. Biol. Chem.*, 234, 3263 (1959).
192. Ito, E., and Strominger, J. L., *J. Biol. Chem.*, 235, PC5, 7 (1960); 237, 2689, 2696 (1962).

193. Strominger, J. L., Ito, E., and Threnn, R. H., *J. Am. Chem. Soc.*, **82,** 998 (1960).
194. Strominger, J. L., Scott, S. S., and Threnn, R. H., *Federation Proc.*, **18,** 334 (1959).
195. Comb, D. G., Chin, W., and Roseman, S., *Biochim. et Biophys. Acta*, **46,** 394 (1961).
196. Ito, E., Ishimoto, N., and Saito, M., *Arch. Biochem. Biophys.*, **80,** 431 (1959).
197. O'Brien, P. J., and Zilliken, F., *Biochim. et Biophys. Acta*, **31,** 543 (1959).
198. Barry, G. T., and Goebel, W. F., *Nature*, **179,** 206 (1957).
199. Comb, D. G., Shimizu, F., anf Roseman, S., *J. Am. Chem. Soc.*, **81,** 5513 (1959).
200. Jourdian, G. W., Shimizu, F., and Roseman, S., *Federation Proc.*, **20,** 161 (1961).
201. Cooksey, K. E., Anwar, R. A., Roy, C., and Watson, R. W., *Arch. Biochem. Biophys.*, **94,** 541 (1961).
202. Kennedy, E. P., and Weiss, S. B., *J. Biol. Chem.*, **222,** 193, (1956).
203. Borkenhagen, L. F., and Kennedy, E. P., *J. Biol. Chem.*, **227,** 951 (1957).
204. Weiss, S. B., Smith, S. W., and Kennedy, E. P., *J. Biol. Chem.*, **231,** 53 (1958).
205. Sribney, M., and Kennedy, E. P., *J. Am. Chem. Soc.*, **79,** 5325 (1957).
206. Herbert, E., and Potter, V. R., *J. Biol. Chem.*, **222,** 453 (1956).
207. Lieberman, I., Berger, L., and Giminez, W. T., *Science*, **124,** 81 (1956).
208. Williams-Ashman, H. G., and Banks, J., *J. Biol. Chem.*, **223,** 509 (1956).
209. Kaufer, J. N., and Kennedy, E. P., *J. Biol. Chem.*, **237,** PC270 (1962).
210. Paulus, H., and Kennedy, E. P., *J. Am. Chem. Soc.*, **81,** 4436 (1959); *J. Biol. Chem.*, **235,** 1303 (1960).
211. Redman, C. M., and Hokin, L. E., *Federation Proc.*, **19,** 309 (1960).
212. Baddiley, J., and Mathias, A. P., *J. Chem. Soc.*, 2723 (1954).
213. Baddiley, J., Buchanan, J. G., Carss, B., Mathias, A. P., and Sanderson, A. R., *Biochem. J.*, **64,** 599 (1956).
214. Baddiley, J., Buchanan, J. G., Carss, B., and Mathias, A. P., *Biochem. et Biophys. Acta*, **21,** 191 (1956).
215. Clarke, P. H., Glover, P., and Mathias, A. P., *J. Gen. Microbiol.*, **20,** 156 (1959).
216. Baddiley, J., Buchanan, J. G., Mathias, A. P., and Sanderson, A. R., *J. Chem. Soc.*, 4186 (1956).
217. Baddiley, J., Buchanan, J. G., and Carss, B., *J. Chem. Soc.* 1869 (1957).
218. Shaw, D. R. D., *Biochem. J.*, **66,** 56P (1957); **82,** 297 (1962).
219. Baddiley, J., Buchanan, J. G., Carss, B., and Mathias, A. P., *J. Chem. Soc.*, 4583 (1956).
220. Baddiley, J., Buchanan, J. G., and Carss, B., *J. Chem. Soc.*, 4058 (1957).
221. Baddiley, J., *Proc. Chem. Soc.*, 177 (1959).
222. Armstrong, J. J., Baddiley, J., Buchanan, J. G., Davison, A. L., Kelemen, M. V., and Neuhaus, F. C., *Nature*, **184,** 247 (1959).
223. Saukkonen, J. J., *Nature*, **192,** 816 (1961).
224. Nikaido, H., and Kokura, K., *Biochem. Biophys. Research Communs,.* **6,** 304 (1961).
225. Cabib, E., and Leloir, L. F., *J. Biol. Chem.*, **206,** 779 (1954).
226. Ginsburg, V., and Kirkman, H. N., *J. Am. Chem. Soc.*, **80,** 3481 (1958).
227. Denamur, R., Fanconneau, G., and Guntz, G., *Compt. rend.*, **246,** 2820 (1958).

228. Pontis, H. G., James, A. L., and Baddiley, J., *Biochim. et Biophys. Acta*, **33**, 588 (1959); *Biochem. J.*, **75**, 428 (1960).
229. Heath, E. C., *Biochim. et Biophys. Acta*, **39**, 377 (1960).
230. Ginsburg, V., O'Brien, P. J., and Hall, C. W., *J. Biol. Chem.*, **237**, 497 (1962).
231. Su, J. C., and Hassid, W. Z., *J. Biol. Chem.*, **235**, PC36 (1960); *Biochemistry*, **1**, 474 (1962).
232. Munch-Petersen, A., *Arch. Biochem. Biophys.*, **55**, 592 (1955).
233. Ginsburg, V., *J. Am. Chem. Soc.*, **80**, 4426 (1958).
234. Ginsburg, V., *J. Biol. Chem.*, **235**, 2196 (1960).
235. Ginsburg, V., *J. Biol. Chem.*, **236**, 2389 (1961).
236. Markovitz, A., *Biochem. Biophys. Research Communs.*, **6**, 250 (1961).
237. Sugino, Y., *J. Am. Chem. Soc.*, **79**, 5074 (1957); *Biochim. et Biophys. Acta*, **40**, 425 (1960).
238. Potter, R. L., and Buettner-Janusch, V., *J. Biol. Chem.*, **233**, 462 (1958).
239. Kennedy, E. P., Borkenhagen, L. F., and Smith, S. W., *J. Biol. Chem.*, **234**, 1998 (1959).
240. Strominger, J. L., and Scott, S. S., *Biochim. et Biophys. Acta*. **35**, 552 (1959).
241. Okazaki, R., *Biochem. Biophys. Research Communs.*, **1**, 34 (1959); *Biochim. et Biophys. Acta*, **44**, 478 (1960).
242. Okazaki, R., Okazaki, T., and Kuriki, Y., *Biochim. et Biophys. Acta*, **38**, 384 (1960).
243. Baddiley, J., and Blumsom, N. L., *Biochim. et Biophys. Acta*, **39**, 376 (1960).
244. Blumsom, N. L., and Baddiley, J., *Biochem. J.*, **81**, 114 (1961).
245. Baddiley, J., Blumsom, N. L., Girolamo, A., and Girolamo, M., *Biochim. et Biophys. Acta*, **50**, 391 (1961).
246. Barber, G. A., and Neufeld, E. F., *Biochem. Biophys. Research Communs.*, **6**, 44 (1961); Barber, G. A., *Biochemistry*, **1**, 463 (1962).
247. Burger, M., Glaser, L., and Burton, R. M., *Biochim. et Biophys. Acta*, **56**, 172 (1962).
248. Kornfeld, S., and Glaser, L., *J. Biol. Chem.*, **236**, 1791 (1961); *Biochim. et Biophys. Acta*, **42**, 548 (1960).
249. Pazur, J. H., and Shuey, E. W., *J. Biol. Chem.*, **236**, 1780 (1961).
250. Pazur, J. H., and Shuey, E. W., *J. Am. Chem. Soc.*, **82**, 5009 (1960).
251. Okazaki, R., Okazaki, T., and Strominger, J. L., *Federation Proc.*, **20**, 85 (1961).
252. Kornfeld, S., and Glaser, L., *Federation Proc.*, **20**, 84 (1961).
253. Glaser, L., and Kornfeld, S., *J. Biol. Chem.*, **236**, 1795 (1961).
254. Glaser, L., *Biochim. et Biophys. Acta*, **51**, 169 (1961).
255. Okazaki, R., Okazaki, T., Strominger, J. L., and Michelson, A. M., *J. Biol. Chem.*, **237**, 3014 (1962).
256. Kornfeld, S., and Glaser, L., *Biochim. et Biophys. Acta*, **56**, 184 (1962).
257. Bernstein, S., and McGilvery, R. W., *J. Biol. Chem.*, **199**, 745 (1952).
258. de Meio, R. H., Wizerkaniuk, M., Schreibman, I., *J. Biol. Chem.*, **213**, 439 (1955).
259. d'Abramo, F., and Lipmann, F., *Biochim. et Biophys. Acta*, **25**, 211 (1957).
260. Suzuki, S., and Strominger, J. L., *J. Biol. Chem.*, **235**, 257, 267, 274 (1960).
261. Robbins, P. W., and Lipmann, F., *J. Biol. Chem.*, **229**, 837 (1957).
262. Bandurski, R. S., Wilson, L. G., and Squires, C. L., *J. Am. Chem. Soc.*, **78**, 6408 (1956).
263. Robbins, P. W., and Lipmann, F., *J. Am. Chem. Soc.*, **78**, 6409 (1956).

264. Robbins, P. W., and Lipmann, F., *J. Biol. Chem.*, **233**, 681 (1958).
265. Wilson, L. G., and Bandurski, R. S., *J. Am. Chem. Soc.*, **80**, 5576 (1958).
266. Bandurski, R. S., Wilson, L. G., and Asahi, T., *J. Am. Chem. Soc.*, **82**, 3218 (1960).
267. Wilson, L. G., Asahi, T., and Bandurski, R. S., *J. Biol. Chem.*, **236**, 1822 (1961).
268. Hilz, H., Kittler, M., and Knape, G., *Biochem. Z.*, **332**, 151 (1959).
269. Peck, H. D., *Proc. Natl. Acad. Sci. U.S.A.*, **45**, 701 (1959); *Biochim. et Biophys. Acta*, **49**, 621 (1961); *J. Biol. Chem.*, **237**, 198 (1962).
270. Peck, H. D., *Proc. Natl. Acad. Sci. U.S.A.*, **46**, 1053 (1960).
271. Peck, H. D., and Fisher, E., *J. Biol. Chem.*, **237**, 190 (1962).
272. Wilson, L. G., and Bandurski, R. S., *Arch. Biochem. Biophys.*, **62**, 503 (1956).
273. Tsuyuki, H., and Idler, D. R., *J. Am. Chem. Soc.*, **79**, 1771 (1957).
274. Berg. P., *J. Am. Chem. Soc.*, **77**, 3163 (1955).
275. Berg, P., *J. Biol. Chem.*, **222**, 991 (1956).
276. Boyer, P. D., Koeppe, O. J., Luchsinger, W. W., and Falcone, A. B., *Federation Proc.*, **14**, 185 (1955).
277. Talbert, P. T., and Huennekens, F. M., *J. Am. Chem. Soc.*, **78**, 4671 (1956).
278. Stern, J. R., Friedman, D. L., and Menon, G. K. K., *Biochim. et Biophys. Acta*, **36**, 299 (1959).
279. Chantrenne, H., *J. Biol. Chem.*, **189**, 227 (1951).
280. Schachter, D., and Taggart, J. V., *J. Biol. Chem.*, **203**, 925 (1953); **208**, 263 (1954).
281. Moldave, K., and Meister, A., *Biochim. et Biophys. Acta*, **25**, 434, (1957).
282. Maas, W. K., and Novelli, G. D., *Arch. Biochem. Biophys.*, **43**, 236 (1953).
283. Jencks, W. P., and Lipmann, F., *J. Biol. Chem.*, **225**, 207 (1957).
284. Whitehouse, M., Moeksi, H., and Gurin, S., *J. Biol. Chem.*, **226**, 813 (1957).
285. Elliott, W. H., *Biochem. J.*, **62**, 427 433 (1956).
286. Ratner, S., and Petrack, B., *Arch. Biochem. Biophys.*, **65**, 582 (1956).
287. Reed, L. J., Leach, F. R., Koike, M., and Levitch, M. E., *Federation Proc.*, **16**, 236 (1957).
288. Hoagland, M. B., Stephenson, M. L., Scott, J. F., Hecht, L. I., and Zamecnik, P. C., *J. Biol. Chem.*, **231**, 241 (1958).
289. Hoagland, M. B., Keller, E. B., and Zamecnik, P. C., *J. Biol. Chem.*, **218**, 345 (1956).
290. de Moss, J. A., and Novelli, G. D., *Biochim. et Biophys. Acta*, **22**, 49 (1956).
291. Berg, P., *J. Biol. Chem.*, **222**, 1025 (1956); **233**, 601 (1958).
292. Karasek, M., Castelfranco, P., Krishnaswamy, P. R., and Meister, A., *J. Am. Chem. Soc.*, **80**, 2335 (1958).
293. Webster, L. T., and Davie, E. W., *Biochim. et Biophys. Acta*, **35**, 559 (1959).
294. Bergman, F. H., Berg, P., Preiss, J., Ofengand, E. J., and Dieckmann, M., *Federation Proc.*, **18**, 751 (1959).
295. Acs, G., Hartmann, G., Boman, H. G., and Lipmann, F., *Federation Proc.*, **18**, 700 (1959).
296. Zillig, W., Schachtschabel, D., and Krone, W., *Z. physiol. Chem.*, **318**, 100 (1960).
297. Sharon, N., and Lipmann, F., *Arch. Biochem. Biophys.*, **69**, 219 (1957).
298. Kalyankar, G. D., and Meister, A., *J. Am. Chem. Soc.*, **81**, 1515 (1959); *J. Biol. Chem.*, **234**, 3210 (1959).
299. Berg, P., *J. Biol. Chem.*, **222**, 1015 (1956).
300. Moldave, K., Castelfranco, P., Meister, A., *J. Biol. Chem.*, **234**, 841 (1959).
301. Jencks, W. P., *Biochim. et Biophys. Acta*, **24**, 227 (1957).

302. Weiss, S. B., Zachau, H. G., and Lipmann, F., *Arch. Biochem. Biophys.*, **83**, 101 (1959).

303. Chantrenne, H., *Biochim. et Biophys. Acta*, **4**, 484, (1950). *Nature*, **160**, 603 (1947); **164**, 576, (1949).

304. Katchalsky, A., and Paecht, M., *J. Am. Chem. Soc.*, **76**, 6042 (1954).

305. Castelfranco, P., Moldave, K., and Meister, A., *J. Am. Chem. Soc.*, **80**, 2335 (1958).

306. Reith, W. S., *Nature*, **178**, 1393 (1956).

307. Gilbert, D. A., and Yemm. E. W., *Nature*, **182**, 1745 (1958).

308. Hansen, R. G., and Hageman, E., *Arch. Biochem. Biophys.*, **62**, 511 (1956).

309. Schuurs, A. H. W. M., de Kloet, S. R., and Koningsberger, V. V., *Biochem. Biophys. Research Communs.*, **3**, 300 (1960).

310. Pontis, H. G., *Biochim. et Biophys. Acta*, **25**, 417 (1957).

311. Ginsburg, V., O'Brien, P. J., and Hall, C. W., *Biochim. et Biophys. Acta*, **55**, 220 (1962).

312. Niemierko, W., Dydnska, M., Drabikowski, W., Kakol, I., and Zaluska, H., *Acta Biol. Exptl.*, **17**, 373 (1957).

313. Ishihara, H., *J. Biochem.*, (*Tokyo*), **47**, 196 (1960).

314. Habermann, V., *Biochim. et Biophys. Acta*, **32**, 297 (1959).

315. Medvedev, Z. A., and Zabolotsky, N. N., *Zhur. Khim.*, *Biol. Khim.*, Abstr. No. 15523 (1959).

316. Hoagland, M. B., *Rec. Trav. Chim.*, **77**, 623 (1958).

317. Koningsberger, V. V., van der Grinten, C. O., and Overbeek, J. T., *Biochim. et Biophys. Acta*, **26**, 483 (1957).

318. Harris, G., Davies, J. W., and Parsons, R., *Nature*, **182**, 1565 (1958).

319. Davies, J. W., Harris, G., and Neal, G. E., *Biochim. et Biophys. Acta*, **51**, 95 (1961).

320. Gilbert, D. A., and Yemm, E. W., *Nature*, **182**, 1745 (1958).

321. Schuurs, A. H. W. M., and Koningsberger, V. V., *Biochim. et Biophys. Acta*, **44**, 167 (1960).

322. Harris, G., and Davies, J. W., *Nature*, **184**, 788 (1959).

323. Davies, J. W., and Harris, G., *Proc. Roy. Soc.*, **151B**, 537 (1960).

324. Davies, J. W., and Harris, G., *Biochim. et Biophys. Acta*, **45**, 28 (1960).

325. Harris, G., and Neal, G. E., *Biochim. et Biophys. Acta*, **47**, 122 (1961).

326. Dirheimer, G., Weil, J. H., and Ebel, J. P., *Compt. rend.*, **246**, 3384 (1958).

327. Cerna, J., Grunberger, D., and Sorm, F., *Collection Czechslov. Chem. Communs.*, **26**, 1212 (1961).

328. Wilken, D. R., and Hansen, R. G., *Federation Proc.*, **19**, 309 (1960).

329. Weinstein, C., Seifter, S., and Berkman, J. I., *Federation Proc.*, **19**, 234 (1960).

330. Ondarza, R. N., and Aubanel, M., *Biochim. et Biophys. Acta*, **44**, 381 (1960).

331. Szafranski, P., Sulkowski, E., and Golaszewski, T', *Nature*, **184**, 1940 (1959).

332. Szafranski, P., Sulkowski, E., Golaszewski, T., and Heller, J., *Acta Biochim. Polon.*, **7**, 151 (1960).

333. Szafranski, P., and Bagdasarian, M., *Nature*, **190**, 719 (1961).

334. Hase, E., Mihara, S., Otsuka, H., and Tamiya, H., *Arch. Biochem. Biophys.*, **83**, 170 (1959); *Biochim. et Biophys. Acta*, **32**, 298 (1959).

335. Hase, E., and Mihara, S., *J. Gen. Appl. Microbiol.*, **5**, 221 (1960).

336. Hase, E., Mihara, S., and Tamiya, H., *Biochim. et Biophys. Acta*, **39**, 381 (1960).

337. Brown, A. D., *Biochem. J.*, **71**, 5P (1959).

338. Bergkvist, R., *Acta. Chem. Scand.*, **12**, 364 (1958).
339. Potter, J. L., and Dounce, A. L., *J. Am. Chem. Soc.*, **78**, 3078 (1956).
340. Prokof'ev, M. A., Antonovich, E. G., and Bogdanov, A. A., *Biokhimiya*, **25**, 931 (1960).
341. Ellfolk, N., and Katunuma, N., *Arch. Biochem. Biophys.*, **81**, 521 (1959).
342. Wilken, D. R., and Hansen, R. G., *J. Biol. Chem.*, **236**, 1051 (1961).
343. Penn, N. W., *Federation Proc.*, **19**, 350 (1960).
344. Walter, H., *Nature*, **188**, 643 (1960).
345. Miettinen, J. K., and Savioja, T., *Biochem. J.*, **76**, 66P (1960).
346. Davies, J. W., and Harris, G., *Biochim. et Biophys. Acta*, **45**, 39 (1960).
347. Baddiley, J., and Todd, A. R., *J. Chem. Soc.*, 648 (1947).
348. Baddiley, J., Clark, V. M., Michalski, J. J., and Todd, A. R., *J. Chem. Soc.*, 815 (1949).
349. Badddiley, J., Michelson, A. M., and Todd, A. R., *J. Chem. Soc.*, 582 (1949).
350. Michelson, A. M., and Todd, A. R., *J. Chem. Soc.*, 2487 (1949).
351. Corby, N. S., Kenner, G. W., and Todd, A. R., *J. Chem. Soc.*, 3669 (1952).
352. Kenner, G. W. Todd, A. R., and Weymouth, F. J., *J. Chem. Soc.*, 3675 (1952).
353. Kenner, G. W., Todd, A. R., Webb, R. F., and Weymouth, F. J., *J. Chem. Soc.*, 2288 (1954).
354. Corby, N. S., Kenner, G. W., and Todd, A. R., *J. Chem. Soc.*, 1234 (1952).
355. Michelson, A. M., *J. Chem. Soc.*, 1957 (1958).
356. Beránek, J., and Smrt, J., *Collection Czechslov. Chem. Communs.*, **25**, 2029 (1960).
357. Szer, W., and Shugar, D., *Acta Biochim. Polon.*, **8**, 235 (1961).
358. Michelson, A. M., unpublished work.
359. Griffin, B. E., and Todd, A., *J. Chem. Soc.*, 1389 (1958).
360. Forrest, H. S., Mason, H. S., and Todd, A. R., *J. Chem. Soc.*, 2530 (1952).
361. Christie, S. M. H., Kenner, G. W., and Todd, A. R., *J. Chem. Soc.*, 46 (1954).
362. Michelson, A. M., and Todd, A., *J. Chem. Soc.*, 3459 (1956).
363. Shabarova, Z. A., Satarova, L. G., and Prokof'ev, M. A., *Doklady Akad. Nauk S.S.S.R.*, **123**, 864 (1958).
364. Shvachkin, Y. P., Syrtsova, L. A., and Prokof'ev, M. A., *Zhur. Obshchet Khim.*, **30**, 2462 (1960).
365. Kenner, G. W., Reese, C. B., and Todd, A. R., *J. Chem. Soc.*, 546 (1958).
366. Christie, S. M. H., Elmore, D. T., Kenner, G. W., Todd, A. R., and Weymouth, F. J., *J. Chem. Soc.*, 2947 (1953).
367. Shuster, L., Kaplan, N. O., and Stolzenbach, F. E., *J. Biol. Chem.*, **215**, 195 (1955).
368. De Luca, C., and Kaplan, N. O., *J. Biol. Chem.*, **223**, 569 (1956).
369. Baddiley, J., Buchanan, J. G., and Letters, R., *J. Chem. Soc.*, 1067 (1957).
370. Baddiley, J., Buchanan, J. G., Letters, R., and Sanderson, A. R., *J. Chem. Soc.*, 1731 (1959).
371. Ikehara, M., Ohtsuka, E., Kitagawa, S., Yagi, K., and Tonomura, Y., *J. Am. Chem. Soc.*, **83**, 2679 (1961).
372. Bachhawat, B. K., Woessner, J. F., and Coon, M. J., *Federation Proc.*, **15**, 214 (1956).
373. Avison, A. W. D., *J. Chem. Soc.*, 732 (1955).
374. Berg, P., *J. Biol. Chem.*, **222**, 1015 (1956).
375. Kellerman, G. M., *J. Biol. Chem.*, **231**, 427 (1958).
376. Moyed, H. S., and Lipmann, F., *J. Bacteriol.*, **73**, 117 (1957).
377. Peng, C. H. L., *Biochim. et Biophys. Acta*, **22**, 42 (1956).

378. Whitehouse, M., Moeksi, H., and Gurin, S., *J. Biol. Chem.*, **226,** 813 (1957).
379. Vignais, P. V., and Zabin, I., *Biochim. et Biophys. Acta,* **29,** 263 (1958).
380. Reed, L. J., Leach, F. R., and Loike, M., *J. Biol. Chem.*, **232,** 123 (1958).
381. Khorana, H. G., and Vizsolyi, J. P., *J. Am. Chem. Soc.*, **81,** 4660 (1959).
382. Zetsche, F., Lüscher, E., and Meyer, H. E., *Chem. Ber.*, **71,** 1088 (1938).
383. Khorana, H. G., and Todd, A. R., *J. Chem. Soc.*, 2257 (1953).
384. Lowenstein, J. M., *Biochem. Preparations*, **7,** 5 (1960).
385. Huennekens, F. M., and Kilgour, G. L., *J. Am. Chem. Soc.*, **77,** 6716 (1955).
386. Kenner, G. W., Todd, A. R., and Webb, R. F., *J. Chem. Soc.*, 2843 (1954).
387. Smith, M., and Khorana, H. G., *J. Am. Chem. Soc.*, **80,** 1141 (1958).
388. Way, J. L., Dahl, J. L., and Parks, R. E., *J. Biol. Chem.*, **234,** 1241 (1959).
389. Hughes, N. A., Kenner, G. W., and Todd, A. R., *J. Chem. Soc.*, 3733 (1957).
390. Kennedy, E. P., *J. Biol. Chem.*, **222,** 185 (1956).
391. Smith, M., Moffat, J. G., and Khorana, H. G., *J. Am. Chem. Soc.*, **80,** 6204 (1958).
392. Paulus, H., and Kennedy, E. P., *J. Am. Chem. Soc.*, **81,** 4436 (1959); *J. Biol. Chem.*, **235,** 1303 (1960).
393. Baddiley, J., Buchanan, J. G., and Sanderson, A. R., *J. Chem. Soc.*, 3107 (1958).
394. Baddiley, J., Buchanan, J. G., and Fawcett, C. P., *J. Chem. Soc.*, 2192 (1959).
395. Reichard, P., and Ringertz, N. R., *J. Am. Chem. Soc.*, **81,** 878 (1959).
396. Rhodes, W. C., and McElroy, W. D., *J. Biol. Chem..* **233,** 1528 (1958).
397. Oertel, G. W., *Arch. Biochem. Biophys.*, **85,** 564 (1959).
398. Oertel, G. W., and Agashe, B. D., *Biochim. et Biophys. Acta,* **45,** 1 (1960).
399. Berg, P., *J. Biol. Chem.*, **233,** 608 (1958).
400. Lambert, R., Zilliken, F., and Gurin, S., *Angew. Chem.*, **70,** 571 (1958).
401. Moldave, K., Castelfranco, P., and Meister, A., *J. Biol. Chem.*, **234,** 841 (1959).
402. McCorquodale, D. J., and Mueller, G. C., *Arch. Biochem. Biophys.*, **77,** 13 (1958).
403. Baddiley, J., and Hughes, N. A., *Advances in Enzymology*, **22,** 157 (1960).
404. Harris, G., and Davies, J. W., *Nature*, **184,** 788 (1959).
405. Tuboi, S., and Huzino, A., *Arch. Biochem. Biophys.*, **86,** 309 (1960).
406. Harris, G., and MacWilliam, I. C., *J. Chem. Soc.*, 2053, (1961).
407. Talbert, P. T., and Huennekens, F. M., *J. Am. Chem. Soc.*, **78,** 4671 (1956).
408. Atherton, F. R., Morrison, A. L., Cremlyn, R. J. W., Kenner, G. W., Todd, A. R., and Webb, R. F., *Chem. and Ind. (London)*, 1183 (1955).
409. Chase, B. H., Kenner, G. W., Todd, A. R., and Webb, R. F., *J. Chem. Soc.*, 1371 (1956).
410. Cramer, F., and Baldauf, H. J., *Angew. Chem.*, **72,** 627 (1960); Cramer, F., Scheit, K. H., and Baldauf, H. J., *Chem. Ber.*, **95,** 1657 (1962).
411. Wittman, R., and Cramer, F., *Angew. Chem.*, **73,** 220 (1961).
412. Stokes, H. N., *Am. Chem. J.*, **15,** 198 (1893).
413. Clark, V. M., Kirby, G. W., and Todd, A. R., *J. Chem. Soc.*, 1497 (1957).
414. Chambers, R. W., and Khorana, H. G., *J. Am. Chem. Soc.*, **80,** 3749 (1958).
415. Baddiley, J., Buchanan, J. G., and Letters, R., *J. Chem. Soc.*, 2812 (1956).
416. Rathlev, T., and Rosenberg, T., *Arch. Biochem. and Biophys.*, **65,** 319 (1956).
417. Jencks, W. P., and Lipmann, F., *J. Biol. Chem.*, **225,** 207 (1957).
418. Borgström, B., *Acta Chem. Scand.*, **12,** 1533 (1958).
419. Ueda, T., and Ohtsuka, E., *Chem. and Pharm. Bull. (Tokyo)*, **7,** 740 (1959).
420. Koerner, J. F., and Varadarajan, S., *J. Biol. Chem.*, **235,** 2688 (1960).

421. Chambers, R. W., and Moffatt, J. G., *J. Am. Chem. Soc.*, **80**, 3752 (1958).
422. Chambers, R. W., *J. Am. Chem. Soc.*, **81**, 3032 (1959).
423. Chambers, R. W., Shapiro, P., and Kurkov, V., *J. Am. Chem. Soc.*, **82**, 970 (1960).
424. Lengyel, P., and Chambers, R. W., *J. Am. Chem. Soc.*, **82**, 752 (1960).
425. Moffatt, J. G., and Khorana, H. G., *J. Am. Chem. Soc.*, **80**, 3756 (1958).
426. Ueda, T., *Chem. and Pharm. Bull. (Tokyo)*, **8**, 464 (1960).
427. Kochetkov, N. K., Budowsky, E. I., and Shibaev, V. N., *Biochim. et Biophys. Acta*, **53**, 415 (1961).
428. Honjo, M., Furukawa, Y., Imai, K., Moriyama, H., and Tanaka, K., *Chem. and Pharm. Bull. (Tokyo)*, **8**, 750 (1960); **10**, 225 (1962).
429. Ueda, T., and Ohtsuka, E., *Chem. and Pharm. Bull. (Tokyo)*, **7**, 389 (1959).
430. Baddiley, J., Hughes, N. A., and James, A. L., *J. Chem. Soc.*, 2574 (1961). See also reference 472.
431. Kessler, D., Moss, B., and Chambers, R. W., *Biochim. et Biophys. Acta*, **38**, 549 (1960).
432. Tanaka, K., Honjo, M., Sanno, Y., and Moriyama, H., *Chem. and Pharm. Bull. (Tokyo)*, **8**, 749 (1960); **10**, 220 (1962).
433. Moffatt, J. G., and Khorana, H. G., *J. Am. Chem. Soc.*, **83**, 649 (1961).
434. Roseman, S., Distler, J. J., Moffatt, J. G., and Khorana, H. G., *J. Am. Chem. Soc.*, **83**, 659 (1961).
435. Agranoff, B. W., and Bradley, R. M., *Federation Proc.*, **20**, 281 (1961).
436. Moffatt, J. G., and Khorana, H. G., *J. Am. Chem. Soc.*, **83**, 663 (1961).
437. Michelson, A. M., *Chem. and Ind. (London)*, 1267 (1960).
438. Michelson, A. M., in press.
439. Michelson, A. M., and Letters, R., in press.
440. Michelson, A. M., Dondon, J., and Grunberg-Manago, M., *Biochim. et Biophys. Acta*, **55**, 529 (1962).
441. Michelson, A. M., and Wold, F., in press.
442. Michelson, A. M., *Biochim. et Biophys. Acta*, **50**, 605 (1961).
443. Michelson, A. M., *Ann. Revs. Biochem.*, **30**, 133 (1961).
444. Riess, J., and Ourisson, G., *Bull. soc. chim.*, 1243 (1961).
445. Michelson, A. M., Strasbourg Meeting on RNA and Polyphosphates, July, 1961.
446. Cramer, F., and Wittmann, R., *Chem. Ber.*, **94**, 322, 328 (1961).
447. Anand, N., Clark, V. M., Hall, R. H., and Todd, A. R., *J. Chem. Soc.*, 3665 (1952).
448. Hasselbach, W., *Acta Biol. et Med. Ger.*, **2**, 13 (1959) [*Chemical Abstracts*, **54**, 9944 (1960)].
449. Clark, V. M., Hutchinson, D. W., and Todd, A. R., *Nature*, **187**, 59 (1960); *J. Chem. Soc.*, 722 (1961).
450. Andrews, K. J. M., *J. Chem. Soc.*, 1808 (1961).
451. Brown, D. M., and Hamer, N. K., *Proc. Chem. Soc.*, 212 (1960).
452. Cramer, F., and Winter, M., *Chem. Ber.*, **92**, 2761 (1959).
453. Cramer, F., and Schaller, H., *Chem. Ber.*, **94**, 1634 (1961).
454. Goldman, L., Marsico, J. W., and Anderson, G. W., *J. Am. Chem. Soc.*, **82**, 2969 (1960). See also reference 475.
455. Cramer, F., Schaller, H., and Staab, H. A., *Chem. Ber.*, **94**, 1612 (1961).
456. Staab, H. A., Schaller, H., and Cramer, F., *Angew. Chem.*, **71**, 736 (1959).
457. Staab, H. A., *Ann.*, **609**, 75 (1957).
458. Schaller, H., Staab, H. A., and Cramer, F., *Chem. Ber.*, **94**, 1621 (1961).
459. Wasserman, H. H., and Cohen, D., *J. Am. Chem. Soc.*, **82**, 4435 (1960).

460. Woodward, R. B., Olofson, R. A., and Mayer, H., *J. Am. Chem. Soc.*, **83**, 1010 (1961).
461. Sanno, Y., and Tanaka, K., *Chem. and Pharm. Bull. (Tokyo)*, **8**, 753 (1960); **10**, 231 (1962).
462. Jacobson, B., and Davidson, E. A., *Nature*, **189**, 663 (1961).
463. Windmueller, H. G., and Kaplan, N. O., *J. Biol. Chem.*, **236**, 2716 (1961).
464. Cramer, F. D., and Weimann, G., *Chem. and Ind. (London)*, 46 (1960).
465. Harris, G., and Wiseman, A., *Biochim. et Biophys. Acta*, **55**, 374, 775, 929 (1962).
466. Harris, G., and Wiseman, A., *Biochim. et Biophys. Acta*, **55**, 396 (1962).
467. Pazur, J. H., Kleppe, K., and Cepure, A., *Biochem. Biophys. Research Communs.*, **7**, 157 (1962).
468. Strominger, J. L., unpublished work.
469. Okazaki, T., Okazaki, R., Strominger, J. L., and Suzuki, S., *Biochem. Biophys. Research Communs.*, **7**, 300 (1962).
470. Roseman, S., *Proc. Natl. Acad. Sci., U.S.A.*, **48**, 437 (1962).
471. Kobata, A., *Biochem. Biophys. Research Communs.*, **7**, 346 (1962).
472. Carlson, D. M., and Hansen, R. G., *J. Biol. Chem.*, **237**, 1260 (1962).
473. Barber, G. A., *Biochem. Biophys. Research Communs.*, **8**, 204 (1962).
474. Mandelstam, P., Loercher, R., and Strominger, J. L., *J. Biol. Chem.*, **237**, 2683 (1962).
475. Cramer, F., and Neunhoeffer, H., *Chem. Ber.*, **95**, 1664 (1962).
476. Bernhauer, K., and Wagner, F., *Biochem. Z.*, **335**, 453 (1962).

Chapter 5*

BIOSYNTHESIS OF NUCLEOTIDES, NUCLEOTIDE ANHYDRIDES, AND POLYNUCLEOTIDES

Biochemical routes leading to the synthesis of nucleotides and their derivatives have been established to a large extent[1] and will be described very briefly. Much of the earlier information was derived from tracer studies *in vivo*; other methods include the use of biochemical mutants (particularly of *Neurospora*) and direct examination of purified enzyme systems *in vitro*. The various schemes are to some extent idealised in that they are constructed from results obtained with a wide, but not all-embracing, variety of micro-organisms and organs.

It may be noted that all the biosynthetic intermediates involved in the *de novo* synthesis of purine and pyrimidine nucleotides possess functional groups (carboxyl or phosphate) that are essentially completely ionised at physiological pHs; uncharged metabolites are generally excretory or catabolic products. A possible reason for " the importance of being ionised " may lie in the more efficient retention of ionised compounds within the cell or its organelles.[2]

A second principle, " the importance of not being ionised " may underlie many of the biochemical reactions of nucleoside-5′ polyphosphates.

Purine Nucleotides

Pigeons and their excreta have played an important part in studies on the *de novo* synthesis of purines. Degradation of the uric acid formed from isotopically labelled compounds both *in vivo* and *in vitro* identified the origin and location of the precursor atoms of the purine ring as shown.

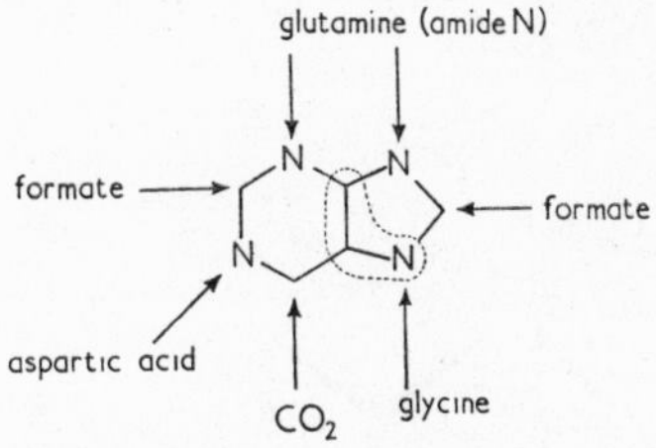

* Since this chapter is a severely abbreviated account included as background information for chemists rather than as a survey of use to biochemists, full documentation has not been attempted.

Further work showed that hypoxanthine was formed from the same metabolites and that the immediate precursor of the free purine was inosine-5' phosphate. By means of partially purified enzyme systems from pigeon liver the various intermediates in the sequence have been isolated (except ribosylamine-5 phosphate) and identified. Pyrophosphorylation of ribose-5 phosphate by ATP gives ribose-1 pyrophosphate-5 phosphate which reacts with glutamine to produce inorganic pyrophosphate, glutamic acid and ribofuranosylamine-5 phosphate. Further reaction of this amine with glycine and ATP gives the glycyl derivative which is then formylated by an anhydroformyl derivative of tetrahydrofolic acid (arising from the reaction of formate with ATP and tetrahydrofolic acid). Subsequently a glycinamidine compound is formed by the action of glutamine and ATP. Ring closure of this formylglycinamidine derivative of ribose-5 phosphate (ATP is again required) gives 5-amino-1-β-D-ribofuranosylimidazole-5' phosphate. Carboxylation gives the 5-aminoimidazole-4 carboxylic acid which with aspartic acid and ATP yields a succinyl derivative that is cleaved to fumaric acid and 5-amino-1-β-D-ribofuranosyl-imidazole-4-carboxamide-5' phosphate. Formylation of the amino group (with N^{10}-formyltetrahydrofolic acid) gives a formamido compound and this is converted into inosine-5' phosphate by cyclisation.

Adenine and guanine nucleotides are then formed by a series of interconversions. Amination of inosine-5' phosphate occurs by the action of aspartic acid and guanosine-5' triphosphate to give an intermediate adenylosuccinic acid with subsequent cleavage to fumaric acid and adenosine-5' phosphate.

Conversion of inosinic acid into guanylic acid depends on the intermediate formation of xanthosine-5' phosphate by an oxidation process involving NAD and a dehydrogenase. Transfer of the amide nitrogen of glutamine to C2 of xanthylic acid gives guanosine-5' phosphate, probably by simultaneous interaction of the xanthylic acid with ATP and glutamine. In bacterial systems ammonia rather than glutamine is the source of this amino group (compare amination of uridine-5' phosphate).

Alternate routes for the de novo synthesis of purine nucleotides have not been identified so far and it is likely that the pathway described above is quite general. Enzymic systems utilising free purines do exist however, such as glycosylation by a phosphorolytic reaction with ribose-1 phosphate (or 2-deoxyribose-1 phosphate) to give the nucleoside, which is then phosphorylated by ATP. Alternatively, an enzymically catalysed pyrophosphorolysis with ribose-1 pyrophosphate-5 phosphate gives the nucleotide directly.

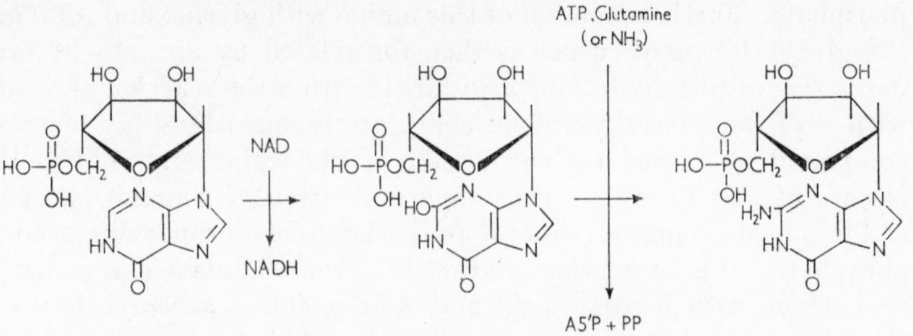

ATP, Glutamine (or NH_3)

NAD

NADH

A5'P + PP

While the effect of an analogue inhibitor can be expressed in several ways, many of the purine analogues that inhibit cell metabolism are biologically active only when converted into the nucleotide by such enzymic reactions, and indeed the resistance of certain mutants of *Streptococcus faecalis* to 6-mercaptopurine and 8-azaguanine is because the cells lack the ability to convert the analogue into the nucleotide by pyrophosphorolysis of ribose-1 pyrophosphate-5 phosphate.

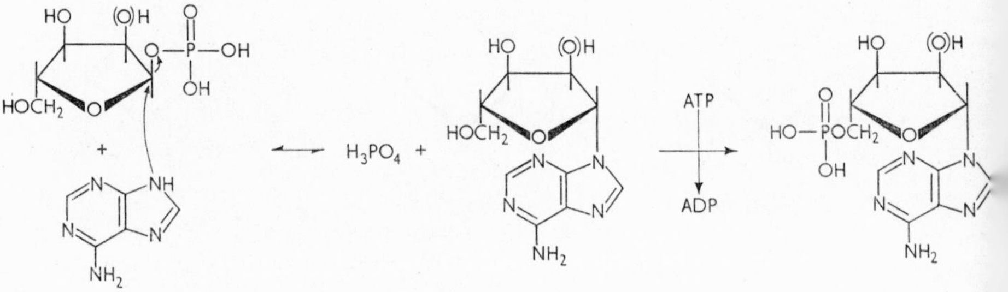

H_3PO_4 +

ATP

ADP

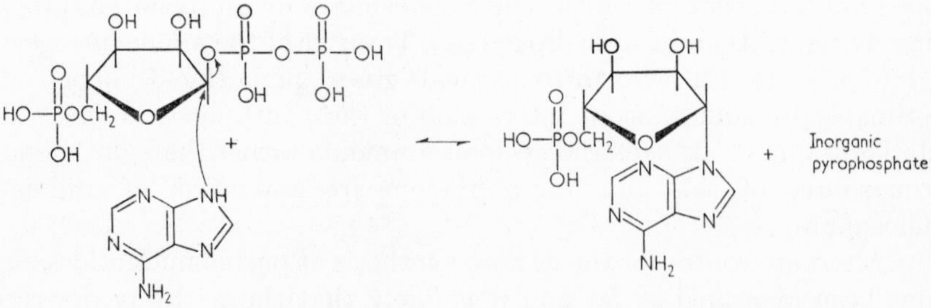

Inorganic pyrophosphate

PYRIMIDINE NUCLEOTIDES

The main route for the *de novo* synthesis of pyrimidines involves formation of orotic acid from simple precursors. Aspartic acid is carbamylated by the action of carbamyl phosphate (formed from ammonia, carbon dioxide and adenosine-5′ triphosphate) to give carbamyl-L-aspartic acid (ureidosuccinic acid) which on ring closure is converted into dihydroorotic acid. Enzymic oxidation gives orotic acid which with ribose-1 pyrophosphate-5 phosphate forms orotidine-5' phosphate. This is then converted into uridine-5' phosphate by the action of a decarboxylase.

Deoxyuridine-5' phosphate ⟶ Thymidine-5' phosphate

An alternative pathway may be of significance in avian liver. This sequence involves transformation of carbamyl-β-alanine ribotide to dihydrouridine-5' phosphate followed by oxidation to the nucleotide.

Other enzymic syntheses have been demonstrated that are analogous to the glycosylation of orotic acid by ribose-1 pyrophosphate-5 phosphate but which will proceed with uracil and other bases. The sequential actions of pyrimidine nucleoside phosphorylase (which also effects

I*

transglycosylation because of the reversible nature of the reaction) and pyrimidine nucleoside kinase provide a mechanism occurring under certain conditions of nucleotide synthesis.

These last mechanisms are of particular significance in the interference of pyrimidine metabolism by analogues such as 4-azauracil (or the nucleoside). In tumour tissues, 4-azauracil is converted into the nucleoside and nucleoside-5′ phosphate and it is likely that the primary biochemical lesion responsible for retardation of tumour growth by 4-azauridine is the inhibition of orotidine-5′ phosphate decarboxylase by 4-azauridine-5′ phosphate. In general, however, routes other than that via orotic acid are probably of greater significance as catabolic sequences.

The key intermediate, uridine-5′ phosphate, is converted into the other pyrimidine nucleotides by various reactions. Phosphorylation with ATP gives uridine-5′ triphosphate which on amination (by the action of ATP and ammonia in bacteria, or ATP and glutamine in mammalian systems) forms cytidine-5' triphosphate. Conversion of uridine-5' phosphate into 2'-deoxyuridine-5' phosphate by an as yet unknown process followed by reaction with N^5,N^{10}-methylene tetrahydrofolic acid (or formaldehyde and tetrahydrofolic acid) yields thymidine-5' phosphate (and dihydrofolic acid). Mechanisms for the biosynthesis of 5-methyl-2'-deoxycytidylic acid have not been elucidated, but enzymic hydroxymethylation of deoxycytidine-5' phosphate to 5-hydroxymethyl-2'-deoxycytidine-5' phosphate by the action of formaldehyde and tetrahydrofolic acid has been established in studies on the metabolism of T-even bacteriophages. (Cytosine is completely replaced by the 5-hydroxymethyl derivative in the DNA of these viruses.) In contrast with the methylation process involved in biosynthesis of DNA thymine, the immediate source of the methyl group for RNA thymine (and the methylated purines present in RNA) appears to be methionine, presumably activated as the S-adenosyl derivative.

Free thymine can also be converted into the deoxynucleotide by enzymic reactions analogous to those described for uracil, but it is probable that these mechanisms are likewise mainly catabolic in function. Again, however, they are of significance in chemotherapeutic studies; inhibition of the methylation of deoxyuridylic acid to thymidine-5′ phosphate by 5-fluorouridine and 5-fluoro-2′-deoxyuridine is

undoubtedly a result of the prior formation of the nucleotide analogue. As in the case of bacterial resistance to purine analogues, strains of *E. coli* that are resistant to growth inhibition by 5-fluorouracil lack the capacity to catalyse pyrophosphorolytic formation of nucleotides from pyrimidine bases (including uracil) and ribose-1 pyrophosphate-5 phosphate, though active enzyme preparations can be obtained from drug sensitive organisms. Another resistance mechanism involving alteration of the active site in thymidylate synthetase, so that the enzyme is no longer effectively inhibited by 5-fluorouracil nucleotides, has been identified in a line of Ehrlich ascites carcinoma.

While the biosynthetic mechanisms involved in the formation of deoxynucleotides are undefined as yet, a number of *in vivo* and *in vitro* studies using nucleosides isotopically labelled in both the sugar and base moieties suggest that the ribosyl compounds (both purine and pyrimidine) are directly reduced to 2′-deoxyribosyl derivatives without cleavage of the glycosyl linkage. The conversion of uridine and cytidine (or the 5′ phosphates) into the corresponding deoxy compounds by soluble extracts of *Salmonella typhimurium* LT-2 possibly involves deoxyribosyl transferring enzymes but other studies with preparations from chick embryos suggest that direct reduction of cytidine and guanosine occurs at the nucleoside-5′ phosphate level. More definitive evidence has been obtained with enzyme preparations from *Escherichia coli* which catalyse the conversion of cytidine-5′ phosphate into deoxy-cytidine-5′ phosphate probably via cytidine-5′ pyrophosphate and deoxycytidine-5′ pyrophosphate, reduced coenzyme II (NADPH$_2$) acting as co-factor in the reduction stage. Uridine-5′ pyrophosphate is also converted into 2′-deoxyuridine-5′ pyrophosphate and it is likely that the mechanism of reduction is common to all the nucleotides.

Inhibition of Purine and Pyrimidine Metabolism

As may be expected, purine and pyrimidine analogues (such as 8-azaguanine and 5-fluorouracil) that act as carcinostatic agents or inhibitors of cellular metabolism do not act in a uniform manner. Some, as the free base, inhibit the utilisation of free purines or pyrimidines, while others, effective as the nucleotide, inhibit a specific reaction in the *de novo* synthesis of nucleotides. Inhibition of the polymerisation processes leading to nucleic acids or incorporation into the nucleic acids (RNA or DNA) with subsequent disruption of the normal cell chemistry represent other modes of action of such compounds. The *in vivo* operation and effectiveness of a particular analogue thus depends on its form (free base, nucleoside or nucleotide), the enzymic reactions to which it is susceptible, and the reactions for which it is an effective inhibitor.

$$NH_2COCH_2CH_2\overset{\underset{NH_2}{|}}{C}HCOOH \qquad N_2CHCO-O-CH_2\overset{\underset{NH_2}{|}}{C}HCOOH$$

Glutamine   Azaserine

$$N_2CHCOCH_2CH_2\overset{\underset{NH_2}{|}}{C}HCOOH$$

DON (6-Diazo-5-oxo-L-norleucine)

Other types of antimetabolite can function as inhibitors of the *de novo* synthesis of nucleotides. Two such compounds, azaserine and 6-diazo-5-oxo-L-norleucine, act antagonistically to glutamine and are particularly effective in inactivating the enzyme catalysing the conversion of formylglycinamide ribotide into formylglycinamidine ribotide. Competitive inhibition occurs in the other enzymic reactions involving glutamine such as the formation of ribosylamine-5' phosphate, and the amination of uridine-5' phosphate and xanthosine-5' phosphate.

CONTROL OF THE BIOSYNTHESIS OF NUCLEOTIDES

The regulation of the complex system of coupled chemical reactions known as cell metabolism is clearly of vital importance. With respect to purine biosynthesis, a number of possible control mechanisms are now known to exist which depend on the suppression of the synthesis of a metabolite by the metabolite itself, or a related compound or end product. This so called " feedback " inhibition can occur by interference with either the action or the synthesis of the enzyme responsible for the production of the metabolite. Thus the activity of phosphoribosylpyrophosphate amido transferase (which catalyses the synthesis of ribosylamine-5 phosphate from glutamine and ribose-1 pyrophosphate-5 phosphate) is markedly inhibited by AMP, ADP, ATP, GMP, GDP and IMP but not by a large number of other purine or pyrimidine derivatives. In certain bacterial mutants with a genetic block leading to the accumulation of aminoimidazole precursors any of the purines can act as a feedback inhibitor if the genetic block does not interfere with purine interconversion. However, when this interconversion is prevented adenine becomes a specific inhibitor (decreasing the accumulation of imidazole precursors) and the feedback control therefore operates at a level involving adenine (or adenosine or the nucleotide) rather than purines in general. Conversion of guanosine-5' phosphate into adenine compounds (via a reductive deamination of GMP to inosine-5' phosphate) is markedly inhibited by adenosine-5' triphosphate, suggesting a possible control of the synthesis of adenine nucleotides from guanine derivatives. The relations between this negative type of control of the rate of synthesis and concentration of nucleotides in the cell and the positive aspects of reciprocal requirement such as the necessity of ATP for the synthesis of guanosine-5' phosphate and of GTP for adenosine-5' phosphate production are undoubtedly complex. As previously mentioned, feedback control can also be achieved by suppression of the synthesis of an enzyme; an example is the effect of guanine on the formation of inosine-5' phosphate dehydrogenase in bacterial mutants lacking xanthosine-5' phosphate aminase.

It is possible that further control mechanisms operate on the various conversions among nucleosides and nucleotides. These conversions include deamination of cytidine, adenosine and guanosine and their derivatives to the corresponding hydroxy compounds, phosphorolysis of nucleosides and pyrophosphorolysis of nucleotides, trans-N-glycosylation of nucleosides (an enzymic transfer involving the direct exchange of deoxyribose from one acceptor to another), phosphorylation of nucleosides and dephosphorylation of nucleotides, and reduction of ribonucleotides to deoxynucleotides. The observation that enzymic conversion of cytidine nucleotides into the deoxynucleotides by chick embryo extracts is strongly inhibited by deoxyadenosine-5' triphosphate, deoxyguanosine-5' triphosphate and to a lesser extent by thymidine-5' triphosphate but not by deoxycytidine-5' triphosphate suggests a possible homoeostatic mechanism governing the synthesis of deoxynucleic acids. At a higher metabolic level a balance is presumable maintained between nucleoside polyphosphates and nucleic acids, while integration of the variety of nucleotide anhydrides (coenzymes) employed in wider metabolic processes adds another order of complexity to the organisation evolved in living systems.

PSEUDOURIDINE

As yet, little is known of the metabolism and significance of 5-ribosyluracil. An approximately equal distribution of tracer is found in the cytidylic, uridylic and ψ-uridylic acids of yeast ribonucleic acid following incorporation of 6-^{14}C orotic acid. Enzyme extracts from a creek-mud pseudomonad catalyse the conversion of ψ-uridine into uridine. A 3,5-diribosyluracil intermediate has been suggested. The conversion is inhibited by thymine and 5-hydroxymethyluracil but not by 4-methyluracil or 5-bromouracil. A possible function of the nucleotide in biologically active ribonucleic acids may lie in the acylating properties of N^3-acyluracils. The "bifunctional" hydrogen bonding capacity of pseudouridine may be significant for maintenance of secondary or tertiary structure of the nucleic acid.

The chemical properties (e.g. bromination, photolysis) of uracil suggest that electrophilic substitution at C5 of the pyrimidine ring occurs fairly readily. A purely speculative mechanism* for the biosynthesis of pseudouridine-5' phosphate would involve ribose-1 pyrophosphate-5 phosphate in a manner analogous to that evident in the biosynthesis of uridine-5' phosphate, with possibly a 4-hydroxy-4,5-dihydro-5-glycosyl intermediate. (See chemical formation of C—C bonds by alkyl pyrophosphates, p. 294).

BIOSYNTHESIS OF NUCLEOTIDE ANHYDRIDES[3]

A number of connected pathways are known whereby adenosine-5' triphosphate is produced (in excess of that consumed) by the oxidation of carbohydrates, fats and amino acids. Thus in the oxidation of glucose,

*Present indications are that the pathway involves glycosylation of uridine by a nucleoside donor followed by cleavage of the N-glycosyl bond.

ADP is phosphorylated to ATP by the action of the metabolic intermediates glyceroyl phosphate-3 phosphate or *enol*pyruvate-2 phosphate.

Other mechanisms for the formation of ATP are coupled more
directly with the utilisation of oxygen by the cytochrome systems of
electron or hydrogen transfer (oxidative phosphorylation) and with
related photosynthetic systems in which light provides the necessary

energy (photophosphorylation). Again, the essential steps seem to
involve phosphorylation of ADP to ATP rather than a phosphorylation
of adenosine-5' phosphate (AMP). However, the three nucleotides are
directly related by the myokinase type of reaction in which AMP is
reversibly phosphorylated by ATP with the formation of two molecules
of ADP.

$$AMP + ATP \leftrightharpoons 2ADP$$

Other compounds that are in biochemical equilibrium with ATP are
phosphocreatine and (in invertebrates) phosphoarginine; they may be
regarded as reserve compounds available in muscle for the rapid
production of ATP by phosphorylation of ADP. The reversible reaction
between polyphosphate and ADP to form ATP, catalysed by an enzyme
from *Escherichia coli*, suggests that in micro-organisms polyphosphate
may possess a similar function.

Directly or indirectly, ATP is involved in the synthesis of the large
number of nucleotide anhydrides that have been identified. For reasons
which are discussed later, phosphorylation of nucleoside-5' phosphates

(both ribo and deoxyribo) to the corresponding pyrophosphates and triphosphates probably always occurs by a stepwise process, that is by phosphorylation rather than pyrophosphorylation.

$$ATP + NMP \leftrightarrows ADP + NDP$$

(NMP = UMP, CMP, GMP, AMP or deoxynucleoside-5' phosphates).

Nucleoside monophosphate kinases also catalyse transphosphorylation between any of the nucleoside-5 triphosphates and adenosine-5' phosphate,

$$NTP + AMP \leftrightarrows NDP + ADP$$
(NTP = UTP, CTP, ITP or ATP)
$$UTP + UMP \leftrightarrows UDP + UDP$$
$$GTP + GMP \leftrightarrows GDP + GDP$$

while nucleoside-5' pyrophosphate kinases catalyse transphosphorylation between a nucleoside-5' triphosphate and a nucleoside-5' pyrophosphate.

$$ATP + UDP \leftrightarrows ADP + UTP$$
$$ATP + GDP \leftrightarrows ADP + GTP$$
$$GTP + UDP \leftrightarrows GDP + UTP$$
$$UTP + IDP \leftrightarrows UDP + ITP$$

The various nucleoside-5' triphosphates are then used for the biosynthesis of diesterified pyrophosphate derivatives such as uridine diphosphate glucose, flavin adenine dinucleotide, guanosine diphosphate mannose, cytidine diphosphate choline and nicotinic acid adenine dinucleotide, by a pyrophosphorolytic reaction with the appropriate monoesterified phosphate.

$$NTP + ZMP \leftrightarrows NPPZ + PP$$

(N = nucleoside, Z = glucose, ribofuranosylnicotinic acid etc.)

Finally, mixed anhydrides of the nucleotides (generally adenylic acid) with acids other than phosphates are formed by the action of the nucleoside-5' triphosphate on the appropriate acid.

$$ATP + H_2SO_4 \leftrightarrows Adenylyl\ sulphate + PP$$
$$ATP + CH_3COOH \leftrightarrows Adenylyl\ acetate + PP$$
$$ATP + R\text{-}CH.COOH \leftrightarrows Amino\text{-}acyl\ adenylate + PP$$
$$\qquad\quad |$$
$$\qquad NH_2$$

Nucleic Acids

As in the biosynthesis of mononucleotides, so with polynucleotides is it necessary to draw distinctions between *in vitro* enzymic mechanisms which may be largely catabolic in function and those which truly represent biosynthetic routes for the *de novo* formation of nucleic acids *in vivo*. Certain enzymes that catalyse the hydrolysis of internucleotide linkages can also effect transphosphorylation under suitable conditions to give new internucleotide linkages. The substrates (e.g. cytidine-2′,3′ cyclic phosphate, adenosine-3′ benzyl phosphate) are diesterified phosphates and the reactions, which are transesterifications rather than syntheses, have little bearing on the biosynthesis of diesterified phosphate as present in nucleic acids. While the major functions of such hydrolytic enzymes as the ribonucleases and spleen phosphodiesterase may be purely degradative, the significance of the high specificity sometimes shown and of the resultant products (oligonucleotides, nucleoside-3′ phosphates) remains obscure, particularly in view of the general metabolic activity of nucleoside-5′ phosphates.

In recent years, enzyme systems which catalyse the synthesis of polyribonucleotides and of polydeoxyribonucleotides from nucleoside-5′ polyphosphates have been studied extensively. Polyribonucleotide phosphorylase, first discovered by Grunberg-Manago and Ochoa[4] in *Azotobacter vinelandii*, catalyses the reversible synthesis of polyribonucleotides of high molecular weight ($\sim 10^5$ to 2×10^6) from ribonucleoside-5′ pyrophosphates with release of orthophosphate.

$$x\,NPP \leftrightharpoons (NP)_x + xP$$
$$N = \text{ribonucleoside-5′}$$

Similar enzymes have been obtained from a variety of sources and the system appears to be of widespread occurrence, particularly in bacteria. By use of the enzyme from *Azotobacter*, homopolymers of the major ribonucleotides and of 3-β-D-ribofuranosylthymine-5′ phosphate have been prepared from the corresponding nucleoside-5′ pyrophosphates. In addition, copolymers from mixtures of two or more ribonucleoside-5′ pyrophosphates were obtained, including a copolymer of adenylic, cytidylic, guanylic and uridylic acids, similar in many respects to isolated ribonucleic acids. Approximately equal labelling of the nucleoside-3′ (or -2′ and -3′) phosphates formed by the action of spleen diesterase (or alkali) on copolymers containing ^{32}P introduced as adenosine-5′ phosphate or uridine-5′ phosphate indicated a random distribution of nucleotides. Contrary to earlier reports, polymers are readily formed from 5-bromouridine-5′ pyrophosphate (and from the 5-chloro and 5-iodo analogues) by the action of *Azotobacter* polynucleotide phosphorylase. Homopolymers of 2-thiouridylic acid, N^1-methyluridylic acid, N^1,5-dimethyluridylic acid, xanthylic acid, and N^6-hydroxyethyladenylic acid have also been prepared. However, 4,5-dihydrouridine-5′ pyrophosphate was not active as a substrate. Elucidation of the structure of these linear polymers showed that, as in the naturally occurring polyribonucleotides, the internucleotide linkage was exclusively 3′—5′.

With highly purified enzyme preparations, polymerisation occurred only after a lag period; this lag could be overcome by the addition of small amounts of polynucleotide or oligonucleotide primers (natural, enzymically or chemically synthesised) including dinucleotides. The polymer chains are formed by successive additions of mononucleotides to the unesterified C3′ hydroxyl group of the terminal nucleoside residue; primers containing a free 3′ hydroxyl group such as P5′A3′P5′A or A3′P5′U are incorporated by this process. Polymerisation of guanosine-5′ pyrophosphate shows an absolute requirement for this type of primer. With the other nucleotides a second type of " primer ", oligonucleotides containing a terminal -3′ phosphate such as A3′P5′A3′P and A3′P5′U3′P, are also effective in overcoming the lag period though they are not incorporated into the polymeric products. In the reverse of the synthetic action of the enzyme, polynucleotides are readily phosphorolysed to give nucleoside-5′ pyrophosphates. Dinucleotides and dinucleoside phosphates are not attacked, and the rate of phosphorolysis is dependent on both the molecular structure of the polymer (that is the nature of the bases and location of the end group phosphate) and the macromolecular conformation. Thus enzymically synthesised homopolymers are rapidly phosphorolysed as are small oligonucleotides containing a terminal 5′ phosphate, whereas oligonucleotides (up to pentanucleotide) with a terminal 3′ phosphate are not. As with the synthetic process, the phosphorolytic reaction is stepwise (from the end bearing an unesterified 3′-hydroxyl group), the final products being nucleoside-5′ pyrophosphates and terminal dinucleotide. Phosphorolysis of multi-stranded chains (such as a mixture of polyadenylic and polyuridylic acids) and of copolymers is considerably depressed. The relative increase in the rate of phosphorolysis of ribonucleic acid specimens with increase in temperature is related to the thermally induced hyperchromic effects shown by the polynucleotides. Since this type of hyperchromic effect may be regarded as resulting (indirectly) from the cleavage of hydrogen bonds, phosphorolysis thus depends to a large extent on the conformation of the polynucleotide and in particular on the amount of hydrogen bonding involved. Polynucleotide phosphorylase also appears to catalyse transfer of nucleoside monophosphate units from a polynucleotide donor to another polynucleotide acceptor. Further, catalysis of phosphate exchange in a nucleoside-5′ pyrophosphate can occur in the absence of net polymer formation.

Polynucleotide phosphorylases that catalyse the synthesis of polynucleotides from nucleoside-5′ pyrophosphates have been obtained from other bacteria. In general they are similar to the *Azotobacter* enzyme though some differences in requirements and action are evident.

It is yet uncertain whether this type of enzymic system represents a major pathway of synthesis of RNA *in vivo*. While the random distribution of nucleotides found in copolymers prepared by the use of polynucleotide phosphorylase does not necessarily militate against such a function, the low substrate affinities would necessitate fairly high local concentrations of nucleoside-5′ pyrophosphates. It may well be that the role of the enzyme lies largely in the interconversion of " storage " or non-functional ribonucleic acids and nucleoside-5′ pyrophosphates.

It is likely that ribonucleoside-5′ triphosphates are the true immediate precursors of RNA. A somewhat special type of incorporation of nucleotides into specific ribonucleic acids involves the attachment of cytidylic and adenylic end groups in the order RNA-C3′P5′C3′P5′A by the action of cytidine-5′ triphosphate and adenosine-5′ triphosphate (with the liberation of inorganic pyrophosphate). This common " CCA " terminal grouping is found in the low molecular weight " soluble " ribonucleic acids that are active as carriers of amino acids in the biosynthesis of protein. Brief treatment with venom diesterase liberates these terminal units and destroys biological activity. This can be restored by incubation of the product with a fractionated enzyme system and ribonucleoside-5′ triphosphates. Fractionation of transfer RNA-protein complexes yielded partially-purified enzyme systems which catalyse pyrophosphorolysis of the three terminal nucleotides only, in the presence of inorganic pyrophosphate. Reincorporation of labelled nucleotides followed by alkaline hydrolysis (with transfer of ^{32}P from the 5′ position to the 2′ or 3′ hydroxyl group of an adjacent nucleotide) gave strong indications that the fourth nucleoside residue is adenosine, that is, for much of the RNA the common terminal grouping is -ApCpCpA. Similar work in which the labelled polymer was degraded by pancreatic ribonuclease (again with transfer of ^{32}P) showed that some 65% of the material contained a pyrimidine-ACCA terminal, and a further 17% contained pyrimidine-GCCA at the amino acid acceptor end. Other terminal sequences indicated from examination of the digest were p3′GACCA (3·1%), p3′AGCCA (3·6%), p3′AACCA (1·1%), p3′UCCA (7·2%), and p3′AUCCA (1·4%) all of which would be preceded by a pyrimidinenucleotide. Thus heterogeneity begins at the fourth nucleotide from the acceptor end.[5]

Several other systems which incorporate terminal ribonucleotides into RNA have been described. These may be unrelated to specific *de novo* synthesis since ribonucleic acids are probably formed by the stepwise addition of nucleotides, and terminal portions are likely to be more susceptible to reversible pyrophosphorolysis than internal nucleotides.

However, an important factor in apparent end group incorporation may well lie in the absence of the appropriate ribonucleoside-5' triphosphate. Some thirteen different nucleosides have been identified in a variety of ribonucleic acids; attempts to effect enzymic polymerisation of four of the major nucleotides may therefore be subject to severe limitations with respect to the formation of polymer chains of any considerable length. Nevertheless, direct evidence for the synthesis of polyribonucleotides from ribonucleoside-5' triphosphates by mammalian systems does exist. For example, extracts of calf thymus nuclei have been fractionated to give enzyme preparations that catalyse the formation of polyadenylic acid sequences (25–100 nucleotides long) from adenosine-5' triphosphate. In the presence of primer RNA, cytidine-5' triphosphate is converted into polycytidylic acid sequences by a partially purified enzyme (distinct from that specific for ATP) from the same source. With another mammalian system (rat liver nuclei) the mononucleotide portion of cytidine-5' triphosphate (^{32}Pα) is incorporated by intrapolynucleotide linkages rather than terminally. Incorporation is markedly stimulated in the presence of ATP, GTP, and UTP while both ribonuclease and deoxyribonuclease cause a marked reduction of incorporation.

Recently, the deoxyribonuclease-sensitive incorporation of ribonucleotides into RNA by cell free bacterial extracts (*Escherichia coli*, *Micrococcus lysodeikticus*, *Lactobacillus arabinosus*, and *Azotobacter vinelandii*) has been described. All four classical ribonucleoside-5' triphosphates (or the monophosphates and a triphosphate generating system) must be present as well as deoxynucleic acid. Added DNA from a variety of sources (*E. coli*, T2 bacteriophage or calf thymus) is effective in stimulating the incorporation. The product has the usual properties of ribonucleic acids. It is degraded by ribonuclease, and alkaline hydrolysis after incorporation of ^{32}P-labelled uridine-5' phosphate gives a mixture of nucleoside-2'(3') phosphates all of which are labelled. Further evidence of other than end group incorporation is given by the continued liberation of radioactivity and ultra-violet absorbing material at parallel rates by the action of venom diesterase. Alternatively, correlation of inorganic phosphate and ^{32}P released by crude venom has been used.

Nearest neighbour sequence analysis (^{32}P-labelled substrates) and estimation of base ratios of the RNA produced, using DNA primers of widely different base composition, suggest that the RNA formed is complementary to the DNA primer. With oligothymidylic acid as primer, only adenosine-5' triphosphate was used from a mixture of the ribonucleoside-5' triphosphates, to give polyadenylic acid. Similar use of an enzymically synthesised copolymer of thymidylic and deoxyadenylic acids (containing the bases in perfect alternating sequence) as primer for RNA polymerase from *Escherichia coli* gave a product containing adenylic and uridylic acids only (even in the presence of the other nucleotides). Alkaline hydrolysis (with concomitant transfer of ^{32}P) showed that the adenine and uracil residues alternated, and hence the primer determines both the composition of the product and the sequence of bases. (Partially purified bacterial RNA polymerase can also be primed by polyribonucleotides; a separate enzyme from the DNA-dependent polymerase is possibly involved.)

Further evidence of the complementary nature of the RNA produced from a given DNA primer has been obtained by specific complex formation on heating and annealing mixtures of primer DNA and product RNA. With equimolar amounts of the two polynucleotides hybrid complexes are formed, and renaturation of DNA is excluded owing to the greater stability of the hybrid. Hybrid formation is specific for the primer DNA and does not occur with other deoxynucleic acids, even though these may possess similar base compositions. Hence average composition, nearest neighbour analysis, and entire sequence complementarity all indicate the dominating role of nucleotide sequence in primer DNA in determining the nature of the enzymically synthesised RNA. With the particular bacterial system used (*Micrococcus lysodeikticus*) hybrids of template and product do not appear to be formed as intermediates in synthesis, in contrast with DNA polymerase. Further, there is no change in the density of the template DNA after enzymic synthesis of RNA and denaturation (strand separation) of DNA does not appear to occur. Hence either the DNA double helix acts as a template without unwinding, or the mechanism involves single stranded oligonucleotide segments of DNA, only a small region immediately surrounding the site of ribonucleotide addition being unwound, the process " caterpillaring " down the double helix. Physical studies of the product RNA will be of considerable interest since one might expect complementary double stranded material; present indications are that the immediate product is single stranded, but is rapidly transformed into double helices.

In other bacterial RNA–polymerase systems the product appears to consist in part of a DNA–RNA complex which is dissociated by heating to 100°. With plant extracts (isolated chromatin of pea embryos) the RNA remains bound in a DNA–RNA–protein complex and is released in a form susceptible to attack by ribonuclease only by preliminary treatment with deoxyribonuclease or by heating to 60° for a brief period; the nucleic acid stoichiometry of the complex appears to be RNA : DNA equals 1 : 2. Since the dissociation temperature is lower than that required to denature DNA it was concluded that release of RNA (and DNA) from the complex is due to denaturation of protein.

However, it is also likely that any triple stranded polynucleotide complex would possess a lower stability than a double stranded complex.

For many years nucleic acids have been segregated into two groups, the ribonucleic acids and the deoxyribonucleic acids. The discovery of an enzyme system (from *Escherichia coli*) which catalyses the incorporation of the mononucleotide moiety of cytidine-5′ triphosphate and other ribonucleoside-5′ triphosphates (in the presence of all four major deoxynucleoside-5′ triphosphates) into DNA type material indicates that this classification might need to be revised. The product is at least partially susceptible to hydrolysis by alkali, ribonuclease, or deoxyribonuclease. Enzymic degradation gave dinucleotides containing the ribonucleotide and a deoxyribonucleotide. The usual labelling methods using ^{32}P and specific enzymic degradations showed that conversion of ribonucleotide into deoxyribonucleotide did not occur and that linkage was from the 5′ position of the ribonucleotide to the 3′ hydroxyl group of a deoxyribonucleotide. Another enzyme, from calf thymus nuclei (but distinct from RNA or DNA polymerase), catalyses incorporation of ribonucleotides or deoxyribonucleotides into terminal positions of DNA.

Radioactive labelling techniques have been used extensively in this work. They depend on the transfer of ^{32}P from 5′-nucleotides to the 3′ hydroxyl group of receptor nucleotides as indicated by alkaline (or spleen diesterase) cleavage of the internucleotide linkage; the alternate cleavage to nucleoside-5′ phosphates by snake venom diesterase provides a useful control since all the activity should remain in the original nucleotide. End group incorporation is demonstrated by a marker (e.g. ^{14}C) in the nucleoside moiety of the triphosphate; specific hydrolysis of the polymer product gives the terminal nucleoside, the activity of which, relative to that of the nucleoside-2′(3′) phosphates, provides a measure of terminal incorporation.

········ cleavage by alkali or spleen diesterase
———— cleavage by venom diesterase

Enzymic synthesis of polydeoxynucleotides from deoxynucleoside-5′ triphosphates (with concomitant release of inorganic pyrophosphate) was first achieved by Kornberg and his associates,[6] using a purified enzyme from *Escherichia coli*. The system, which probably closely resembles the *in vivo* biosynthetic mechanism, requires the presence of all four major deoxynucleoside-5' triphosphates and a deoxynucleic acid " primer " as well as magnesium ions. On the basis of a number of chemical (including base ratios), biochemical and physical properties the product (molecular weight $\sim 5 \times 10^6$) cannot be distinguished from the primer DNA even when prepared from distorted relative amounts of the deoxynucleoside-5' triphosphates. Net synthesis of some twenty times the primer DNA (from various sources) has been obtained so far. Substrate affinities are very high.

$$x(dATP + dCTP + DGTP + dTTP) \rightarrow DNA + 4xPP$$

Omission of any one nucleoside-5' triphosphate (or of the other components) greatly reduces polymer synthesis; in the presence of a single deoxynucleoside-5' triphosphate (P^{32} labelled) a small amount of incorporation occurs, primarily by reaction of the labelled nucleotide with the nucleoside end groups of the primer DNA. Very few further additions to the new (radioactive) end groups occur, as shown by sequential liberation of deoxynucleotides from the product by the action of snake venom diesterase. Certain analogues of the natural deoxynucleoside-5' triphosphates can also act as substrates and are incorporated in the polymer product. Thus, to varying extents, the deoxynucleoside-5' triphosphates of uracil and 5-bromouracil effected specific replacement of thymine while cytosine could be replaced by 5-methylcytosine or 5-bromocytosine, and guanine by hypoxanthine (but not by xanthine). The specificity of the replacement is in accord with the base-pairing relationships in the double helix structure for deoxynucleic acids advanced by Watson and Crick. It is significant that kinases for the phosphorylation of deoxyuridine-5' phosphate to the triphosphate do not seem to occur in *Escherichia coli*, although 5-bromouracil is converted into the deoxynucleoside-5' triphosphate via the nucleoside monophosphate. In the normal sense, the polymerisation reaction is not significantly reversible, as befits the metabolic stability of DNA. However, in the presence of a large excess of inorganic pyrophosphate some pyrophosphorolysis, particularly of newly added terminal nucleotides, can be achieved.

Enzyme preparations that catalyse the synthesis of DNA from the deoxynucleoside-5' triphosphates have now been obtained from a number of animal tissues and tumours.

The replication of sequences in the enzymic (*E. coli*) synthesis of DNA has been examined, using ^{32}P labelled substrates and primer DNA samples isolated from viral, bacterial, and animal sources. Diesterase hydrolysis of the resultant polydeoxynucleotides to deoxynucleoside-3' phosphates followed by estimation of the distribution of activity showed that all sixteen possible dinucleotide (nearest neighbour) sequences were present in each case, that the pattern was unique, non-random, and reproducible and was not predicted by the base composition of the DNA; and that enzymic replication involved base pairing of adenine and thymine, and of guanine and cytosine, in two strands running in opposite directions (that is, of opposite " polarity ") as in the Watson–Crick model.

Studies on the primer requirements for calf thymus polymerase have shown that release of hydrogen bonds is a prerequisite for priming action and that single strands or (perhaps more accurately) single stranded regions are the actual priming sites. Thus non-priming DNA is readily converted into active primer by heat denaturation. Similarly, the single stranded DNA from bacteriophage ϕX–174 is active, as are oligodeoxynucleotides from pancreatic deoxyribonuclease digests of DNA.

In the absence of demonstrable primer, but after a 2–5 hour lag period, polymerase from *E. coli* catalyses the *de novo* synthesis of a double stranded copolymer of deoxyadenosine-5' phosphate and thymidine-5' phosphate in perfect alternating sequence. Some 80% utilisation of the two deoxynucleoside-5' triphosphates was obtained, but negligible amounts of added deoxyguanosine-5' triphosphate or deoxycytidine-5' triphosphate were incorporated. The physical properties of the products (molecular weight $\sim 5 \times 10^6$) were similar to those of doubly stranded DNA, and thymidine-5' triphosphate could be replaced by 5-bromo-2'-deoxyuridine-5' triphosphate. Thymidylic-deoxyadenylic acid copolymer acted as a primer for the synthesis of identical polymeric material and eliminated the lag phase. The results suggest an autocatalytic pattern of development for the course of polymer formation involving rapid replication after an initial *de novo* phase during which the first few polymer molecules are synthesised. Combination of template and product has been demonstrated by use of the A-T copolymer as primer for an analogous 5-bromo-2'-deoxyuridylic plus deoxyadenylic acid copolymer. Hybrid material, containing 5-bromouracil in one strand only, could be isolated from the reaction mixture. A second type of product has been obtained from deoxyguanosine-5' triphosphate and deoxycytidine-5' triphosphate; this consists of hydrogen bonded double strand material containing the two homopolymers. As previously mentioned, in the presence of suitable primer and the four major deoxyribonucleoside-5' triphosphates the *E. coli* polymerase gives a product very similar to deoxynucleic acid, with unity relationships between adenine and thymine, and between guanine and cytosine.

The Chemical Basis of the
Reactions of Nucleotide Anhydrides

The concept of " high energy " phosphate bonds introduced by Lipmann[7] in 1941 has undoubtedly been of considerable value in biochemistry for the thermodynamic description of various enzymic reactions involving organic phosphates. However, from a chemical view the term (which refers to free energy of hydrolysis) can be somewhat misleading.[8] Again from a purely chemical view, it is perhaps unnecessary to draw a further verbal distinction between simple esters of phosphoric acid and anhydrides of organic phosphates (with phosphoric or other acids), phosphoramidates or enol phosphates. The general characteristics and distinctions implicit in the terms ester and acid anhydride are described in most text books of organic chemistry and will not be discussed here. However, it may be as well to indicate that the division of phosphoric acid derivatives into two groups on the basis of free energies of hydrolysis is somewhat meretricious since in fact a complete range of such values could be obtained by a choice of compounds no more judicious than that shown in the compilation of tables of " low-energy " and " high-energy " phosphates.

The free energy of hydrolysis of phosphate derivatives can be related to a number of features which include the relative resonance stabilisation of the substance and its hydrolysis products, tautomeric stabilisation of the products, electrostatic repulsion effects, and ionisation and solvation effects.[9-11] Resonance stabilisation is of considerable significance when the compound gives hydrolytic products with relatively higher resonance stabilisation. Thus inorganic phosphate and adenosine-5' phosphate possess many more permissible resonance forms than are available per phosphate in adenosine-5' pyrophosphate; in adenosine-5' triphosphate the number of resonance forms per phosphate residue is even further reduced by the " opposing " resonance effect (i.e. the incompatibility of forms with charges of the same sign on adjacent atoms). This effect also applies to anhydrides of nucleotides with acids other than phosphoric such as carboxylic, sulphuric and amino acids as well as to phosphoramidates such as phosphocreatine, phosphoarginine and adenosine-5' phosphoramidate. The number of resonance forms varies with the ionic species involved (e.g. H_3PO_4, $H_2PO_4^-$, HPO_4^{2-}, PO_4^{3-} have 23, 25, 29 and 35 contributing structures respectively).

In the case of certain enol phosphates such as phosphoenol pyruvate, in addition to the " opposing resonance " effect, an important contribution to the free energy of hydrolysis is provided by tautomeric change from the enol to the more stable keto form in the product. The

lectrostatic effect, the result of repulsion among similarly charged
groups is of some significance in compounds such as nucleoside-5′
riphosphates and to a lesser extent in phosphoenolpyruvate and
ucleoside-5′ pyrophosphates. Ionisation and solvation effects arise
rom ionisation of liberated dissociating groups in the products of

$$
\underset{\substack{\; \\ \;}}{N-O-\overset{\overset{O}{\|}}{\underset{\underset{O^-}{|}}{P}}-O-\overset{\overset{O}{\|}}{\underset{\underset{O^-}{|}}{P}}-O^-} \longrightarrow N-O-\overset{\overset{O}{\|}}{\underset{\underset{O^-}{|}}{P}}-O^- + HO-\overset{\overset{O}{\|}}{\underset{\underset{O^-}{|}}{P}}-O^-
$$

$$
N-O-\overset{\overset{O}{\|}}{\underset{\underset{O^-}{|}}{P}}-O-\overset{\overset{O}{\|}}{\underset{\underset{O^-}{|}}{P}}-O-\overset{\overset{O}{\|}}{\underset{\underset{O^-}{|}}{P}}-O^- \longrightarrow N-O-\overset{\overset{O}{\|}}{\underset{\underset{O^-}{|}}{P}}-O-\overset{\overset{O}{\|}}{\underset{\underset{O^-}{|}}{P}}-O^- + HO-\overset{\overset{O}{\|}}{\underset{\underset{O^-}{|}}{P}}-O^-
$$

$$
N-O-\overset{\overset{O^-}{|}}{\underset{\underset{O^-}{|}}{P^\pm}}-O-\overset{\overset{O^-}{|}}{\underset{\underset{O^-}{|}}{P^\pm}}-O-\overset{\overset{O^-}{|}}{\underset{\underset{O^-}{|}}{P^\pm}}-O^-
$$

$$
{}^-O-\overset{\overset{O}{\|}}{\underset{\underset{O^-}{|}}{P}}-OH \qquad {}^-O-\overset{\overset{O^-}{|}}{\underset{\underset{O^-}{|}}{P^\pm}}-OH \qquad {}^-O-\overset{\overset{O^-}{|}}{\underset{\underset{O^-}{|}}{P}}\overset{+}{=}OH \qquad HO-\overset{\overset{O}{\|}}{\underset{\underset{O^-}{|}}{P}}=O
$$

$$
N-O-\overset{\overset{O}{\|}}{\underset{\underset{O^-}{|}}{P}}-OCOCH_3 \longrightarrow N-O-\overset{\overset{O}{\|}}{\underset{\underset{O^-}{|}}{P}}-O^- + CH_3COO^-
$$

$$
N-O-\overset{\overset{O}{\|}}{\underset{\underset{O^-}{|}}{P}}-O\underset{\underset{{}^+NH_3}{|}}{COCH}-R \longrightarrow N-O-\overset{\overset{O}{\|}}{\underset{\underset{O^-}{|}}{P}}-OH + R-\underset{\underset{{}^+NH_3}{|}}{CHCOO^-}
$$

$$
N-O-\overset{\overset{O}{\|}}{\underset{\underset{O^-}{|}}{P}}-O\underset{\underset{NH_2}{|}}{COCH}-R \longrightarrow N-O-\overset{\overset{O}{\|}}{\underset{\underset{O^-}{|}}{P}}-O^- + R\underset{\underset{NH_2}{|}}{CHCOO^-}
$$

$$
H_2C=\underset{\underset{\overset{O}{\underset{\diagdown}{\;}}\;}{|}}{C}-COO^- \longrightarrow CH_3COCOO^- + HO-\overset{\overset{O}{\|}}{\underset{\underset{O^-}{|}}{P}}-O^-
$$

hydrolysis. Each of the above mentioned causes of high free energy of
hydrolysis in a compound is dependent on pH to a greater or lesser
degree; a pH shift from 6 to 8 (covering the secondary dissociation of
phosphoric acid) thus has a relatively large effect ($\sim 1\cdot4$ kcal at $38°$)
on the free energy of hydrolysis of ATP to ADP. Metal ions can also
have a relatively large effect on the value of the free energy of hydrolysis,

by complex formation. Thus, for the hydrolysis of ATP to ADP and phosphoric acid at pH 7·5 and 37° in the absence of magnesium ions (or other divalent cations) the free energy of hydrolysis is approximately − 9·3 kcal, while the value for hydrolysis of magnesium ATP is − 7·0 kcal (at pH 7 and 37°).

Although thermodynamic treatments can indicate the equilibrium position of a given reaction (some conclusions drawn from such equilibria are scarcely relevant to *in vivo* biological conditions) such studies do not reveal why certain phosphates are more effective phosphorylating agents than others. In this respect it is perhaps not unduly otiose to state that adenosine-5' triphosphate itself is not an effective phosphorylating agent; by means of certain catalysts however, the activation energy can be sufficiently lowered so that phosphorylation of hydroxyl and other groups occurs readily.

Within the past ten years knowledge of the possible mechanisms operating in biochemical phosphorylation reactions has grown considerably and it is pertinent at this stage to reiterate briefly some of the chemical properties of esterified phosphates and phosphate anhydrides.[12-14]

PHOSPHORYLATION

Fully esterified pyrophosphates are efficient chemical phosphorylating agents in the presence of tertiary base, the activity depending to a large extent on the nature of the alkyl or aryl groups. Thus tetrabenzyl pyrophosphate is a relatively feeble phosphorylating agent for weak nucleophiles such as alcohols, while tetraphenyl pyrophosphate is a much stronger agent, and in the case of tetra-p-nitrophenyl pyrophosphate the reagent is sufficiently reactive to render base catalysis unnecessary. In general, the activity of a fully esterified pyrophosphate as a phosphorylating agent is directly related to the acidic strength of the component di-alkyl (or -aryl) phosphates, that is, the greater the positive charge on the phosphorus atoms, the stronger is the anhydride as a phosphorylating agent. With unsymmetrically substituted pyrophosphates (such as P^1-diphenyl P^2-dibenzyl pyrophosphate) phosphorylation occurs so that the product is normally derived from the weaker of the two acids composing the anhydride.

Since both phosphorus atoms of the anhydride molecule carry a positive charge to some extent (that of the stronger acid component being the more positive) any approaching nucleophile would presumably attack both atoms. As the P=O group in phosphate anhydrides shows little if any additive property, such attacks are successful only if there is simultaneous expulsion of a group on the other side of the phosphorus atom.* Expulsion of the more stable anion (that of the stronger acid) thus favours attacks culminating in attachment of the nucleophile to the less positive phosphorus atom and phosphorylation is predominantly by the weaker of the two phosphates composing the anhydride. With the stronger phosphorylating agents of this type, ionisation (or effective ionisation caused by interaction with the tertiary base normally present) presumably occurs but the result is precisely the same with mixed anhydrides since the phosphorylium cation is formed from the weaker of the two acids.

Reagents of this type (including phosphorochloridates) have been used extensively for the phosphorylation of alcohols (such as the syn-

* It must be remembered that both $HO—\overset{\overset{O}{\|}}{\underset{\underset{OH}{|}}{P}}—OH$ and the sometimes favoured $HO—\overset{\overset{O^-}{|}}{\underset{\underset{OH}{|}}{P^+}}—OH$ are merely symbolic approximations to structural representation. To speak of a P=O group is meaningful only if this is kept in mind; more correctly a polarised P—O bond is implied. The phosphorus atom (in the compounds discussed) is tetrahedral, and like carbon is subject to nucleophilic displacement with " inversion ". Optically active phosphorus compounds (with respect to the P atom) are known.

thesis of nucleotides from nucleosides); they are also very effective for the phosphorylation of amines.

In a similar manner, mixed anhydrides from diesterified phosphate and sulphonic acids act as phosphorylating agents when the sulphonic acid is stronger than the phosphate; sulphonylation occurs when the reverse is true. In these cases, however, the effect of the environment can become very noticeable. Thus in dioxan solution, the mixed anhydride from methanesulphonic acid (or ethanesulphonic acid) and uridine-2′,3′ cyclic phosphate is a *sulphonylating* agent in the presence of tri-n-butylamine (a sterically hindered base) and the product is 5′-*O*-methanesulphonyl (or ethanesulphonyl)-uridine-2′,3′ cyclic phosphate. In pyridine solution, the same intermediate is a *phosphorylating* agent and the products are methanesulphonic acid and polyuridylic acids of various chain lengths. The pyridine presumably acts " catalytically " by formation of a phosphopyridinium derivative. (Other factors such as relative ionisation and solvation may be involved. See p. 278. A related effect is probably evident in the formation of a mixture of polyadenylic acids (terminating in 5′-benzyl phosphite groups) and adenosine-2′,3′ cyclic phosphate-5′ benzyl phosphite from the mixed anhydride of adenosine-2′,3′ cyclic phophate and benzyl phosphorous acid in dioxan solution in the presence of pyridine (see also p. 439).

Mixed anhydrides from diesterified phosphates and carboxylic acids (or amino acids) act as acylating rather than phosphorylating agents since diesterified phosphates almost invariably will be stronger acids than carboxylic acids. Thus acetyl diphenyl phosphate is an acetylating agent, this function being accentuated by the additive properties of the C=O group; on hydrolysis at all pHs a C—O bond will be broken rather than the corresponding P—O linkage.

ANION EXCHANGE

In addition to phosphorylating relatively weak nucleophiles such as alcohols and amines, fully esterified pyrophosphates readily phosphorylate acids i.e. they undergo anion exchange. Again, it is the net effect of expulsion of the more stable anion (that is, the stronger acid) which determines the course or direction of the exchange reactions. Thus tetraphenyl pyrophosphate reacts with dibenzyl phosphoric acid (a weaker acid) to give P^1-diphenyl P^2-dibenzyl pyrophosphate which then undergoes further nucleophilic displacement by dibenzyl phosphate anion with formation of tetrabenzyl pyrophosphate.

While control of fully esterified mixed anhydride intermediates is difficult owing to the rapidity with which nucleophilic displacement of a stronger acid by a weaker acid occurs, a considerable measure of control can be exerted when the intermediate anhydride contains an acidic dissociation. Thus treatment of uridine-5′ phosphate with tetraphenyl pyrophosphate in dioxan solution (in the presence of tri-n-butylamine) gives a quantitative yield of P^1-uridine-5′ P^2-diphenyl pyrophosphate.

N = purine or pyrimidine base

Under these conditions the ionic nature of the triester diminishes the ease of attack by nucleophilic reagents (reduction of the electrophilic character of the phosphorus atoms, and electrostatic shielding) so that further exchange to liberate the more stable anion with formation of P^1,P^2-di(uridine-5′) pyrophosphate does not occur.

While such P^1-nucleoside-5′ P^2-diphenyl pyrophosphate intermediates are relatively stable in the presence of a hindered tertiary base in dioxan solution, they readily undergo further exchange reactions by attack of suitable nucleophiles with displacement of the stronger acid (diphenyl phosphoric acid) of the anhydride in *pyridine* solution. As might be expected, the nucleophile must possess a less stable anion than the acid displaced, and as with fully esterified anhydrides attack is predominantly if not exclusively at the phosphorus atom of the weaker acid of the intermediate anhydride. Suitable nucleophiles include carboxylic acids, amino acids, peptides, sulphate, phosphate, phosphite, pyrophosphate, triphosphate, riboflavin-5' phosphate, sugar phosphates and pantetheine-4' phosphate. These reactions bear a formal

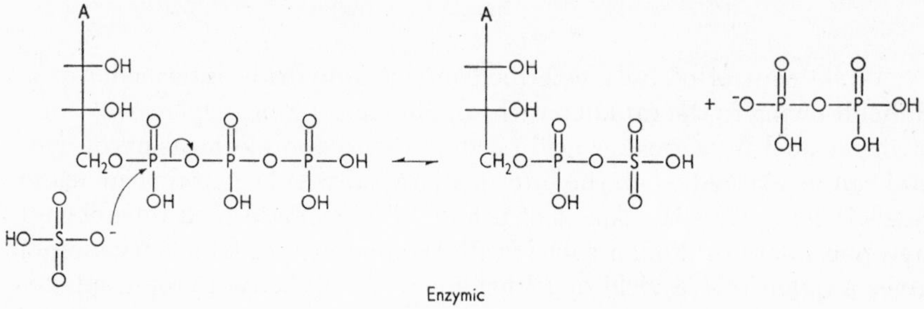

Enzymic

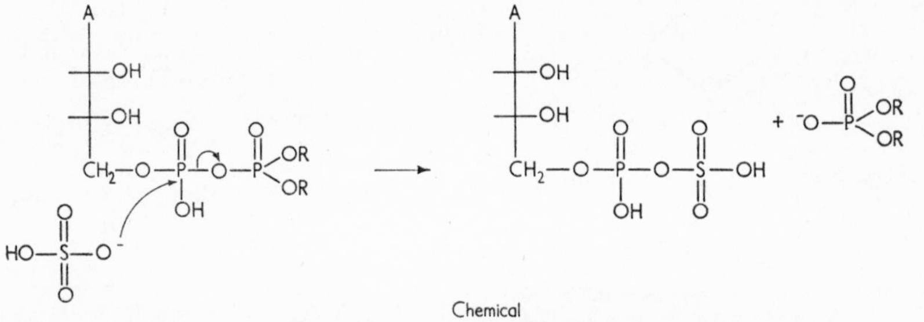

Chemical

analogy with enzymic syntheses of nucleotide mixed anhydrides from the nucleoside-5' triphosphate and monoesterified phosphate (or other acids), that is, the diphenyl phosphate group is chemically equivalent to the biological use of a pyrophosphate residue.

Although the term " stronger acid " can be used as a rough guide in determining the direction of the chemical reaction, more accurately this should be displacement of the more stable anion, under the prevailing local conditions. This of course is related, as in the case of the biochemical reactions, to a number of features which include the relative resonance stabilisation of the intermediate and its products, electrostatic repulsion effects, ionisation and solvation effects. (Change of solvent will have a marked influence on the last three factors.) In the case of certain chemical phosphorylating agents related to phosphoenol-pyruvic acid (such as diethyl-α-ethoxy-β-β-dichlorovinyl phosphate and the imidoyl phosphate intermediates from carbodi-imides) tauto-meric stabilisation of the products plays an important part.

As has been indicated, tri-esterified pyrophosphates are not as reactive as tetraesters of pyrophosphoric acid. Diesterified (P^1,P^2) pyrophosphates are even less reactive. Again one may ascribe this decreased reactivity to the negatively charged oxygen atoms which not only reduce the electrophilic character of the phosphorus atoms considerably, but also provide some degree of electrostatic shielding from attack by nucleophiles. Nevertheless, under suitable conditions, even P^1,P^2-diesters of pyrophosphoric acid can act as phosphorylating agents not only with respect to anion exchange reactions, but also for the phosphorylation of alcoholic hydroxyl groups providing they are suitably situated with respect to the pyrophosphate linkage. Thus alkaline cleavage of uridine diphosphate glucose and of flavin adenine dinucleotide gives glucose-1,2 cyclic phosphate and riboflavin-4',5' cyclic phosphate respectively. A proximal hydroxyl group of suitable configuration decreases the stability of the pyrophosphate linkage since under the same conditions of hydrolysis P^1,P^2-di-(adenosine-5') pyro-phosphate is completely stable. A further example of chemical phos-phorylation by P^1,P^2-diesterified pyrophosphate (providing an alcoholic hydroxyl group is suitably situated) is to be found in the degradation of coenzyme A to yield pantetheine-2',4' cyclic phosphate. Closely related to this type of reaction is the intra-phosphorylation which occurs when adenosine-5' triphosphate is treated with aqueous barium hydroxide.

R = Uridine-5'   (UDPG)
    Adenosine-5'   (FAD)
    Thymidine-5'   (TDPG)
    Cytidine-5'   (CDP-glycerol)

Chelation of barium ion with phosphate residues undoubtedly plays an important part in the reaction mechanisms that lead to the formation of adenosine-3',5' cyclic phosphate and adenosine-2'(or 3'),5' diphos-phate, among numerous other products. Equally important is the specific location of the sugar hydroxyl groups.

Since diesterified (P^1,P^2) pyrophosphates can phosphorylate weakly nucleophilic hydroxyl groups under certain conditions, it is not sur-

N.N.   K

prising that they will undergo anion exchange with suitably nucleophilic anions in reactions that are analogous to the biochemical pyrophosphorolysis of nucleotide anhydrides such as UDPG and FAD. Again, for the reaction to be chemically feasible, the direction must be such that a stronger acidic dissociation (more stable anion) is displaced by a weaker acid. Thus treatment of P^1,P^2-di (adenosine-5') pyrophosphate with inorganic pyrophosphate in pyridine solution gives a mixture of adenosine-5' triphosphate, adenosine-5' pyrophosphate, and adenosine-5' phosphate. Effectively, this is displacement of the secondary dissociation of adenosine-5' phosphate ($pK_2 = 6 \cdot 0$) by the tertiary dissociation of inorganic pyrophosphate ($pK_3 = 6 \cdot 54$). The

adenosine-5' pyrophosphate presumably arises by further attack of inorganic pyrophosphate on the γ phosphate of the initially formed adenosine-5' triphosphate, since direct cleavage of adenosine from the di-adenosine pyrophosphate is most unlikely, and indeed is not observed.

The decreasing order of reactivity of tetraesters, triesters and diesters of pyrophosphoric acid has been indicated. A further decrease is observed with mono-esterified pyrophosphate. Nevertheless, non-enzymic phosphorylation by such derivatives can be observed since acidic calcium (or sodium) salts of nucleoside-5' pyrophosphates in the solid state are slowly converted into mixtures containing the nucleoside-5' triphosphate, a process equivalent to the myokinase type of enzymic reaction. (However, it may be noted that symmetrical diesterified pyrophosphates such as P^1,P^2-di-adenosine-5' pyrophosphate are considerably more resistant to acidic or alkaline hydrolysis than are monoesterified pyrophosphates such as adenosine-5' pyrophosphate. Disparity in positive charge on the two phosphorus atoms is as significant as the absolute value. This is particularly demonstrated by the extreme instability of P^1,P^1-diesterified pyrophosphates; monomeric metaphosphate intermediates are probably involved). Finally, inorganic pyrophosphoric acid is a very weak phosphorylating agent indeed and is effective only at elevated temperatures (200–300°).

ADENYLYL SULPHATE

Anhydrides of nucleotides with inorganic acids other than phosphoric acid may be considered in a similar manner. Sulphuric acid is

$$\text{A}-\text{O}-\overset{O}{\underset{H^{18}O^-}{\overset{\|}{P}}}-\text{O}-\overset{O}{\overset{\|}{S}}-\text{O}^- \longrightarrow \text{A}-\text{O}-\overset{O}{\underset{^{18}OH}{\overset{\|}{P}}}-\text{O}^- + \text{SO}_4^{=}$$

a stronger acid than phosphoric acid or monoalkyl phosphates and hence adenylyl sulphate is a mixed anhydride from a relatively weak acid (adenosine-5' phosphate) and a strong acid. The anhydride is therefore considerably less stable than is adenosine-5' pyrophosphate. Chemical hydrolysis presumably occurs by nucleophilic attack at the phosphorus rather than the sulphur atom, that is, on hydrolysis in $H_2^{18}O$, the heavy oxygen will appear in the resultant adenosine-5'

Enzymic

phosphate and not in the sulphate. Other mechanisms can be envisaged however.

A biochemical example of nucleophilic attack at the phosphorus atom of adenylyl sulphate is to be found in the enzymic pyrophosphorolysis (or phosphorolysis) of the compound.

Adenylyl sulphate-3′ phosphate, " active sulphate ", functions as a biochemical sulphating agent (attack at the sulphur atom) rather than

a nucleotide donor.* The two types of reaction provide examples of control exerted by enzymes which is similar to the chemical control of the course of the reaction of methanesulphonyl anhydrides of nucleoside-2′,3′ cyclic phosphates.

MIXED ANHYDRIDES OF NUCLEOTIDES WITH CARBOXYLIC ACIDS

Much the same considerations apply to the reactions of nucleotide anhydrides of carboxylic and amino acids except that due account must now be taken of the strongly additive character of the C=O group. Effectively this means that the anhydride acts as an acylating agent not only when the phosphate moiety is a stronger acid than the

* Non-enzymic sulphation in the presence of charcoal has also been reported.

carboxylic acid (i.e. displacement of the more stable anion) but also when the carboxylic acid is stronger than the phosphoryl dissociation liberated.[15] In the latter case nucleophilic attack at the more positive atom is facilitated by the additive properties of the group attacked. Adenylyl acetate therefore acts as an acylating agent rather than a phosphorylating agent with respect to weak nucleophiles such as alcoholic (or aqueous) hydroxyl groups. Under anhydrous conditions, however, anion exchange with suitable nucleophiles can occur with displacement of the stronger acid (i.e. the carboxylic acid). Since the

A = Adenosine-5′

additive property of the C=O group is an activating effect, anion exchange by nucleophilic attack at the nucleotide moiety is considerably slower than exchange by attack at the carboxyl component. Treatment of adenylyl acetate with adenosine-5′ phosphate therefore results in the formation of P^1,P^2-di(adenosine-5′) pyrophosphate, the more rapid exchange with acetate merely re-producing adenylyl acetate. (It may be noted that the anhydride from acetic acid and adenosine-5′ phenyl phosphate would act as an acylating agent only, that is, nucleophilic attack would be preferentially at the carbonyl group rather than the phosphorus atom under practically all possible conditions.)[15]

Since no additive properties are involved, the resultant P^1,P^2-di-(adenosine-5′) pyrophosphate is quite stable towards nucleophilic attack by acetate anions; successful attack would involve displacement of a less stable dissociating group by a more stable anion.

Again because of the additive properties of the $C{=}O$ group, treatment of thymidylyl acetate with phosphoric acid in pyridine solution gives thymidine-5' phosphate (rather than the pyrophosphate) and acetyl phosphate. Further attack by inorganic phosphate (a stronger nucleophile than thymidine-5' phosphate) then occurs at both the carboxyl and phosphate moieties of acetyl phosphate but only in the latter case is a new product, inorganic pyrophosphate, formed. Apart from being stable to attack by acetate ion (since a less stable anion would need to be displaced) pyrophosphate is probably (in pyridine solution) more nucleophilic than inorganic phosphate and would react further with acetyl phosphate. The final products from the action of inorganic phosphate on thymidylyl acetate in anhydrous pyridine are therefore thymidine-5' phosphate, acetate, pyrophosphate and higher polyphosphates.

T=Thymidine-5'

Amino acid anhydrides of nucleotides behave in a similar fashion. The presence of the α-amino group increases the positive charge on the carbonyl group (i.e. increase in acidic strength owing to electrostatic effects) and the amino acid anhydrides of nucleotides are considerably less stable than the corresponding anhydrides with carboxylic acids, unless the amino function is blocked. This increase in reactivity is also evident in the 2'(or 3') amino-acyl esters of ribonucleotides compared with the 2'(or 3') acyl derivatives, but even these latter are considerably less stable than simple alkyl esters that lack an adjacent hydroxyl group, such as the 3'- or 5'-esters of the deoxyribonucleosides. A possible explanation may be found in hydrogen bonding of the vicinal *cis* hydroxyl group with the carbonyl group, thereby facilitating nucleophilic attack at this carbon atom. Infrared spectra of 3',5'-di-O-acetyladenosine and 2',3'-di-O-acetyladenosine indicated the presence of such hydrogen bonding in the former compound.[16] However, extensive studies of the reactivity of a number of model amino acid esters (e.g. of 3-hydroxytetrahydrofuran, and *cis* and *trans* diol systems) and of esters of the different nucleosides showed that other factors are involved.[17–19] Evaluation of the kinetic data derived from rates of cleavage of the esters by hydroxylamine and by saponification at pH 9·8 indicated that the reactivity of the ester linkage is affected strongly by the acid component, by the ring oxygen of the sugar and by the neighbouring hydroxyl group. Inductive and steric effects as well as hydrogen bonding may well play significant roles in what has been loosely termed a new type of high energy bond. An adjacent phosphate group can also exert a marked influence,[31] possibly as a result of nucleophilic attack by phosphate anion at the carbonyl group of the ester to give a transitory amino-acyl phosphate anhydride. (This would not

necessarily yield a cyclic phosphate on hydrolysis.) Presence of a phosphate group, even when fully esterified and at the 5′ position, also increases the " acidity " of the 2′-hydroxyl group (with respect to reaction with diazomethane) in ribonucleoside derivatives such as uridine-5′ phosphate[16, 32] and adenosine-3′,5′ cyclic phosphate.[16]

At pH 6·0 to 8·5 adenylyl tryptophan behaves as an acylating agent, spontaneous breakdown occurring to give amino-acyl esters (of the secondary sugar hydroxyl groups) as well as some polytryptophan. However, as with acetyl adenylate, under anhydrous conditions nucleophilic attack at the phosphorus atom in aminoacyl adenylates can occur. Thus carbobenzyloxyglycyl adenylate (as the tri-n-butylammonium salt) is relatively stable in dioxan solution, but in pyridine it is converted into di-adenosine-5′ pyrophosphate.[20]

As in pyrophosphate derivatives, stereochemical considerations can play an important part in the reactivity of carboxylic anhydrides of nucleotides. This is shown by a comparison of the mixed anhydrides obtained by treating uridine-5′ phosphate and uridine-3′ phosphate with ethyl chloroformate. The former is relatively stable, but the latter has only a transient existence, being converted into uridine-2',3' cyclic phosphate even in aqueous solution. Specific location (and configuration) of the adjacent 2'-hydroxyl group in the ethyl carbonate anhydride of uridine-3' phosphate not only leads to increased reactivity (relative to attack of water molecules on the analogous uridine-5' phosphate anhydride) but also provides a directive effect in that the anhydride is a phosphorylating agent, and nucleophilic attack is at the phosphorus atom exclusively rather than the carbonyl group.

The behaviour of non-esterified phosphate anhydrides such as acetyl phosphate, carbamyl phosphate or amino-acyl phosphates, is dependent on the ionic species present, together with environmental factors such as divalent metal ions. Under conditions where the additive character of the $C=O$ group is less effective than nucleophilic displacement of the stronger anion, then such compounds will act as phosphorylating rather than acylating agents. In addition to forming polypeptides, amino acid-phosphoric acid anhydrides will also phosphorylate adenosine-5' phosphate to give adenosine-5' pyrophosphate in aqueous solution. Similarly, treatment of sodium (or potassium) phosphate with acetic anhydride causes quantitative conversion to trimetaphosphate, and treatment of phosphoric acid with acetyl chloride and acetic anhydride gives acetyl polyphosphoric acids.[21] In each case the intermediate acetyl phosphate acts as a phosphorylating agent. In general, however, phosphorylation is considerably slower than acylation (cf. rates of hydrolysis of acetyl phosphate when acid or base catalysed C—O cleavage is involved compared with the spontaneous P—O cleavage at pHs 3–6). It may be noted that glyceroyl phosphate-3 phosphate acts solely as a biochemical phosphorylating rather than acylating agent, that is, the more stable carboxylate ion (pK approximately 4·5) is liberated, rather than a tertiary phosphate dissociation (pK approximately 12) at physiological pH values. Disparity in strength (electrophilic character) of the acids forming the anhydride has been mentioned as an important factor in the reactivity of unsymmetrical diesterified pyrophosphates. The same is true of phosphate-carboxylate anhydrides. Acetyl phosphate (respective pKs approximately 4·5 and 12) is more reactive as a phosphorylating agent than are acyl nucleotides or acetyl phenyl phosphate (respective pKs 4·5 and 6·5). A monomeric metaphosphate intermediate is possibly involved in the first case (P—O cleavage is catalysed by pyridine, suggesting formation of an active quaternary pyridinium phosphoramidate). The latter cases probably involve direct nucleophilic attack at the phosphorus atom and this is a slower process; however, formation of monomeric metaphosphate as a rate determining step cannot be excluded entirely.

With respect to attack at the carbonyl group, a second substituent on the phosphate facilitates acyl transfer; phenyl benzoyl phosphate is a good benzoylating agent and diacetyl phosphate is more reactive than monoacetyl phosphate.[15] Even greater reactivity may be expected with acetyl diphenyl phosphate.

Acid	pK liberated	~ 0.9
PH 3-6	pK liberated	~ 4.5
Alkali	pK liberated	~ 12

OTHER PHOSPHORYLATING AGENTS

Enol-phosphates containing groups that cause strong electron shifts away from the P—O linkage (that is, they increase the electrophilic character of the phosphorus) are chemical phosphorylating agents, and bear a formal resemblance to phosphoenol pyruvate in its biochemical activities. Examples of such enol-phosphates include diethyl α-ethoxy-β-carboxyethylvinyl phosphate and diethyl α-ethoxy-ββ-dichlorovinyl phosphate.

Other enol phosphates that are not sufficiently reactive to phosphorylate directly may do so under oxidising conditions, that is, by

K*

external electron withdrawal. Related to such compounds are quinol monophosphates and diphosphates; in the presence of bromine (or iodine) or ceric salts such esters will phosphorylate inorganic phosphate in aqueous solution to give pyrophosphate. Similar oxidative phosphorylation is observed with esters of thiolphosphoric acid and iodine, the reaction being initiated by oxidation at the sulphur atom.

Imidoyl phosphates and related derivatives are nitrogen analogues of enol phosphates. In the protonated form they react readily with anions to give anhydrides, and much less readily with weaker nucleophiles such as alcohols to give esters.

Phosphoramidates are effective phosphorylating agents providing the structure is such that protonation occurs on nitrogen rather than on oxygen. Although diesterified imidazole phosphates are sufficiently reactive to phosphorylate alcohols, the simpler phosphoramidates such as benzyl phosphoramidate are phosphorylating agents for anions only, and dibenzyl phosphoramidate is relatively inert.

TRANSPHOSPHORYLATION

The effect of a suitably located hydroxyl group of correct configuration (and conformation) on the reactivity of P^1,P^2-diesterified pyrophosphates has been discussed in connection with intramolecular phosphorylation. A similar effect is apparent in tri-, di- and monoesters of phosphoric acid and this gives rise to intramolecular transphosphorylation. Whereas thymidine-5' dibenzyl phosphate is relatively stable at neutral pH, uridine-3' dibenzyl (or dimethyl) phosphate is unstable over the whole pH range, decomposing to a mixture of the monoesters of uridine-2' and uridine-3' phosphate together with traces of uridine-2',3' cyclic phosphate. Intermolecular transphosphorylation can be achieved with tri-esterified phosphates containing strong electron-withdrawing groups. For example, tri-p-nitrophenyl phosphate on treatment with methanol gives methyl di-p-nitrophenyl phosphate and p-nitrophenol.

The alkaline hydrolysis of diesterified phosphates possessing a *cis* vicinal hydroxyl group is thought to proceed via a pentacovalent intermediate transition state (on the basis of studies with ^{18}O) and presumably similar intermediates are involved in the formation of thymidine-3',5' cyclic phosphate from thymidine-3' p-nitrophenyl phosphate, and in the migration (i.e. transphosphorylation) of benzyl phosphate on partial acidic hydrolysis of cytidine-3' benzyl phosphate. Acid or base catalysed intermolecular transesterification of ribo-nucleoside-2',3' cyclic phosphates with primary alcohols readily gives the nucleoside-2' (or -3') alkyl phosphate; in the former case, protonation of the phosphate increases the electrophilic character of the phosphorus atom and in the latter case, formation of an alkoxy anion increases the nucleophilic character of the alcohol.

Finally, acid catalysed transesterification of monoesterified phosphate occurs readily with the -2′ (or -3′) phosphates of the ribonucleosides. The ease of this reaction, which does not occur in alkaline solution, is a result of protonation of the phosphate group, thus assisting nucleophilic attack by the suitably located -3′ (or -2′) hydroxyl group.

In addition to the increase in electrophilic character of the phosphorus atom, removal of electrostatic shielding by suppression of ionisation is probably of importance.*

MONOMERIC METAPHOSPHATE[12]

A number of chemical reactions of phosphate mixed anhydrides (or their imidoyl equivalents) containing a free phosphoryl dissociation probably proceed via a monomeric metaphosphate intermediate. For example, alcohols can be esterified by monesters of phosphoric acid by use of the chloride of a very strong acid in the presence of pyridine. An intermediate mixed anhydride (or the product of interaction of the acid

chloride with an initially formed P^1,P^2-di-alkyl pyrophosphate) probably breaks down to the monomeric alkyl metaphosphate and the anion of the strong acid. Similar considerations can be applied to the phosphorylation of alcohols (including polynucleotide synthesis) by the action of dicyclohexylcarbodi-imide on monoesters of phosphoric acid. A related use of trichloracetonitrile, in which the imidoyl phosphate intermediate contains a strong electron-withdrawing group prior to protonation, presumably involves a monomeric metaphosphate intermediate also.

* Protonation of the phosphate group is clearly more effective than ionisation of an alcoholic hydroxyl group (and of all phosphate dissociations).

Since pyridine is normally used as solvent for these reactions, similar mechanisms could give rise to active phosphoramidate intermediates. In effect such intermediates are actually equivalent to monomeric metaphosphate, and can be regarded as " base-metaphosphate complexes " which would be formed from monomeric metaphosphate in any case.

CHEMICAL FORMATION OF C—O, C—N AND C—C BONDS

Alkylating properties of phosphate esters are apparent in a number of chemical reactions that lead to the formation of C—O, C—N and C—C bonds. Treatment of tribenzyl phosphate (or tetrabenzyl pyrophosphate) with N-methylmorpholine gives a benzyl N-methylmorpholinium salt; the related method of debenzylation by anionic fission has also been used. As may be expected, the nature of the esterifying groups exerts a considerable influence; tri-n-propyl phosphate is resistant towards dealkylation by bases or salts, but n-propyl diphenyl phosphate is readily dealkylated. (Diphenyl phosphate is a stronger acid than dipropyl phosphate.)

Alkylation to a nitrogen atom of the guanine moiety occurs when solutions of 2′,3′-O-isopropylideneguanosine-5′ di-p-nitrophenyl phosphate are heated. Under sufficiently vigorous conditions, and with a suitably positioned oxygen, alkylation can also occur in the absence of full esterification. Thus treatment of uridine (or cytidine) with polyphosphoric acid gives O^2,2′-cyclouridine (or -cytidine)-5′ phosphate probably via an intermediate 2′-polyphosphate derivative. Intramolecular O-alkylation has also been observed in the solvolysis of dibenzyl *trans*-2-hydroxycyclohexyl phosphate with hydroxide ions or with potassium t-butoxide; the products include a considerable proportion of cyclohexane oxide (and dibenzyl phosphate).[22]

Solvolysis of tetrabenzyl pyrophosphate with n-propanol in the presence of sterically hindered tertiary amines (such bases are not catalytic and merely prevent autocatalysed solvolysis, by neutralising the acid formed) gives mainly benzyl propyl ether and tribenzyl pyrophosphate by intermolecular *O*-alkylation. Bases such as pyridine or 2,6-lutidine catalyse solvolysis by P—O rather than C—O cleavage and the same pyrophosphate then acts as a phosphorylating agent to yield n-propyl dibenzyl phosphate.[23]

Finally, the formation of C—C bonds by means of phosphate esters is demonstrated by reactions in which debenzylation of fully esterified benzyl phosphates or pyrophosphates by the action of phenol gives rise to o- and p-benzylphenol.[24]

CONCLUSIONS[13]

The following points of possible biochemical interest may be drawn from a purely chemical study of the reactions of phosphate esters and nucleotide anhydrides.

(1) Nucleophilic attack at a phosphorus atom in a pyrophosphate is normally successful only if there is simultaneous expulsion of a group on the opposite side of the phosphorus atom. Expulsion of the more stable anion (under the local conditions of pH and cation concentration) effectively means phosphorylation by the weaker of the two acids forming the anhydride.

(2) The additive properties of the carbonyl group in carboxylic anhydrides both activate and direct the course of the reaction.

(3) Base catalysis (formation of pyridinium derivatives) also has a directing effect and may be equivalent to the effect of imidazole residues in certain enzymes.

(4) Possible solvent effects: the dielectric properties of the solvent may affect the electronic distribution in the anhydride and will certainly affect the ionisation properties of reactants and products. This may be related to changes in dielectric constant near protein surfaces.

(5) Suppression of ionisation increases activity owing to an increase in the positive charge on the phosphorus atoms and removal of the electrostatic shielding effect. Chemically, this is achieved by esterification or use of acidic solutions. Biochemically a similar result is obtained by binding of the substrate to the protein.

(6) Stereochemical effects. For example, specific location of a hydroxyl group not only leads to attack at a specific part of the anhydride but also results in greater reactivity and to exclusion of general hydrolysis by water molecules.

(7) The conformation of the anhydride when bound to the enzyme surface may be of significance in directing attack at a particular phosphorus atom with easy expulsion of an anion from the opposite side of the phosphorus atom.

BIOCHEMICAL ASPECTS

In no small measure, the biological importance of derivatives of phosphoric acid can be related to the multitude of reactions that they undergo under relatively mild conditions, rather than to any unique properties. Esters and anhydrides of phosphoric acid are neither too stable, nor too unstable, under conditions normally obtaining in living systems and their immediate environment. Further, the presence of three ionising groups (one strongly acidic, one with a dissociation in the general physiological pH region and one equivalent in many respects to an alcoholic hydroxyl group), and the variation of ionisation by ester or anhydride formation, gives phosphoric acid a flexibility in action which to a large extent would be absent in living systems based on silicate or sulphate. Numerous examples of the effect of the ionisation state on the energy of activation and reactivity of phosphate derivatives have been given. Underlying certain of the biochemical functions of organic phosphates is the atomic structure of phosphorus itself; this is such that in many activated complexes the reactants are actually bonded to each other, that is, the complex represents a chemical compound rather than a special orientation of unbonded molecules or molecular fragments.[25]

The chemical factors governing the rate and direction of reactions involving organic phosphates mainly concern the location of the substrate hydroxyl group or phosphate (or other functional groups) with respect to the operative part of the organic phosphate, presence or absence of base catalysis, and the distribution of charge in the anhydride or ester. Chemically, the charge distribution can be varied by a number of means such as suppression of specific phosphoryl dissociations by ester formation or by use of acidic conditions (e.g. the proton-catalysed interconversions of nucleoside-2′ and -3′ phosphates and of nucleoside-2′

and -3′ alkyl phosphates, migrations that do not occur in alkaline solution) and by forming mixed anhydrides from acids of disparate strengths. " Catalytic " and directive effects of complex formation with certain polyvalent metal ions have also been observed in a non-enzymic chemical sense. Biochemically, similar control may be exerted by such factors as the conformation of nucleoside-5′ polyphosphates, metal bonding of the substrate and the enzyme, and hydrogen bonding from the enzyme to dissociating groups and to the $P{=}O$ group, equivalent to protonation. (In view of the resonance involved in phosphates, distinction between the $P{=}O$ and a $P{-}O^-$ group is purely formal.) Formation of cation-substrate complexes, such as magnesium ATP, probably increases the electrophilic character of the phosphorus atoms (by preventing ionisation) and almost certainly results in a charge-directing effect favouring attack at a particular phosphorus atom, depending on the precise stereochemistry of the complex. With enzyme–metal–substrate complexes in which the metal acts as a bridge between the enzyme and the substrate, the free energy of activation is probably decreased significantly.

While direct nucleophilic attack at a positively charged phosphorus atom with rear displacement may well be of considerable significance for a variety of enzymic reactions, alternate mechanisms involving intermediate formation of " monomeric metaphosphate " as the active phosphorylating agent may operate in some instances. In certain cases, reaction (phosphorylation) or complex formation of the substrate with imidazole or other basic residues in the enzyme may occur (corresponding in a crude fashion to the pyridine catalysis observed chemically), and in others a three dimensional complex of enzyme, reactants and products may be involved. It is therefore not surprising that generalities concerning requirements and mode of action of enzymic reactions with organic phosphate substrates are not immediately evident. Even for a simple hydrolytic reaction such as the chemical hydrolysis of glucose-1 phosphate some half dozen mechanisms may be involved under various conditions. However, it is clear that " nearly all chemical processes catalysed by enzymes have similar counterparts in so-called organic or non-enzymic reactions ".[26] Further, although enzymic reactions are normally operative in aqueous solutions, one of the functions of some enzymes is undoubtedly to position the reactants so that water molecules are virtually excluded, that is, to create local " anhydrous " conditions. A direct comparison with chemical reactions in anhydrous media is therefore not unduly extravagant. It may also be noted that the enzyme surface not only positions the reactants and creates a suitable environment, but at some stage the substrate must be bound to this surface (in whatever way may be postulated) and hence is invariably modified to some extent (as is the enzyme). In many ways therefore, analogies between enzymic and non-enzymic reactions are perhaps more realistic when in the latter case the organic phosphate is modified in a chemical sense rather than identical with the enzyme substrate. Finally, from the stereospecific requirements shown by many enzymes it is perhaps not unreasonable to assume that concerted reactions involving simultaneous participation of both electrophilic and nucleophilic groups occur fairly frequently. A chemical analogy of this type of reaction is the formation of $O^2,5'$-cyclothymidine from $5'$-iodo-$5'$-deoxythymidine, " catalysed " by silver ion.

Mechanisms for a number of the enzymic reactions concerned in the biosynthesis of nucleotides and their derivatives have been indicated by tracer studies, particularly with ^{18}O, although the role of the enzyme in most cases is subject to speculation as yet.[27] Both nucleoside-$5'$ triphosphates and nucleoside-$5'$ pyrophosphates can act as enzymically catalysed phosphorylating agents. As may be expected, the former are much stronger (being mixed anhydrides of phosphoric acid and nucleoside-$5'$ pyrophosphate) and will readily phosphorylate alcohols whereas the nucleoside-$5'$ pyrophosphates are effective in general only for strong nucleophiles such as anions, for example nucleoside-$5'$ pyrophosphates (nucleoside monophosphokinases). An exception is to be found in the polymerisation reaction catalysed by polynucleotide phosphorylase where nucleophilic attack by a $3'$-hydroxyl group at the α phosphorus atom of a ribonucleoside-$5'$ pyrophosphate gives polyribonucleotides.

With nucleoside-$5'$ triphosphates nucleophilic attack can occur at two loci, the α or the γ phosphorus atoms, resulting in bond cleavage A—O—P$+$O—P—O—P or A—O—P—O—P—O$+$P. Various kinases catalyse phosphorylation of alcohols (such as glucose, glycerol and nucleosides) and anions (such as nucleoside-$5'$ phosphates and -$5'$ pyrophosphates) by attack at the γ phosphate of ATP. Biochemical examples of the first type of reaction, involving release of inorganic pyrophosphate by anion exchange, are many and varied. They include the reversible enzymic syntheses of P^1,P^2 diesterified pyrophosphates such as uridine diphosphate glucose and flavin adenine dinucleotide, and of nucleotide mixed anhydrides with carboxylic and amino acids.

As mixed anhydrides of pyrophosphoric acid and nucleoside-5′ phosphate, the nucleoside-5′ triphosphates are also capable of donating the mononucleotide moiety to weakly nucleophilic hydroxyl groups as in enzymic syntheses of deoxynucleic acid and ribonucleic acid.

The effect of metal complexing (or hydrogen bonding) of the β phosphate of nucleoside-5' pyrophosphates is indicated in the enzymic synthesis of polyribonucleotides from such substrates, where the normally stronger acid (nucleoside-5' phosphate) is used to " phosphorylate " a 3' hydroxyl group. (It may be noted that divalent cation complexes of nucleoside-5' triphosphates are more stable than those of nucleoside-5' pyrophosphates which are themselves markedly more stable than analogous complexes of P^1,P^2 diesterified pyrophosphates.) In addition to decreasing the free energy of activation of the rate determining step,[28] this metal bridging of enzyme and reactants also exerts a powerful charge-directing effect. It is possible that phosphate exchange in such systems may occur readily in the absence of polymer formation, owing to non-specific attack of inorganic phosphate, a much more powerful nucleophile than a nucleoside-3' hydroxyl group. An analogous enzymic anion exchange reaction leading to synthesis of nucleotide coenzymes by nucleophilic attack at the α phosphorus atom of nucleoside-5' pyrophosphates has not been described in detail as yet, but is probably evident in the formation of adenyl-5'-yl sulphate from ADP and inorganic sulphate with liberation of orthophosphate. More recently, the phosphorolysis of guanosine diphosphate mannose (to give guanosine-5' pyrophosphate and mannose-1 phosphate) by purified yeast extracts has been reported. It is likely that many more reactions of this type will be discovered.

The nature of the stereochemical control involved in nucleophilic displacement of alkoxy group (nucleoside-3') by phosphate in the phosphorolysis of polyribonucleotides to give nucleoside-5' pyrophosphates rather than the -3' pyrophosphates is not known. This specificity may be a consequence of the general conformation of polynucleotides (and oligonucleotides) which could lead to preferential attack at the more exposed portion of the phosphorus atom opposite to the 3' position.

No unequivocal example of enzymic pyrophosphorylation by nucleophilic attack at the β phosphorus atom of a nucleoside-5' triphosphate has been described. Possible explanations for this may lie in the conformations adopted by such derivatives of triphosphoric acid, as well as in electrostatic shielding, or shielding by the enzyme itself in substrate-enzyme complexes, which would tend to restrict successful attack at the β phosphorus atom with rear displacement of nucleoside-5' phosphate (or of inorganic phosphate in the case of transfer of nucleoside-5' pyrophosphate). As in the numerous cases of anion exchange reactions, bond cleavage in the enzymic hydrolysis of nucleoside-5' triphosphates to nucleoside-5' phosphate and inorganic pyrophosphate occurs by nucleophilic attack at the α rather than the β phosphorus atom.[29] Pyrophosphorylation of ribose-5 phosphate by nucleophilic attack of an α-D-ribose hydroxyl group at the β phosphorus atom of ATP has been claimed[30] for the enzymic synthesis of α-D-ribose-1 pyrophosphate-5 phosphate. However, the experimental results (using ^{32}P labelled ATP) indicated only that the β and γ phosphates were transferred as a single entity, and provided no unambiguous evidence of the mechanism involved. A possible alternate mechanism may lie in nucleophilic attack at C1 of β-D-ribose-5 phosphate with inversion, the reaction being assisted to some extent by hydrogen bonding between the C1 hydroxyl group and the 5-phosphate group.

In general, nucleoside-5' triphosphates appear to play a much more extensive biochemical role than do the corresponding nucleoside-5' pyrophosphates. Regarding ADP and ATP purely as chemical reagents one might expect ATP (an anhydride of AMP and inorganic pyrophosphate) to be a stronger nucleotide donating agent than ADP (an anhydride of AMP and inorganic phosphate) since pyrophosphate is a " stronger " acid than orthophosphate (where " stronger " includes all the relevant factors such as ability to form complexes with metal ions) and the stronger the acids forming the mixed phosphate anhydride (that is, the greater the positive charges on the phosphorus atoms) the more effective the reagent. Hence kinetically, the nucleoside triphosphate is a more effective nucleotide donating agent than the pyrophosphate whether one considers nucleophilic attack at the nucleotide α phosphorus atom by a strong nucleophile (such as an alkyl phosphate) or by a weak nucleophile (such as an alcoholic hydroxyl group). Thermodynamically, that is, with respect to the equilibrium position of the reaction, definition of the reaction conditions is of course all important. However, under the same environmental conditions in the pH range 6–8, one might expect reaction B to proceed further in the direction left to right than reaction A if the *difference* in resonance stabilisation, ionisation, solvation, metal ion and electrostatic effects between the products and ATP (reaction B) is greater than the difference between products and ADP (reaction A).

(A)

(B)

ROH = Alcohol, alkyl phosphate or inorganic sulphate

A comparison of the equilibrium constants for polynucleotide phosphorylase and DNA polymerase, or of any pair of analogous reactions involving phosphorolysis versus pyrophosphorolysis, would presumably suggest that this is indeed the case.

Chemically, one requires a reaction that goes completely, (that is, an equilibrium position far to the right) and also proceeds in a finite time. From an experimental point of view it is difficult to separate the thermodynamic effect of blocking phosphoryl dissociations (hence giving products that are more stable than the anhydride starting material under the conditions employed) from the kinetic effect resulting from an increase in positive charge on the phosphorus atoms (that is, increasing the electrophilic character). To this extent then, the concept of " high-energy bonds " is justifiable, despite the chemical criticism it has been subjected to.

The enzymic synthesis of lecithin from cytidine diphosphate choline and a diglyceride is an example of biochemical " phosphorylation " of alcoholic hydroxyl groups by P^1, P^2 diesterified pyrophosphates.

Several other reactions involving transfer of alkyl phosphate from CDPX to an alcohol are known. Examples of enzymic anion exchange with diesterified pyrophosphates include the reaction catalysed by uridylyl transferase, as well as conversion of UDPG or FAD into UTP or ATP by the action of inorganic pyrophosphate.

Examples of alkylation by phosphate derivatives include the

enzymic syntheses of nucleosides and nucleotides from the free base and α-D-ribose-1 phosphate or α-D-ribose-1 pyrophosphate-5 phosphate. In each case the reaction involves nucleophilic displacement of a phosphate (or pyrophosphate) residue, with inversion, to yield β nucleoside derivatives from the α-sugar phosphates. A further example, involving alkylation of a tertiary nitrogen atom, lies in the biosynthesis of thiamine phosphate from the hydroxymethylpyrimidine pyrophosphate and the thiazole phosphate.

Related alkylations occur in the formation of carbon–oxygen bonds, as in the enzymic synthesis of type III pneumococcal capsular polysaccharide (polycellobiuronic acid) from uridine diphosphate glucose and uridine diphosphate glucuronic acid (with inversion at C1 of the transferred glycosyl units) and of glycogen (with retention of configuration) from primer oligosaccharide and uridine diphosphate glucose. Another enzymic reaction analogous to the C—O solvolysis of tetrabenzyl pyrophosphate is to be found in the synthesis of "active methionine" from methionine and adenosine-5' triphosphate. In this case the adenosine moiety is transferred to form a C—S bond, with coincident liberation of orthophosphate and inorganic pyrophosphate.

Concerted reaction of the substrates has been proposed in mechanisms for enzymic syntheses of C—N bonds that involve displacement of a hydroxyl group by an amino residue (derived from glutamine or ammonia) by the action of adenosine-5' triphosphate. For example, in the amination of xanthosine-5' phosphate to guanosine-5' phosphate, concerted action by both acidic and basic groups results in simultaneous cleavage of the C—O bond, formation of the C—N bond, and cleavage of adenosine-5' triphosphate (which acts as an electrophilic activator of the C—O linkage) to adenosine-5' phosphate and inorganic pyrophosphate (nucleophilic attack at the α phosphorus atom). Similar cleavage of adenosine-5' triphosphate occurs in the amidation (by glutamine) of nicotinic acid adenine dinucleotide to nicotinamide adenine dinucleotide, but conversion of uridine-5' triphosphate into cytidine-5' triphosphate involves cleavage of ATP into inorganic orthophosphate and adenosine-5′ pyrophosphate (nucleophilic attack at the γ phosphorus atom). The tautomeric shifts shown (e.g. uridine as 6-hydroxy rather than 6-keto), corresponding to ionisation, could well be induced by the enzyme at neutrality. (cf. Chemical amination of 6-thiouridine, but

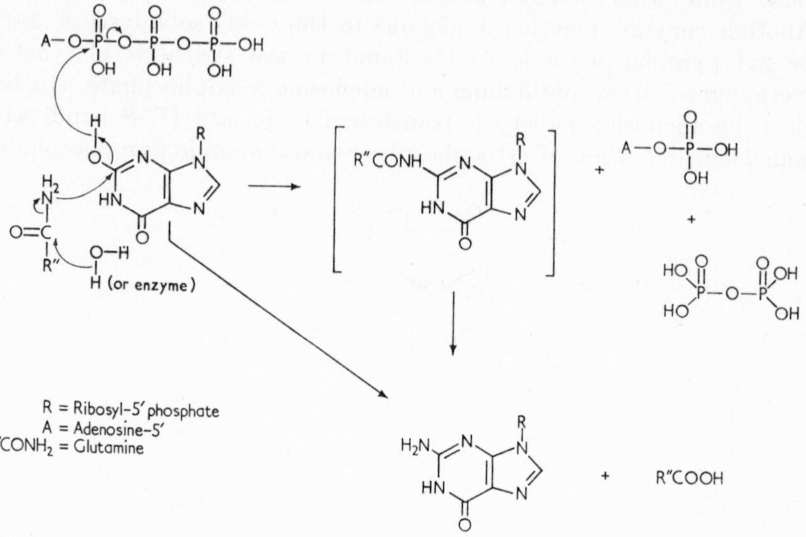

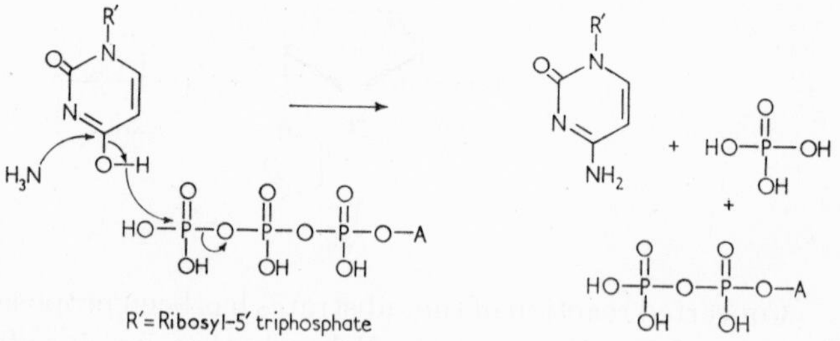

R = Ribosyl-5′ phosphate
A = Adenosine-5′
R″CONH₂ = Glutamine

R′ = Ribosyl-5′ triphosphate

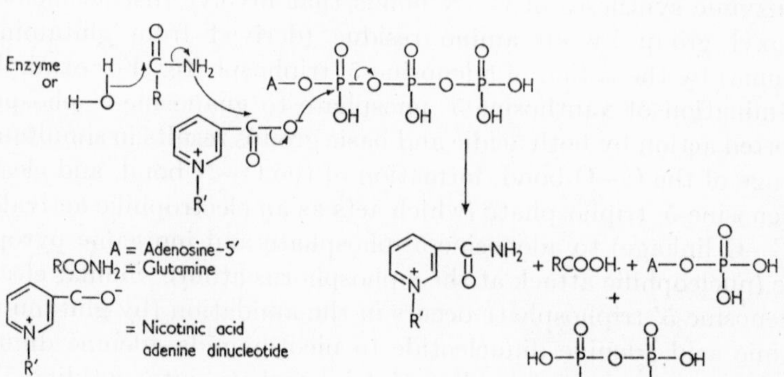

Enzyme or

A = Adenosine-5′
RCONH₂ = Glutamine

= Nicotinic acid adenine dinucleotide

not uridine. Compare also the high reactivity of uridine derivatives such as O^2-ethyluridine and $O^2,2'$ (or 3' or 5')-cyclouridine in which the pyrimidine is held in a tautomeric form facilitating attack by amines at C2. Similarly O^6-ethyluridine and $O^6,5'$-cyclo-pseudouridine are readily aminated at C6 with displacement of oxygen simply by treatment with ethanolic ammonia.)

Similar concerted mechanisms have been proposed for the enzymic synthesis of glycinamide ribotide from glycine, ribosylamine-5 phosphate and adenosine-5' triphosphate, and for the enzymic synthesis of formylglycinamidine ribotide by the action of glutamine and adenosine-5' triphosphate on formylglycinamide ribotide. Such mechanisms can also be applied to the formation of adenylosuccinic acid from inosine-5' phosphate, aspartic acid and guanosine-5' triphosphate. (All these examples appear to involve nucleophilic attack at the γ phosphorus

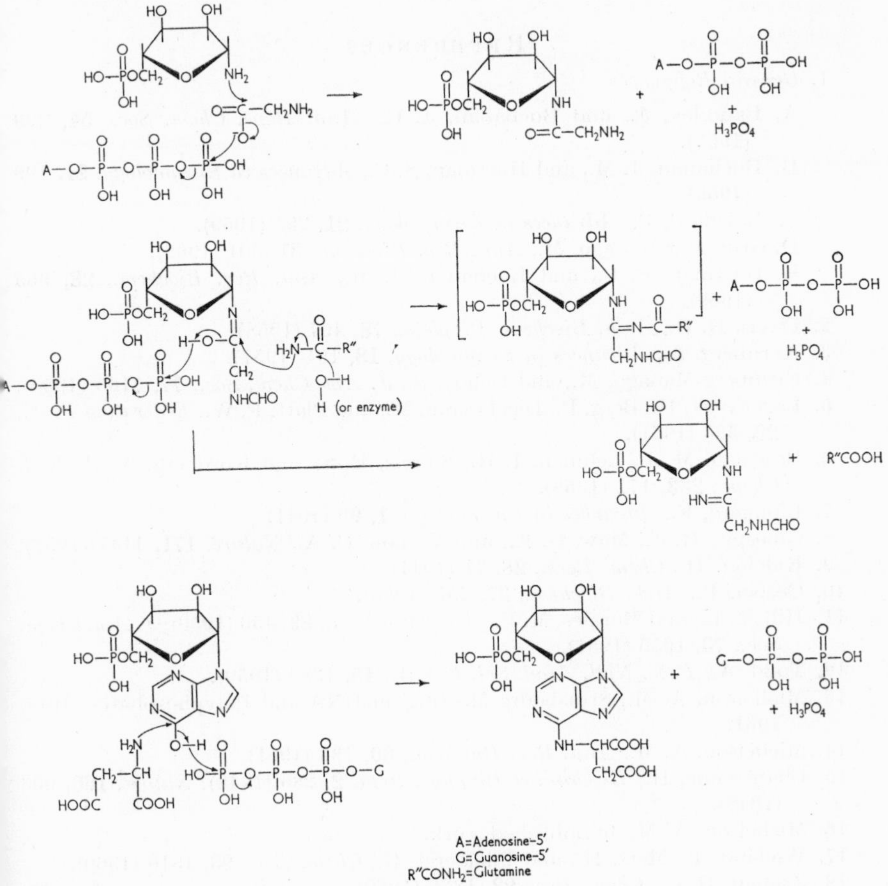

A = Adenosine-5'
G = Guanosine-5'
R"CONH$_2$ = Glutamine

atom of the nucleoside-5' triphosphate, to liberate orthophosphate and nucleoside-5' pyrophosphate.)

CATABOLISM OF NUCLEOTIDES

Stereochemical factors assisting protonation of the sugar lactol oxygen may be significant in the enzymic cleavage of nucleosides to free base and sugar (as distinct from phosphorolysis reactions). In addition, the nature of the binding of substrate to enzyme may well affect the stability of the glycosyl linkage. Decreased glycosyl bond stability as a result of substituents in the heterocyclic ring system and of strain induced in the sugar has been mentioned earlier (p. 26). Similarly, chemically achieved variation of the electron density at C2 or C8 in purines (by substitution elsewhere in the ring) can lead to ready attack at these centres; this may bear on the enzymic oxidation of adenine and guanine to uric acid.

REFERENCES

1. *General References*

    A. Baddiley, J., and Buchanan, J. G., *Ann. Reps. Chem. Soc.*, **54,** 329 (1957).
    B. Buchanan, J. M., and Hartman, S. C., *Advances in Enzymology*, **21,** 199 (1959).
    C. Reichard, P., *Advances in Enzymology*, **21,** 263 (1959).
    D. Grunberg-Manago, M., *Ann. Rev. Biochem.*, **31,** 301 (1962).
    E. Hartman, S. C., and Buchanan, J. M., *Ann. Rev. Biochem.*, **28,** 365 (1959).
2. Davis, B. D., *Arch. Biochem. Biophys.*, **78,** 497 (1958).
3. Kornberg, A., *Advances in Enzymology*, **18,** 191 (1957).
4. Grunberg-Manago, M., and Ochoa, S., *J. Am. Chem. Soc.*, **77,** 3165 (1955).
5. Lagerkvist, U., Berg, P., Dieckmann, M., and Platt, F. W., *Federation Proc.*, **20,** 363 (1961).
6. Bessman, M. J., Lehman, I. R., Simms, E. S., and Kornberg, A., *J. Biol. Chem.*, **233,** 171 (1958).
7. Lipmann, F., *Advances in Enzymology*, **1,** 99 (1941).
8. Gillespie, R. J., Maw, G. A., and Vernon, C. A., *Nature*, **171,** 1147 (1953).
9. Kalckar, H., *Chem. Revs.*, **28,** 71 (1941).
10. Oesper, P., *Arch. Biochem.*, **27,** 255 (1950).
11. Hill, T. L., and Morales, M. F., *Arch. Biochem.*, **29,** 450 (1950); *J. Am. Chem. Soc.*, **73,** 1656 (1951).
12. Todd, A., *Proc. Natl. Acad. Sci. U.S.A.*, **45,** 1389 (1959).
13. Michelson, A. M., Strasbourg Meeting on RNA and Polyphosphates, July, 1961.
14. Michelson, A. M., *Ann. Rev. Biochem.*, **30,** 133 (1961).
15. Chantrenne, H., *Biochim. et Biophys. Acta*, **2,** 286 (1948); *Nature*, **160,** 603 (1947).
16. Michelson, A. M., unpublished work.
17. Wieland, T., Merz, H., and Pfleiderer, G., *Chem. Ber.*, **93,** 1816 (1960).
18. Zachau, H. G., *Chem. Ber.*, **93,** 1822 (1960).

19. Zachau, H. G., and Karau, W., *Chem. Ber.*, **93**, 1830 (1960).
20. Michelson, A. M., and Letters, R., in press.
21. Grunze, I., Thilo, E., and Grunze, H., *Chem. Ber.*, **93**, 2631 (1960).
22. Brown, D. M., and Hamer, N. K., *J. Chem. Soc.*, 406 (1960).
23. Dudek, G. O., and Westheimer, F. H., *J. Am. Chem. Soc.*, **81**, 2641 (1959).
24. Kenner, G. W., and Mather, J., *J. Chem. Soc.*, 3524 (1956).
25. Schmulbach, C. D., Wazer, J. R. V., and Irani, R. R., *J. Am. Chem. Soc.*, **81**, 6347 (1959).
26. Buchanan, J. M., and Hartman, S. C., *Advances in Enzymology*, **21**, 230 (1959).
27. *General References*
   A. Koshland, D. E., in " *The Mechanism of Enzyme Action* " ed. by McElroy, W. E., and Glass, B., The Johns Hopkins Press, 1954.
   B. Kornberg, A., *Advances in Enzymology*, **18**, 191 (1957).
   C. Buchanan, J. M., and Hartman, S. C., *Advances in Enzymology*, **21**, 199 (1959).
28. Ingraham, L. L., and Green, D. E., *Science*, **128**, 310 (1958).
29. Cohn, M., *Biochim. et Biophys. Acta*, **37**, 344 (1960).
30. Khorana, H. G., Fernandes, J. F., and Kornberg, A., *J. Biol. Chem.*, **230**, 941 (1958).
31. Shabarova, Z. A., Hughes, N. A., and Baddiley, J., *Biochem. J.*, **83**, 216 (1962).
32. Szer, W., and Shugar, D., *Biokhimiya*, **26**, 840 (1961).

Chapter 6

ORGANIC CHEMISTRY OF NUCLEIC ACIDS

The nucleic acids are polymeric substances that can be degraded to mononucleotides by a variety of means. For general convenience, polymers of mononucleotides will be referred to as oligonucleotides when the number of monomer units per molecule is between two and seven (approximately) and as polynucleotides when this number exceeds seven.* As with many macromolecules, the concept of molecule becomes rather vague at very large molecular weights owing to aggregation and disaggregation processes which may occur with greater or lesser ease. Again for general convenience, molecule should refer only to a structure formed entirely by covalent bonds; a macromolecule is a very large single molecule (which may contain intramolecular secondary bonds in addition to the covalent bonding); aggregates should be described as such and, when this is known, further defined as di-, tri- or polymolecular to indicate the number of molecules or strands involved in the complex.

Nucleic acids were originally so-called because they were isolated from cell nuclei. Subsequently, two main classes of nucleic acid were defined, one being typified by the nucleic acid isolated from thymus and the other by yeast nucleic acid. Later work has shown that classification by origin (e.g. plant or animal) is misleading and that in fact both kinds of nucleic acid occur in all types of cell. Both are present in the nucleus but in many cells the bulk of the nucleic acid (ribonucleic acid) is located in the cytoplasm. Since biological distinctions tend to vagueness, particularly when applied to quasi-living systems such as viruses, a chemical description has been found most convenient and nucleic acids are now classified as deoxyribonucleic or ribonucleic depending on the nature of the major sugar component. Ribonucleic acid is found mainly in the cytoplasm while deoxyribonucleic acid is confined, possibly exclusively, to the cell nucleus. Further major distinctions are to be found in the pyrimidine composition of the two kinds of nucleic acid and, to a lesser degree, in the nature of the proteins with which the acids are generally associated.

Although the low stability of nucleic acids was recognised by the earliest workers, for many years rather drastic isolation procedures were used. Partly because of this, the examination of nucleic acids with particular reference to base composition, molecular weight, and the

* This is an operational definition, but a physical justification is also possible.

308

number of secondary phosphoryl dissociations relative to primary dissociations gave results which, though perhaps characteristic of the grossly degraded specimens studied, were scarcely relevant to nucleic acids *in vivo*. With the advent of milder extraction methods a more accurate picture has become available, but even now, only the more general outlines of the structures of nucleic acids are known.

Ribonucleic Acids

ISOLATION OF RIBONUCLEIC ACIDS

Methods used for the extraction of ribonucleic acids are partly dependent on the nature of the organ or organism. In the early method used by Levene,[1] alkali was added to a thick paste of yeast, the mixture stirred with picric acid, filtered, and the nucleic acid precipitated from the filtrate by addition of hydrochloric acid. Such rather drastic procedures ensure that the nucleic acid obtained differs considerably from " native " ribonucleic acid. For the isolation of ribonucleic acids bearing some resemblance to those occurring in the living cell it is necessary to avoid the use of extreme conditions of pH or temperature; at the same time, enzymic degradation must be inhibited as far as possible. Extraction of ribonucleoproteins with isotonic sodium chloride solution has been used extensively.[2, 3] Dissociation of the nucleic acids and proteins can be achieved by a variety of methods such as treatment with chloroform–octyl alcohol mixtures,[4] with sodium dodecyl sulphate,[5] strontium nitrate[6] or alcohol[7] or by digestion of the protein fraction with trypsin.[8] Again, the efficacy of each method is determined by the nature of the ribonucleoprotein. Guanidine hydrochloride (a protein denaturant) is useful for the inactivation of enzymes during extraction;[9] an approach involving adsorption of ribonucleases on bentonite after a preliminary treatment with zinc ions has been used for the isolation of ribonucleic acids and undegraded ribonucleoproteins from yeast.[10]

The isolation of ribonucleic acids from homogenates of mammalian tissues, from micro-organisms and viruses, by extraction with phenol and water at room temperature is particularly advantageous since proteins and deoxyribonucleic acids are precipitated, ribonuclease is inhibited and very good yields of highly polymerised products are obtained.[11–14] Direct extraction of yeast with aqueous phenol has been used for the large scale preparation of amino acid " transfer " ribonucleic acids.[15] Under the conditions employed, little of the high molecular weight material is released from the organism. Combined with a rapid purification of the RNA on ECTEOLA[16] or DEAE[17, 18] cellulose anion exchange material, the extraction procedure gives relatively pure " transfer " nucleic acid in quantity.

FRACTIONATION

Other than a number of viral ribonucleic acids, the majority of polyribonucleotides as isolated are undoubtedly complex mixtures containing polymers of various chain lengths, nucleotide sequences and base composition (presence or absence of minor bases). Partial fractionation has been achieved by a number of approaches, but until satisfactory characterisation is developed, the degree of purity or homogeneity of ribonucleic acids will remain difficult to define. The specific enzymic reaction of amino acids (via the amino-acyl adenylates) with " transfer " ribonucleic acids may provide a means of estimating the purity of these relatively low molecular weight polyribonucleotides, and certainly provides a measure of their biochemical homogeneity.

Methods of fractionation include precipitation with neutral salts,[19-21] electrophoresis,[22, 23] chromatography on calcium phosphate,[24-26] and precipitation with dihydrostreptomycin.[27] Recently, fractional dissociation of nucleic acid–histone complexes, previously used for deoxynucleic acids, has been extended to the fractionation of ribonucleic acids.[28] In all fractions the ratio of 6-amino- to 6-keto-nucleosides was close to unity. Some degree of fractionation occurs in the phenol extraction procedure,[29-32] possibly as a result of differential binding of nucleic acids to proteins. Cellulose anion exchange materials such as ECTEOLA and DEAE are now being used extensively for the fractionation not only of ribonucleic acids,[33, 34] including amino acid-specific transfer ribonucleic acids,[35] but also ribonucleoproteins[36] and even virus preparations.[37] Neutral or near neutral salt solutions are normally used for elution. The capacity of these exchangers to fractionate material ranging from mononucleotide isomers[38] and oligonucleotides of different chain lengths or composition[39-42] to polynucleotides of extremely high molecular weight is a striking feature of the method.* Separation of valine-labelled RNA from unlabelled acceptor RNA on DEAE–dextran columns has been reported.[43] Modified cellulose exchangers in which nucleosides, particularly adenosine and guanosine (instead of triethanolamine), are bound to cellulose with epichlorohydrin have also been used for the fractionation of ribonucleic acids.[44] A related use of ECTEOLA cellulose, depending on specific hydrogen bonding ability, might lie in loading ECTEOLA with denatured DNA from a particular organism (extremely high ionic strength is required for removal of the DNA) for fractionation or isolation of operationally defined informational RNA, using solutions of decreasing ionic strength for elution. Transfer ribonucleic acid has been separated into material with increased specificities for tyrosine and for leucine by chromatography on a tertiary aminoalkyl ether of starch (Cato 2, formerly Cato 8

* Greatly improved separation of oligonucleotides and small polynucleotides can be obtained by ion-exchange chromatography in the presence of urea to eliminate secondary binding forces. [569]

anion exchanger).[45, 46] Chromatography on hydroxyapatite gave good separation of valine- and phenylalanine-specific ribonucleic acids.[47]

Partial fractionation of ribonucleic acids can also be effected by counter-current distribution;[48] using this technique almost complete separation of alanine- from tyrosine-active ribonucleic acids[49, 50] and of tyrosine- from valine-acceptor fractions[17] in the mixture of so-called " soluble ", " transfer " or " acceptor " ribonucleic acids was obtained. With 400 transfers in a phosphate buffer–formamide–isopropanol system, partial or complete separation of ribonucleic acids specific for a number of different amino acids was achieved.[51] Though in no case could complete purity and homogeneity be claimed, the method provides a convenient preliminary fractionation.[557] The distribution of threonine- and leucine-specific ribonucleic acids suggested that these are heterogeneous (though not necessarily so) in transfer RNA from yeast.[51] Other solvent systems have also been used with considerable success.[52–55]

Successful separation of specific transfer ribonucleic acids has been achieved by partition chromatography using a phosphate buffer (containing magnesium ions)–formamide–isopropanol solvent on silicic acid. Good separation of tyrosine-, tryptophan-, histidine-, valine- and alanine-active acceptor RNA was obtained,[56] and a considerably improved recovery of RNA (80%) is possible.[57]

Some purification[58] of transfer ribonucleic acids specific for valine and for proline is possible using fractional precipitation with spermine at pH 5·6. The pH is rather critical, and studies[59] with enzymically synthesised homopolymers (all of which are precipitated between pH 4·1 and 6·8) and the helical complexes therefrom, indicate that whereas polyadenylic–polyuridylic acid complex is precipitated by spermine at pH 5·1 to 6·8, the analogous polyinosinic–polycytidylic acid forms a spermine complex that is soluble between these pH limits. However, on acidification to pH 4·5 immediate aggregation occurs, possibly owing to destruction of the helical complex by protonation of the cytosine residues. The results suggest a rather marked compositional (or possibly structural) heterogeneity in transfer nucleic acids.

Partial separation of a specific amino acid transfer ribonucleic acid has been achieved by chemical treatments. Amino acids esterifying the 3' (or 2') hydroxyl group of the terminal nucleoside of ribonucleic acids isolated from yeast by extraction with phenol were removed at pH 10. The mixture was then labelled specifically with ^{14}C-L-valine by means of an amino acid-activating enzyme fraction. Periodate oxidation of the unesterified 2', 3' cis hydroxyl groups gave ribonucleic acids (other than the valine protected polymers) containing a terminal dialdehyde. Formation of the hydrazone with 2-hydroxy-3-naphthoic acid hydrazide followed by coupling with tetrazotised o-dianisidine gave dye-bound nucleic acid, together with the valine specific RNA. A twelvefold enrichment of the latter was obtained by fractional precipitation at a two phase interface.[60] More conveniently, virtually pure valine protected RNA can be separated from dye bound nucleic acid by chromatography on DEAE–dextran columns.[43] A number of other fractionation techniques could doubtless be applied and the method (and its possible modifications) offers considerable promise. One such modification

and possible polymers

involves coupling the periodate oxidised ribonucleic acids (other than the specific amino-acyl-RNA) with a phenylhydrazine resin obtained from p-aminobenzyl cellulose by diazotisation and then reduction with sodium borohydride.[61] Alternatively, the RNA-dialdehyde can be coupled with a water-soluble polyacrylic acid hydrazide; a tenfold enrichment of L-valine-labelled RNA has been attained in this way.[52, 62] The method is reproducible and can be used for large amounts of material. Coupling with aminoethylcellulose has also been employed.[566]

Another approach with considerable potential value uses cross-linked polydiazostyrene formed by the reaction of polyaminostyrene with nitrous acid, and is based on observations that diazonium compounds react readily with certain amino acids forming covalently linked derivatives. At pH 7 to 8·5 only tyrosine and histidine react rapidly. Preparations of " transfer " ribonucleic acids fully esterified with amino acids were stirred with the insoluble polydiazostyrene which combined with the tyrosine and histidine labelled nucleic acids only. Incubation at pH 10 released the two specific polynucleotides by cleavage of the amino-acyl ester linkage. Further separation was then achieved by re-esterification with tyrosine using a purified tyrosine-activating

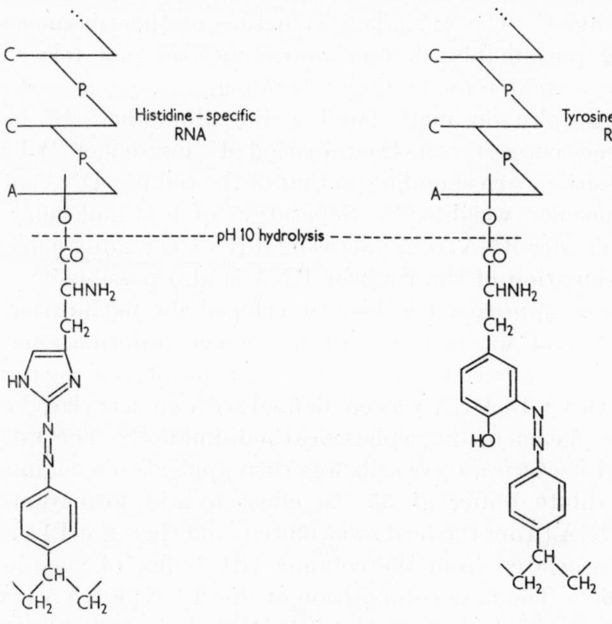

Histidine – specific
RNA

Tyrosine – specific
RNA

pH 10 hydrolysis

enzyme and repetition of the polydiazostyrene treatment. No reaction occurred with the unesterified histidine-specific ribonucleic acid which was left in solution, whereas the tyrosine-specific nucleic acid was released as before, by mild alkaline treatment. Both fractions were almost pure with respect to their amino acid receptor specificity.[63] Preliminary observations indicated that the valine-specific ribonucleic acid could be esterified with the dipeptide tyrosylvaline, with obvious possibilities.

Preliminary work on the use of " tailor-made " chromatographic materials employing hydrogen bonds (presumably) rather than salt or covalent linkages has been reported. The p-nitrobenzoyl ester of a partly acetylated cellulose was reduced to the amino derivative and this was diazotised and coupled with guanine (at C8) to give a product containing one guanine residue per fifteen glucose units.[64] The material readily adsorbed ribonucleic acids from salt solutions of high ionic strength (conducive to the formation of hydrogen bonds); elution with solutions of decreasing ionic strength gave fractions with significant differences in base composition in the case of low molecular weight RNA from yeast. Contrary to possible expectation, a marked increase in cytosine content during the course of elution was not observed, and factors other than complementary hydrogen bonding (such as molecular weight, nucleotide sequence and the irregular distribution of 8-substituted guanine residues in the chromatographic material) are possibly involved. The secondary structure of the ribonucleic acids themselves is presumably of some importance, in that relatively few bases may be available for hydrogen bonding.

Chromatography on methylated serum albumin[551, 552] has been used with some success for the fractionation of " messenger " ribonucleic acids (composition corresponding to that of the cellular DNA) of widely different molecular weights.[553] Separation of low molecular weight amino acid transfer RNA from microsomal RNA is readily achieved;[558] further fractionation of the transfer RNA is also possible.[568]

An ingenious approach has been developed for purification of T4-specific RNA and for isolation of messenger (informational) RNA corresponding to a restricted genetic segment of the bacteriophage DNA. Denatured T4 DNA was condensed with an acetylated cellulose phosphate by means of dicyclohexylcarbodi-imide.[562] The total RNA from infected *Escherichia coli* cells was then applied to a column of this material in dilute buffer at 55° to effect hybrid formation. Non-complexed RNA (from the host) was eluted, and then the T4 messenger RNA was dissociated from the column with buffer of very low ionic strength at 65°. The base composition of this T4 type RNA (free of *E. coli* RNA) resembled that of the T4 DNA bound to the cellulose phosphate, providing further evidence that adsorption resulted from specific formation of complementary hydrogen bonded hybrid RNA–DNA complexes. Similar treatment of the bulk T4 messenger RNA on a second column containing DNA from a T4 deletion mutant, r 1272 (that is, DNA lacking a specific stretch of nucleotides), then resulted in separation of RNA specific for the r II region of the bacteriophage genome (this RNA is not adsorbed by the column) from messenger RNA corresponding to the available DNA binding sites (adsorbed by the column).[562]

More recent studies have shown that physical entrapment of DNA in cellulose acetate or agar gels can be effected readily (in the absence of any chemical agent); DNA immobilised in this way forms hydrogen bonds with complementary molecules and hence can be used for purification and isolation of specific RNA.[570]

A related technique involving specific complex formation with relatively short chains has been described.[563] Covalent binding of small polythymidylic acids to cellulose was achieved by esterification of hydroxyl groups with the terminal 5'-phosphate residues in an oligo-nucleotide mixture, using dicyclohexylcarbodi-imide as reagent. At 4° hexa-deoxyadenylic acid was retained by the column and thus could be separated from hexa-thymidylic acid; the oligoadenylic acid was eluted at 35° Fractionation of amino acid transfer RNA may be possible by this method.[563]

GENERAL STRUCTURE OF RIBONUCLEIC ACIDS

While it was soon realised that ribonucleic acids were composed essentially of four mononucleotide units, for many years precise information concerning the internucleotide linkages was lacking, and a great deal of imagination was therefore expended on this problem. The many suggested structures included pyrophosphate, polyphosphoric, ether, and phosphoramidate linkages, but the relatively simple tetranucleotide structure proposed by Levene[65, 66] which contained phosphodiester linkages between the sugar components of the nucleosides best fitted the facts as then known. In view of the odium now associated with the tetranucleotide theory of the structure of nucleic acids it is perhaps relevant to mention that it was considerably more accurate than the trinucleotide theory[67, 68] with which it was in opposition, and that as Levene himself wrote " On the other hand, it must be borne in mind that the true molecular weight of nucleic acids is as yet not known. The tetranucleotide theory (sic) is the minimum molecular weight and the nucleic acid may as well be a multiple of it."[69] Moreover, it is likely that the material then called nucleic acid was of very low molecular weight, with an average chain length of five or six nucleotides. Later work by Gulland and his co-workers suggested a modification of the theory embodied in the phrase " statistical tetranucleotide,"[70] but it was not until the application of modern analytical techniques in 1949 that the highly unsatisfactory situation was clarified.

At that time it was known that ribonucleic acids could be hydrolysed with alkali to mononucleotides, then thought to be exclusively nucleo-side-3' phosphates. A general structure for ribonucleic acids, with 2'-3' phosphodiester linkages, had been advanced by Levene and Tipson,[71] the assumption being made that the 2' linkage would be considerably less stable than the -3' phosphate ester bonds, thus giving rise to nucleoside-3' phosphates exclusively on alkaline hydrolysis. However, when ribonucleic acid was treated with snake venom (which contains a phosphomonoesterase specific for nucleoside-5' phosphates) inorganic phosphate and nucleosides were obtained.[72, 73] Further, X-ray diffraction studies of ribonucleic acid by Astbury suggested that the principal internucleotide linkage was 2'–5' or 3'–5' rather than 2'–3'.[74] On the other hand, no direct chemical evidence of a 5' phosphate linkage was available and indeed the absence of 5' phosphorylated derivatives in acid-hydrolysates of ribonucleic acid, in spite of their known stability, was in apparent conflict with a 2'(or 3')–5' internucleotide linkage. The stability of deoxyribonucleic acid (necessarily 3'–5' linked) towards alkali, in contrast with the instability of ribonucleic acid, was also held to indicate a different type of linkage at that time. In contradiction to this, the action of pancreatic ribonuclease on ribonucleic acid gave periodate-resistant oligonucleotide mixtures which, after removal of monoesterified phosphate by treatment with phosphomonoesterase, consumed periodate, indicating that the terminal phosphate was located at a 2' or 3' hydroxyl group and, since nucleoside was not liberated, that linkage through other than the 2' or 3' hydroxyl groups also occurred.[75]

$$
\begin{array}{c}
\text{Base–sugar–P(=O)–OH} \\
\text{Base–sugar–P(=O)–OH} \\
\text{Base–sugar–P(=O)–OH} \\
\text{Base–sugar–P(=O)–OH}
\end{array}
$$

The application of paper chromatographic methods to the rapid analysis of purine and pyrimidine bases[76, 77] in hydrolysates of small quantities of ribonucleic acids soon showed that molar equivalence of these bases was exceptional, rather than the general rule. Of even greater significance was the observation that separation of the mixture of nucleotides in an alkaline digest of ribonucleic acid by means of ion exchange chromatography gave isomeric pairs of nucleotides, later shown to be the nucleoside-2' and -3' phosphates.[78] While these isomers were not interconverted in alkali, acid readily catalysed the migration of the phosphate residue between the 2' and 3' hydroxyl groups. The same analytical technique yielded the 5'-phosphates of adenosine, cytidine, guanosine and uridine (among other products) from intestinal phosphodiesterase hydrolysates of ribonucleic acids that had been treated previously with ribonuclease.[79] Considerably higher yields of the nucleoside-5' phosphates were obtained by the action of snake venom diesterase on ribonucleic acids from yeast and calf liver; the digests also contained free nucleosides and nucleoside-2'(3'),5' diphosphates.[80]

In 1952 the problem of the general structure of nucleic acids was resolved by Brown and Todd, and the apparently conflicting lines of evidence neatly reconciled.[81] It had been shown previously in studies using radioactive phosphorus that the acid-catalysed isomerisation of α or β glycerophosphates was intramolecular, proceeding via a cyclic phosphate intermediate.[82] It was also known that whereas glycerol-α phosphate was stable to alkali, the methyl ester was readily converted into methanol and a mixture of glycerol-α and -β phosphates on hydrolysis with alkali or with dilute acid. A tri-esterified cyclic phosphate " orthoester " intermediate was postulated[83, 84] to explain the much lower stability of such diesters of phosphoric acid containing a glycerol (or ethylene glycol) residue compared with simple phosphate diesters lacking a vicinal hydroxyl group. Fonó further suggested (in 1947) that the rapid degradation of ribonucleic acid by treatment with alkali,

in contrast with the stability shown by deoxyribonucleic acid, was dependent on the *cis* hydroxyl group at C2′ of the ribose residues (absent in deoxynucleic acids) and that with respect to hydrolysis, the ribonucleic acids and glycerol alkyl phosphates were analogous.[84]

Similar properties were shown by a number of simple synthetic nucleotide derivatives such as adenosine-2′ benzyl phosphate and adenosine-3′ benzyl phosphate.[81, 85] These were readily hydrolysed (by acidic or alkaline treatment) to benzyl alcohol and a mixture of adenosine-2′ and -3′ phosphates in each case. The postulated adenosine-2′,3′ cyclic phosphate intermediate was synthesised and characterised; the properties of this cyclic phosphate were in full accord with those required of such an intermediate.[86] Further work verified these observations for a number of alkyl esters of ribonucleoside-2′ and -3′ phosphates all of which, in contrast with adenosine-5′ benzyl phosphate, were readily degraded with concomitant phosphate migration under acidic or alkaline conditions.[86, 87]

A general structure for ribonucleic acid was therefore advanced, in which the nucleoside units were bridged by recurring phosphodiester linkages between the 3'(or 2') hydroxyl group and the 5' hydroxyl group of adjacent nucleosides.[81] Alkaline degradation would then be expected to give nucleoside-2',3' cyclic phosphates by exclusive fission

of the C5'—O—P bond, followed by further hydrolysis to a mixture of nucleoside-2' and -3' phosphates. The presence of these postulated nucleoside-2',3' cyclic phosphates was demonstrated in hydrolysates of ribonucleic acid using suitable mild alkaline conditions and the mechanism advanced received immediate confirmation.[88]

The necessity of a neighbouring hydroxyl group (stereochemical requirements further define this as *cis* vicinal) for the formation of cyclic phosphate intermediates thus explains the alkali-stability of deoxyribonucleic acid and of such synthetic diesters as adenylyl-5′ : 5′-uridine (adenosine-5′ uridine-5′ phosphate).[89] By virtue of its stability, the type of internucleotide linkage present in the latter compound can be excluded from ribonucleic acids except as a very minor proportion. Similarly, the possibility of alternate 2′–2′ and 3′–3′ inter-

nucleotide linkages (such structures would be degraded by alkali in a stepwise fashion rather than by simultaneous attack at many points in the chain) can be excluded for a number of reasons, such as the almost quantitative production of nucleoside-5′ phosphates from ribonucleic acids by the action of venom phosphodiesterase.[90] The specificity of this enzyme for esters of nucleoside-5′ phosphates[91] (and the nature of

the products) is strong evidence for involvement of the 5′ hydroxyl groups, while the production of nucleosides and nucleoside-2′(3′),5′ diphosphates in equal small amounts is readily accounted for by a recurring 3′(or 2′)–5′ internucleotide structure since these compounds would arise from the end units of such structures.[92]

While at this stage chemical hydrolytic methods were not available for discrimination between a 3'–5' and a 2'–5' internucleotide linkage, evidence for the probably exclusive occurrence of a 3'–5' structure was obtained from studies on the enzymic hydrolysis of ribonucleic acid and of simple nucleotide derivatives. A number of nucleases which catalyse the hydrolysis of nucleic acids to smaller fragments have been isolated from various sources. Pancreatic ribonuclease,[93] one of a group of enzymes showing high specificity for ribonucleic acids, has been studied extensively and the mode of action elucidated. Earlier work indicated that the enzyme acted at pyrimidine nucleotide sites since the larger non-dialysable residues from enzymic digests of ribonucleic acid were considerably enriched in purine content;[94] pyrimidine mononucleotides were also liberated but no free purine mononucleotides.[75, 95, 96] Further studies based on acidic and alkaline hydrolysis of the products obtained by consecutive treatment of ribonucleic acid by ribonuclease and prostatic phosphomonoesterase led to the conclusion that the specificity of ribonuclease was such that nucleic acids were degraded to mixtures of pyrimidine mononucleotides and purine oligonucleotides containing a terminal pyrimidine nucleoside-2'(or 3') phosphate unit.[75, 97]

$$\text{RNA} \xrightarrow{\text{RNAase}} \text{Py} + \text{PuPy} + \text{PuPuPy} + \text{Pu} \ldots \text{PuPy}$$

(Py = pyrimidine nucleotide; Pu = purine nucleotide.)

Fractionation of ribonuclease digests of ribonucleic acids by ion exchange chromatography,[98] paper electrophoresis, and paper chromatography[99] fully confirmed the conclusion based on study of crude mixtures, and led to an examination of the properties of individual oligonucleotide components. Brief treatment with ribonuclease (or incubation under dialysis conditions) showed that pyrimidine nucleoside-2',3' cyclic phosphates (and oligonucleotides with a terminal 2',3' cyclic phosphate)[100] were formed initially by a transphosphorylation mechanism and that subsquent action of the enzyme effected hydrolysis of these cyclic phosphates to the corresponding -3' phosphate. Treatment of synthetic uridine-2',3' cyclic phosphate and cytidine-2',3' cyclic phosphate with pancreatic ribonuclease likewise gave the nucleoside-3' phosphate exclusively, by unidirectional cleavage of the C2'—O—P ester bond, while the specificity of the enzyme for pyrimidine nucleotide derivatives was further demonstrated by the lack of action on adenosine-2',3' cyclic phosphate and guanosine-2',3' cyclic phosphate.[101] Thus exhaustive treatment of ribonucleic acid by ribonuclease gives pyrimidine nucleoside-3' phosphates and oligonucleotide products with a terminal 3' phosphate group. Alkaline hydrolysis of the latter yields mixtures of the 2′ and 3′ phosphates of the purine nucleosides, and the 3′ phosphates only of the pyrimidine nucleosides. (Migration of monoesterified phosphate does not occur under alkaline conditions). The specific action of ribonuclease in producing pyrimidine mononucleotides from sites in the nucleic acid with two or more adjacent pyrimidine residues and oligonucleotides from sites where purine nucleotides are flanked by pyrimidine nucleotides was then further defined by studies on the enzymic hydrolysis of simple esters of the mononucleotides. While alkyl (benzyl, methyl, and ethyl) esters of pyrimidine nucleoside-3′ phosphates were readily converted into the free 3′ nucleotides via the nucleoside-2′,3′ cyclic phosphate, analogous esters of the pyrimidine nucleoside-2′ phosphates (or of the purine nucleoside-2′ or -3′ phosphates) were completely unaffected. Hence,

Pyrimidine nucleoside – 3′ phosphates
Purine nucleoside – 2′ and – 3′phosphates

in ribonucleic acid all the pyrimidine nucleotide residues are linked via a 3′ phosphate rather than a 2′ phosphate group.[87] Finally, the use of a spleen nuclease that degraded ribonucleic acid to both purine and pyrimidine nucleotides esterified at the 3′ hydroxyl group, without intermediate formation of nucleoside-2′,3′ cyclic phosphates,[102-104] fully defined the general internucleotide linkage as 3′–5′. The specificity of this enzyme (and of others from intestine, potato and rye-grass) was likewise established by the use of simple synthetic substrates. While cytidine-3′ benzyl phosphate and adenosine-3′ benzyl phosphate were hydrolysed to the corresponding-3′ phosphates, the enzyme preparations had no action on esters of nucleoside-2′ phosphates.[105]

No unequivocal evidence for branching in ribonucleic acids either by triesterification of phosphate residues, or by attachment of polynucleotide chains to the 2′-hydroxyl groups of nucleosides in a primary strand has yet appeared. In the main, and probably *in toto*, the ribonucleic acids are linear polymers of mononucleotides united by 3′–5′ phosphodiester linkages.

Molecular weight estimations of ribonucleic acids have often been conflicting, partly because the size of the molecule depends greatly on the pre-treatment. This can give rise not only to low values (by enzymic or chemical rupture of covalent bonds), but also to misleadingly high molecular weights (by aggregation of distinct linear chains). Apart from alteration of the nucleic acid coincident with extraction, within the living cell there is undoubtedly considerable variation in the chain lengths of ribonucleic acids with different biological functions, and direct extraction therefore gives a complex mixture. Molecular weights for ribonucleic acids range from approximately 15,000 (corresponding to some 50 nucleotides) to $2 \cdot 1 \times 10^6$. The latter figure has been reported for freshly isolated ribonucleic acid from tobacco mosaic virus and corresponds to a chain length of approximately 6000 nucleotides since the nucleic acid appears to exist as a single coiled chain.[106] Most commercial preparations of ribonucleic acid from yeast have an average chain length of some 6 or 7 nucleotides, after purification.

MODE OF ACTION OF PANCREATIC RIBONUCLEASE

Pancreatic ribonuclease (IA) has been used extensively; it is an enzyme of relatively low molecular weight (13,683) and a considerable portion can be removed by digestion with carboxypeptidase[107] or pepsin[108] with retention of enzymic activity. However, carboxymethylation of a single histidine group (in the imidazole moiety) causes complete loss of activity;[109] the histidine concerned has been unequivocally identified as that nearest to the C-terminal end of the ribonuclease molecule.[110, 111] The amino acid sequence of the enzyme has been virtually established.[112–115] Further work suggests that residues 119 (histidine), 121 (aspartic acid), 15 (asparagine), and 41 (lysine) are all at, or near, the active site.[116] Artificially induced microheterogeneity in ribonuclease may result from differences in secondary and tertiary structure rather than in a primary sequence of amino acids.[117]

Evidence of the hydrolysis of polyadenylic and polyinosinic acid to mononucleotides by rather large amounts of ribonuclease has been presented.[118] Non-enzymic catalysis has not been excluded entirely.* Similar results have been reported for purine containing oligonucleotides that are resistant to pancreatic ribonuclease using standard procedures.[119] Under suitable conditions the enzyme shows " synthetic " activity. Apart from repolymerisation of nucleoside-2',3' cyclic phosphates, 3'-alkyl esters can be obtained by treatment of uridine-2',3' cyclic phosphate with ribonuclease and primary alcohols. As in the case of chemical reaction with sodium alkoxides, secondary and tertiary alcohols are not effective.[120]

The specificity of pancreatic ribonuclease for esters of pyrimidine

* Cleavage of poly 8-azaguanylic acid[571] provides a more convincing demonstration of wider specificity for pancreatic ribonuclease.

ribonucleoside-3′ phosphates has been discussed previously. Further definition of the structural requirements has been obtained from a study of the action, or lack of action, of the enzyme on a wide range of derivatives, some of which are listed in Table 6-I.

TABLE 6-I.

Compound	Enzymic hydrolysis	Reference
Methyl α (or β)-ribofuranoside-2′,3′ cyclic phosphate	—	121
Ethylene glycol-1,2 cyclic phosphate	—	122
Polyglycerophosphate	—	123
Nucleoside esters of ribose-3 phosphate	—	124
Nucleoside esters of ribitol-3 phosphate	—	124
Esters of ribofuranosylureidopropionic acid 3′ phosphate	—	125
Uridine-2′,3′ cyclic phosphate 5′-pyrophosphate	+	126
5′-Deoxyuridine-2′,3′ cyclic phosphate	+	18
5′-O-Methanesulphonyluridine-2′,3′ cyclic phosphate	+	127
5′-Bromo-5′-deoxyuridylyl-3′ : 5′ adenosine	+	127
Poly 5′-thiouridylic acid	+	127
Internucleotide linked 2-thiouridylic acid	+	128
5-Methyluridine-2′,3′ cyclic phosphate	+	129, 130
Poly 5-methyluridylic acid	+	131
5-Halogenouridine-2′,3′ cyclic phosphate	+	130, 132
Poly 5-chloro (or bromo or iodo) uridylic acid	+	132
Esters of 4,5-dihydrouridine-3′ phosphate	+	125
Poly 4,5-dihydrouridylic acid	+	133
Pseudouridine-2′,3′ cyclic phosphate	+	129, 130
Poly pseudouridylic acid	+	134
N^6-Acetylcytidine-2′,3′ cyclic phosphate	+	18
N^1-Methyluridine-3′ methyl phosphate	—	135
Poly N^1-methyluridylic acid	—	132, 133
Uridine-3′,5′ cyclic phosphate	—	136
Cytidine-3′,5′ cyclic phosphate	—	136

The results suggest that the specificity lies in the presence and location of functional groups found only in the pyrimidine nucleosides, in accord with the postulate[125] that hydrogen bonding of the carbonyl oxygen at C2 of the pyrimidine ring with the 2′-hydroxyl group of the sugar increases the nucleophilic character of this hydroxyl group (and may well account for any differences in the conformation of the sugar in purine nucleosides compared with pyrimidine nucleosides), thus facilitating nucleophilic attack at the phosphorus atom and formation of the nucleoside-2',3' cyclic phosphate. (Some support for this concept may be found in a greater resistance towards chemical hydrolysis shown by polypurine-nucleotides compared with polypyrimidine-nucleotides). A planar pyrimidine ring system is presumably necessary to preserve stereochemical aspects of the interaction, hence the resistance to enzymic attack shown by esters of ribofuranosylureidopropionic acid 3' phosphate but not by dihydropyrimidine derivatives. Kinetic studies with a variety of substrates fit such a mechanism and also indicate that the nature of the alkyl component in esters of pyrimidine nucleoside-3' phosphates can have a marked effect.[561] Thus in the series CpA, CpG, CpC, and CpU (where p represents a 3'–5' internucleotide linkage from left to right, and A, C, G, and U are the respective ribonucleosides) rates of hydrolysis are in the ratio 3000:500:240:27. This may be a consequence of π-electron interaction between the bases, increase in polarisability and nucleophilic character of the cytidine residue being dependent on the extent of interaction.[561]

In agreement with the mechanism, substrate derivatives are obtained from ψ-uridine since in this nucleoside a carbonyl oxygen is also suitably located relative to the 2'-hydroxyl group.[137–139] With uridine-3',5' cyclic phosphate and cytidine-3',5' cyclic phosphate the necessary structural elements with respect to the aglycon are present, but in these cases nucleophilic attack by the 2'-hydroxyl group at the phosphorus atom of the 3'-phosphate ester is rendered impossible as a result of the stereochemistry of the 3',5' cyclic phosphate group.[136]

Further assistance is possibly provided by electron donation from the enzyme to the pyrimidine ring by partial or entire withdrawal of a proton.[139] Similarly, electron withdrawal from a tautomeric form of the pyrimidine nucleoside-2',3' cyclic phosphate by the enzyme could provide both direction and assistance for cleavage to a 3' phosphate. Such mechanisms receive some support from the behaviour of derivatives of N^1-methyluridine and N^6-acetylcytidine.

A somewhat different mechanism of action for pancreatic ribonuclease, involving the two histidine residues numbered 119 and 48 (or 105), has been advanced.[140] Essentially this involves shift of a proton from one imidazole residue to the other as shown in the schematic representation (page 326).

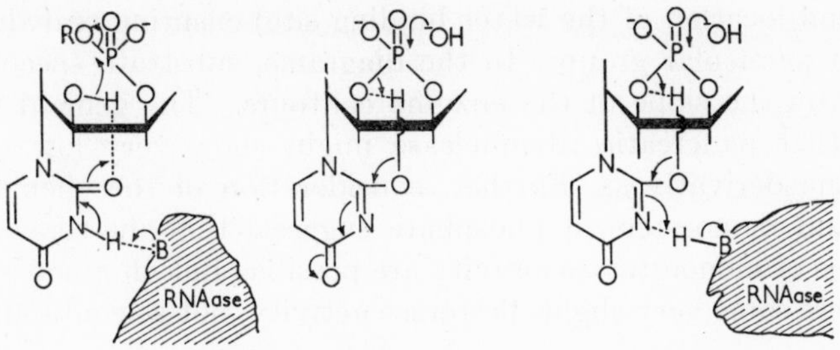

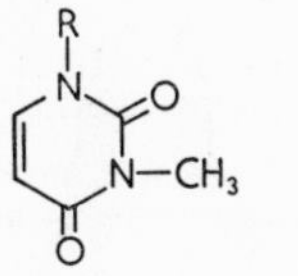

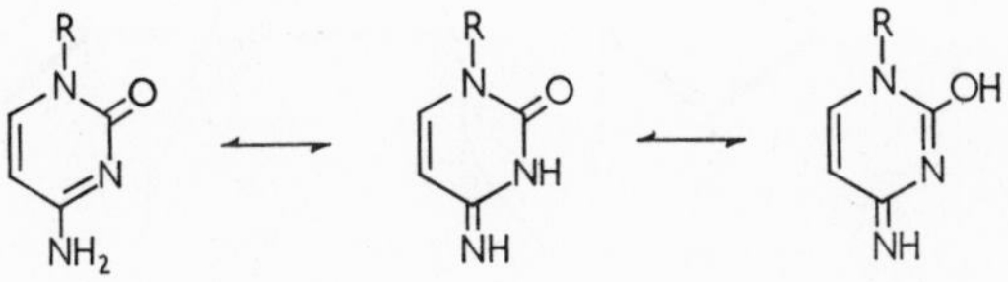

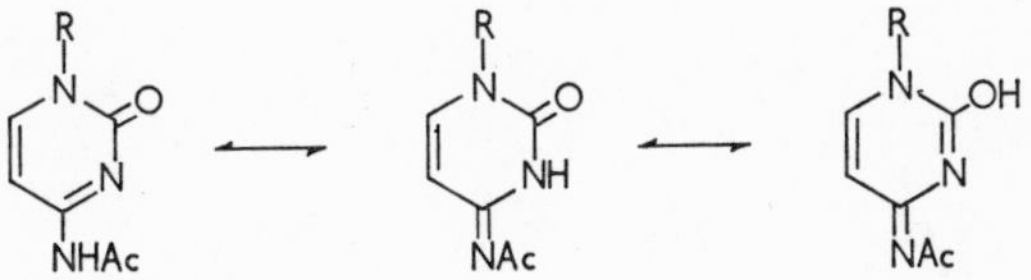

It may be noted that in this scheme " activation " of water molecules as well as of the organic substrate is suggested. The hypothetical mechanism can be applied in a quite general way as a mode of action for a variety of diesterases such as the takadiastase ribonucleases, spleen diesterase on RNA (giving 3' phosphates without intermediate formation of a 2',3' cyclic phosphate) and on 2',3' cyclic phosphates (giving nucleoside-2' phosphates), and venom diesterase on polynucleotides (giving nucleoside-5' phosphates), and for monesterases. Pentacovalent phosphate transition states are presumably involved though these are not shown in the diagrammatic representations. The various resonance structures permissible for the phosphate group should also be remembered.

Substrate specificity lies in the availability of binding sites in the protein for the pyrimidine or purine bases; specific action (to cleave a 3' O—P or a 5' O—P linkage) lies not in intramolecular hydrogen bonding in the substrate, but in nucleophilic attack at a particular aspect of the phosphorus atom (determined by the conformation of the enzyme and location of the water binding site) ensuring rear displacement of a particular group. In the diagrams, substrate specificity is indicated by the slope of the enzyme contours. The general scheme suggests that pancreatic ribonuclease might show very low activity with purine derivatives. Further, consideration of the chemistry of diesters and monoesters of phosphate suggests that diesterases completely free of monoesterase activity are possible, but all monoesterases may possess some very slight diesterase activity, not as contamination,

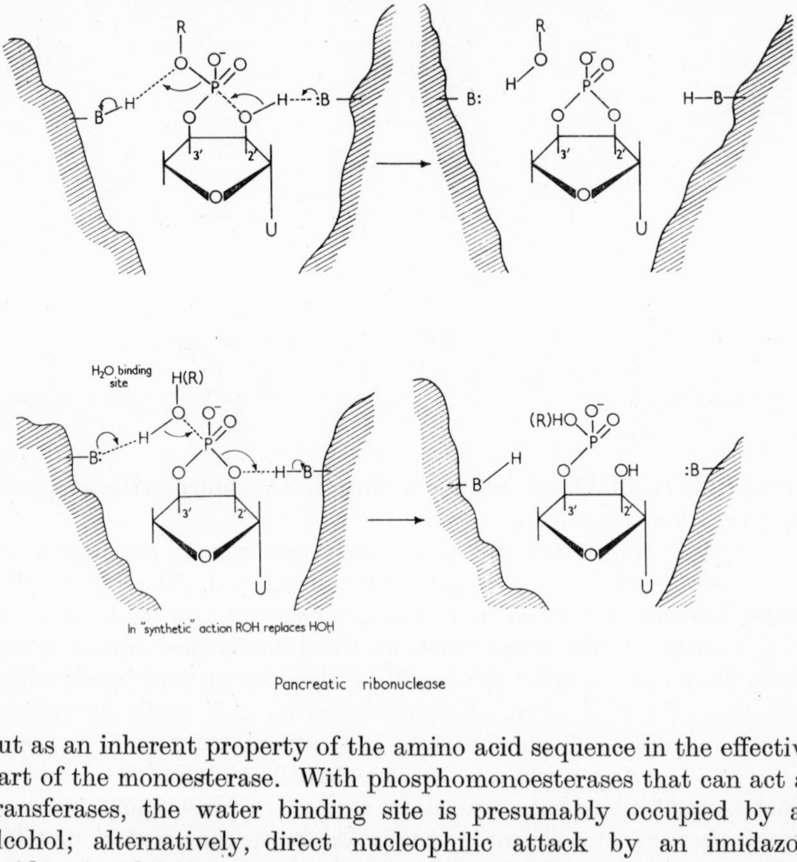

Pancreatic ribonuclease

but as an inherent property of the amino acid sequence in the effective part of the monoesterase. With phosphomonoesterases that can act as transferases, the water binding site is presumably occupied by an alcohol; alternatively, direct nucleophilic attack by an imidazole residue in the enzyme to give an intermediate phosphoramidate derivative, which then undergoes further reaction, may be postulated.

As indicated, pancreatic ribonuclease catalyses two reactions (reversible transphosphorylation to give a-2′,3′ cyclic phosphate and irreversible hydrolysis of this cyclic phosphate) albeit at quite different rates. A more distinct separation of these activities has not been observed, in terms of substrate specificity. Differential effects occur in

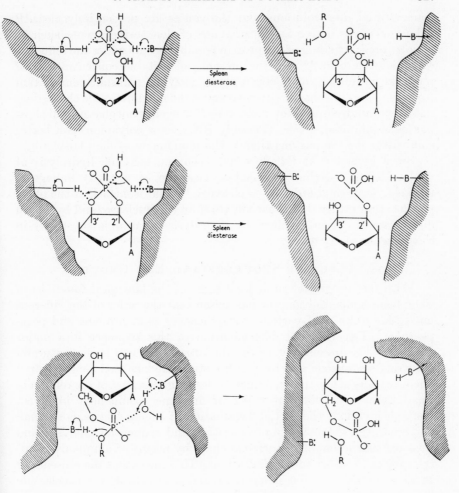

Spleen diesterase

Spleen diesterase

Snake venom diesterase

Phosphomonoesterase

concentrated urea solutions, but the causes are not entirely clear.[141]
(The enzyme is active in the presence of denaturing agents such as
8 molar urea; refolding of the protein possibly occurs under the influence
of ribonucleic acid.)[142]   In the presence of suitable concentrations of
polyacid inhibitors, inactivation of the enzymic transphosphorylation
(to give cyclic phosphates with cleavage of the polynucleotide chain) does
not occur, but hydrolysis of nucleoside-2′,3′ cyclic phosphates to 3′ phosphates in inhibited.[143, 144]   (Possibly RNA, as a polyanion, is a better
competitor for the enzyme than is the monomeric cyclic phosphate.)

Since inversion at C2′ does not occur on enzymic hydrolysis of
nucleoside-2′,3′ cyclic phosphates, cleavage of a C—O linkage is
unlikely. Confirmation of P—O cleavage,[145] that is, attack at the phosphorus atom rather than a carbon atom by ribonuclease (and by spleen
diesterase) has been obtained by hydrolysis of suitable substrates in
the presence of $H_2^{18}O$.

NUCLEOTIDE SEQUENCE AND END GROUPS

With the recognition of at least some of the biological functions of
ribonucleic acids, the concept has arisen that the order of the different
nucleotide units is of particular significance, as in proteins and poly-
peptides.   Experimental determination of this sequence is a major
problem of the present day; as yet, the largest fragment from a naturally
occurring ribonucleic acid for which a structure has been demonstrated
unequivocally is less than ten nucleotides long. Because of the relatively
small number of different types of monomer component involved,
methods involving the partial degradation of ribonucleic acids to small
polynucleotides, followed by separation and sequential analysis, and
then reconstruction of the original chain by means of unique overlaps,
are subject to rather severe limitations. To some extent the presence of
small amounts of minor nucleotides and alkali-stable internucleotide
linkages in the nucleic acid will be of assistance in this approach.
Stepwise degradation of the ribonucleic acid itself is perhaps feasible
with nucleic acids containing 50–100 nucleotides; sequential analysis
of the only preparations that are known (or strongly suspected) to be
homogeneous presents formidable logistic difficulties.   In addition to
such drawbacks, the purification and separation of crude mixtures of
polynucleotides into single molecular species is not entirely resolved,
though considerable advances have been made.   Until completely
homogeneous preparations are available, little progress in determination
of the primary structure of nucleic acids can be achieved. Nevertheless
these problems will undoubtedly be solved, and a number of techniques
now being developed, such as the radioactive labelling of end groups to
increase sensitivity in detection, will facilitate their solution.

While little is known of the actual order of nucleotides in ribonucleic acids, other than that all possible binary sequences can occur,
methods are available for determining the relative distribution of
nucleotides and small oligonucleotide tracts within the chain, and significant differences have been observed in various plant virus ribonucleic
acids. Further, given a sufficiently homogeneous polynucleotide, end
groups can be characterised by relatively simple means; quantitative
estimation of these end groups relative to the total mononucleotide
content gives the chain length. This, coupled with a molecular weight
determined by physical methods then leads to an estimate of the
number of strands in a given macromolecular aggregate. More directly,

the number of chains can be evaluated from a study of the initial
kinetics of enzymic degradation.

Although nucleic acids can possess either a terminal 3′ phosphate or
a terminal 5′ phosphate group,[146] and hence they may be regarded as
polymers of nucleoside-3′ or -5′ phosphates (this distinction has little
real meaning), there is no direct evidence of the mechanisms involved in
the biosynthetic control of chain length and there is little justification
for ignoring other possibilities. Neglecting possible non-nucleotide
terminal components, four types of nucleic acid may be envisaged with
(1) no terminal phosphate, (2) a terminal 5′ phosphate, (3) a terminal 3′
phosphate (or 2′,3′ cyclic phosphate), (4) phosphate residues at each
end (5′ and 3′) of the molecule. Each of these could be converted into
the other by suitable enzymic degradation either *in vivo* or during
isolation.

The left end in each of the above representations of nucleic acids will be termed the head units and the nucleoside component at the right is the tail. From a consideration of the mechanisms previously described, it can be seen that although alkaline hydrolysis converts the bulk of the chain to nucleoside-2' and -3' phosphate, in type (1) the tail unit appears as free nucleoside, in type (2) the head is liberated as nucleoside-2',5' and -3',5' diphosphate and the tail as nucleoside, while in type (4) the head unit appears as nucleoside-2',5' and -3',5' diphosphate but no free nucleoside is liberated. Type (3) yields nucleoside-2' and -3' phosphates only. Enzymic hydrolysis using spleen diesterase (specific for esters of nucleoside-3' phosphates) would give the same results. However, with rattlesnake venom diesterase (specific for esters of nucleoside-5' phosphates) complementary information is obtained. Thus type (1) gives the head nucleoside and the rest of the chain as nucleoside-5' phosphate, type (2) gives nucleoside-5' phosphate only, from type (3) a head nucleoside and a tail nucleoside-3'(2'),5' diphosphate is obtained while type (4) yields the tail nucleoside-3'(2'),5' diphosphate. By the use of alkaline and venom diesterase hydrolysis on the same specimen therefore, both the head and tail nucleotide units can be identified, as well as the type of polynucleotide.

Type	(1) head tail	(2) head tail	(3) head tail	(4) head tail
Alkali	− +	+ +	− −	+ −
Venom diesterase	+ −	− −	+ +	− +

As previously mentioned, the chain length of the polynucleotide can be determined by quantitative estimation of terminal units. With certain small polymers hydrolysis of the terminal phosphate(s) by the action of purified phosphomonoesterase gives an independent estimate of chain length from the ratio of total phosphate to liberated inorganic phosphate; re-examination of the residual polynucleotide affords confirmation of the nature of the terminal units. Such methods are somewhat restricted by the high degree of purity required for the enzymes concerned, and by the variation in activity shown by monoesterases (and diesterases) with different polymer chain lengths. However, nucleic acids of both types 2 and 3 have been identified (albeit in heterogeneous mixtures of ribonucleic acids) the latter possibly arising mainly from degradative processes.[92]

Examination of the alkaline hydrolysis products of rabbit liver transfer RNA indicated chains approximately 100 nucleotides long, containing guanosine-5' phosphate and adenosine terminal units.[147] Somewhat shorter chain lengths (approximately 40 nucleotides) for the corresponding RNA from rat liver have been reported but again alkaline hydrolysis yielded nucleosides (mainly adenosine and guanosine) and molar amounts of guanosine-2'(3'),5' diphosphate equivalent to the nucleosides, in addition to the mixture of nucleoside-2'(3') phosphates.[148] Guanosine-5' phosphate and adenosine end groups were also found in the soluble RNA from *Escherichia coli*.[149] Diffusion and sedimentation studies indicated a molecular weight of 35,000 but analysis of the hydrolysis products indicated a chain length of approximately 62 nucleotides, that is, a molecular weight approximately 18,500. It is of interest that phenylalanine-specific RNA from *Escherichia coli* does not possess a guanosine-5' phosphate end group, since no guanosine-2'(3'),5' diphosphate was found on alkaline hydrolysis.[47] Similar results have been reported for wheat germ " soluble " RNA but considerably less guanosine-2'(3'),5' diphosphate was obtained relative to adenosine.[150] Alkaline hydrolysis of " insoluble " (in 3 M sodium chloride) RNA from wheat germ gave all four classical nucleosides in quantities indicative of a mean chain length of 1200 nucleotides, that is, a mean molecular weight approximately 4×10^5.

No evidence of a terminal 5' phosphate in tobacco mosaic virus ribonucleic acid has been found[151] though short polynucleotide chains bearing 5' phosphomonester end groups may be associated with some virus preparations.[152]

Periodate oxidation of ribonucleic acids containing a terminal nucleoside esterified at the 5' hydroxyl group only, gives the corresponding dialdehyde. Treatment of this with [^{35}S]-thiosemicarbazide in aqueous solution provides a sensitive method for the detection of terminal nucleoside residues.[153] No such residues were found in ribonucleic acids from tobacco mosaic virus or turnip yellow mosaic virus.[153] Although no clear-cut stoichiometry was obtained by the application of this procedure to tobacco mosaic virus ribonucleic acid, before and after treatment with prostrate monoesterase, the results indicated that at least some terminal monoesterified phosphate was located at a 3'(or 2') hydroxyl group.[154] The amount of inorganic phosphate released from ^{32}P labelled virus suggested that each chain contained one terminal phosphate rather than two. However, later results indicate that no terminal phosphomonoester group is present in the infective nucleic acid and that such end groups arise by cleavage of the polynucleotide chains.[155] Since these chains contain some 6000 nucleotides, the difficulties associated with such studies can be appreciated. Alkaline hydrolysis of ^{14}C labelled tobacco mosaic virus RNA yielded 1 mol of adenosine per chain, but no significant amounts of nucleoside-2'(3'),5' diphosphate, suggesting a definitive structure* for the RNA as shown, despite the previously mentioned results using periodate oxidation.[156, 556]

Methanolysis of RNA (catalysed by methoxide ions) provides a suitable approach for the determination of terminal units bearing a 2' or 3' phosphate group.[157] Whereas internal diesterified internucleotide linkages give rise to methyl esters of the nucleoside-2' and -3' phosphates, the end group is unaffected and is liberated as free nucleotide (without phosphate migration). Methanolysis of adenosine-2' dimethyl phosphate gives adenosine, in contrast with the alkaline hydrolysis of such compounds. The method has been applied to calf liver RNA and to a commercial preparation of yeast RNA.

A method for labelling 5' phosphomonoester end groups involving treatment of the RNA (or ribonuclease digests) with di-isopropyl-carbodi-imide and aniline (^{14}C labelled) has been developed.[564] Terminal 5' phosphate groups are converted into phosphoroanilidates (3' phosphate end groups appear as 2',3' cyclic phosphates) which can be detected after enzymic degradation of the poly (or oligo) nucleotides (to enrich resistant labelled nucleotide sequences) and fractionation on DEAE cellulose. Results with amino acid transfer RNA indicate that whereas most of the chains end with guanosine-5' phosphate, terminal adenosine-5' phosphate and uridine-5' phosphate residues are also present; gross heterogeneity appears in the adjacent nucleotides with unfractionated RNA. The method is presumably applicable also to polydeoxynucleotides.

The specific action of pancreatic ribonuclease can also indicate terminal groups. In addition to the pyrimidine nucleoside-3' phosphates, and oligonucleotides, that are present in ribonuclease digests of yeast ribonucleic acid, five nucleosides (adenosine, cytidine, guanosine, pseudouridine and uridine) have been isolated, indicating tail nucleoside units esterified through the 5' hydroxyl group to the 3' phosphate of a pyrimidine nucleotide. Among larger fragments that gave rise to nucleosides on alkaline hydrolysis, adenylyl-3':5' uridine and adenylyl-3':5' cytidine have been identified, and likewise they indicate terminal (tail) portions of polynucleotide chains.[158] The same

---

* Enzymic hydrolysis of the RNA indicates that the terminal adenosine is linked to a pyrimidine nucleotide.[572]

nucleic acid yielded small amounts of nucleosides and nucleoside-2'(3'),5' diphosphates on alkaline hydrolysis and clearly it is in the main composed of a variety of type (2) polynucleotides. Adenosine-2',3' cyclic phosphate and guanosine-2',3' cyclic phosphate have also been identified in pancreatic ribonuclease digests.[158, 159] They possibly represent terminal tail units from polynucleotides of type (3) or (4) or alternatively arise from the action of contaminating ribonucleases of different specificity.

Ribonuclease treatment of amino acid labelled " transfer " RNA yields the 2'(3')-aminoacyl ester of adenosine, the free nucleoside being readily obtained by mild alkaline hydrolysis.[434] This end group has also been reported for nuclear transfer RNA.[160]

Ribonucleases of high specificity are of considerable value since they not only cleave the nucleic acid into oligonucleotides, which in many cases have been separated and the structures determined, but also indicate the distribution of nucleotides in a general sense. Thus the proportion of pyrmidine nucleoside-3' phosphates (relative to the total pyrimidine content of the nucleic acid) liberated by the action of pancreatic ribonuclease has been found to vary considerably. From the known specificity of the enzyme, the liberation of a high percentage of the total pyrimidine as free nucleotide indicates tracts of two or more pyrimidines, whereas a relatively small release as mononucleotide indicates that the bulk of the pyrimidine is attached (from a 5' hydroxyl group) to the 3' phosphate of a purine nucleotide unit. The finding that some 50% in each case of the total cytidylic, uridylic, and pseudouridylic acids but only 10–20% of the thymine nucleotide is liberated from the saline-soluble ribonucleic acids of yeast is of interest in this connection.[161] Significantly greater quantities of pyrimidine nucleotides were isolated from tobacco mosaic virus ribonucleic acid of M strain, than from strains TMV, HR and YA after exhaustive digestion with pancreatic ribonuclease, hence the distribution of pyrimidine nucleotides in M strain RNA differs from that in strains TMV, HR or YA[162] (compare with following results).

Successive paper electrophoresis and paper chromatography provides a convenient mapping procedure for the nucleotides and oligonucleotides (up to tetranucleotide) present in ribonuclease digests.[163] Separation, identification and estimation of these fragments gives some information on the nature and frequency of nucleotide sequences in different ribonucleic acids. Although all possible binary sequences do occur, the actual distribution of nucleotides is far from random. Significant quantitative differences in the products obtained by degradation of the nucleic acids by pancreatic ribonuclease were not observed between strains M and TMV of tobacco mosaic virus, but several striking differences were noted between strain HR and the other two, indicating altered patterns of nucleotide sequence.[164, 165]

Recently, ribonucleases with an even greater specificity than that shown by the major component of the crystalline pancreatic enzyme, have been examined.   Two from " Takadiastase Sankyo " are of particular interest in that their action is complementary to that of pancreatic ribonuclease.[166]   Thus takadiastase ribonuclease T1 is specific for esters of guanosine-3' phosphate, that is, it catalyses the cleavage of internucleotide linkages between a guanosine-3' phosphate residue and the 5' hydroxyl group of an adjacent nucleotide, via formation of guanosine-2',3' cyclic phosphate residues.[167, 168]   The ultimate products from yeast ribonucleic acid are guanosine-3' phosphate (some 40% of the total guanine) and oligonucleotides containing a terminal guanosine-3' phosphate residue.   As with pancreatic ribonuclease, the transphosphorylation step is reversible[169, 170] and the enzyme catalyses polymerisation of guanosine-2',3' cyclic phosphate to oligo- and possibly poly-guanylic acid as well as transphosphorylation to the 5' hydroxyl group of nucleosides (to give dinucleoside phosphates such as guanylyl-3' : 5'-uridine and guanylyl-3' : 5'-adenosine), nucleoside-3' phosphates, and nucleoside-2',3' cyclic phosphates.   Extremely high specificity of ribonuclease T1 has been demonstrated by digestion of amino acid-acceptor RNA with the nuclease, followed by enzymic removal of terminal monoesterified phosphate groups and then alkaline hydrolysis of the mixture.[171]   All the guanine appeared as guanosine (hence all guanylyl-3' : 5' bonds were cleaved), but the methylated guanine derivatives (1-methylguanine and 2-dimethylamino-6-hydroxypurine) were recovered as nucleotides (as were adenine and the pyrimidine bases) showing that 3' : 5' phosphodiester linkages from these compounds are resistant to enzymic hydrolysis by ribonuclease T1.

In contrast with RNAase T1, ribonuclease T2 cleaves internucleotide linkages between an adenosine-3' phosphate unit and the 5' hydroxyl group of an adjacent nucleotide, to give oligonucleotides with a terminal adenosine-3' phosphate residue, and adenosine-3' phosphate (from adenylic acid tracts).[172]   Very small amounts of the mononucleotide were liberated from yeast ribonucleic acid, in contrast with the large amounts of guanylic acid released by RNAase T1. The distribution of the two nucleotides in the nucleic acid thus appears to be quite different.   Although intermediate formation of adenosine-2',3' cyclic phosphate residues (either as mononucleotides or as terminal units of oligonucleotides) could not be detected in ribonuclease T2 digests, the enzyme does hydrolyse the cyclic phosphate to adenosine-3' phosphate, and also catalyses transphosphorylation to produce oligoadenylic acids. Under suitable conditions the polymerisation reactions presumably can be reduced to negligible proportions, and it is likely that the takadiastase ribonucleases will be of value for determination of the structure of oligoribonucleotides, in addition to their application in studies of nucleotide distribution in ribonucleic acids.

Treatment of tobacco mosaic virus RNA with RNAase T1 liberated some 26·9% of the total guanine as mononucleotide, that is, this proportion occurs (it is claimed) as clusters of two or more consecutive guanylic residues.[173] Di-, tri- and tetra-nucleotides ending in guanosine-3′ phosphate were also formed. However, an independent estimate of the guanosine-3′ phosphate and guanosine-2′,3′ cyclic phosphate produced by the action of purified RNAase T1 on tobacco mosaic virus RNA showed that some 55·7% of the total guanine* was liberated (compared with a theoretical 24·0% for random distribution of bases).[174] A similar treatment of yeast RNA liberated 48·7% of the total guanine; for random distribution only 27·5% would be expected. However, a considerably lower figure has also been reported.[559] Fractionation on ECTEOLA of the polypurine oligonucleotides (containing a pyrimidine nucleotide end group) from pancreatic ribonuclease digests of RNA indicated that the products of higher molecular weight were particularly rich in guanylic acid residues, that is, tracts of guanylic acid do occur.[175]

Distribution of adenylic acid residues in tobacco mosaic virus RNA has been estimated by quantitative analysis of the products resulting from the combined action of pancreatic ribonuclease and takadiastase ribonuclease T1. From the known specificities of these enzymes the degradation may be expressed generally as RNA → C3′P + U3′P + G3′P + (A3′P)$_n$5′C3′P + (A3′P)$_n$5′U3′P + (A3′P)$_n$5′G3′P the products being preceded by C3′P, U3′P or G3′P in each case in the intact nucleic acid. For the viral nucleic acid it is claimed that some 56·6% of the total adenine occurs as single units (19·1% as ApCp, 19·6% as ApUp and 17·9% as ApGp); a further 37·8% occurs in stretches of 2 or 3 units (followed, approximately equally, by Cp, Up or Gp).[176]

A crystalline extracellular ribonuclease has been isolated from culture media of *Bacillus subtilis*. The action is complementary to that of pancreatic ribonuclease and the enzyme catalyses specific hydrolysis of purine ribonucleoside-3′ phosphate ester linkages.[177] Other ribonucleases that cleave all the internucleotide linkages in ribonucleic acids, to yield nucleoside-3′ phosphates (or 2′,3′ cyclic phosphates), have been isolated from pea[178, 179] and tobacco leaves.[180] With these enzymes some linkages are broken more rapidly than others but no absolute specificity has been observed. A possibly useful property of rye-grass ribonuclease lies in the considerable reduction in rate of hydrolysis with decrease in size of the polynucleotide substrate, so that

* Another estimate[567] is 19%.

substantial amounts of many oligonucleotide intermediates accumulate in the enzymic digest.[181] The enzyme splits oligonucleotides regardless of the nature of the end groups.

A highly active (and remarkably stable) ribonuclease is present in water washings of human fingers, alive[182] or dead, and in finger prints; inactivation of biologically active ribonucleic acids may sometimes be a result of handling procedures.

A rather refined approach to nucleotide sequence in certain viral nucleic acids, such as tobacco mosaic virus RNA, may lie in the stepwise removal of protein subunits from the native virus by mild treatment with detergent, followed by specific enzymic attack on the exposed portion of the nucleic acid core.[183]

STRUCTURE OF OLIGORIBONUCLEOTIDES

While the elucidation of nucleotide sequence in ribonucleic acids lies in the future, the structures of a number of oligonucleotides isolated

from the natural polymers have been fully established by biochemical and chemical methods. The structure of a trinucleotide with a terminal 5′ phosphate is unequivocally determined by alkaline hydrolysis; e.g.

P5′G3′P5′A3′P5′U yields guanosine-2′(3′),5′ diphosphate, adenosine-2′(3′) phosphate and uridine. An indication of the tail unit is provided by alkaline hydrolysis of a trinucleotide possessing a terminal 3′ phosphate, since G3′P5′A3′P5′U3′P yields a mixture of the -2′ and-3′ phosphates of guanosine and of adenosine but the -3′ phosphate only of uridine. Confirmation is readily obtained by removal of the terminal phosphoryl group by the action of monoesterase (to give G3′P5′A3′-P5′U) followed by alkaline hydrolysis. The actual sequence is established by treatment of the dephospho intermediate with snake venom diesterase to yield guanosine, adenosine-5′ phosphate and uridine-5′ phosphate.[184]

Other enzymes, including ribonucleases, can be used in a similar fashion and the structure of many small oligonucleotides could be established by these means. However, it is clear that for larger oligoribonucleotides a method of stepwise degradation is virtually essential. Such a method has been developed, based on the extremely ready

elimination reactions undergone by phosphate esters of β-aldehydo and β-keto alcohols under very mild alkaline conditions.[185, 186] Periodate oxidation of adenosine-5′ phosphate or adenosine-5′ benzyl phosphate gave the corresponding dialdehyde compounds, the 5′ phosphoryl residue being β to one of the aldehyde groups. Mild alkaline treatment (pH 10·5 at room temperature) rapidly removed the phosphate (or benzyl phosphate) group, leaving an oxidised nucleoside residue (easily converted into adenine).[187]

A number of di- and tri-ribonucleotides have been stepwise degraded in this way and their structures decisively established, and in principle the method could be applicable to larger oligoribonucleotides.[188] Thus treatment of A3′P5′G3′P5′C3′P with phosphomonoesterase gave the corresponding trimer with a free cis glycol group. Periodate oxidation yielded the dialdehyde which at pH 10·5 was rapidly degraded to the dinucleotide A3′P5′G3′P and a cytosine derivative (converted into cytosine by acidic hydrolysis). Repetition of the entire process with the dinucleotide liberated guanine and adenosine-3′ phosphate. In addition to the determination of nucleotide sequence, this method also distinguishes between a 3′–5′ and a 2′–5′ internucleotide linkage in dinucleotides since phosphate migration does not occur.

Recently the method has been considerably improved by the use of cyclohexylamine at pH 6·2 for degradation of the periodate oxidised product. Quantitative conversion of the terminal nucleoside into the free base, and hydrolysis of the phosphodiester linkage to a 3′ monoesterified phosphate of the penultimate nucleoside occurs almost instantaneously at room temperature.[189, 190] Use of a lysine buffer also gives quantitative cleavage under milder conditions and in a shorter time than with the procedure originally described (using a glycine buffer).[191] It may be noted that the presence of pseudouridine in a polynucleotide chain will not cause a block to sequence studies (despite suggestions to the contrary[192]) even though a 5-substituted uracil, rather than uracil, will be liberated by phosphate elimination.

A more detailed examination showed that treatment of the dialdehyde from adenosine-5' phosphate with a primary amine at pH > 9 resulted in quantitative formation of Schiff's base.[190] Under neutral

or mildly acidic conditions this was cleaved to an aglycon fragment and inorganic phosphate. Reduction of the Schiff's base with sodium borohydride gave an acid-stable product. A quantitative yield of phosphate and aglycon fragment was also obtained by treatment of the periodate oxidised nucleotide with a primary amine in the pH range 6–8, probably via formation of a di-α-hydroxy amine. The initial cleavage leaves at least part of the ribose attached to the purine (or pyrimidine) but under alkaline conditions, or at pH 1, fission of the glycosyl bond occurs to give the free heterocyclic base.

CHEMICAL HYDROLYSIS OF RIBONUCLEIC ACIDS

The mechanisms involved in the alkaline hydrolysis of ribonucleic acids are undoubtedly of general significance regardless of the alkali used. However, with many preparations of ribonucleic acid quantitative degradation has not been observed and some alkali-resistant linkages appear to be present. To some extent the exceptional resistance to alkaline degradation of certain oligoribonucleotides (for example, di- and tri-adenylic acids)[193] may be a result of the opposing effects of interplanar interaction between the bases (hindering a necessary displacement) and repulsion between charged phosphate groups, that is, an internucleotide linkage in a small oligonucleotide is more stable than the same linkage in the middle of a large polynucleotide.[194] Further, since alkaline hydrolysis of ribonucleic acid involves trans-phosphorylation to give 2′,3′ cyclic phosphate intermediates, differences in the ease of phosphorylation of nucleoside-2′ hydroxyl groups might well be reflected in the relative stabilities of internucleotide linkages between the various nucleosides. Polyguanylic acid (mixed 2′–5′ and 3′–5′ linkages) is markedly more resistant to dilute alkali than is the analogous polyuridylic acid[18] and thus, under suitable hydrolytic conditions, degradation of ribonucleic acids could give rise to guanine oligonucleotide tracts carrying a terminal nucleoside-2′(3′) phosphate (or -2′,3′ cyclic phosphate) other than guanylic acid. The nucleophilic character of the 2′ hydroxyl group in the pyrimidine nucleoside residues may be enhanced by hydrogen bonding with the C2 carbonyl oxygen of the pyrimidine ring, and hence the internucleotide linkages most readily broken by mild alkali would be those cleaved by pancreatic ribonuclease.* In accord with this, by far the major portion of the dinucleotides obtained by partial alkaline hydrolysis of ribonucleic acid are resistant to ribonuclease degradation, that is, they are of the type purine nucleoside-3′-P-5′-purine (or pyrimidine) nucleoside-2′(3′) phosphate.[119, 193]

Hydrolysis of RNA by a variety of metal hydroxides such as lead, cadmium, zinc, or aluminium hydroxide gives varying amounts of nucleoside, nucleotide, and oligonucleotide material.[195] Degradation of yeast RNA by lanthanum hydroxide leaves a resistant fraction.[196] All sixteen possible dimer sequences derived from the four classical bases have been isolated from bismuth hydroxide (pH 4) hydrolysates of ribonucleic acid;[197] the action of weakly basic anion exchange resins gives dinucleotides preponderantly.[198] With the latter method, migration of unhydrolysed phospho-diester bonds (isomerisation of a

---

* Recent kinetic studies on the alkaline hydrolysis of amino acid transfer RNA in 1 N KOH at 25° suggest that there is an initial rapid random cleavage followed by step-wise hydrolysis of oligonucleotides, terminal location conferring decreased stability. The rate constants for the release of cytidylic, uridylic, and guanylic acid were very similar (1st order kinetics during the initial 6–8 hours), but significantly greater (approximately 2 fold) than that for adenylic acid.[555] Since ionisation of the 2′-hydroxyl group occurs at pH 12–13 (and this is important since cleavage of the chain involves nucleophilic attack by this group) a comparison with the kinetics of milder alkaline hydrolysis would be of interest. Slightly different pK values for the 2′-hydroxyl group can be expected in the various nucleotides.

3'–5' to a 2'–5' linkage) occurs, in contrast with the action of dilute alkali on simple esters of the ribonucleotides.

In addition to this type of increased resistance to cleavage of internucleotide linkages (relative to those in ribonucleic acid), there is some evidence for components or linkages that may be termed alkali-stable. In view of the difficulties associated with the preparation of ribonucleic acids that are pure even in the most general sense, it is essential that covalent linkage of such components to the original ribonucleic acid be established. Alkaline hydrolysates of fractions of RNA from frog eggs are reported to contain 10–20% of resistant residues.[199] Some of these may be nucleoside diphosphates, particularly in view of the oligonucleotide nature of the " RNA " preparation.

More decisive evidence of alkali-stable dinucleotide sequences in ribonucleic acid from several sources has been reported. This stability results from the presence of 2' substituted compounds, probably 2'-O-methyl nucleotide derivatives.[119, 200, 201] Degradation of the isolated dinucleotides by treatment with phosphomonoesterase followed by periodate oxidation and phosphate elimination yielded substituted mononucleotides; on dephosphorylation these gave nucleoside compounds that did not consume periodate. In chromatographic behaviour the sugar component was identical with 2(or 3)-O-methylribose.[200] Methylation of such hydroxyl groups in ribonucleic acid would confer resistance to degradation by both alkali and pancreatic ribonuclease.[202]

Degradation of ribonucleic acids with potassium t-butoxide[203] (or barium carbonate)[204] gives the nucleoside-2',3' cyclic phosphates. These are also obtained by treating solutions of the ribonucleic acid in formamide with ammonia.[205]

Mild acidic hydrolysis of ribonucleic acids yields mononucleotides by mechanisms similar to those elucidated for alkaline degradation, though coincident cleavage of the glycosyl linkage in the purine nucleotides gives a rather complex mixture. More vigorous hydrolysis gives mainly the purine bases and the pyrimidine nucleotides.[206] Hydrolysis of ribonucleic acid solutions buffered at pH 4 gives good yields of the nucleosides.[207] Brief treatment of yeast ribonucleic acid with strong hydrochloric acid gives low yields of small oligonucleotides, some of which have been isolated by ion exchange chromatographic methods.[208] Further examination of the products by paper chromatography showed the presence of dinucleotide sequences not found in pancreatic ribonuclease digests and indicated that all possible sequences of the four classical bases were present in yeast ribonucleic acid.[209] Acidic hydrolysis of purine nucleoside-3' pyrimidine nucleoside-5' phosphates produces a ribose (3') ester of the pyrimidine nucleoside-5' phosphate. Further treatment with sodium carbonate then gives the pyrimidine nucleoside-5′ phosphate by elimination of phosphate β to the ribose aldehydo group.[210]

HYDRAZINOLYSIS

The reaction of hydrazine with pyrimidine nucleotides has been described in connection with structural studies on the liberated ribose phosphates. Hydrazinolysis of yeast ribonucleic acid gives a product, ribo-apyrimidinic acid, which contains reducing ribose residues and is almost free of pyrimidine bases.[211, 212] The material, probably of relatively short chain length, is not hydrolysed by pancreatic ribonuclease IA.[213]

DEAMINATION AND ACTION OF FORMALDEHYDE

Deamination of ribonucleic acids by treatment with nitrous acid converts nucleotide residues possessing an amino group to the corresponding hydroxy compounds without significant chain scission.[214] Alteration of very few of the residues causes loss of biological activity.[215, 216] Treatment of tobacco mosaic virus ribonucleic acid with formaldehyde also destroys infectivity; the reaction appears to be specific for the amino groups of the bases,[217, 218] and presumably involves formation of Schiff's bases, or aminomethylol and methylene derivatives. In the case of adenine residues, initial attack may occur at N^1 of the purine ring system.

TREATMENT WITH WATER-SOLUBLE CARBODI-IMIDES

An addition reaction specific for uridine and guanosine nucleotides involving reaction with cyclohexyl 2-(N-methylmorpholinyl)-ethyl carbodi-imide toluenesulphonate in aqueous solution at pH 8 has been described.[554] Such substitution in the case of the pyrimidine (at N^1) confers resistance to the action of pancreatic ribonuclease; treatment of RNA followed by digestion with the enzyme gives large fragments (since only the cytidyl-3′-yl linkages are cleaved), cytidylic acid, and only traces of uridine-3′ phosphate. (The blocking group is hydrolysed at pH 10·5 after removal of the enzyme).[554]

TREATMENT WITH HYDROXYLAMINE

The action of aqueous hydroxylamine on tobacco mosaic virus RNA has been examined.[219] Purine nucleosides are not attacked but uridine is rapidly degraded under mild conditions (pH 10) to 5-iso-oxazolone and ribosylurea; further treatment of the latter compound with hydroxylamine gives urea and ribose oxime. At alkaline pH, cytidine reacts very slowly but at pH 6 cytidine residues in the RNA react some thirty times faster than the uridine components, and are converted into what appear to be uridine-6-oxime derivatives.[219, 220] Fairly specific base elimination or alteration, without extensive cleavage of the chain, is thus possible. Removal of the uracil residues from a polynucleotide in this way prevents cleavage of the chain by pancreatic ribonuclease at these points.[221] Treatment of *E. coli* ribosomal RNA with hydroxylamine at pH 10 gave a product which on digestion with ribonuclease yielded oligonucleotides but no uridylic acid. Similar treatment at pH 6 yielded material from which no cytidylic acid was liberated by enzymic hydrolysis; however, alkaline hydrolysis showed no decrease in cytidylic acid content, probably owing to reversibility of the initial addition of hydroxylamine (at the 4,5 double bond) to cytidine.[221] Mechanisms for the action of hydroxylamine on cytidine similar to those advanced for 3-methylcytosine have been proposed (see p. 374).

BASE COMPOSITION OF RIBONUCLEIC ACIDS

For many years the results of the laborious and rather crude analyses of ribonucleic acid by the early workers were held to indicate equimolar proportions of two purine (adenine and guanine) and two pyrimidine (uracil and cytosine) bases. More recently, the application of paper chromatographic[222] and to a lesser extent ion exchange techniques has provided rapid and relatively precise analytical methods for the estimation of ribonucleic acid components. Hydrolysis of the nucleic acid by alkali gives the mononucleotides which can then be separated as such, or as nucleosides after dephosphorylation. Alternatively, acidic hydrolysis gives the purine bases and pyrimidine mononucleotides. Spectrophotometric estimation of the separated components after elution from the paper (using electrophoresis[223] or chromatography) or ion exchange resin then gives the molar ratios of the bases.

A large number of perforce heterogeneous preparations of ribonucleic acids from animals, plants, and micro-organisms as well as a variety of viral nucleic acids have now been analysed; a few representative results are given in the table. Since many of the preparations examined were complex mixtures of nucleic acids with various biological functions, subject to various degrees of degradation both extracellular and intracellular (some types of ribonucleic acid are metabolically very active with relatively high turnover rates, and the possibility of significant amounts of " incomplete " ribonucleic acid within the cell cannot be neglected), it is perhaps not surprising that no very obvious quantitative relationships among the bases are apparent, even if they actually exist *in vivo*. It is of some interest however, that the ribonucleic acid most widely studied by the early workers, that from yeast, does appear to contain equimolar proportions of the bases. A judicious choice of the

TABLE 6-II. *Composition of ribonucleic acids*

Source of ribonucleic acid	A	C	G	U	Molar ratios			DNA	Reference
					Purines/Pyrimidines	$\frac{G+U}{A+C}$	$\frac{G+C}{A+U}$	$\frac{G+C}{A+T}$	
Liver—Rabbit	10	14·6	16·9	10·3	1·08	1·11	1·55	—	231
Liver—Rat	10	14·3	17·6	10·8	1·10	1·17	1·53	—	231
Liver—Chicken	10	13·6	17·1	10·6	1·12	1·17	1·49	—	231
Liver—Pig	10	15·3	18·8	9·1	1·23	1·10	1·79	0·69	232
Liver —Calf	10	14·9	17·9	8·4	1·20	1·06	1·78	0·76	9
Spleen — ,,	10	17·7	19·7	8·6	1·13	1·02	2·01	0·76	9
Thymus— ,,	10	13·9	23·8	6·5	1·65	1·27	2·28	0·74	9
Brain—Cat	10	12·0	14·7	9·5	1·15	1·10	1·37	—	233
Eggs—Sea urchin	10	12·3	13·3	9·3	1·07	1·01	1·33	—	234
Eggs—Starfish	10	14·0	15·0	11·0	1·0	1·08	1·38	—	235
Nuclei —Rat liver	10	14·6	12·7	12·2	0·84	1·01	1·23	—	236
Mitochondria— ,, ,,	10	15·1	16·9	11·0	1·03	1·11	1·52	—	231
Microsomes — ,, ,,	10	17·1	17·9	9·9	1·03	1·03	1·76	→	236
Cell sap — ,, ,,	10	16·5	17·3	9·8	1·04	1·02	1·71	—	236
Yeast—Brewers	10	9·2	10·4	9·6	1·08	1·04	1·0	0·56	237
Yeast—Bakers	10	8·5	10·9	9·5	1·16	1·10	1·0	0·56	238

Plant viruses—Tobacco mosaic	10	6·2	8·5	8·8	1·24	1·07	0·78	—	239
Plant viruses—Cucumber	10	7·1	9·9	11·9	1·05	1·27	0·78	—	239
Plant viruses—Wild cucumber mosaic	10	21·9	8·7	14·1	0·52	0·72	1·25	—	240
Plant viruses—Turnip yellow mosaic	10	16·8	7·6	9·8	0·66	0·65	1·23	—	241
Polio virus	10	7·7	8·4	8·9	1·11	0·98	0·85	—	242
Mouse encephalomyocarditis virus	10	8·5	8·6	9·5	1·03	0·98	0·88	—	243
Serratia marcescens	10	8·5	10·2	8·3	1·2	1·0	1·02	1·45	224
Escherichia coli (U.S.A.)	10	8·5	10·2	8·3	1·2	1·0	1·02	0·99	224
Escherichia coli (U.S.S.R.)	10	9·3	11·8	7·4	1·31	1·00	1·21	1·09	226
Escherichia coli (glucose medium)	10	8·6	11·3	7·7	1·30	1·02	1·12	—	229
Escherichia coli (broth medium)	10	9·2	12·7	9·7	1·20	1·17	1·11	—	229
Escherichia coli Phenylalanine-specific RNA	10	13·2	15·6	9·8	1·12	1·09	1·46	—	47
Clostridium perfringens	10	7·8	10·5	7·3	1·36	1·00	1·06	0·45	226
Salmonella typhosa	10	9·2	11·8	7·3	1·32	1·00	1·21	1·14	226
Brucella abortus	10	9·8	11·9	7·7	1·26	0·99	1·23	1·37	226
Pseudomonas aeruginosa	10	9·5	12·6	7·8	1·31	1·05	1·24	2·03	226
Sarcina lutea	10	10·4	14·1	8·6	1·27	1·11	1·32	2·57	226
Aspergillus niger	10	10·0	12·0	8·0	1·23	1·0	1·23	1·00	244
Sclerotinia libertiana	10	7·8	10·1	7·8	1·29	1·01	1·01	0·83	244
Pinus sibirica	10	9·7	12·5	7·7	1·27	1·02	1·25	0·675	245
Ginkgo biloba	10	9·8	12·1	8·7	1·20	1·05	1·17	—	246
Magnolia glauca	10	10·0	12·0	8·3	1·20	1·02	1·20	—	246
Allium cepa	10	9·9	12·0	8·3	1·21	1·02	1·20	0·58	245

analytical figures for mammalian ribonucleic acids and analysis of whole cells, or centrifugally prepared cell fractions, revealed that in many instances the ratio of the total 6-keto groups (guanine and uracil) to the sum of the 6-amino residues (adenine and cytosine) was nearly equal to unity.[224] An extensive survey by Belozersky and his co-workers showed that this regularity was even more marked in the ribonucleic acids from higher plants and micro-organisms.[225]

A comparison of the compositions of the deoxyribonucleic acids and the ribonucleic acids from nineteen bacterial species of various systematic groups indicated small differences only in RNA composition, although the DNA composition varied greatly. While no marked conformity between the compositions of the two types of nucleic acid in different species was observed, a possible correlation was noticed since the ratio of guanylic plus cytidylic acids to adenylic plus uridylic acids in the ribonucleic acids tended to increase with an increase in the ratio of guanine plus cytosine to adenine plus thymine in the deoxyribonucleic acids.[226] The value of regression of the first ratio on the second was very small, but the results suggested that whereas most of the cellular ribonucleic acid is relatively independent of the deoxyribonucleic acid, at least part is related, and the two kinds of nucleic acid may even have similar base compositions.[227] More recently, a comparison of the uptake of radioactive phosphate into the nucleoside-2' (and 3') or -5' phosphates obtained by alkaline or venom diesterase hydrolysis of yeast ribonucleic acid indicated that a fraction (with a high turnover rate) of the ribonucleic acid possessed a composition similar to that of yeast deoxynucleic acid, uracil being equivalent to thymine.[228] Further studies have confirmed the presence of such RNA in a variety of micro-organisms.

Relatively marked differences in the base ratios for RNA from *Escherichia coli* determined by two different groups of workers may be noted (see Table 6-II). To some extent this may be a result of environment-induced changes.[229] Base ratios of the total RNA of *E. coli* grown on a glucose medium and in a nutrient broth–yeast extract medium illustrate this further complication in the interpretation of RNA composition.[229] These changes are associated with the ribosomal RNA, the composition of which varies during the normal growth cycle.[230]

Rather large compositional differences have been observed among purified amino acid acceptor ribonucleic acids from yeast.[55] For alanine-, tyrosine-, and valine-specific nucleic acids the " empirical " formulae were

$$A_{11}C_{25}G_{29}U_{17}\psi U_3; \ A_{19}C_{22}G_{26}U_{14}\psi U_4; \ \text{and} \ A_{17}C_{23}G_{25}U_{16}\psi U_4$$

respectively.

Minor Components of Ribonucleic Acids

Although ribonucleic acids are undoubtedly mainly composed of nucleotides derived from adenine, guanine, cytosine and uracil, complete elucidation of the composition of such polymers is beset with a number of difficulties. The possible presence of very small amounts of non-nucleotide components has been ignored till recently, largely because of the convenience of using quantitative accounting with respect to ultra-violet absorption only. Also, a decision between artifact and genuine component is not always easy; the stability or instability of the combination is no criterion of covalent or non-covalent bonding with polyelectrolytes of high molecular weight such as the nucleic acids. It is now known that in certain ribonucleic acids a terminal adenosine residue is esterified at the 2′ or 3′ hydroxyl group by a single amino acid. (Analogy with acetyl derivatives of adenosine suggests that they are 3′ esters exlusively). The existence of peptide derivatives of nucleic acids has been indicated repeatedly, and in addition the possibility of some relatively unstable covalent linkages between protein and nucleic acid in ribonucleoproteins cannot be entirely disregarded. To some extent problems of minor non-nucleotide components of ribonucleic acid are semantic, and could be resolved by a suitably precise definition of nucleic acid.

In addition to providing rapid analytical methods, the application of ion exchange and paper chromatographic techniques has led to the separation of a number of minor nucleotide components in ribonucleic acids. Many of these have now been identified and shown to occur in rather small quantities, corresponding to ~ 0.05–4% of the uracil residues. The bases from which such trace nucleotides are derived include thymine, 5-methylcytosine, 2-methyladenine, 6-methylaminopurine, 6-dimethylaminopurine, 1-methylguanine, 2-methylamino-6-hydroxypurine and 2-dimethylamino-6-hydroxypurine.[247–252] Recently, 1-methyladenine has been identified in the " soluble " ribonucleic acids from pig, and rat livers.[253] Under alkaline conditions, 1-methyladenosine and the corresponding nucleotide are converted into derivatives of 6-methylaminopurine.[254] Identification of 1-methyladenine in a ribonucleic acid is thus dependent on the nature of the hydrolytic procedure used. Reinvestigation of the composition of low molecular weight RNA from rat liver, pig liver, yeast, wheat germ, and *Escherichia coli* using acidic hydrolysis showed that only the bacterial RNA contained 6-methylaminopurine, although all the preparations gave some of the corresponding nucleotide on alkaline hydrolysis.[255] The mammalian and plant nucleic acids all contained 1-methyladenine, but owing to acidic ring cleavage (to give 5-aminoimidazole-4-N-methyl-carboxamide)[254] the amounts present in hydrolysates were some 50% lower than indicated by the 6-methylaminopurine nucleoside-2′(3′) phosphate produced by alkaline hydrolysis of the RNA. It is of interest that deoxynucleic acids from *E. coli* (and from coliphages) also contain 6-methylaminopurine but no 1-methyladenine.

The mechanism of " migration " of the methyl group from N^1 to the adjacent extranuclear amino group under alkaline conditions is probably similar to that occurring in pyrimidine derivatives. This has been shown to involve hydrolytic ring fission followed by cyclisation with the extranuclear amino group.[256] Thus rearrangement of the N^1-methyl

derivative of 2-aminopyrimidine (labelled with ^{15}N in the amino group) in hot alkali gave 2-methylaminopyrimidine which on acidic hydrolysis gave 2-hydroxypyrimidine enriched in ^{15}N, and methylamine free of label. A similar mechanism has been advanced for the rearrangement of 4-amino-5-nitroso-6-hydroxypyrimidines by the action of acid anhydrides to give cyano-*s*-triazines.[257] Analogy with these reactions and with the effect of alkali on N^1-alkylinosine and N^3,5′-cycloadenosine suggests that alkaline re-arrangement of N^1-methyladenylic acid to the 6-methylaminopurine nucleotide proceeds via a 5-formylamino-imidazole-4-(*N*-methyl)-carboxamidine intermediate.

It may be noted that all the minor nucleotides mentioned so far are methylated derivatives of the four major bases. In most cases the corresponding nucleosides and nucleotides, as well as the free bases, have been identified after appropriate degradation;[258] the isolation of a 5' phosphate after hydrolysis of the nucleic acid by treatment with venom diesterase (or of the nucleoside by the action of crude snake venom), and of a mixture of 2' and 3' phosphates after alkaline hydrolysis, indicates that the trace nucleotide occurs as an integral part of the polynucleotide in a normal 3'–5' phosphodiester linkage.[259] In all the nucleosides that have been rigorously examined, the sugar is ribose and the glycosyl linkage is at the normal position.

Another type of nucleotide component has been identified as 5-β-D-ribofuranosyluracil phosphate (pseudouridylic acid);[260–263] since certain ribonucleic acids contain some 25 moles of this component per 100 moles of uridine, it may be regarded as a major rather than a minor nucleotide.

All the ribonucleic acids examined from bacteria, plants, and animal tissues contain several minor bases. However, the quantitative distribution in ribonucleic acids from various sources is not uniform, and indeed considerable variation occurs in nucleic acid fractions from a given cell (see Table 6-III). Thus yeast ribonucleic acids that are soluble in molar sodium chloride contain considerably more pseudouridine than those that are not.[261] More precisely, this component is concentrated in the so-called " soluble " or " transfer " ribonucleic acid of the cell (though a significant amount appears to be present in the high molecular weight ribosomal RNA) and the content seems to be directly proportional to the ability of the ribonucleic acid to accept amino acids; the most active ribonucleic acid (with respect to incorporation of leucine) so far isolated contains approximately 5·6 molar % of pseudouridine.[250, 264–267] Substantially greater amounts of the methylated bases are also present in the " soluble " cytoplasmic fractions of the cell ribonucleic acid,[251, 268, 269] compared with high molecular weight ribosomal RNA. A further marked increase in the amounts of the methylated purines (particularly 2-methylamino-6-hydroxypurine) has been observed in the " soluble " ribonucleic acids from tumour tissue compared with those from liver cells.[269]

Since " transfer " ribonucleic acid has a chain length of 50–100 nucleotides it is clear that certain of the minor nucleotides are not present in all the nucleic acid molecules in a given crude fraction (this would require minimum amounts of approximately 4–8 moles of base per 100 moles of uracil), but are components of particular polynucleotide chains contained in the preparation. The precise significance of these nucleotides is unknown as yet; they may be expected to exert some influence on the macromolecular conformation of the nucleic acid.

TABLE 6-III.

A. Minor nucleotides

Component	Rat liver microsomes[268]	"Soluble" (U.S.A.)[268]	Moles/100 moles of uracil	
			"Soluble" (N.Z.)[269]	"Soluble" (mammary adenocarcinoma)[269]
Pseudouridine	7·5	25	—	—
5-Methylcytosine	0·4	10	—	—
1-Methyladenine	0·5	8·1	·78	4·20
6-Methylaminopurine	0·1	0·1	·55	1·16
6-Dimethylaminopurine	0·1	3·3	·86	1·03
1-Methyl guanine	0·1	2·3	5·2	12·40
2-Methylamino-6-hydroxypurine	0·1	3·0	1·36	3·20
2-Dimethylamino-6-hydroxypurine	0·1			

B. Nucleotide composition of "soluble" RNA from Escherichia coli,[253] rat liver[270] and yeast[267]

Component base	Moles nucleotide/100 moles uridylic acid		
	E. coli	Rat liver	Yeast
Adenine	135	120	99
Guanine	214	222	134
Cytosine	193	220	118
Uracil	100	100	100
Pseudouridine	14	24	27
5-Methyluracil	7·3		
2-Methyladenine	2·0		
6-Methylaminopurine	0·7		
1-Methylguanine	0·7		
$\dfrac{\text{Purines}}{\text{Pyrimidines}} =$	1·12	0·99	0·95
$\dfrac{\text{6-amino}}{\text{6-keto}} =$	0·98	0·98	0·83

None of the minor nucleotides (or pseudouridylic acid) has been definitely found in tobacco mosaic virus or turnip yellow mosaic virus.

RIBONUCLEIC ACID COMPLEXES

The nucleic acids are polyelectrolytes and as such readily form complexes with other polyelectrolytes. Thus admixture of aqueous solutions of ribonucleic acids[271] (or small polynucleotides)[272] and basic protamines or histones precipitates a complex which may be regarded as a conglomeration of salt-like combinations of acid and base. Dissociation can normally be achieved by dissolution in strong saline, presumably by a mass action effect of sodium and chloride ions; dilution reprecipitates the complex. Similar acid-base complexes are also formed between nucleic acids (or oligonucleotides) and synthetic lysine poly-peptides[273, 274] or such polybasic compounds as spermine,[274, 275] spermidine,[274] and putrescine.[275] Changes in secondary structure may also be involved since spermine inhibits the enzymic degradation of ribonucleic acid by ribonuclease.[276] Polyphosphate, which occurs in a number of organisms, also forms complexes with ribonucleic acids.[277] The properties of polyphosphate–ribonucleic acid complexes isolated from *Aspergillus niger* indicate their actual existence as such and not as secondary products formed by precipitation.[278] Such complexes can be purified by electrophoresis, a technique which readily separates simple mechanical mixtures of the components.[279]

Biologically, the most important complexes are the ribonucleo-proteins. Little is known of the precise chemical nature of the combination between the nucleic acid and the protein though in many nucleo-proteins, such as the crystalline plant viruses, the components are arranged in a definite pattern with the nucleic acid surrounded by a " protective " protein coat. X-ray studies of ribonucleoprotein particles of cellular origin and of the ribonucleic acid derived therefrom suggests that the protein matrix determines the conformation of the ribonucleic acid moiety.[280]   Reversible dissociation of high molecular weight ribonucleoprotein sub-units occurs readily[281] and it is likely that a variety of binding forces are involved. These include the coulombic attractions of oppositely charged ions, the attraction of dipoles, and hydrogen bonds. Strong evidence for other than electrostatic bonds has been provided by electrophoretic examination of ribonucleoprotein, ribonucleic acid, and protein, and by the effect on the electrophoretic behaviour of the ribonucleoprotein produced by treatment with urea, a procedure generally held to weaken hydrogen bonds.[282] The ratio of nucleic acid to protein in isolated ribonucleoproteins varies considerably and it is likely that specific arrangements exist in the more rigidly characterised cellular complexes, as with the plant viruses. Some

80–90% of the total cellular RNA in *Escherichia coli* occurs as ribonucleoprotein particles.[283] These particles have been separated into four major fractions by centrifugation.[283] All four components are approximately spherical or ellipsoid[284] and contain some 63% of ribonucleic acids. The ribonucleic acid moieties of ribonucleoproteins are of very high molecular weight, unlike the " soluble " ribonucleic acid fraction (molecular weight approximately 3×10^4). Two main components with molecular weights approximately 0.6×10^6 and 1.8×10^6 have been isolated from animal and plant tissues,[32, 285] and it is likely that a single RNA molecule is present per ribonucleoprotein particle.[285, 286] Unlike the free nucleic acid, in many instances the ribonucleoprotein is resistant to attack by nucleases[287] and gradual dissociation of the complex is among the prerequisites for enzymic cleavage;[288] a measure of protection against ultraviolet radiation is also afforded by the protein shell of tobacco mosaic virus.[289] Artificial " nucleoproteins " can be prepared from free nucleic acid and cytoplasmic proteins.[290]

Stable complexes of nucleic acids are also formed by interaction with metal ions, particularly polyvalent ions. For example, ribonucleic acid forms a complex with beryllium ions[291] that is stable to dialysis. Binding with other divalent metal ions such as magnesium and calcium also occurs, mainly by ion pair formation with adjacent primary phosphoryl groups.[292] The interaction of other metals such as cupric ions, probably involves metal chelation between the bases in addition, particularly with the purine residues.[293] Considerable stabilisation of the infectivity of plant and animal viral ribonucleic acids can be achieved by the addition of Ni^{++}, the optimal ratio being one nickel ion per nucleotide.[25, 294] Significant amounts of chromium, manganese, nickel, iron, aluminium, copper, zinc, cadmium, lead, and other metals with a total molar ratio of 1/50 of the phosphate residues, have been observed in ribonucleic acids from diverse biological sources.[295, 296] Such complexes are extremely stable and separation of the metals by dialysis or by the action of chelating agents is very difficult; indeed, stable mixed complexes of beef liver ribonucleic acid, ferrous ion, and 1,10-phenanthroline are readily formed.[296] While the presence of some of these metals in ribonucleic acid is probably chance contamination, it has been suggested that metals may bear a functional relationship to protein synthesis and the transmission of genetic information. Possible roles may lie in maintenance of the conformation of the ribonucleic acid molecule by chelation of purine and pyrimidine bases or by crosslinking in helical regions,[297] and in the linkage of nucleic acid to protein in ribonucleoprotein.[296] The interaction of metal ions (and of amino acids) with ribonucleic acids causes rather complex changes in the sedimentation rate,[298] as may be expected for changes in conformation or aggregation.   Disintegration of bacterial ribonucleoprotein into several sub-units on treatment with versene[299] has been observed, as has association and dissociation of various ribonucleoproteins in response to changes in magnesium concentration.[300-303] Removal of magnesium ions by dialysis from the antiviral agent helanine (a ribonucleoprotein from *Penicillium funiculosum*) causes loss in activity.[304]

Spermidine and putrescine have been identified in ribosomal fractions from *Escherichia coli*. Spermidine exerts a stabilising effect (which is enhanced by the addition of magnesium ions) on these nucleo-proteins, which otherwise tend to decompose.[305] In addition, poly-peptides, amino acids, and 1,3-diaminopropane have been identified on cleavage of the nucleoprotein particles by removal of magnesium ions with ethylenediamine tetra-acetic acid. The diamines are present in amounts sufficient to neutralise at least one third of the ribonucleic acid phosphoryl dissociations.[306]

Deoxyribonucleic Acids

ISOLATION OF DEOXYRIBONUCLEIC ACIDS

Except for spermotozoa, living cells normally contain considerably more ribonucleic than deoxyribonucleic acid. Methods of isolation of deoxyribonucleic acids have been influenced considerably by the fortunate circumstance that whereas ribonucleoproteins and ribo-nucleic acids are soluble in dilute (0·15 M) sodium chloride, deoxy-ribonucleoprotein complexes are virtually insoluble. The homogenized organ or organism is therefore thoroughly washed with dilute saline, the deoxyribonucleic acid is extracted from the residue with strong salt solutions, and then precipitated by the addition of ethanol.[307, 308] Alternatively, elution of the residue with water gives a solution from which the deoxyribonucleoprotein is precipitated by adjustment of the salt concentration.[309-312] Cleavage of the nucleoprotein, which in the main is a salt-like complex between polybasic and polyacidic electro-lytes, is readily achieved by dissolution in strong saline[313, 314] or by treatment with potassium thiocyanate.[315] Much of the protein can be removed by the addition of ethanol (the protamines or histones remain in solution),[316] or by emulsification with chloroform and amyl, or octyl, alcohol (the protein forms a chloroform gel).[4, 317] Treatment with detergents has also been used extensively.[318] More recently, deoxy-ribonucleic acids have been isolated by extraction with aqueous *p*-aminosalicylate–phenol solutions.[319] Using this method, some preparations of deoxyribonucleic acid contained residual protein whereas others were virtually protein-free, indicating that the protein–nucleic acid binding varies in different tissues.[320] A convenient modification involves homogenization of mammalian tissues in 0.15 M phenolphthalein diphosphate followed by addition of phenol to precipitate DNA (free of RNA) in good yield.[321, 322] With bacteria that are susceptible to lysozyme a preliminary treatment with this enzyme (to effect disrupture of the cell wall) is advantageous.[323] Alternatively, lysis with sodium lauryl sulphate is often successful, and has yielded biologically active, highly polymerised DNA (molecular weight 8 to 12×10^6) from a variety of bacterial species.[324] Mammalian spermatozoa require digestion with trypsin (or an equivalent procedure) before extraction of the deoxyribonucleic acid is attempted.[325] For bull or human sperm, pretreatment with 2-mercaptoethanol (followed by trypsin digestion) is particularly advantageous for breaking down the impervious keratin-like membrane surrounding the sperm head.[326] The requirement for a reducing agent (oxidising or mercaptide forming agents are not effective) suggests some type of sulphur-containing linkage between the DNA and the protein coat. Acidic hydrolysis of DNA isolated from bull sperm showed the presence of some 0.1% of amino acids (or protein) with a high serine content.[326]

The isolated deoxyribonucleic acids, however obtained, are mixtures of different molecular species, except those from certain types of bacteriophage. In addition to being composed of polymers with different sequences of nucleotides, most preparations are either paucidisperse as a result of hydrodynamic shear during isolation, or they are polydisperse with respect to molecular weight partly owing to degradation, enzymic or otherwise, coincident with isolation and partly because of polymolecular aggregative processes. As with ribonucleic acids therefore, the fractionation of isolated deoxyribonucleic acids into homogeneous molecular (or specific aggregate) species is of considerable importance.

FRACTIONATION

An early method of separation involved fractional dissociation of deoxyribonucleoprotein (e.g. nucleohistone) gels by extraction with aqueous sodium chloride of increasing molarity. In this way, deoxyribonucleic acid preparations were separated into a number of fractions characterised by different ratios of adenine plus thymine to guanine plus cytosine, the guanine-cytosine enriched fractions tending to be more readily liberated.[327-331] Similar results were obtained by chromatographic procedures using gradient elution of the deoxyribonucleic acids with sodium chloride solutions from histone adsorbed on kieselguhr.[332] In an improved version of this method, purified fractions of histone were coupled by diazo linkages from tyrosine and histidine groups in the proteins to p-aminobenzyl cellulose.[333] Fractionation of nucleic acids on methylated serum albumin (kieselguhr support) has also been described.[551, 552, 558] Elution from the column with salt solutions of increasing strength is dependent on molecular size, composition (nucleic acids with a high guanine-cytosine content are eluted more readily), and secondary structure (denatured DNA is more firmly bound than native material). A naturally occurring poly deoxyadenylic-thymidylic acid component has been isolated from DNA of the marine crab *Cancer borealis* by means of this technique.[558] Deoxyribonucleic acids have also been fractionated by gradient elution from columns of calcium phosphate,[334, 335] but perhaps the most valuable column chromatographic methods yet developed lie in the use of cellulose anion exchange materials.

ECTEOLA cellulose anion exchanger has proved strikingly successful for the fractionation of deoxyribonucleic acids. The procedure is highly reproducible, gives quantitative recoveries and is applicable to material with a molecular weight from several hundred to several million.[336-341] Molecular size and shape are important factors in the fractionation, although the nature and distribution of the bases probably have some influence. While complete homogeneity of individual fractions cannot be claimed (in view of the nature of deoxyribonucleic acids it is unlikely that this will be attained by the application of any single technique) the method has high resolving power. In addition to fractionation of polydeoxyribonucleotides characterised by differences in molecular weight, effective separations of deoxyribonucleic acid from polyadenylic acid or ribonucleic acid and from deoxyribonucleic acid of identical source (*E. coli*) but in which thymine was partly replaced by 5-bromouracil, were obtained. There is no significant destruction of biologically active deoxyribonucleic acids as a result of adsorption to and elution from ECTEOLA, and a considerable fractionation of pneumococcal transforming DNA has been achieved. Of interest, is the observation that many different fractions showed the same qualitative type of biological activity, although they varied quantitatively. Partial resolution of different transforming activities was also obtained. As might be expected, chromatographic profiles of isolated deoxyribonucleic acids are greatly influenced by the method of preparation. Examination of the relative purine and pyrimidine contents of different fractions of a calf thymus deoxynucleic acid preparation showed wide variations of the base ratios. In particular, although the ratio of purines to pyrimidines was always close to unity, the adenine to thymine and guanine to cytosine ratios were significantly different from the value of 1·0 frequently obtained, which arises from the complementarity of specific bases in the double helical secondary structure of deoxyribonucleic acid. This indicates either that single chains of polydeoxyribonucleotides were present in the mixture (as artefacts or as genuine *in vivo* constituents) or that an absolute base-pairing system of the type normally associated with a double helical structure for deoxyribonucleic acid, is not entirely essential, that is, some non-complementarity (possibly involving " looping out " of mis-matched segments) may be present in certain fractions of double stranded DNA.

GENERAL STRUCTURE OF DEOXYRIBONUCLEIC ACIDS

As with the ribonucleic acids, early attempts to express relationships among the smaller components of deoxynucleic acid included a number of what would now be considered rather grotesque structures, many of which could be dismissed on aesthetic grounds with as much justification as lay in the scientific reasons on which they were based. Despite the careful inaugural work by Miescher, who isolated relatively high molecular weight polymers, later studies were made with extensively degraded materials. The technical difficulties then associated with the examination of deoxynucleic acids are perhaps indicated in an early biochemical preparation of deoxynucleosides[342] by Levene and London (1929). In this procedure, a solution of the deoxynucleic acid was passed through a segment of the gastrointestinal tract of a live dog, using a gastric fistula to establish a clean and empty segment. After suitable incubation of the eluate (collected from an intestinal fistula), the deoxynucleosides were isolated by laborious procedures to give a maximal yield of 1·5 grams of deoxyguanosine from 200 grams of nucleic acid, the other deoxynucleosides being obtained in much smaller quantities. Subsequent refinements of the method (calf gut enzymes and arsenate inhibition of phosphomonoesterase) yielded the deoxymononucleotides; these were considered to be 3' or 5' phosphate esters, but precise structural definition could not be made.[343] Mild acidic hydrolysis of deoxynucleic acid gave a mixture from which diphosphates of thymidine and deoxycytidine were isolated; a 3',5' diphosphate structure was assigned to both compounds.[344] More vigorous acidic conditions caused complete cleavage of glycosyl linkages to give the purine and pyrimidine bases. In marked contrast with ribonucleic acid, deoxynucleic acid was found to be stable to mild treatment with alkali. Deamination of oligodeoxynucleotides by the action of nitrous acid could be effected without significant further degradation.[345]

On the basis of rather dubious diagnostic methods (tritylation followed by toluene-*p*-sulphonylation and treatment with sodium iodide) thymidine was assumed to possess a furanose structure.[346, 347] In 1935, Levene and Tipson suggested a 3'–5' phosphodiester linked structure for the so-called tetranucleotide unit of deoxynucleic acid, in which pyrimidine deoxynucleotides alternated with purine deoxynucleotides.[347] The major part of this structure, though now known to be correct in certain respects, was based entirely on assumptions and analogies, some more reasonable than others. In particular, the isolation of 2-deoxyribose from deoxyguanosine and the identification of a fura- nose structure in thymidine (to some extent confirmed by the failure of the nucleoside to react with borate) provided scant justification for the concept that the sugar moiety in all the deoxynucleosides was 2-deoxy-D-ribofuranose.

By 1939 it was realised that the molecular weight of deoxynucleic acid was largely dependent on the severity of the method of isolation and the tetranucleotide theory was suitably modified. However, the misconception of a minimum repeating tetranucleotide unit containing the four bases in a defined order persisted and it was not until the advent of reasonably accurate simple analytical methods that the term tetra- nucleotide lost completely its associated overtones of meaning.

With the identification of the deoxynucleotides obtained from deoxynucleic acid by the action of intestinal diesterase as -5′ phos- phates,[348] it became clear that the principle internucleotide linkage involved 3′–5′ phosphodiester groupings, and Brown and Todd advanced the same general structure for deoxynucleic acids as for ribonucleic acids, together with an explanation for the contrasting stabilities towards acid and alkali shown by the two types of polymer.[81] As previously mentioned, deoxynucleic acid shows the normal stability to alkaline hydrolysis characteristic of dialkyl phosphates, whereas ribonucleic acid is readily degraded owing to the presence of vicinal *cis* hydroxyl groups.

Subsequently the constituent deoxynucleosides were fully established as β-D-2-deoxyribofuranosyls,[91] and confirmation of the general structure of DNA was afforded by a comparison of the properties of a synthetic dithymidine dinucleotide containing a 3'–5' internucleotide linkage with those of oligonucleotides obtained by enzymic degradation of deoxynucleic acid.[349]

STRUCTURE OF OLIGODEOXYNUCLEOTIDES

Complete elucidation of the primary structure of deoxyribonucleic acids poses an array of problems even more formidable than in the case of ribonucleic acids, and little has been achieved as yet. Nevertheless, some progress has been made in the determination of base sequence in single stranded oligodeoxynucleotides. Such degradation products are readily obtained from deoxyribonucleic acids by the action of deoxyribonucleases. Pancreatic deoxyribonuclease[350] (deoxyribonuclease I) is active in neutral solution, requires magnesium or certain other divalent cations and has a minimum molecular weight[351] of 61,566. The enzyme catalyses hydrolysis of DNA to a complex mixture, from which deoxynucleoside-5' phosphates ($\sim 1\%$), a number of dinucleotides ($\sim 16\%$), trinucleotides, and larger oligodeoxynucleotides carrying a terminal 5' phosphate group, have been separated by paper chromatography and electrophoresis[352] and by ion-exchange techniques.[353] Although the specificity of the mode of action of deoxyribonuclease I has not been defined completely, it is clear that cleavage occurs at the 3' O—P linkage. Examination of the dinucleotides containing both a purine and a pyrimidine base indicated that such compounds were almost entirely 5'P—Py—3'P—5'Pu, the isomeric 5'P—Pu—3'P—5'Py sequences being virtually absent. The suggestion that purine-3'—P-5' pyrimidine linkages are preferentially attacked[354] received strong confirmation from hydrolysis of the trinucleotide (deoxy) A3'P5'A3'P5'T3'P to (deoxy) A3'P5'A and thymidine-3',5' diphosphate by deoxyribonuclease I. Since related dinucleotides were unaffected a minimal chain length of three nucleotides appears to be necessary for cleavage of the purine-pyrimidine linkage in oligodeoxynucleotides containing a terminal 3' phosphate.[355] Preliminary results using chemically prepared oligodeoxynucleotides as substrates indicate that homopolymers of deoxyadenylic, deoxycytidylic and thymidylic acid larger than the trinucleotide are all cleaved by the enzyme, but oligodeoxyadenylic acid is attacked significantly faster than the pyrimidine compounds.[356]

Streptococcal deoxyribonuclease (streptodornase) likewise cleaves the 3′ phosphate internucleotide bond to give 5′ phosphate terminated fragments of variable length. The products are mainly oligodeoxynucleotides with a chain length greater than 2, though small amounts of dinucleotides and traces of mononucleotides are also formed.[357] Analysis of the products indicated a preferential cleavage of -P5′-pyrimidine-3′—P5′-purine linkages, that is, the action is complementary to that of pancreatic deoxyribonuclease I. The same pH and metal ion requirements are shown by the two enzymes and both are endonucleases (cleavage along the whole chain rather than stepwise attack).[357] The traces of mononucleotides present in the digestion mixtures in each case may represent terminal nucleotides from DNA chains. It is not entirely clear whether the initial action of all such enzymes on undenatured double helical DNA structures involves cleavage of internucleotide linkages followed by separation of oligonucleotide strands[358] or cleavage of the hydrogen bonds and separation of the DNA chains followed by hydrolysis of covalent bonds. There is some evidence that the initial action of deoxyribonuclease involves a structural change before hydrolysis.[359]

Deoxyribonucleases with an acidic pH optimum and no requirement for magnesium ions have been isolated from mammalian[360-363] and bacterial[364] sources, and are commonly termed deoxyribonuclease II. They further differ from deoxyribonuclease I in that cleavage of the internucleotide linkage occurs between the phosphate and a C5′ oxygen to give oligodeoxynucleotides containing a terminal 3′ monoesterified phosphate group.[365, 366] Hydrolysis of DNA with splenic deoxyribonuclease II occurs rapidly to give polydeoxynucleotides with an average chain length of 10. Subsequent hydrolysis is considerably slower.[367]

A similar specificity, resulting in products bearing a terminal 3′ phosphate group, is shown by a nuclease isolated from the culture medium of *Micrococcus pyogenes*.[368-371] Nucleoside-3′ phosphates and di- and trinucleotides bearing a 3′-monoesterified phosphate are obtained from ribonucleic and deoxyribonucleic acids and from enzymically synthesised poly ACGU,[372] but when biochemically prepared polyadenylic, polyuridylic or polycytidylic acid, or the two stranded copoly (deoxyadenylic-thymidylic) acid are used as substrates, only mono- and dinucleotides are found in a limit digest. Chemosynthetic polyguanylic acid (containing 2′-5′ and 3′-5′ phosphodiester linkages) is resistant to hydrolysis although the analogous polyadenylic acid is partially hydrolysed. This is probably a consequence of the extremely easy aggregation of oligoguanylic acids compared with other oligonucleotides. The resistance of -3'P5'–G linkages is further indicated by the very small amounts of deoxyguanosine-3' phosphate that are liberated from DNA, the major mononucleotide components being deoxyadenosine-3' phosphate, thymidine-3' phosphate, and to a lesser extent, deoxycytidine-3' phosphate. Examination of the rate of liberation of various fragments from native and from heat denatured deoxynucleic acids indicated a strong preferential initial attack at nucleotide stretches containing the bases adenine and thymine, the result of a " conformational specificity " arising from the weaker hydrogen bonding of adenine-thymine base pairs relative to the less readily disrupted guanine-cytosine segments in the double helix. Subsequently, when larger amounts of single stranded polynucleotides are present, the specificity broadens and fragments containing guanine and cytosine begin to accumulate. The preferential attack by this enzyme at " denatured regions " of deoxynucleic acid suggests a possible use as a structural probe for cleavage at loci containing a specific sequence of three or four nucleotides.[372]

The action of micrococcal diesterase on tobacco mosaic virus RNA has also been examined.[373] Again a combination of endo- and exo-cleavage was observed, the latter presumably stepwise from the 3'-phosphate end of oligonucleotides produced by endo-action, but the final products (using a large excess of enzyme) were mono- and dinucleotides exclusively, even with oligonucleotides terminated by guanosine-3' phosphate (obtained by the action of takadiastase ribonuclease T1 on the viral nucleic acid).

A phosphodiesterase that is also of considerable potential value has been isolated from *Escherichia coli*.[374] Slight activity only was shown with intact double stranded deoxyribonucleic acid, but the same material after heat denaturation was rapidly hydrolysed to deoxy-nucleoside-5' phosphates, as was the single stranded deoxynucleic acid from bacteriophage ϕX–174. The action is exonuclease and involves stepwise attack from the 3'-hydroxyl end of the chain. Dinucleotides are not cleaved so that degradation of a polynucleotide chain gives mononucleotides and the terminal dinucleotide bearing a 5' mono-esterified phosphate group. The enzyme can thus be used for both determination of chain length and end group analysis. In accord with this specificity, enzymic hydrolysis of a deoxyribonuclease I digest of calf thymus deoxynucleic acid (average chain length of the oligonucleo-tide mixture approximately four nucleotides) gave a mixture of some 50% mononucleotides and 50% dinucleotides. Unlike rattlesnake venom diesterase, the *Escherichia coli* enzyme is completely active against bacteriophage deoxynucleic acids containing glucosidic 5-hydroxymethylcytosine residues.[374]

Structural analysis of oligodeoxynucleotides (including those obtained from deoxynucleic acids by chemical hydrolysis) can be achieved in much the same way as for oligoribonucleotides. End

groups are determined by the use of venom diesterase[352, 354, 375] (cleavage to deoxynucleoside-5' phosphates and terminal units) and spleen diesterase (cleavage to deoxynucleoside-3' phosphates and terminal units).[376–378] Hydrolysis with the latter enzyme, equivalent to alkaline degradation of oligoribonucleotides, is necessary because of the stability to alkali shown by the deoxynucleotide polymers. With certain oligonucleotides, a preliminary treatment with monoesterase is necessary since small oligmers containing a terminal 5′ phosphate are resistant to attack by spleen diesterase, and those with a terminal monoesterified 3′ phosphate are not readily hydrolysed by venom diesterase.[379] Longer chains are attacked by the diesterases regardless of the position of the terminal phosphate,[376-378] but become more resistant to the action of prostatic monoesterase with increase in chain length.[357]

Both spleen and venom diesterases act in a stepwise fashion, but are complementary, in that the former enzyme liberates mononucleotides beginning from the polynucleotide end bearing a 5′ hydroxyl group (head) and purified venom diesterase acts stepwise from the end bearing a 3′ hydroxyl group (tail).[380] The potentialities of such enzymes for stepwise analysis of polynucleotides have not been fully exploited, beyond demonstration of the structures of trinucleotides and various homopolymers of thymidylic acid.[381] Despite the claims that have been made, controlled liberation of nucleotides from polymers containing several different bases would be a more convincing demonstration of the utility of the method, particularly since interference by differing rates of hydrolysis of different purine–pyrimidine sequences might be expected to obscure precise interpretation. A disadvantage of spleen diesterase lies in the capacity of the enzyme to catalyse transfer reactions leading to the synthesis of higher homologues, and with venom diesterase, degradation of oligonucleotides containing a terminal 3′ phosphate does not occur by stepwise attack from the 3′ phosphate end of the molecule since nucleosides and nucleotides appear before liberation of nucleoside-3′,5′ diphosphates.[382] Even highly purified preparations of the latter diesterase appear to retain some endonuclease activity. Nevertheless, stepwise liberation of terminal nucleotides has proved useful for differentiating between terminal addition and true synthesis, when labelled deoxynucleotides are incorporated into DNA chains.[383, 384]

A possibly useful refinement of methods used for end group determination involves methylation of the terminal monoesterified phosphate group in oligonucleotides by the action of dicyclohexylcarbodi-imide and methanol. Subsequent hydrolysis yields the methyl ester of the end nucleotide or of a terminal oligonucleotide sequence using the appropriate hydrolytic method. Sensitivity could probably be increased considerably by the use of [^{14}C]-methanol.[385] The method has not as yet been applied with success to polyribonucleotides (or to deoxynucleic acids). More conveniently, the terminal phosphate group in oligodeoxynucleotides can be labelled by treating the oligmer with ethylchloroformate and tri-n-butylamine in aqueous solution. Reaction under such mild conditions appears to be confined to secondary phosphoryl dissociations present only in terminal phosphate groups. Subsequent treatment with diesterase yields mononucleotides and terminal nucleotide-ethyl carbonate anhydride. Alternatively, crude snake venom can be used since the terminal anhydride is resistant to hydrolysis whereas the mononucleotides are further degraded to nucleosides.[18] A preliminary examination has indicated that the method is also applicable to polyribonucleotides containing a terminal 5′ phosphate group.

A procedure for the stepwise degradation of oligodeoxynucleotides has been developed. This involves catalytic oxidation of a terminal 5′ CH_2OH group to a carboxylic acid residue, followed by phosphate elimination from the 3′ position (see p. 35).

NUCLEOTIDE SEQUENCE IN DEOXYNUCLEIC ACIDS

The comprehensive determination of nucleotide sequence in deoxy-nucleic acids is restricted by a variety of factors such as the difficulty of obtaining homogeneous material with chain lengths of 10,000 to 200,000 mononucleotides, the small number of different mononucleotides involved, and the polymolecular nature of DNA aggregates. At present therefore, little is known of the actual sequence of bases in deoxyribo-nucleic acid chains. Nevertheless it is clear that, as in ribonucleic acids, all possible binary sequences of nucleotides are present since they are liberated by chemical or enzymic hydrolysis. A simple repeating pattern containing the major nucleotides in a defined order therefore does not occur,* though of course this has not been rigorously proven for all molecular species in a given preparation. Gross differences among deoxynucleic acids from various sources have been established by simple analysis of the base composition and by quantitative comparison of the oligonucleotides and non-dialysable enzyme-resistant polydeoxynucleotide tracts released by the action of deoxy-ribonucleases.[386, 387] At a higher level of organisation, differences have been detected by following the specific activity of chromatographically separated polydeoxynucleotide fractions from a heated mixture of ^{32}P labelled DNA and unlabelled DNA of different origin.[388] While some of the degradation observed on heating aqueous solutions of deoxynucleic acids may result from simple hydrolysis of phosphodiester linkages, a more probable explanation lies in the fission of purine (particularly guanine) glycosyl linkages[389] at pH 7 followed by phosphate elimination from the deoxyribose residues and cleavage of polynucleo-tide chains.

Direct comparison of deoxynucleic acids from different sources has been achieved by means of chemical treatments that depend on pre-ferential removal of all, or nearly all, of the purine residues. These

* An exception is the copoly deoxyadenylic–thymidylic acid from crab, mentioned on p. 355. It has been shown[573] that at least 93% of the adenine and thymine residues are arranged in a perfect alternating sequence.

studies also indicate that the quantitative distribution of different bases, and sequences of bases, is non-random in the heterogeneous materials examined.

APURINIC ACIDS

Purine-free products obtained by treating deoxynucleic acid with dilute mineral acid were first described some seventy years ago and given the name "thymic acid".[390] Subsequently the presence of cytosine as well as thymine was demonstrated,[391] though the misnomer persisted until replaced by the term apurinic acid.[392] The formation of such products is a result of the extreme instability of purine–deoxyglycosyl linkages in acidic solution compared with pyrimidine–glycosyl bonds and phosphodiester linkages. Although quite mild conditions

Pu = Purine
Py = Pyrimidine

(such as hydrolysis[392] at 37° and pH 1·6 or treatment[393] with ion exchange resins) are now used for the preparation of apurinic acids, coincident cleavage of phosphodiester linkages does occur and the products are much reduced with respect to chain length and have molecular weights[394, 395] of 3500 to 15,000 compared with several million for the original polymers. As with hydrolysis in neutral solution, the ready elimination of phosphate from non-glycosyl deoxyribose units is a major cause of chain fission.

Apurinic acids show the reducing properties characteristic of non-glycosyl sugars and also react with such typical reagents as hydroxylamine, 2,4-dinitrophenylhydrazine, mercaptans and Schiff's reagent.[395] Polarographic studies have indicated the presence of some free aldehyde groups,[396] as may be expected from the general properties of 2-deoxyribose. Reduction with sodium borohydride converts the deoxyribose phosphate residues into 2-deoxyribitol esters,[394] probably with some coincident chain cleavage.

As mentioned previously, more vigorous acidic hydrolysis of DNA yields the -3',5' diphosphates of thymidine and deoxycytidine.[397-400] Originally described as hexose derivatives, these nucleotides were of some significance in considerations of the structure of deoxynucleic acids. Subsequently the sugar was identified as 2-deoxyribose[401] but the formation of considerable amounts of the diphosphates by acidic cleavage of DNA was disputed on somewhat questionable grounds.[402] A reinvestigation using modern techniques fully confirmed the original observations that major amounts of the pyrimidine deoxynucleoside-3',5' diphosphates,[403] and very much smaller quantities of the -3' and -5' monophosphates of thymidine and deoxycytidine,[91] could be isolated from acidic digests of DNA. The presence of more complex pyrimidine deoxynucleotide products (mainly di- and tri-nucleotides possessing an extra terminal phosphate) was also indicated. In view of the relative amounts of deoxynucleoside monophosphates and diphosphates it was suggested that acidic hydrolysis of DNA did not proceed solely by random fission of internucleotide linkages, but that the initial removal of purine residues was followed by preferential cleavage of phosphate from the resultant non-glycosyl deoxyribose residues giving rise to pyrimidine deoxynucleoside-3',5' diphosphates from each part of the polynucleotide chain where a pyrimidine was flanked by purines.[403]

Examination of the products obtained by acidic hydrolysis of the benzyl esters of the various deoxynucleotides provided confirmation of such a preferential mechanism. Thus both deoxyguanosine-3' benzyl phosphate and deoxyadenosine-3' benzyl phosphate are rapidly hydrolysed to the respective purine and 2-deoxyribose-3 benzyl phosphate. Further degradation of the sugar derivative then gives benzyl phosphoric acid. Similarly, benzyl phosphoric acid is rapidly released from the 2-deoxyribose-5 benzyl phosphate initially produced by the action of acid on deoxyadenosine-5' benzyl phosphate. Benzyl esters of the pyrimidine deoxynucleotides are relatively stable however, and under the same conditions the final products are unchanged benzyl esters and small (but significant) amounts of free nucleotides and other degradation products.[91] A plausible explanation for the preferential fission involved may be found in the properties of phosphate esters of β-aldehydo alcohols[404, 405] which suggest that elimination of the phosphate group at C3 of deoxyribose residues (β to the actual or latent aldehyde group of the sugar) should occur extremely readily.[406] Further, since mild acidic treatment of 2-deoxyribose is known to yield ω-hydroxylaevulic aldehyde,[407] ready fission of phosphate from C5 of degraded deoxyribose groups may also be expected[91] in view of the instability of α-keto phosphate esters.[408]　　The acidic hydrolysis of deoxynucleic acids therefore involves hydrolysis of purine glycosyl linkages followed by cleavage of phosphate diester linkages from C3 and C5 of deoxyribose units flanking pyrimidine deoxynucleosides or tracts of two or more pyrimidine nucleotides to give products containing both a 3' and a 5' terminal monoesterified phosphate.

Alternative hydrolytic mechanisms involving the C4 hydroxyl group of the acyclic form of purine-freed deoxyribose residues to give 3,4 or 4,5 cyclic phosphates appear to be of little significance since such intermediates would give pyrimidine deoxynucleosides or poly (pyrimidine deoxynucleotides) devoid of terminal monoesterified phosphate. The small amounts of deoxynucleoside-3' and -5' phosphates that are formed may result from such mechanisms or from secondary hydrolysis of the phosphate enriched deoxynucleotides and oligodeoxynucleotides initially produced.

Comprehensive studies of the acidic hydrolysis of a number of dideoxynucleotides (isolated from enzymic digests of DNA) fully confirmed the general mechanisms outlined above and extended them to the subsequent hydrolysis of polypyrimidine fragments.[409] Thus (deoxy) P5'C3'P5'A was rapidly degraded quantitatively to deoxycytidine-3',5' diphosphate (and adenine) while the isomeric dinucleotide (deoxy) P5'A3'P5'C yielded deoxycytidine-5' phosphate. Prolonged hydrolysis cleaves cytosine glycosyl linkages and to a lesser extent thymine linkages, the rate being markedly dependent on the number of phosphate residues attached to the sugar. (Deoxycytidine and thymidine are considerably less stable than the phosphate esters, particularly the 3',5' diphosphates). Under the general hydrolytic conditions used, the dinucleotide (deoxy) P5'C3'P5'C was slowly degraded to cytosine (mainly from the monoesterified deoxynucleoside), deoxycytidine-3',5' diphosphate, and small amounts of deoxycytidine-5' phosphate. In similar fashion, acidic treatment of a mixture of isomeric dinucleotides containing both thymidine and deoxycytidine yielded the corresponding deoxynucleoside-3',5' diphosphates, the greater stability of thymine glycosyl linkages relative to those of cytosine having a considerable influence on the ratio of the products.[409]

Further examination of acidic digests of deoxynucleic acids showed that pyrimidine oligodeoxynucleotides of the series (pyrimidine deoxynucleoside)$_n$(phosphate)$_{n+1}$ were indeed present, in addition to the simple deoxynucleoside-3',5' diphosphates, and that they formed the bulk of the pyrimidine nucleotide degradation products, in accord with the elimination mechanisms described.[410, 411] A number of dinucleoside triphosphates, trinucleoside tetraphosphates and higher oligodeoxynucleotides were separated by ion exchange chromatography and all possible sequences involving cytosine and/or thymine shown to exist.

Quantitative determination of the pyrimidine deoxynucleoside-3',5' diphosphates and smaller oligonucleotides released from deoxynucleic acids by acidic hydrolysis under standard conditions (the so-called method of differential distribution analysis)[411] using approximate corrections for secondary hydrolytic reactions led to estimates of the distribution of thymine and cytosine. Comparison of the results with deoxynucleic acids from a number of sources showed that the distribution of pyrimidines (and hence presumably of purines) varied in preparations of different origin (and in different fractions of a particular preparation). In general, a considerably greater proportion of the thymine occurred as single units flanked by purines compared with the cytosine, and some 70% of the total pyrimidines occured as oligonucleotide tracts of three or more successive pyrimidines. In all cases the results were considered to indicate that the distribution of components was far from random (although the heterogeneity of the deoxynucleic acids examined might reasonably have been expected to lead to an overall appearance of randomness), the yields of low molecular weight products being considerably less than those predicted by a mathematical treatment.[411]

Application of the same procedure to rye germ deoxyribonucleic acid which contains a relatively high proportion of the minor component 5-methylcytosine gave similar results with respect to the distribution of thymine and cytosine.[412] In addition, 5-methyl-2'-deoxycytidine-

3′,5′ diphosphate and the unresolved isomeric mixtures of dinucleoside triphosphates derived from 5-methylcytosine and cytosine or thymine respectively were estimated.[413]   A non-random distribution of the minor base could also be inferred since less than a theoretical 25% (for randomness) of the total 5-methylcytosine appeared as the deoxynucleoside-3′,5′ diphosphate corresponding to single units originally flanked by purine bases.   Moreover, the distribution of this base as reflected in the relative amounts appearing as deoxynucleoside-3′,5′ diphosphate or as components of pyrimidine di-deoxynucleoside triphosphates (originally stretches of two pyrimidines flanked by purines) was significantly different from that of cytosine.[412]   Examination of various fractions of the rye germ deoxyribonucleic acid obtained by fractional dissociation of the nucleoprotein provided further evidence that 5-methylcytosine is not equivalent to cytosine in a structural sense and does not " replace " cytosine in a random manner.   Nevertheless, the unity relationships arising from the complementary nature of the double helical structure of DNA were maintained.[412]   (That is, the total guanine in each fraction was equal to the sum of the cytosine and 5-methylcytosine).

An analogous cleavage of deoxynucleic acid under very mild conditions occurs on treatment with formic acid containing small amounts of primary or secondary aromatic amines, particularly diphenylamine.[414] The mechanism of the reaction or the function of the base (which is necessary) is not yet clear, but possibly involves enamine formation with the initially produced apurinic acids, followed by phosphate elimination. As with direct acidic hydrolysis very little of the deoxynucleoside monophosphates are formed, the appropriate amount of phosphate appears as inorganic phosphate, and the major nucleotide products form a series with the general structure (pyrimidine deoxynucleoside)$_n$(phosphate)$_{n+1}$.   To facilitate separation and estimation, the complex mixture of products was treated with phosphomonoesterase (relatively free of diesterase activity) to remove terminal phosphate groups, and the resultant mixture of deoxynucleosides (from the-3′,5′ diphosphates), dinucleoside phosphates, and higher homologues was analysed by paper chromatographic methods.   Considerably more of the mono- and dipyrimidine fragments were recovered from calf thymus deoxynucleic acid by this approach compared with the previously described degradation, but nevertheless a slight bias in favour of three or more consecutive pyrimidines (61% against a theoretical 50% for random sequence) was observed.   A significant difference between the amounts of the two sequential isomers (deoxy) P5′C3′P5′T3′P and (deoxy) P5′T3′P5′C3′P provided stronger evidence that the arrangement of nucleotides was not random.[415]   The ratio of these two sequences (originally flanked by purines) varied widely in deoxynucleic acids of different origin as shown in Table 6-IV.[416]

TABLE 6-IV.

Origin of DNA	Molar ratio (deoxy)C3′P5′T/(deoxy)T3′P5′C
Sea urchin	0·8
E. coli	0·9
Calf thymus	1·4
Herring	1·6
Salmon	1·7

Detailed examination of the products of diphenylamine–formic acid degradation of four bacterial and four animal species showed that each DNA differed from the others, and from a random polynucleotide. However, there was no obviously consistent pattern and no general tendency for the pyrimidines to be bunched together in a non-random fashion,[417] in contrast with estimates obtained by direct acidic hydrolysis of deoxynucleic acids. Discrepancies between the two methods could arise from the presence of diesterase activity in the phosphomonoesterase used; both approaches are subject to a variety of experimental inaccuracies.

In yet another attempt at determination of the distribution of pyrimidines in deoxynucleic acids, mercaptalation of deoxyribose residues originally bound to purines, followed by chain cleavage with alkali was examined. Treatment of herring-roe DNA with ethanethiol in the presence of hydrochloric acid gave a low yield of mercaptalated polymer which on alkaline hydrolysis gave a number of smaller degradation products.[418] The use of mercaptoacetic acid in the presence of anhydrous zinc chloride and sodium sulphate gave more quantitative results.[419, 420] Alkaline degradation of the *aldehydo*apurinic acid di-(carboxymethyl)dithioacetal prepared from calf thymus deoxynucleic acid gave a large number of components, including oligonucleotides containing at least three consecutive pyrimidines. The mechanism of alkaline hydrolysis is analogous to that evident in the hydrolysis of ribonucleic acids owing to the availability of a hydroxyl group at C4 of the acyclic deoxyribose residues, so that a range of products of the form (pyrimidine)$_n$(phosphate)$_{n-1}$ is obtained, that is, pyrimidines flanked by purines appear as the deoxynucleosides while sequences of two or more pyrimidines are converted into the analogous oligonucleotide devoid of terminal monoesterified phosphate. However, random hydrolysis of cyclic phosphate intermediates gives two other

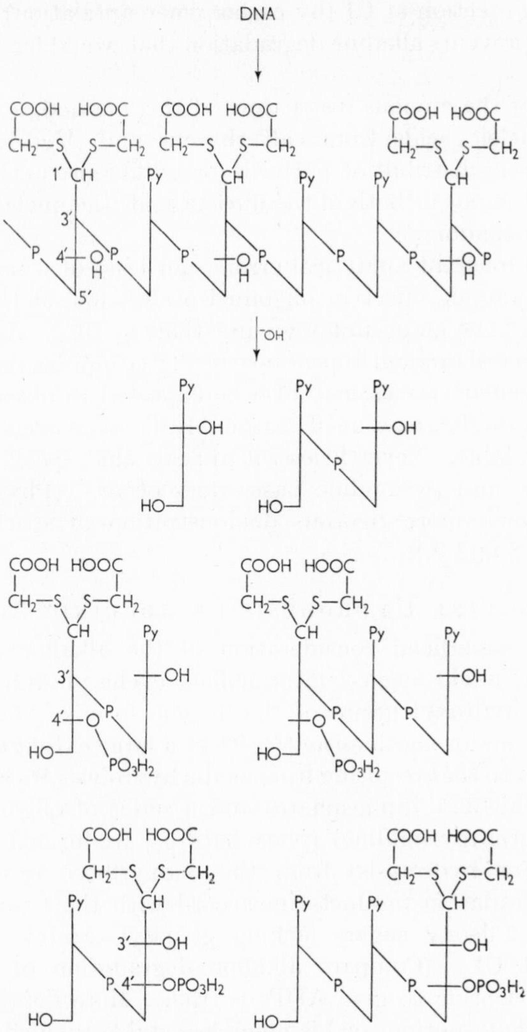

DNA

↓

COOH HOOC   COOH HOOC   COOH HOOC
 | | | | | |
CH₂—S S—CH₂ CH₂—S S—CH₂   CH₂—S S—CH₂
  1′ CH   Py   CH   Py   Py   CH

 3′
  P 4′ O P   P   O P   P   O P
        H   H   H
     5′

↓ ⁻OH

     Py   Py   Py
      —OH   —OH
          P
   HO—   HO—

COOH HOOC   COOH HOOC
 | | | |
CH₂—S S—CH₂   CH₂—S S—CH₂
   CH   Py   CH   Py   Py
 3′   —OH   —OH
 4′ O P   —O P   P
HO—   HO—
     PO₃H₂   PO₃H₂

     COOH HOOC   COOH HOOC
      | | | |
     CH₂—S S—CH₂   CH₂—S S—CH₂
 Py   CH   Py   Py CH
     3′ —OH   —OH
   P 4′ —OPO₃H₂   P P —OPO₃H₂
HO—   HO—

series of products containing a terminal 2-deoxy-*aldehydo*-D-ribose di(carboxymethyl)dithioacetal-4 phosphate residue attached to either a terminal 5′ phosphate or a terminal 3′ phosphate of the oligonucleotide. Blockage of the hydroxyl group at C4 of the sugar by a phosphate group prevents further cyclisation involving the adjacent phosphodiester linkage, and such products are therefore stable to mild alkaline treatment. Small amounts of a fourth type of product, pyrimidine deoxynucleotide residues flanked by deoxyribose mercaptal 4 phosphate at both the 3′ and 5′ phosphate ends, might also be expected. It may be noted that protection at C1 (by carboxymercaptalation) of the deoxy-ribose units prevents alkaline degradation that would lead to phosphate elimination.

In spite of the obvious restrictions of this method, a comparison of the deoxynucleic acids from calf thymus and *Mycobacterium phlei* showed different distribution patterns (or a difference in the degradative process), and in one or both of the nucleic acids the nucleotide distribution was non-random.[421]

Owing to inherent analytical errors, not least of which is a neglect of the hypochromic effect in oligonucleotides, few of the results discussed above have an accuracy greater than $\pm$ 10%. A second major factor, the overall random appearance of a large number of different non-random molecular species may also be expected to obscure particular types of non-randomness until reasonably homogeneous deoxynucleic acids are available. Nevertheless, it appears that specific distribution of the purine and pyrimidine bases does occur. (Physical methods provide a much more rigorous demonstration of specific sequence. See chapters 8 and 9.)

ALKALINE HYDROLYSIS OF APURINIC ACIDS

Although superficial consideration of the alkaline hydrolysis of apurinic acids might suggest intermediate cyclic phosphate formation with the C4 hydroxyl group of the acyclic form of the deoxyribose residues as a major mechanism,[422, 423] to a large extent degradation is closely similar to that resulting from acidic hydrolysis.[18, 424] Pyrimidine deoxynucleoside-3',5' diphosphates and a series of oligonucleotides of the general form (pyrimidine)$_n$(phosphate)$_{n+1}$ are formed by phosphate elimination (or hydrolysis) from the deoxyribose residues (or the resultant degradation products) in accord with the known properties of esters of 2-deoxy sugars lacking glycosyl, acetal, or mercaptal protection at C1. (Compare alkaline degradation of nicotinamide adenine dinucleotide to give ADP; p. 159.) More detailed studies[425] have shown that apurinic acid is much less stable than ribonucleic acid at pH 10, and that alkaline degradation gives an $\alpha\beta$-unsaturated aldehyde phosphate (presumably the result of β-elimination of phosphate from the 3' position of adjacent purine-free deoxyribose units) in addition to oligonucleotides. The amount of this product suggests that at least 45% of the degradation proceeds by a β-elimination mechanism; other hydrolytic processes are not excluded for the remainder and some degradation may occur via cyclic phosphate formation (though extremely small amounts of free pyrimidine deoxy-nucleosides are produced). Nevertheless, mild acidic treatment of DNA (to remove purines) followed by alkaline hydrolysis offers an alternative approach to the distribution of pyrimidines. Correction for the pyrimidine glycosyl cleavage encountered in the more vigorous acidic treatments would be unnecessary, and separation and estimation of the products would be facilitated by a preliminary treatment with phosphomonoesterase to remove terminal monoesterified phosphate residues.

Apurinic acid is also degraded on heating neutral unbuffered solutions of the sodium salt.[426] There is a rapid loss of free aldehyde groups (but not of reducing properties) followed by a slower release of inorganic phosphate and of the free base cytosine (up to 95% of the total cytosine after 20 hours at 100°). Thymidylic acid and thymidine oligonucleotides with an equimolar ratio of thymine to phosphate are also formed; these possibly contain a terminal 5' phosphate exclusively (phosphate elimination from C3 of adjacent deoxyribose residues and, in the absence of alkaline degradation of the sugar, 4,5 cyclic phosphate formation in deoxyribose units next to thymidine-3' phosphate linkages).

DISTRIBUTION OF PURINE NUCLEOTIDES IN DEOXYNUCLEIC ACID

Since in most deoxynucleic acids the molar ratio of purines to pyrimidines is equal to unity, the distribution of the purines is largely characterised by the pyrimidine distribution. Acceptance of a strictly complementary nature for the polynucleotide chains of the double helical DNA aggregate further implies that, for instance, the distribution of the sequence G3'P5'A is identical with that of T3'P5'C (that is, C5'P3'T). Nevertheless, independent determination of purine distribution is desirable, even for the grossly heterogeneous mixtures normally examined.

Selective oxidation of thymine, cytosine and guanine residues in

DNA with potassium permanganate gave a product which on alkaline degradation yielded a number of adenine components by phosphate elimination from ureido sugar residues.[424] Some 62% of the total adenine appeared as tri-deoxyadenosine tetraphosphate, a further 22% being accounted for by the dimer (deoxyadenosine)$_2$(phosphate)$_3$.

Studies of the enzymic (streptodornase) hydrolysis of deoxyribonucleic acids indicate that most of the nucleotides occur as sequences of pyrimidines up to 10 units long, with corresponding tracts of purines.[357]

Hydrazinolysis of DNA followed by alkaline degradation of the apyrimidinic acids may be of value for the determination of purine distribution.* The process would be analogous to the alkaline hydrolysis of apurinic acids.

OTHER DEGRADATIVE TREATMENTS

OF DEOXYRIBONUCLEIC ACID

Treatment of pyrimidine nucleotides with hydrazine gives acyclic derivatives which are readily degraded to the sugar phosphate.[427] Although some cleavage of phosphodiester linkages probably occurs, hydrazinolysis of deoxyribonucleic gives polymeric products that are almost free of pyrimidines but retain the purine deoxynucleotides present in the original nucleic acid. Further treatment of this " apyrimidinic acid " with dilute acid gives a poly(deoxyribose phosphate) type of product which, it is claimed, can also be prepared by hydrazinolysis of apurinic acid.[428]

Hydroxylamine reacts rapidly with cytosine and 5-hydroxymethylcytosine (or 5-bromouracil) residues in DNA under mild conditions, whereas thymine or 5-methylcytosine are unaffected.[429] The reagent is strongly mutagenic and possibly acts by attack at C6 of the pyrimidine

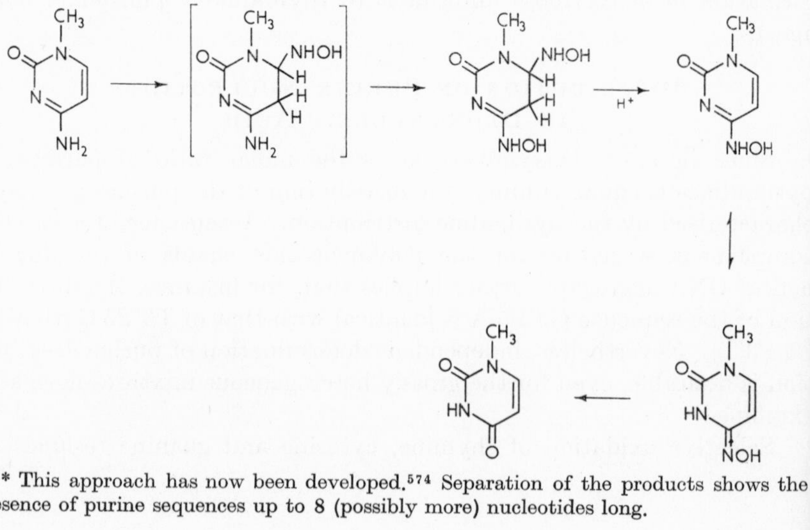

* This approach has now been developed.[574] Separation of the products shows the presence of purine sequences up to 8 (possibly more) nucleotides long.

ring to give intermediates that are converted into uracil. However, studies with 3-methylcytosine and cytidine as model compounds suggest that initial attack is at the 4,5 double bond and that the reaction sequence is as shown.[221, 430]

Although ribonucleic acids react with formaldehyde under mild conditions, presumably by Schiff's base or methylol formation with the amino groups, undenatured polystranded deoxynucleic acids are unaffected by this reagent (in that no spectral changes are observed) probably owing to the protection afforded by the hydrogen bonded based pairing system of the double helical structure. Native single stranded and denatured deoxynucleic acids are sensitive to formaldehyde.[217, 218, 431]

Alkylating agents such as dimethyl sulphate and "nitrogen mustards" react with deoxyribonucleic acids[432] under very mild conditions of pH and temperature.[433, 436, 437] Alkylation of the purine and pyrimidine bases occurs; studies with the individual deoxynucleotides and analysis of the products in acidic digests of DNA treated with the reagents mentioned showed that the order of reactivity of the bases was guanine > adenine > cytosine > thymine and that in the case of the guanine residues the major reaction[433, 436, 437] was alkylation at N^7. Methylation of adenylic acid in aqueous solution at pH 7 gives N^1 and N^3 derivatives; further treatment with alkali causes "migration" of the N^1 methyl group to the extranuclear 6-amino group.[438] Thus the adenine residues in DNA are presumably alkylated at the pyrimidine moiety, in contrast with guanine residues which are attacked at the imidazole ring. Under suitable conditions an appreciable number of the phosphate groups are esterified when DNA is treated with "nitrogen mustard"[439] or dimethyl sulphate,[433] the resultant triesterified phosphate residues being relatively unstable. With bifunctional alkylating agents cross linking between different parts of the same DNA chain or between different chains can occur. Degradation of DNA treated with monofunctional reagents yielded 7-alkylguanines; similarly, di(guanin-7-yl) derivatives were obtained by the use of difunctional alkylating agents.[440] It may be noted that RNA containing 7-alkyl-guanosine residues is stable in neutral aqueous solution, but alkylated DNA decomposes spontaneously with the loss of alkylated guanine products (owing to the instability of the deoxyglycosyl linkage). Subsequent cleavage of the sugar phosphate strand is then possible. With difunctional reagents double strand fission can occur fairly readily owing to the relatively high proportion of neighbouring alkylations in opposing strands (about 25%). Breaks in both strands within 2 to 6 nucleotides of each other (and hence drop in molecular weight) by the use of monofunctional alkylating agents would be rare.[440] In many respects the chemical action of these agents (radiomimetics) parallels the biological effect of high energy radiation such as X-rays in causing mutations, damage to chromosomes, and inhibition of tumours.[441]

Treatment of DNA with aqueous bromines causes extensive destruction of the guanine and cytosine residues. Thymine is affected to a lesser extent, and the adenine components are virtually unaffected.[442-445]

Deoxyribonucleic acids are stable to mild alkaline conditions, but more vigorous treatment with hot alkali gives a complex mixture of oligodeoxynucleotides.[446-448] Considerable destruction of cytosine and adenosine residues occurs, in addition to deamination of cytosine to uracil.[449, 450]

BASE COMPOSITION OF DEOXYRIBONUCLEIC ACIDS

Relative proportions of the various component mononucleotides in deoxyribonucleic acid preparations are normally obtained by quantitative acidic hydrolysis to the free base (best with formic acid) followed by paper chromatographic separation and spectrophotometric estimation.[451-455] In addition to the long recognised components (adenine, cytosine, guanine, and thymine), other bases have been identified in hydrolysates, and the derived nucleotides isolated. Small amounts of 5-methylcytosine occur in deoxyribonucleic acids from a number of mammalian, fish and insect sources and relatively large amounts occur in wheat germ deoxyribonucleic acid.[456, 457] The deoxynucleoside,[458] -5' phosphate,[459] and -3',5' diphosphate[403, 413] from 5-methylcytosine have been isolated from suitable digests of deoxyribonucleic acid. Another methylated base, 6-methylaminopurine, has been identified as a minor constituent of deoxyribonucleic acids from various micro-organisms (*Escherichia coli*, *Aerobacter aerogenes*, *Mycobacterium tuberculosis*, and *Pneumococcus*) and viruses (*E. coli* bacteriophage T2 and *Salmonella C* bacteriophage).[460] Isolation of the deoxynucleoside and its phosphate indicates that the base is a true component of the nucleic acid. The amount of 6-methylaminopurine present in the deoxynucleic acids of *Escherichia coli* 15T⁻ (a thymine requiring strain) increases from 2% of the adenine present to some 15% when the organism is grown under conditions of thymine starvation or in the presence of thymine analogues such as 5-aminouracil or 2-thiothymine.[460]

Statements that these minor bases replace other specific bases, that is, a corresponding amount of cytosine is replaced by 5-methylcytosine in the deoxynucleic acid[461] may possess meaning in spite of the heterogeneous nature of the nucleic acids analysed, though further claims with respect to distribution can scarcely be considered until at least a relatively homogeneous fraction of deoxynucleic acid is examined.

Major exceptions* to the general composition occur with deoxynucleic acids of the *Escherichia coli* bacteriophages T2, T4 and T6. These nucleic acids are marked by a complete absence (within the sensitivity of the analytical methods used) of cytosine, and the presence of 5-hydroxy-methylcytosine in major quantities.[462] Much of this component has glucoside residues at the 5-hydroxymethyl group[463-465] and both monogluco-[463-467] and digluco-5-hydroxymethyl-2'-deoxycytidine-5' phosphate[466, 468] (as well as 5-hydroxymethyl-2'-deoxycytidine-5' phosphate)[463-465, 467, 469] have been isolated from bacteriophage DNA by treatment with deoxyribonuclease followed by snake venom diesterase. Although deoxynucleic acids from all three bacteriophages contain much the same amount of 5-hydroxymethylcytosine, the ratio of glucose to this pyrimidine base is significantly different,[468] being 0·81 for T2 bacteriophage, 1·08 for T4 and 1·71 for T6.

The presence of combined glucose confers resistance to attack by a number of enzymes including phosphomonoesterase,[470] venom diesterase, and deoxyribonuclease.[463-465, 471] Thus deoxynucleic acid from bacteriophage T2 is more readily degraded by pancreatic deoxyribonuclease than is DNA from bacteriophage T6. Further, the successive action of deoxyribonuclease and venom diesterase on the deoxynucleic acids from all three bacteriophages (T2, T4 and T6) yields deoxynucleoside-5' phosphates together with a large proportion of diesterase-resistant oligodeoxynucleotide fragments.[466] Most of the viral 5-hydroxymethylcytosine is present in these oligodeoxynucleotides but 5-hydroxymethyl-2'-deoxycytidine-5' phosphate and the monoglucoside were isolated from the mononucleotide fraction of T2 DNA digests. Similarly, the diglucoside, the free nucleotide and a small amount of the monoglucoside were obtained from T6 DNA. Enzymic digests of T6 DNA also yielded a dinucleotide containing adenine and 5-hydroxymethylcytosine diglucoside.[466] Since venom diesterase is highly specific for nucleoside-5' phosphate alkyl esters but shows little specificity for the nature of the alkyl or aryl group (benzyl, phenyl, nucleoside-2', nucleoside-3', nucleoside-5') it might be expected that this dinucleotide was 5-diglucosido-5-hydroxymethyl-2'-deoxycytidylyl-5' : 3'-deoxyadenosine-5' phosphate rather than the isomeric deoxyadenylyl-5' : 3'-5-diglucosido-5-hydroxymethyl-2'-deoxycytidine-5' phosphate. That this was indeed the case was readily shown by degradation of the dinucleotide with formic acid and diphenylamine to yield a monophosphate of 5-hydroxymethyldeoxycytidine diglucoside rather than the 3',5' diphosphate.[466] Presumably the diesterase-resistant oligodeoxynucleotide fragments mentioned previously consist mainly of glucosidic 5-hydroxymethyl-2'-deoxycytidylic acid tracts bearing a terminal deoxynucleoside-5' phosphate other than the gluco-

*Deoxynucleic acids from bacteriophages SP2 and 8 (host, *Bacillus subtilis*) are also exceptional. Thymine is replaced by uracil in the former and by 5-hydroxymethyluracil in the latter.[575]

sidic pyrimidine nucleotide. Similarly, liberation of glucosidic mononucleotides from the DNA by the combined action of pancreatic
deoxyribonuclease and venom diesterase may result from an initial
cleavage by the nuclease to give oligodeoxynucleotides bearing a
terminal glucosidic 5-hydroxymethyl-2'-deoxycytidine-5' phosphate
(attached to a non-glucosidic nucleotide) and these are further degraded
by the diesterase.

Deoxynucleic acids from T*even* bacteriophages are completely
hydrolysed to deoxynucleotide-5' phosphates by a phosphodiesterase
from *Escherichia coli*. Chromatographic analysis of the products showed
that for T2 bacteriophage, 25% of the total hydroxymethylcytosine
content is nonglucosylated, 70% is monoglucosylated (a-glucosidic
linkage as shown by studies with a- and β-glucosidase) and 5% contains
a β-diglucoside in α-glycosidic linkage with the hydroxylmethyl group.
In T4 DNA, all of the pyrimidine is monoglucosylated but 70% of the
residues are linked in an α-configuration and 30% contain a β-glucosidic
linkage. In T6 25% of the hydroxymethylcytosine is free, 3% is monoglucosylated (α-linkage) and 72% occurs as an α-linked β-diglucoside.[472]
The disaccharide has been identified as 6-*O*-β-D-glucopyranosyl-D-
glucose (gentiobiose).[560]

Introduction of simple and reasonably accurate chromatographic
methods engendered analysis of numerous preparations of DNA. In
the course of this analytic orgasm, deoxynucleic acids of mammalian[473]
(including human),[473, 474] avian,[475] piscine,[476] plant,[477] microbial[478]
and viral[479] origin have been examined, and only the more exotic or
extreme forms of life have escaped attention. A few results are given in
the table. In spite of the fact that the vast majority of the materials
were far from homogeneous, a number of generalities concerning the
purine and pyrimidine composition of deoxynucleic acids have emerged.
The most significant of the regularities noted is that the molar ratios of
adenine to thymine and of guanine to cytosine are equal to (or very
close to) unity.[480] From this, it follows that the total purines (adenine
and guanine) are equal to the total pyrimidines (thymine and cytosine)
and that the number of 6-amino groups (adenine and cytosine) is the
same as that of 6-keto groups (thymine and guanine). An explanation
for the molar equality of adenine and thymine and of guanine and
cytosine (including 5-methylcytosine or 5-hydroxymethylcytosine) was
subsequently provided by Watson and Crick[481] who postulated (on
X-ray evidence) a double helical secondary structure for deoxynucleic
acid in which the bases of one polynucleotide chain are specifically
paired by hydrogen bonding with the bases in the other chain, the specific
pairings being adenine–thymine and guanine–cytosine (or substituted
cytosine). This not only establishes the unity relationships described

above but also, rather unfortunately, indicates an analytical difficulty in that the molar ratios of the component mononucleotides, or the frequency of specific sequences, in most deoxynucleic acids (however homogeneous) with respect to occurrence in the *same* chain cannot be determined without prior denaturation (separation) and fractionation of the complementary polynucleotides. Exceptions to this occur with natural single stranded deoxynucleic acids[482] such as that from bacteriophage ϕX174, and it is not impossible that at least some of the cellular deoxyribonucleic acids are likewise unmated.

Other numerical aspects of the composition of deoxynucleic acids have been developed from a study of the ratio of adenine plus thymine to cytosine plus guanine (or of adenine or thymine to guanine or cytosine). As with ribonucleic acids, the presence of equimolar proportions of the constituent bases is rather rare and the majority of deoxynucleic acids fall into either of the two groups characterised by an excess or a deficit of adenine and thymine relative to guanine and cytosine.[491-493] Considerable differences in this ratio occur among the deoxynucleic acids isolated from different forms of life, a preponderance of adenine and thymines being characteristic of mammals to some extent. Significant differences in composition have not been observed in deoxyribonucleic acid preparations from different organs of the same animal, but statistical analysis of the appropriate data led to the discovery that the ox is different from man.[473]

While it is obvious that all deoxynucleic acids must fall into one of three groups (adenine plus thymine greater than, equal to, or less than cytosine plus guanine) the biological significance of this ratio remains obscure, particularly since fractionation of total isolates can give deoxyribonucleic acids of each of the three types from the same source. Changes in the nucleic acid composition of experimentally evolved forms of certain intestinal bacteria are of some interest. Transition of *Escherichia coli*, *Salmonella typhosa* and *Shigella dysenteria* to " alkaliproducing forms " is accompanied by a notable change in the ratio of cytosine plus guanine to adenine plus thymine from 1·1 to approximately 2·0. In the " neutral forms ", the ratio is reduced to 0·7–0·8. Only slight changes in the composition of the ribonucleic acids were observed.[494] Although complete correspondence with taxonomic systematics has by no means been observed, the specific compositions of the deoxynucleic acids reflect definite phylogenetic and taxonomic interrelations between species, particularly in micro-organisms.[495, 496] Much smaller variations in composition are observed with DNA from higher organisms, both plants and animals.

High homogeneity of microbial DNA is observed in density gradient (caesium chloride) centrifugation.[497, 498] This density homogeneity

TABLE 6-V. Composition of deoxyribonucleic acids

Source	Molar ratios					$\dfrac{A+T}{G+C(+5\ MeC)}$	Reference
	A	T	G	C	5 MeC		
Ox thymus	10	9·8	7·3	7·3	—	1·36	473
Ox liver	10	10·1	7·3	7·3	—	1·37	473
Sheep thymus	10	9·7	7·3	7·2	—	1·36	473
Sheep liver	10	10·0	7·1	7·1	—	1·41	473
Pig thymus	10	9·6	6·8	6·9	—	1·43	473
Pig liver	10	10·1	6·7	6·7	—	1·44	473
Man thymus	10	9·5	6·4	6·4	—	1·52	473
Man liver	10	10·0	6·4	6·6	—	1·54	473
Man spleen	10	10·1	7·2	6·7	—	1·42	475
Man sperm	10	10·2	6·2	6·0	—	1·67	483
Man sperm	10	9·8	7·5	7·5	—	1·47	326
Hen erythrocytes	10	10·1	7·9	7·7	—	1·29	475
Herring sperm	10	9·9	8·0	7·4	0·7	1·23	484
Salmon sperm	10	9·8	7·0	6·9	—	1·43	476
Sea urchin sperm	10	9·5	6·3	6·0	0·6	1·52	484
Drosophila	10	10·1	8·9	5·9	2·9	1·13	485
Pinus silvirica	10	10·4	7·1	5·0	1·7	1·48	477
Papaver somniferum (Poppy)	10	10·1	7·0	5·0	1·8	1·46	477
Allium cepa (onion)	10	9·8	5·8	4·0	1·7	1·72	477
Wheat germ (U.S.S.R.)	10	10·2	9·3	7·1	2·5	1·07	477

	Molar ratios				5-Hydroxy-methyl C	$\dfrac{A+T}{G+5\text{-}HOCH_2C}$	Reference
	A	T	G	C			
Wheat germ (U.S.A.)	10	9·9	8·3	6·2	2·2	1·19	457
Yeast	10	10·5	6·0	5·5	—	1·79	486
Clostridium perfringens	10	10·3	4·6	4·4	—	2·22	487
Proteus vulgaris	10	9·8	6·6	6·9	—	1·47	487
Escherichia coli	10	10·0	10·9	11·0	—	0·92	487
Salmonella typhosa	10	10·0	11·4	11·2	—	0·88	487
Aerobacter aerogenes	10	10·3	13·5	13·1	—	0·76	487
Pseudomonas aeruginosa	10	9·6	19·6	20·2	—	0·49	487
Sarcina lutea	10	10·6	26·8	26·2	—	0·39	487
Actinomyces viridochromogenes	10	9·7	27·5	28·0	—	0·36	487
Aspergillus niger	10	10·0	10·0	10·0	—	1·00	488
Sclerotinia libertiana	10	10·0	8·3	8·4	—	1·20	488
E. coli Bacteriophage T5	10	10·2	6·4	6·4	—	1·57	479
E. coli Bacteriophage T7	10	10·0	9·2	9·2	—	1·09	489
Bacteriophage φX174	10	13·1	10·6	8·2	—	1·23	490
Drosophila eggs	10	9·7	8·1	6·3	—	1·37	550

E. coli Bacteriophage	Molar ratios			5-Hydroxy-methyl C	$\dfrac{A+T}{G+5\text{-}HOCH_2C}$	Reference
	A	T	G			
T2r	10	10·0	5·6	5·2	1·84	479
T4r +	10	10·2	5·7	5·0	1·89	479
T6r +	10	10·0	5·6	5·1	1·86	479

presumably reflects a composition homogeneity (since composition determines the density characteristics) which is remarkable, in that among a number of microbial species (covering a wide range of guanine–cytosine content) few, if any, DNA molecules appear to possess a common composition.

COMPLEXES OF DEOXYRIBONUCLEIC ACID

As mentioned previously, deoxyribonucleic acids are frequently prepared by cleavage of an isolated nucleic acid–protein complex. The protein moiety is generally highly basic and of relatively low molecular weight. Nucleoprotamines[499] occur in the ripe spermatozoa of many fish genera, and nucleohistones[500, 501] have been isolated from the nuclei of mammalian cells. A striking similarity among the nucleohistones from a number of vertebrates with respect to the content of arginine, lysine and histidine has been observed.[502] These complexes with relatively simple basic proteins are distinguished from another kind of deoxynucleoprotein which has been isolated from avian tubercle bacilli.[503] Unlike the nucleohistones and nucleoprotamines, this is soluble in isotonic saline and contains protein that is not strongly basic. A further example is " avidin ", isolated from hen eggs.[547, 548]

While many preparations of nucleohistone have been artefacts arising from dissociation and reassociation in the course of isolation, the original combination of histones and deoxyribonucleic acid *in vivo* is undoubtedly specific, at least in part, and the nucleoprotein is a definite structural complex rather than a loose association of the two components.[504–506] Using suitably refined methods of isolation, a physically well-defined deoxyribonucleohistone has been isolated from calf thymus in high yield,[507] though the lack of gel formation is possibly a result of hydrodynamic shear and protease activity during isolation.[508, 509, 549] Examination by a number of macromolecular methods showed that the material consisted of completely dispersed deoxyribonucleoprotein particles of high assymmetry containing nearly equal amounts of deoxyribonucleic acid and protein, with a molecular weight of $18·5 \times 10^6$. Dissociation gave a deoxyribonucleic acid with a molecular weight of 8×10^6 suggesting a single deoxyribonucleic acid moiety in the nucleoprotein. The protein units appear to be rather evenly distributed along the DNA chains, possibly in an α-helical conformation in the large groove of the double stranded DNA helix. The histone has a stabilising effect[507] on the DNA structure since isolated DNA underwent thermal denaturation at 60–70° whereas denaturation of the nucleoprotein (at the same ionic strength) occurred at 80–90°. Considerable protection is also afforded against enzymic degradation by deoxyribonuclease, both in " native " nucleohistones and in artificially prepared complexes,[510-512] and against damage by high energy irradiation.[513, 514] While the conjugated proteins have a definite structure which persists in solutions of very low ionic strength, high salt concentrations effect cleavage (partial or otherwise) of the essentially linear salt-like binding, to liberate phosphoryl groups and amino residues which on recombination form non-specific cross linkages between different DNA and histone chains (or with added protein or nucleic acid) to give complexes of variable composition and ill-defined structure.[505] Aggregation may also occur by association between portions of the histone from different nucleoprotein particles, leading to gelation.[507] A study of the metachromasy induced in toluidine blue by a calf thymus nucleohistone that carried a net negative charge approximately one seventh that of DNA showed that the uncombined phosphate groups occurred in sequences,[504] possibly owing to the absence of a complete histone subunit from the linear particle.

Artificial complexes between deoxynucleic acids and protamines,[515] histones,[516] polylysine, polyvinylamine,[517] and a wide variety of proteins have been described.[518-520] Complex formation with bovine serum albumin induced by heat results from the thermal denaturation of both components, binding being mainly by hydrogen bonds.[521] Up to 1800 albumin molecules can be bound by one DNA molecule,[521, 522] and the protective action of thymus deoxyribonucleic acid on thermal coagulation of albumin solutions[520] can be ascribed to this binding which prevents self-aggregation. Similar considerations can be applied to the hindering effect exerted by DNA on the cleavage of proteins by trypsin, that is, the effect operates on the substrate rather than the enzyme.[523] However, studies on the inhibition of chymotrypsin activity by DNA using synthetic substrates suggest that stoichiometric complexes between the enzyme and the nucleic acid are also formed. Maximum inhibition occurred at a 20 : 1 protein–DNA ratio corresponding to approximately four nucleotide units per molecule of chymotrypsin.[524] With trypsin this ratio was found to be 7 : 1.

Although the major constituents are nucleohistones, mammalian chromosomes also contain small amounts of deoxyribonucleoproteins involving non-histone proteins. These complexes appear to possess covalent linkages between the components since it is claimed that enzymic degradation gives oligodeoxynucleotide fragments attached to short peptides.[525]

Putrescine and spermidine have been identified as components of certain bacterial viruses (T2, T3, and T4 bacteriophage)[526, 527] and may indeed neutralise up to 50% of the deoxyribonucleic acid phosphoryl dissociations.[526] Such polyamines readily form stable complexes with DNA and a possible function (as non-specific cations)[528] is the preservation of the bacteriophage DNA in an infective conformation.[529] Cadaverine in particular protects the protoplast infecting agent derived from T2 bacteriophage,[529] and spermine is particularly effective for increasing the stability of transforming DNA (from *Bacillus subtilis*) to heat inactivation.[530] Both spermine[531] and cadaverine[532] inhibit degradation of DNA by deoxyribonuclease, possibly by the purely physical effect of coating the polynucleotide chain, or by increasing the conformational stability. Further studies on the effects of diamines[435] on the thermal transition of DNA from calf thymus, and from coliphage T2 have shown that stabilisation (manifested by a raised denaturation temperature) is a function of the concentration and chain length of the diamine.[533] For the series $NH_2(CH_2)_nNH_2$ where $n = 2$–8, a maximum effect (approximately $5°$) was found with cadaverine ($n = 5$), presumably reflecting stereochemical factors involved in any bridge-like structures. Measurements were made at high ionic strength to damp out non-specific counterion effects. Under these conditions interaction with magnesium ions raised the thermal denaturation temperature of T2 DNA from $83.4°$ to $84.2°$ only. In the presence of cadaverine the figure was $88.6°$. The protection afforded by this amine was found to be directly proportional to the adenine–thymine content of the deoxy-nucleic acid.[534]

Polyvalent metal ions are strongly bound by deoxyribonucleic acids, both " native " and denatured. Tervalent cations[535, 536] and cupric salts[537] yield insoluble complexes, presumably by binding DNA molecules together in lateral aggregates through chelation with phosphate groups (and possibly the purine and pyrimidine bases) of adjacent chains. The interaction of magnesium ions with deoxyribonucleic acid has been studied extensively.[537–541] Direct titration methods (using eriochrome black T as indicator) show that at low concentrations of sodium chloride, magnesium is strongly bound by both undenatured and denatured deoxyribonucleic acids, binding by the former being stronger.[540] In the presence of higher concentrations of sodium ions, binding of the magnesium is considerably reduced and it appears that the primary sites involved are the charged phosphate groups. Under suitable conditions chelation with the purine rings in single stranded or denatured polynucleotides could presumably occur also.[538, 539] Large changes in the rotatory dispersion of DNA on reaction with mercuric chloride have been observed. Reversible conformational changes occur and the process probably involves direct interaction of undissociated mercuric chloride with the heterocyclic bases.[542] Spectral changes indicate formation of two types of complex, one in which there is one mercury atom per two bases; the other probably has a 1 : 1 ratio. Reversal of the interaction (to give DNA that fully retains transforming activity) occurs on treatment with complexing agents such as cyanide or cysteine.[543] Nuclear magnetic resonance studies of proton relaxation enhancement by paramagnetic ion binding in solutions of DNA indicate that ferric ions are bound at interior sites.[544] Thermally denatured deoxyribonucleic acids are precipitated by lead ions; no precipitation occurs with the unheated double helical nucleic acids.[545]

Metal ions may play a significant role in the combination and structural relationships of protein and nucleic acid in deoxyribonucleoproteins. The liberation of DNA from nucleoprotein by simultaneous action of a metal complexing agent and interaction with the protein is of interest.[546]

REFERENCES

1. Levene, P. A., *Biochem. Z.*, **17**, 120 (1909).
2. Kerr, S. E., and Seraidarian, K., *J. Biol. Chem.*, **180**, 1203 (1949).
3. Beale, R. N., Harris, R. J. C., and Roe, E. M. F., *J. Chem. Soc.*, 1397 (1950).
4. Sevag, M. G., Lackman, D. B., and Smolens, J., *J. Biol. Chem.*, **124**, 425 (1938).
5. Kay, E. R. M., and Dounce, A. L., *J. Am. Chem. Soc.*, **75**, 4041 (1953).
6. Pirie, N. W., *Biochem. J.*, **56**, 83 (1954).
7. Markham, R., and Smith, J. D., *Biochem. J.*, **49**, 401 (1951).
8. Beale, R. N., Harris, R. J. C., and Roe, E. M. F., *J. Chem. Soc.*, 1397 (1950).
9. Volkin, E., and Carter, C. E., *J. Am. Chem. Soc.*, **73**, 1516 (1951).
10. Brownhill, T. J., Jones, A. S., and Stacey, M., *Biochem. J.*, **73**, 434 (1959).
11. Westphal, O., Luderitz, O., and Bister, F., *Z. Naturforsch.*, **7b**, 148 (1952).
12. Kirby, K. S., *Biochem. J.*, **64**, 405 (1956).
13. Colter, J. S., and Brown, R. A., *Science*, **124**, 1077 (1956).
14. Gierer, A., and Schramm, G., *Z. Naturforsch.*, **11b**, 138 (1956).
15. Monier, R., Stephenson, M. L., and Zamecnik, P. C., *Biochim. et Biophys. Acta*, **43**, 1 (1960).
16. Osawa, S., *Biochim. et Biophys. Acta*, **43**, 110 (1960).
17. Holley, R. W., Apgar, J., Doctor, B. P., Farrow, J., Marini, M. A., and Merrill, S. H., *J. Biol. Chem.*, **236**, 200 (1961).
18. Michelson, A. M., unpublished work.
19. Crestfield, A. M., Smith, K. C., and Allen, F. W., *J. Biol. Chem.*, **216**, 185 (1955).
20. Miura, K., Kitamura, T., and Kawade, Y., *Biochim. et Biophys. Acta*, **27**, 420 (1958).
21. Littauer, U. Z., and Eisenberg, H., *Biochim. et Biophys. Acta*, **32**, 320 (1959).
22. Hakim, A. A., *J. Biol. Chem.*, **225**, 689 (1957).
23. Bloemendal, H., and Bosch, L., *Biochim. et Biophys. Acta*, **35**, 244 (1959).
24. Main, R. K., Wilkins, M. J., and Cole, L. J., *J. Am. Chem. Soc.*, **81**, 6490 (1959).
25. Burness, A. T. H., and Vizoso, A. D., *Biochim. et Biophys. Acta*, **49**, 225 (1961).
26. Bernardi, G., and Timasheff, S. N., *Biochim. Biophys. Research Communs.*, **6**, 58 (1961).
27. Matoba, K., *Osaka Shiritsu Daigaki Igaku Zasshi*, **7**, 344 (1958).

386   NUCLEOSIDES AND NUCLEOTIDES

28. Lipshitz, R., and Chargaff, E., *Biochim. et Biophys. Acta*, **42**, 544 (1960).
29. Sibatani, A., Yamana, K., Kimura, K., and Okagaki, H., *Biochim. et Biophys. Acta*, **33**, 590 (1959).
30. Yamana, K., and Sibatani, A., *Biochim. et Biophys. Acta*, **41**, 295 (1960).
31. Kimura, K., *Biochim. et Biophys. Acta*, **55**, 22 (1962).
32. Gierer, A., *Z. Naturforsch.*, **13b**, 788 (1958).
33. Bradley, D. F., and Rich, A., *J. Am. Chem. Soc.*, **78**, 5898 (1956).
34. Goldthwait, D. A., *J. Biol. Chem.*, **234**, 3245 (1959).
35. Nishiyama, K., Okamoto, T., Watanabe, I., and Takanami, M., *Biochim. et Biophys. Acta*, **47**, 193 (1961).
36. Taussig, A., and Creaser, E. H., *Arch. Biochem. Biophys.*, **83**, 436 (1959).
37. Brown, F. and Cartwright, B., *Biochim. et Biophys. Acta*, **33**, 343 (1959).
38. Michelson, A. M., *J. Chem. Soc.*, 3655 (1959).
39. Staehelin, M., Peterson, E. A., and Sober, H. A., *Arch. Biochem. Biophys.*, **85**, 289 (1959).
40. Korn, E. D., *Biochim. et Biophys. Acta*, **32**, 554 (1959).
41. Tanaka, K., *Bull. Chem. Soc. (Tokyo)*, **31**, 393 (1958).
42. Staehelin, M., *Biochim. et Biophys. Acta*, **49**, 11 (1961).
43. Stephenson, M. L., and Zamecnik, P. C., *Proc. Natl. Acad. Sci. U.S.A.*, **47**, 1627 (1961).
44. Bosch, L., Wende, G., and Bloemendal, H., *Nature*, **191**, 349 (1961).
45. Smith, K. C., Cordes, E., and Schweet, R. S., *Biochim. et Biophys. Acta*, **33**, 286 (1959).
46. Smith, K. C., Rebhun, S., and Kaplan, H. S., *Analyt. Biochem.*, **1**, 202 (1960).
47. Hartmann, G., and Coy, U., *Biochim. et Biophys. Acta*, **47**, 612 (1961).
48. Kirby, K. S., *Biochem. J.*, **68**, 13P (1958); *Biochim. et Biophys. Acta*, **40**, 193; **41**, 338 (1960).
49. Holley, R. W., Doctor, B. P., Merrill, S. H., and Saad, F. M., *Biochim. et Biophys. Acta*, **35**, 272 (1959).
50. Holley, R. W., and Merrill, S. H., *J. Am. Chem. Soc.*, **81**, 753 (1959).
51. Doctor, B. P., Apgar, J., and Holley, R. W., *J. Biol. Chem.*, **236**, 1117 (1961).
52. Zachau, H. G., Tada, M., Lawson, W. B., and Schweiger, M., *Biochim. et Biophys. Acta*, **53**, 221 (1961).
53. Apgar, J., Holley, R. W., and Merrill, S. H., *Biochim. et Biophys. Acta*, **53**, 220 (1961).
54. Doctor, B. P., and Connelly, C. M., *Biochem. Biophys. Research Communs.*, **6**, 201 (1961).
55. Holley, R. W., Apgar, J., Merrill, S. H., and Zubkoff, P. L., *J. Am. Chem. Soc.*, **83**. 4861 (1961).
56. Everett, G. A., Merrill, S. H., and Holley, R. W., *J. Am. Chem. Soc.*, **82**, 5757 (1960).
57. Everett, G. A., Merrill, S. H., and Holley, R. W., *Federation Proc.*, **20**, 388 (1961).
58. Cantoni, G. L., *Nature*, **188**, 300 (1960).
59. Huang, S. L., and Felsenfeld, G., *Nature*, **188**, 301 (1960).
60. Zamecnik, P. C., Stephenson, M. L., and Scott, J. F., *Proc. Natl. Acad. Sci. U.S.A.*, **46**, 811 (1960).
61. Saponara, A., and Bock, R. M., *Federation Proc.*, **20**, 356 (1961).
62. Portatius, H., Doty, P., and Stephenson, M. L.. *J. Am. Chem. Soc.*, **83**, 3351 (1961).

63. Brown, G. L., 10th Symp. of the Soc. for Gen. Microbiol. Microbial Genetics, ed. Hayes, W., and Clowes, R. C., p. 208 (Cambridge University Press, 1960).
64. Jones, A. S., and Parsons, D. G., Proc. Chem. Soc., 78 (1961).
65. Levene, P. A., J. Biol. Chem., **48**, 119 (1921).
66. Levene, P. A., and Simms, H. S., J. Biol. Chem., **70**, 327 (1926).
67. Steudel, H., Peiser, E., Z. physiol. Chem., **108**, 42 (1919).
68. Jones, W., and Perkins, M. E., J. Biol. Chem., **62**, 557 (1925).
69. Levene, P. A., and Bass, L. W., Nucleic Acids, p. 289 (The Chemical Catalog Company, New York, 1931).
70. Gulland, J. M., Barker, G. R., and Jordan, D. O., Ann. Rev. Biochem., **14**, 175 (1945).
71. Levene, P. A., and Tipson, R. S., J. Biol. Chem., **109**, 623 (1935).
72. Gulland, J. M., and Jackson, E. M., J. Chem. Soc., 1492 (1938); Biochem. J., **32**, 590 (1938).
73. Gulland, J. M., J. Chem. Soc., 1722 (1938).
74. Astbury, W. T., Symposia Soc. Exptl. Biol., **1**, 66 (1947).
75. Schmidt, G., Cubiles, R., and Thannhauser, S. J., J. Cellular Comp. Physiol., **38, S1**, 61 (1951).
76. Vischer, E., and Chargaff, E., J. Biol. Chem., **168**, 781 (1947); **176**, 703 (1948).
77. Hotchkiss, R. D., J. Biol. Chem., **175**, 315 (1948).
78. Cohn, W. E., J. Cellular Comp. Physiol., **38, S1**, 21 (1951).
79. Cohn, W. E., and Volkin, E., Nature, **167**, 483 (1951).
80. Cohn, W. E., and Volkin, E., J. Biol. Chem., **203**, 319 (1953).
81. Brown, D. M., and Todd, A. R., J. Chem. Soc., **52**, (1952).
82. Chargaff, E., J. Biol. Chem., **144**, 455 (1942).
83. Baer, E., and Kates, M., J. Biol. Chem., **175**, 79 (1948); **185**, 615 (1950).
84. Fono, A., Arkiv. Kemi Mineral Geol., **24A**, No. 33, 14, 15 (1947).
85. Brown, D. M., and Todd, A. R., J. Chem. Soc., 44 (1952).
86. Brown, D. M., Magrath, D. I., and Todd, A. R., J. Chem. Soc., 2708 (1952).
87. Brown, D. M., and Todd, A. R., J. Chem. Soc., 2040 (1953).
88. Markham, R., and Smith, J. D., Biochem. J., **52**, 552 (1952).
89. Elmore, D. T., and Todd, A. R., J. Chem. Soc., 3681 (1952).
90. Cohn, W. E., and Volkin, E., Arch. Biochem. & Biophys., **35**, 465 (1952).
91. Michelson, A. M., Tetrahedron, **2**, 333 (1958).
92. Crestfield, A. M., and Allen, F. W., J. Biol. Chem., **219**, 103 (1956).
93. Kunitz, M., J. Gen. Physiol., **24**, 15 (1940).
94. Bacher, J. E., and Allen, F. W., J. Biol. Chem., **183**, 633 (1950).
95. Carter, C. E., and Cohn, W. E., J. Am. Chem. Soc., **72**, 2604 (1950).
96. Magasanik, B., and Chargaff, E., Biochim. et Biophys. Acta, **7**, 396 (1951).
97. Schmidt, G., Cubiles, R., Zöllner, N., Hecht, L., Strickler, N., Seraidarian, K., Seraidarian, M., and Thannhauser, S. J., J. Biol. Chem., **192**, 715 (1951).
98. Volkin, E., and Cohn, W. E., J. Biol. Chem., **205**, 767 (1953).
99. Markham, R., and Smith, J. D., Biochem. J., **52**, 565 (1952).
100. Markham, R., and Smith, J. D., Biochem. J., **52**, 558 (1952).
101. Brown, D. M., Dekker, C. A., and Todd, A. R., J. Chem. Soc., 2715 (1952).
102. Heppel, L. A., Markham, R., and Hilmoe, R. J., Nature, **171**, 1152 (1953).
103. Heppel, L. A., and Whitfield, P. R., Biochem. J., **60**, 1 (1955).
104. Whitfield, P. R., Heppel, L. A., and Markham, R., Biochem. J., **60**, 15 (1955).
105. Brown, D. M., Heppel, L. A., and Hilmoe, R. J., J. Chem. Soc., 40 (1954).

106. Gierer, A., *Nature*, **179**, 1297 (1957); *Z. Naturforsch.*, **13b**, 485 (1958).
107. Rogers, W. I., and Kalnitsky, G., *Biochim. et Biophys. Acta*, **23**, 525 (1957).
108. Ginsburg, A., and Schachman, H. K., *J. Biol. Chem.*, **235**, 115 (1960).
109. Gundlach, H. G., Stein, W. H., and Moore, S., *J. Biol. Chem.*, **234**, 1754 (1959).
110. Barnard, E. A., and Stein, W. D., *Biochem. J.*, **71**, 19P (1959).
111. Stein, W. D., and Barnard, E. A., *J. Mol. Biol.*, **1**, 350 (1959).
112. Anfinsen, C. B., Åqvist, S. E. G., Cooke, J. P., and Jönsson, B., *J. Biol. Chem.*, **234**, 1118 (1959).
113. Hirs, C. H. W., *J. Biol. Chem.*, **235**, 635 (1960).
114. Hirs, C. H. W., Moore, S., and Stein, W. H., *J. Biol. Chem.*, **235**, 633 (1960).
115. Spackman, D. H., Stein, W. H., and Moore, S., *J. Biol. Chem.*, **235**, 648 (1960).
116. Stein, W. H., and Stark, G. R., *Science*, **133**, 1369 (1961).
117. Shapiro, R., and Parker, S., *Biochem. Biophys. Research Communs.*, **3**, 200 (1960).
118. Beers, R. F., *J. Biol. Chem.*, **235**, 2393 (1960).
119. Lane, B. G., and Butler, G. C., *Can. J. Biochem. & Physiol.*, **37**, 1329 (1959).
120. Barker, G. R., and Parsons, M. A., *Chem. and Ind. (London)*, 1009 (1955).
121. Ukita, T., and Irie, M., *Chem. and Pharm. Bull. (Tokyo)*, **6**, 445 (1958).
122. Egami, F., Takagi, M., Hayashi, I., and Takemura, S., *Seikagaku*, **31**, 120 (1959).
123. Michelson, A. M., *Chem. and Ind. (London)*, 1147 (1958).
124. Witzel, H., *Ann.*, **620**, 126 (1959).
125. Witzel, H., *Abstracts 4th Intern. Congr. Biochem. Vienna*, 33 (1958).
126. Michelson, A. M., *Biochim. et Biophys. Acta*, **50**, 605 (1961).
127. Michelson, A. M., *J. Chem. Soc.*, 979 (1962).
128. Mandel, H. G., Markham, R., and Matthews, R. E. F., *Biochim. et Biophys. Acta*, **24**, 205 (1957).
129. Davis, F. F., Carlucci, A. F., and Roubein, I. F., *J. Biol. Chem.*, **234**, 1525 (1959).
130. Ukita, C., and Irie, M., *Chem. Pharm. Bull. (Tokyo)*, **8**, 81 (1960).
131. Griffin, B. E., Todd, A. R., and Rich, A., *Proc. Natl. Acad. Sci. U.S.A.*, **44**, 1123 (1958).
132. Letters, R., and Michelson, A. M., *J. Chem. Soc.*, 71, (1962).
133. Janion, C., and Shugar, D., *Acta Biochim. Polon,.* **7**, 309 (1960).
134. Michelson, A. M., *J. Chem. Soc.*, 3655 (1959).
135. Brown, G. B., and Magrath, D. I., unpublished work.
136. Lipkin, D., unpublished work.
137. Cohn, W. E., *Biochim. et Biophys. Acta*, **32**, 569 (1959).
138. Michelson, A. M., *Acta Biochim. Polon.*, **6**, 335 (1959).
139. Dekker, C. A., *Ann. Rev. Biochem.*, **29**, 454 (1960).
140. Findlay, D., Herries, D. G., Mathias, A. P., Rabin, B. R., and Ross, C. A., *Nature*, **190**, 781 (1961).
141. Kalnitsky, G., Hummel, J. P., and Dierks, C., *J. Biol. Chem.*, **234**, 1512 (1959).
142. Sela, M., Anfinsen, C. B., and Harrington, W. F., *Biochim. et Biophys. Acta*, **26**, 502 (1957).
143. Vandendriessche, L., *Arch. Biochem. Biophys.*, **65**, 347 (1956).
144. Hummel, J. P., Flores, M., and Nelson, G., *J. Biol. Chem.*, **233**, 717 (1958).
145. Hilmoe, R. J., Heppel, L. A., Springhorn, S. S., and Koshland, D. E., *Biochim. et Biophys. Acta*, **53**, 214 (1961).

146. Markham, R., Matthews, R. E. F., and Smith, J. D., *Nature*, **173**, 537 (1954).
147. Singer, M. F., and Cantoni, G. L., *Biochim. et Biophys. Acta*, **39**, 182 (1960).
148. Herbert, E., and Canellakis, E. S., *Biochim. et Biophys. Acta*, **42**, 363 (1960).
149. Zillig, W., Schachtschabel, D., and Krone, W., *Z. physiol. Chem.*, **318**, 100 (1960).
150. Lane, B. G., and Allen, F. W., *Biochim. et Biophys. Acta*, **47**, 36 (1961).
151. Reddi, K. K., and Knight, C. A., *Nature*, **180**, 374 (1957).
152. Matthews, R. E. F., and Smith, J. D., *Nature*, **180**, 375 (1957).
153. Delbecco, R., and Smith, J. D., *Biochem. et Biophys. Acta*, **39**, 358 (1960).
154. Gordon, M. P., Singer, B., and Fraenkel-Conrat, H., *J. Biol. Chem.*, **235**, 1014 (1960).
155. Fraenkel-Conrat, H., and Singer, B., *Vth International Congress of Biochemistry Moscow*, 1961.
156. Sugiyama, T., and Fraenkel-Conrat, H., *Proc. Natl., Acad. Sci. U.S.A.*, **47**, 1393 (1961).
157. Lipkin, D., Dixon, J. S., and Talbert, P. T., *J. Am. Chem. Soc.*, **83**, 4772 (1961).
158. Crestfield, A. M., and Allen, F. W., *Arch. Biochem. Biophys.*, **78**, 334 (1958).
159. Markham, R., and Smith, J. D., *Biochem. J.*, **50**, 38P (1952).
160. Hopkins, J. W., Allfrey, V. G., and Mirsky, A. E., *Biochim. et Biophys. Acta*, **47**, 194 (1961).
161. Davis, F. F., Carlucci, A. F., and Roubein, I. F., *J. Biol. Chem.*, **234**, 1525 (1959).
162. Reddi, K. K., *Biochim. et Biophys. Acta*, **25**, 528 (1947).
163. Rushizky, G. W., and Knight, C. A., *Biochem. Biophys. Research Communs.*, **2**, 66 (1960).
164. Reddi, K. K., *Biochim. et Biophys. Acta*, **32**, 386 (1959).
165. Rushizky, G. W., and Knight, C. A., *Proc. Natl. Acad. Sci. U.S.A.*, **46**, 945 (1960).
166. Sato-Asano, K., and Egami, F., *J. Biochem. (Tokyo)*, **44**, 753 (1959); *Nature*, **185**, 462 (1960).
167. Sato-Asano, K. and Egami, F., *Comp. rend. soc. biol.*, **151**, 1792 (1957).
168. Sato-Asano, K., *J. Biochem. (Tokyo)*, **46**, 31 (1959).
169. Sato-Asano, K., and Egami, F., *Biochim. et Biophys. Acta*, **29**, 655 (1958).
170. Sato-Asano, K., *J. Biochem. (Tokyo)*, **48**, 284 (1960).
171. McCully, K. S., and Cantoni, G. L., *Biochim. et Biophys. Acta*, **51**, 190 (1961).
172. Naoi-Tada, M., Sato-Asano, K., and Egami, F., *J. Biochem. (Tokyo)*, **46**, 757 (1959).
173. Reddi, K. K., *Nature*, **188**, 60 (1960).
174. Miura, K., and Egami, F., *Biochim. et Biophys. Acta*, **44**, 378 (1960).
175. Tanaka, K., *Bull. Chem. Soc. (Tokyo)*, **31**, 393 (1958).
176. Reddi, K. K., *Biochim. et Biophys. Acta*, **42**, 365 (1960).
177. Nishimura, S., *Biochim. et Biophys. Acta*, **45**, 15 (1960).
178. Holden, M. and Pirie, N. W., *Biochem. J.*, **60**, 39 (1955).
179. Markham, R., and Strominger, J. L., *Biochem. J.*, **64**, 46P (1956).
180. Reddi, K. K., *Biochim. et Biophys. Acta*, **28**, 386 (1958); **30**, 638 (1958).
181. Shuster, L., Khorana, H. G., and Heppel, L. A., *Biochim. et Biophys. Acta*, **33**, 452 (1959).
182. Holley, R. W., Apgar, J., and Merrill, S. H., *J. Biol. Chem.*, **236**, PC42 (1961).
183. Commoner, B., Shearer, G. B., and Strode, C., *Proc. Natl. Acad. Sci. U.S.A.*, **44**, 1117 (1958).

184. Volkin, E., and Cohn, W. E., *J. Biol. Chem.*, **205,** 767 (1953).
185. Brown, D. M., Fried, M., and Todd, A. R., *Chem. and Ind. (London)*, 352 (1953).
186. Whitfeld, P. R., and Markham, R., *Nature*, **171,** 1151 (1953).
187. Brown, D. M., Fried, M., and Todd, A. R., *J. Chem. Soc.*, 2206 (1955).
188. Whitfeld, P. R., *Biochem. J.*, **58,** 390 (1954).
189. Yu, C-T., and Zamecnik, P. C., *Biochim. et Biophys. Acta*, **45,** 148 (1960).
190. Khym, J. X., and Cohn, W. E., *J. Biol. Chem.*, **236,** PC9 (1961).
191. Ogur, M., and Small, J. D., *J. Biol. Chem.*, **235,** PC60 (1960).
192. Dlugajczyk, A., and Allen, F. W., *Biochim. et Biophys. Acta*, **51,** 215 (1961).
193. Lane, B. G., and Butler, G. C., *Biochim. et Biophys. Acta*, **33,** 281 (1959).
194. Michelson, A. M., *Acta Biochim. Polon.*, **6,** 335 (1959).
195. Dimroth, K., Witzel, H., Hülsen, W., and Mirbach, H., *Ann.*, **620,** 94 (1959).
196. Miyazaki, M., *Bull. Chem. Soc. (Tokyo)*, **30,** 912 (1957).
197. Dimroth, K., and Witzel, H., *Angew. Chem.*, **68,** 579 (1956); *Ann.*, **620,** 109 (1959).
198. Dimroth, K., and Matthaeus, W., *Angew. Chem.*, **68,** 579 (1956).
199. Finamore, F. J., and Volkin, E., *J. Biol. Chem.*, **236,** 443 (1961).
200. Smith, J. D., and Dunn, D. B., *Biochim. et Biophys. Acta*, **31,** 573 (1959).
201. Biswas, B. B., and Myers, J., *Nature*, **186,** 238 (1960).
202. Egami, F., Ishihara, H., and Shimomura, M., *Z. physiol. Chem.*, **295,** 349 (1953).
203. Lipkin, D., and Talbert, P. T., *Chem. and Ind. (London)*, 143 (1955).
204. Markham, R., and Smith, J. D., *Biochem. J.*, **52,** 552 (1952).
205. Tanaka, K., *J. Biochem. (Tokyo)*, **47,** 398 (1960).
206. Vischer, E., and Chargaff, E., *J. Biol. Chem.*, **176,** 715 (1948).
207. Hayes, D. H., *J. Chem. Soc.*, 1184 (1960).
208. Merrifield, R. B., and Woolley, D. W., *J. Biol. Chem.*, **197,** 521 (1952).
209. Cohn, W. E., and Markham, R., *Biochem. J.*, **62,** 17P (1956).
210. Witzel, H., *Ann.*, **620,** 126 (1959).
211. Takemura, S., *J. Biochem. (Tokyo)*, **44,** 321 (1957).
212. Takemura, S., and Miyazaki, M., *Bull. Chem. Soc. (Tokyo)*, **32,** 926 (1959).
213. Takemura, S., Takagi, M., Miyazaki, M., and Egami, F., *J. Biochem. (Tokyo)*, **46,** 1149 (1959).
214. Fletcher, W. E., Gulland, J. M., Jordan, D. O., and Dibben, H. E., *J. Chem. Soc.*, 30 (1944).
215. Gierer, A., and Mundry, K.-W., *Nature*, **182,** 1457 (1958).
216. Schuster, H., and Schramm, G., *Z. Naturforsch.*, **13b,** 697 (1958).
217. Fraenkel-Conrat, H., *Biochim. et Biophys. Acta*, **15,** 307 (1954).
218. Staehelin, M., *Biochim. et Biophys. Acta*, **29,** 410 (1958).
219. Schuster, H., *J. Mol. Biol.*, **3,** 447 (1961).
220. Zillig, W., Verwoerd, D. W., and Kohlhage, H., Strasbourg meeting on RNA and Polyphosphates, July, 1961.
221. Verwoerd, D. W., Kohlhage, H., and Zillig, W., *Nature*, **192,** 1038 (1961).
222. Magasanik, B., Vischer, E., Doniger, R., Elson, D., and Chargaff, E., *J. Biol. Chem.*, **186,** 37 (1950).
223. Davidson, J. N., and Smellie, R. M. S., *Biochem. J.*, **52,** 594 (1952).
224. Elson, D., and Chargaff, E., *Nature*, **173,** 1037 (1954); *Biochim. et Biophys. Acta*, **17,** 367 (1955).

225. Belozersky, A. N., "Nukleoproteidy i Nukleinovye Kisloty Rasteny i ikh Biologicheskie Znachenie," Izdatel. Akad. Nauk S.S.S.R., Moscow (1959).
226. Spirin, A. S., Belozersky, A. N., Shugaeva, N. V., and Vanyushin, B. F., Biokhimiya, 22, 744 (1957).
227. Belozersky, A. N., and Spirin, A. S., Nature, 182, 111 (1958).
228. Yčas, M., and Vincent, W. S., Proc. Natl. Acad. Sci. U.S.A., 46, 804 (1960).
229. Santer, M., Teller, D. C., and Andrews, W., J. Mol. Biol., 2, 273 (1960).
230. Santer, M., Teller, D. C., and Skilna, L., Proc. Natl. Acad. Sci. U.S.A., 47, 1384 (1961).
231. Crosbie, G. W., Smellie, R. M. S., and Davidson, J. N., Biochem. J., 54, 287 (1953).
232. Chargaff, E., Magasanik, B., Vischer, E., Green, C., Doniger, R., and Elson, D., J. Biol. Chem., 186, 51 (1950).
233. Deluca, H. A., Rossiter, R. J., and Strickland, K. B., Biochem. J., 55, 193 (1953).
234. Elson, D., Gustafson, T., and Chargaff, E., J. Biol. Chem., 209, 285 (1954).
235. Vincent, W. S., Proc. Natl. Acad. Sci. U.S.A., 38, 139 (1952).
236. Elson, D., and Chargaff, E., Phosphorus Metabolism 2, 329 (1952), ed. by McElroy, W. E., and Glass, B., The Johns Hopkins Press.
237. Khouvine, Y., and Robichon-Szulmajster, H., Bull. soc. chim. biol., 34, 1056 (1952).
238. Loring, H. S., Fairley, J. L., and Seagran, H. L., J. Biol. Chem., 197, 823 (1952).
239. Knight, C. A., J. Biol. Chem., 197, 241 (1952).
240. Yamazaki, H., and Kaesberg, P., Nature, 191, 96 (1961).
241. Markham, R., and Smith, J. D., Biochem. J., 49, 401 (1951).
242. Schaffer, F. L., Moore, H. F., and Schwerdt, C. E., Virology, 10, 530 (1960).
243. Faulkner, P., Martin, E. M., Sved, S., Valentine, R. C., and Work, T. S., Biochem. J., 80, 597 (1961).
244. Uryson, S. O., and Belozersky, A. N., Doklady Akad. Nauk S.S.S.R., 132, 708 (1960).
245. Uryson, S. O., and Belozersky, A. N., Doklady Akad. Nauk. S.S.S.R., 125, 1144 (1959).
246. Vanyushin, B. F., and Belozersky, A. N., Doklady Akad. Nauk. S.S.S.R., 127, 455 (1959).
247. Littlefield, J. W., and Dunn, D. B., Nature, 181, 254 (1958); Biochem. J., 70, 642 (1958).
248. Smith, J. D., and Dunn, D. B., Biochem. J., 72, 294 (1959).
249. Amos, H., and Korn, M., Biochim. et Biophys. Acta, 29, 444 (1958).
250. Kemp, J. W., and Allen, F. W., Biochim. et Biophys. Acta, 28, 51 (1958).
251. Davis, F. F., Carlucci, A. F., and Roubein, I. F., J. Biol. Chem., 234, 1525 (1959).
252. Adler, M., Weissmann, B., and Gutman, A. B., J. Biol. Chem., 230, 717 (1958).
253. Dunn, D. B., Smith, J. D., and Spahr, P. F., J. Mol. Biol., 2, 113 (1960).
254. Brookes, P., and Lawley, P. D., J. Chem. Soc., 539, (1960).
255. Dunn, D. B., Biochim. et Biophys. Acta, 46, 198 (1961).
256. Brown, D. J., Nature, 189, 828 (1961).
257. Taylor, E. C., Jefford, C. W., and Cheng, C. C., J. Am. Chem. Soc., 83, 1261 (1961).
258. Dunn, D. B., Biochim. et Biophys. Acta, 38, 176 (1960).

259. Dunn, D. B., and Smith, J. D., *Proc. IVth Internat. Congr. Biochem.*, *Vienna.* (1958) Symposium VII.
260. Cohn, W. E., *Biochim. et Biophys. Acta*, **32,** 569 (1959).
261. Davis, F. F., and Allen, F. W., *J. Biol. Chem.*, **227,** 907 (1957).
262. Yu, C. T., and Allen, F. W., *Biochim. et Biophys. Acta*, **32,** 393 (1959).
263. Scannell, J. P., Crestfield, A. M., and Allen, F. W., *Biochim. et Biophys. Acta*, **32,** 406 (1959).
264. Osawa, S., and Otaka, E., *Biochim. et Biophys. Acta*, **36,** 549 (1959).
265. Otaka, E., and Osawa, S., *Nature*, **185,** 921 (1960).
266. Otaka, E., Hotta, Y., and Osawa, S., *Biochim. et Biophys. Acta*, **35,** 266 (1959).
267. Osawa, S., *Biochim. et Biophys. Acta*, **42,** 244 (1960); **43,** 110 (1960).
268. Dunn, D. B., *Biochim. et Biophys. Acta*, **34,** 286 (1959).
269. Bergquist, P. L., and Matthews, R. E. F., *Biochim. et Biophys. Acta*, **34,** 567 (1959).
270. Herbert, E., and Canellakis, E. S., *Biochim. et Biophys. Acta*, **42,** 363 (1960).
271. Steudel, H., and Peiser, E., *Z. physiol. Chem.*, **122,** 298 (1922).
272. Michelson, A. M., *J. Chem. Soc.*, 1371 (1959).
273. Burger, W. C., and Stahmann, M. A., *J. Biol. Chem.*, **193,** 13 (1951).
274. Razin, S., and Rozansky, R., *Arch. Biochem. Biophys.*, **81,** 36 (1959).
275. Keister, D. L., *Federation Proc.*, **17,** 84 (1958).
276. Herbst, E. J., and Doctor, B. P., *J. Biol. Chem.*, **234,** 1497 (1959).
277. Chayen, R., Chayen, S., and Roberts, E. R., *Biochim. et Biophys. Acta*, **16,** 117 (1955).
278. Belozersky, A. N., and Kulaev, I. S., *Biokhimiya*, **22,** 79 (1957); Kulaev, I. S., and Belozersky, A. N., *Biokhimiya*, **22,** 587 (1957).
279. Kulaev, I. S., and Belozersky, A. N., *Doklady Akad. Nauk. S.S.S.R.*, **120,** 1080 (1958).
280. Franklin, R. E., Klug, A., Finch, J. T., and Holmes, K. C., *Discussions Faraday Soc.*, No. 25, 197 (1958).
281. Chao, F.-C., *Arch. Biochem. Biophys.*, **70,** 426 (1957).
282. Elson, D., *Biochim. et Biophys. Acta*, **27,** 207 (1958).
283. Tissières, A., Watson, J. D., Schlessinger, D., and Hollingworth, B. R., *J. Mol. Biol.*, **1,** 221 (1959).
284. Hall, C. E., and Slayter, H. S., *J. Mol. Biol.*, **1,** 329 (1959).
285. Cheng, P.-Y., *Biochim. et Biophys. Acta*, **37,** 238 (1960).
286. Takanami, M., *Biochim. et Biophys. Acta*, **39,** 152 (1960).
287. Markham, R., and Smith, K. M., *Parasitology*, **39,** 330 (1949).
288. Shigeura, H. T., and Chargaff, E., *Biochim. et Biophys. Acta*, **37,** 347 (1960).
289. Bawden, F. C., and Kleczkowski, A., *Nature*, **183,** 503 (1959).
290. Szafarz, D., *Biochim. et Biophys. Acta*, **6,** 562 (1951).
291. Feldman, I., Havill, J. R., and Neuman, W. F., *Arch. Biochem. Biophys.*, **46,** 443 (1953).
292. Wiberg, J. S., and Neuman, W. F., *Arch. Biochem. Biophys.*, **72,** 66 (1957).
293. Frieden, E., and Alles, J., *J. Biol. Chem.*, **230,** 797 (1958).
294. Cheo, P. C., Friesen, B. S., and Sinsheimer, R. L., *Proc. Natl. Acad. Sci. U.S.A.*, **45,** 305 (1959).
295. Wacker, W. E. C., and Vallee, B. L., *Nature*, **184,** 1399 (1959).
296. Wacker, W. E. C., and Vallee, B. L., *J. Biol. Chem.*, **234,** 3257 (1959).
297. Furva, K., Wacker, W. E. C., Druyan, R., Bartholomay, A. F., and Vallee, B. L., *Proc. Natl. Acad. Sci. U.S.A.*, **46,** 1298 (1960).

298. Brown, R. A., *Proc. Natl. Acad. Sci. U.S.A.*, **47**, 465 (1961).
299. Taussig, A., and Creaser, E. H., *Arch. Biochem. Biophys.*, **83**, 436 (1959).
300. Chao, F.-C., *Arch. Biochem. Biophys.*, **70**, 426 (1957).
301. Ts'O, P. O. P., Bonner, J., and Vinograd, J., *Biochim. et Biophys. Acta*, **30**, 570 (1958).
302. Edelman, I. S., Ts'O, P. O. P., and Vinograd, J., *Biochim. et Biophys. Acta*, **43**, 393 (1960).
303. Petermann, M. L., *J. Biol. Chem.*, **235**, 1998 (1960).
304. Lewis, U. J., Rickes, E. L., McClelland, L., and Brink, N. G., *J. Am. Chem. Soc.*, **81**, 4115 (1959).
305. Cohen, S. S., and Lichtenstein, J., *J. Biol. Chem.*, **235**, 2112 (1960).
306. Zillig, W., Krone, W., and Albers, M., *Z. physiol. Chem.*, **317**, 131 (1959).
307. Mirsky, A. E., and Pollister, A. W., *J. Gen. Physiol.*, **30**, 117 (1946).
308. Schwander, H., and Signer, R., *Helv. Chim. Acta*, **33**, 1521 (1950).
309. Hammarsten, E., *Biochem. Z.*, **144**, 383 (1924).
310. Gulland, J. M., Jordan, D. O., and Threlfall, C. J., *J. Chem. Soc.*, 1129 (1947).
311. Crampton, C. F., Lipshitz, R., and Chargaff, E., *J. Biol. Chem.*, **206**, 499 (1954).
312. Butler, J. A. V., Davison, P. F., James, D. W. F., and Shooter, K. V., *Biochim. et Biophys. Acta*, **13**, 224 (1954).
313. Bang, I., *Beitr. chem. Physiol. u. Path.*, **4**, 331 (1904); **5**, 317 (1904).
314. Hammarsten, E., *Biochem. Z.*, **144**, 383 (1924).
315. Hurst, R. O., *Can. J. Biochem. and Physiol.*, **36**, 1115 (1958).
316. Cohen, S. S., *J. Biol. Chem.*, **158**, 255 (1945).
317. Bawden, F. C., and Pirie, N. W., *Biochem. J.*, **34**, 1278 (1940).
318. Marko, A. M., and Butler, G. C., *J. Biol. Chem.*, **190**, 165 (1951).
319. Kirby, K. S., *Biochem. J.*, **66**, 495 (1957); **70**, 260 (1958).
320. Kirby, K. S., *Biochim. et Biophys. Acta*, **36**, 117 (1959).
321. Kirby, K. S., *Biochim. et Biophys. Acta*, **47**, 18 (1961).
322. Colter, J. S., Brown, R. A., and Ellem, K. A. O., *Biochim. et Biophys. Acta*, **55**, 31 (1962).
323. Vendrely, R., Palmade, C., Vendrely, C., *Nature*, **178**, 1044 (1956).
324. Marmur, J., *J. Mol. Biol.*, **3**, 208 (1961).
325. Zamenhof, S., Shettles, L. B., and Chargaff, E., *Nature*, **165**, 756 (1950).
326. Borenfreund, E., Fitt, E., and Bendich, A., *Nature*, **191**, 1375 (1961). See also reference 565.
327. Chargaff, E., Crampton, C. F., and Lipshitz, R., *Nature*, **172**, 289 (1953).
328. Crampton, C. F., Lipshitz, R., and Chargaff, E., *J. Biol. Chem.*, **211**, 125 (1954).
329. Lipshitz, R., and Chargaff, E., *Biochim. et Biophys. Acta*, **19**, 256 (1956).
330. Lucy, J. A., and Butler, J. A. V., *Nature*, **174**, 32 (1954).
331. Lerman, L. S., *Biochim. et Biophys. Acta*, **18**, 132 (1955).
332. Brown, G. L., and Watson, M., *Nature*, **172**, 339 (1953).
333. Brown, G. L., and Martin, A. V., *Nature*, **176**, 971 (1955).
334. Main, R. K., and Cole, L. J., *Arch. Biochem. Biophys.*, **68**, 186 (1957).
335. Bernardi, G., *Biochem. Biophys. Research Communs.*, **6**, 54 (1961).
336. Bendich, A., Fresco, J. R., Rosenkranz, H. S., and Beiser, S. M., *J. Am. Chem. Soc.*, **77**, 3671 (1955).
337. Bendich, A., Pahl, H. B., Korngold, G. C., Rosenkranz, H. S. and Fresco, J. R., *J. Am. Chem. Soc.*, **80**, 3949 (1958).
338. Rosoff, M., Di Mayorca, G., and Bendich, A., *Nature*, **180**, 1355 (1957).

339. Kondo, N., and Osawa, S, S., *Nature*, **183**, 1602 (1959).
340. Bendich, A., Pahl, H. B., and Beiser, S. M., *Cold Spring Harb. Symp. Quant. Biol.*, **21**, 31 (1956).
341. Bendich, A., Pahl, H. B., Rosenkranz, H. S., and Rosoff, M., *Symp. Soc. Exp. Biol.*, **12**, 31 (1958).
342. Levene, P. A., and London, E. S., *J. Biol. Chem.*, **81**, 711 (1929); **83**, 793 (1929).
343. Klein, W., and Thannhauser, S. J., *Z. physiol. Chem.*, **218**, 173 (1933); **224**, 252 (1934); **231**, 96 (1935).
344. Levene, P. A., *J. Biol. Chem.*, **48**, 119 (1921); **126**, 63 (1938).
345. Bredereck, H., Berger, E., and Richter, F., *Chem. Ber.*, **74**, 338 (1941).
346. Levene, P. A., and Tipson, R. S., *Science*, **81**, 98 (1935).
347. Levene, P. A., and Tipson, R. S., *J. Biol. Chem.*, **109**, 623 (1935).
348. Carter, C. E., *J. Am. Chem. Soc.*, **73**, 1537 (1951).
349. Michelson, A. M., and Todd, A. R., *J. Chem. Soc.*, 2632 (1955).
350. Kunitz, M., *J. Gen. Physiol.*, **33**, 349 (1950).
351. Gehrmann, G., and Okada, S., *Biochim. et Biophys. Acta*, **23**, 621 (1957).
352. Markham, R., and Smith, J. D., *Biochim. et Biophys. Acta*, **8**, 350 (1952).
353. Sinsheimer, R. L., *J. Biol. Chem.*, **208**, 445 (1954); **215**, 579 (1955).
354. de Garilhe, M. P., Cunningham, L., Laurila, U., and Laskowski, M., *J. Biol. Chem.*, **224**, 751 (1957).
355. Potter, J. L., Laurila, U., and Laskowski, M., *J. Biol. Chem.*, **233**, 915 (1958).
356. Ralph, R. K., Smith, R. A., and Khorana, H. G., *Federation Proc.*, **20**, 351 (1961).
357. Potter, J. L., and Laskowski, M., *J. Biol. Chem.*, **234**, 1263 (1959).
358. Schumaker, V, N., Richards, E. G., and Schachman, H. K., *J. Am. Chem. Soc.*, **78**, 4230 (1956).
359. Davis, R. L., MacIntyre, S. B., and Lawton, A. H., *Abstracts 138th Am. Chem. Soc. Meeting*, 54C (1960).
360. Koerner, J. F., and Sinsheimer, R. L., *J. Biol. Chem.*, **228**, 1039 (1957).
361. Koszalka, T. R., Falkenheim, R., and Altman, K. I., *Biochim. et Biophys. Acta*, **23**, 647 (1957).
362. Shimomura, M., and Laskowski, M., *Biochim. et Biophys. Acta*, **26**, 198 (1957).
363. Fredericq, E., and Oth, A., *Biochim. et Biophys. Acta*, **29**, 281 (1958).
364. Cunningham, L., Catlin, B. W., and de Garilhe, M. P., *J. Am. Chem. Soc.*, **78**, 4642 (1956).
365. Laurila, U., and Laskowski, M., *J. Biol. Chem.*, **228**, 49 (1957).
366. Doskočil, J., and Šorm, F., *Biochim. et Biophys. Acta*, **48**, 211 (1961).
367. Koerner, J. F., and Sinsheimer, R. L., *J. Biol. Chem.*, **228**, 1049 (1957).
368. Cunningham, L., *J. Am. Chem. Soc.*, **80**, 2546 (1958).
369. de Garilhe, M. P., Cunningham, L., Laurila, U., and Laskowski, M., *J. Biol. Chem.*, **224**, 751 (1957).
370. Pochon, F., and de Garilhe, M. P., *Bull. soc. chim. biol.*, **42**, 795 (1960).
371. Martin, A., Heppel, L. A., and Hurwitz, J., *J. Biol. Chem.*, **236**, 3014 (1961).
372. Dekker, C. A., *Ann. Rev. Biochem.*, **29**, 458 (1960).
373. Reddi, K. K., *Biochim. et Biophys. Acta*, **47**, 47 (1961).
374. Lehman, I. R., *J. Biol. Chem.*, **235**, 1479 (1960).
375. Sinsheimer, R. L., and Koerner, J. F., *J. Am. Chem. Soc.*, **74**, 283 (1952).
376. Koerner, J. F., and Sinsheimer, R. L., *J. Biol. Chem.*, **228**, 1049 (1957).

377. Heppel, L. A., and Hilmoe, R. J., in *Methods in Enzymology*, II, 565 (Academic Press, Inc., New York, 1955).
378. Hilmoe, R. J., *J. Biol. Chem.*, **235**, 2117 (1960).
379. Heppel, L. A., and Rabinowitz, J. C., *Ann. Rev. Biochem.*, **27**, 621 (1958).
380. Razzell, W. E., and Khorana, H. G., *J. Am. Chem. Soc.*, **80**, 1770 (1958); *J. Biol. Chem.*, **236**, 1144 (1961).
381. Razzell, W. E., and Khorana, H. G., *J. Biol. Chem.*, **234**, 2114 (1959).
382. Felix, F., Potter, J. L., and Laskowski, M., *J. Biol. Chem.*, **235**, 1150 (1960).
383. Adler, J., Lehman, I. R., Bessman, M. J., Simms, E. S., and Kornberg, A., *Proc. Natl. Acad. Sci. U.S.A.*, **44**, 641 (1958).
384. Smellie, R. M. S., Gray, E. D., Keir, H. M., Richards, J., Bell, D., Davidson, J. N., *Biochim. et Biophys. Acta*, **37**, 243 (1960).
385. Khorana, H. G., *J. Am. Chem. Soc.*, **81**, 4657 (1959).
386. Zamenhof, S., and Chargaff, E., *J. Biol. Chem.*, **178**, 531 (1949); **187**, 1 (1950).
387. Brawerman, G., and Chargaff, E., *J. Am. Chem. Soc.*, **73**, 4052 (1951).
388. Astrachan, L., and Volkin, E., *J. Am. Chem. Soc.*, **79**, 130 (1957).
389. Greer, S., and Zamenhof, S., *Federation Proc.*, **18**, 238 (1959).
390. Kossel, A., and Neumann, A., *Chem. Ber.*, **26**, 2753 (1893).
391. Steudel, H., and Brigl, P., *Z. physiol. Chem.*, **70**, 398 (1910–11).
392. Tamm, C., Hodes, M. E., and Chargaff, E., *J. Biol. Chem.*, **195**, 49 (1952).
393. Laland, S. G., *Acta Chem. Scand.*, **8**, 449 (1954).
394. Hurlen, E., Laland, S. G., Cox, R. A., and Peacocke, A. R., *Acta Chem. Scand.*, **10**, 793 (1956).
395. Tamm, C., and Chargaff, E., *J. Biol. Chem.*, **203**, 689 (1953).
396. Lucy, J. A., and Kent, P. W., *Research.* **6**, 49s (1953).
397. Levene, P. A., and Jacobs, W. A., *J. Biol. Chem.*, **12**, 411 (1912).
398. Thannhauser, S. J., and Offenstein, B., *Z. physiol. Chem.*, **114**, 39 (1921).
399. Thannhauser, S. J., and Blanco, G. G., *Z. physiol. Chem.*, **161**, 116 (1926).
400. Levene, P. A., *J. Biol. Chem.*, **126**, 63 (1938).
401. Levene, P. A., and London, E. S., *J. Biol. Chem.*, **83**, 793 (1929).
402. Bredereck, H., and Caro, G., *Z. physiol. Chem.*, **253**, 170 (1938).
403. Dekker, C. A., Michelson, A. M., and Todd, A. R., *J. Chem. Soc.*, 947 (1953).
404. Meyerhof, O., and Lohmann, K., *Biochem. Z.*, **271**, 98 (1934).
405. Foster, A. B., Overend, W. G., and Stacey, M., *J. Chem. Soc.*, **980**, 987 (1951).
406. Brown, D. M., and Todd, A. R., in *The Nucleic Acids*, ed. Chargaff, E., and Davidson, J. N., **1**, 409 (Academic Press, New York, 1955).
407. Deriaz, R. E., Stacey, M., Teece, E. G., and Wiggins, L. F., *J. Chem. Soc.*, 1222 (1949).
408. Fleury, P., Courtois, J., and Desjobert, A., *Bull. Soc. Chim. (France)*, 694 (1948).
409. Shapiro, H. S., Chargaff, E., *Biochim. et Biophys. Acta*, **26**, 596 (1957).
410. Cohn, W. E., and Volkin, E., *Biochim. et Biophys. Acta*, **24**, 359 (1957).
411. Shapiro, H. S., and Chargaff, E., *Biochim. et Biophys. Acta*, **26**, 608 (1957).
412. Shapiro, H. S., and Chargaff, E., *Biochim. et Biophys. Acta*, **39**, 68 (1960).
413. Shapiro, H. S., and Chargaff, E., *Biochim. et Biophys. Acta*, **39**, 62 (1960).
414. Burton, K., and Petersen, G. B., *Biochim. et Biophys. Acta*, **26**, 667 (1957).
415. Burton, K., and Petersen, G. B., *Biochem. J.*, **75**, 17 (1960).
416. Burton, K., *Biochem. J.*, **74**, 35P (1960).
417. Burton, K., *Biochem. J.*, **77**, 547 (1960).
418. Kent, P. W., Lucy, J. A., and Ward, P. F. V., *Biochem. J.* **61**, 529 (1955).
419. Jones, A. S., and Letham, D. S., *J. Chem. Soc.*, 2573 (1956).

420. Jones, A. S., Letham, D. S., and Stacey, M., *J. Chem. Soc.*, 2579, 2584 (1956).
421. Jones, A. S., Stacey, M., and Watson, B. E., *J. Chem. Soc.*, 2454 (1957).
422. Tamm, C., Shapiro, H. S., Lipshitz, R., and Chargaff, E., *J. Biol. Chem.*, 203, 673 (1953).
423. Hodes, M. E., and Chargaff, E., *Biochim. et Biophys. Acta*, 22, 348 (1956).
424. Bayley, C. R., and Jones, A. S., *Trans. Farad. Soc.*, 55, 492 (1959).
425. Bayley, C. R., Brammer, K. W., and Jones, A. S., *J. Chem. Soc.*, 1903 (1961).
426. Ademiec, A., and Shugar, D., *Naturwissenschaften*, 46, 356 (1959).
427. Caputto, R., Leloir, L. F., Cardini, C. E., and Paladini, A. C., *J. Biol. Chem.*, 184, 333 (1950).
428. Takemura, S., *Biochim. et Biophys. Acta*, 29, 447 (1958); *Bull. Chem. Soc. (Tokyo)*, 32, 920 (1959).
429. Freese, E., Bautz, E. K. F., and Freese, E. B., *Proc. Natl. Acad. Sci. U.S.A.*, 47, 845 (1961).
430. Brown, D. M., and Schell, P., *J. Mol. Biol.*, 3, 709 (1961).
431. Sarkar, N. K., and Dounce, A. L., *Biochim. et Biophys. Acta*, 49, 160 (1961).
432. Bredereck, H., Muller, G., and Berger, E., *Chem. Ber.*, 73, 1058 (1940).
433. Reiner, B., and Zamenhof, S., *J. Biol. Chem.*, 228, 475 (1957).
434. Zachau, H., Acs, G., and Lipmann, F., *Proc. Natl. Acad. Sci. U.S.A.*, 44, 885 (1958).
435. Tabor, H., *Biochemistry*, 1, 496 (1962).
436. Lawley, P. D., *Biochim. et Biophys. Acta*, 26, 450 (1957).
437. Lawley, P. D., and Wallick, C. A., *Chem. and Ind. (London)*, 633 (1957).
438. Brookes, P., and Lawley, P. D., *J. Chem. Soc.*, 539 (1960).
439. Butler, J. A. V., Gilbert, L., James, D. W. F., and Ross, W. C. J., *Nature*, 168, 985 (1951).
440. Brookes, P., and Lawley, P. D., *Biochem. J.*, 80, 496 (1961).
441. Alexander, P., *Scientific American*, 202, 99 (1960).
442. Cohn, W. E., *Biochem. J.*, 64, 28P (1956).
443. Suzuki, T., and Ito, E., *J. Biochem. (Tokyo)*, 45, 403 (1958).
444. Ishihara, H., and Suzuki, N., *Nature*, 182, 1302 (1958).
445. Jones, A. S., and Woodhouse, D. L., *Nature*, 183, 1603 (1959).
446. Bredereck, H., and Jochmann, I., *Chem. Ber.*, 75, 395 (1942).
447. Bredereck, H., and Hoepfner, E., *Chem. Ber.*, 75, 1086 (1942).
448. Fischer, F. G., *Naturwissenschaften*, 30, 377 (1942).
449. Hurst, R. O., *Can. J. Biochem. and Physiol.*, 34, 265 (1956).
450. Hurst, R. O., and Kukis, A., *Can. J. Biochem. and Physiol.*, 36, 919 (1958).
451. Vischer, E., and Chargaff, E., *J. Biol. Chem.*, 176, 715 (1948).
452. Daly, M. M., Allfrey, V. G., and Mirsky, A. E., *J. Gen. Physiol.*, 33, 497 (1950).
453. Marshak, A., and Vogel, H. J., *J. Biol. Chem.*, 189, 597 (1951).
454. Wyatt, G. R., and Cohen, S. S., *Biochem. J.*, 55, 774 (1953).
455. Chargaff, E., and Lipshitz, R., *J. Am. Chem. Soc.*, 75, 3658 (1953).
456. Wyatt, G. R., *Nature*, 166, 237 (1950); *Biochem. J.*, 48, 581, 584 (1951).
457. Brawerman, G., and Chargaff, E., *J. Am. Chem. Soc.*, 73, 4052 (1951).
458. Dekker, C. A., and Elmore, D. T., *J. Chem. Soc.*, 2864 (1951).
459. Cohn, W. E., *J. Am. Chem. Soc.*, 72, 2811 (1950); 73, 1539 (1951).
460. Dunn, D. B., and Smith, J. D., *Biochem. J.*, 68, 627 (1958).
461. Chargaff, E., *Federation Proc.*, 10, 654 (1951).

462. Wyatt, G. R., and Cohen, S. S., *Nature*, **170**, 1072 (1952); *Biochem. J.*, **55**, 774 (1953).
463. Volkin, E., *J. Am. Chem. Soc.*, **76**, 5892 (1954).
464. Sinsheimer, R., *Science*, **120**, 551 (1954).
465. Loeb, M. R., and Cohen, S. S., *J. Biol. Chem.*, **234**, 364 (1959).
466. Lichtenstein, J., and Cohen, S. S., *J. Biol. Chem.*, **235**, 1134 (1960).
467. Koerner, J. F., and Varadarajan, S., *J. Biol. Chem.*, **235**, 2688 (1960).
468. Jesaitis, M. A., *Nature*, **178**, 637 (1956); *J. Exptl. Med.*, **106**, 233 (1957).
469. Weed, L. L., and Courtenay, T. A., *J. Biol. Chem.*, **206**, 735 (1954).
470. Sinsheimer, R. L., *Science*, **125**, 1123 (1957).
471. Sinsheimer, R. L., *Proc. Natl. Acad. Sci. U.S.A.*, **42**, 502 (1956).
472. Lehman, I. R., and Pratt, E. A., *J. Biol. Chem.*, **235**, 3254 (1960).
473. Chargaff, E., and Lipshitz, R., *J. Am. Chem. Soc.*, **75**, 3658 (1953).
474. Uzman, L. L., Desoer, C., *Arch. Biochem. Biophys.*, **48**, 63 (1954).
475. Hurst, R. O., Marko, A. M., and Butler, G. C., *J. Biol. Chem.*, **204**, 847 (1953).
476. Chargaff, E., Lipshitz, R., Green, C., and Hodes, M. E., *J. Biol. Chem.*, **192**, 223 (1951).
477. Uryson, S. O., and Belozersky, A. N., *Doklady Akad. Nauk. S.S.S.R.*, **125**, 1144 (1959).
478. Zamenhof, S., Brawerman, G., and Chargaff, E., *Biochim. et Biophys. Acta*, **9**, 402, (1952).
479. Wyatt, G. R., and Cohen, S. S., *Biochem. J.*, **55**, 774 (1953).
480. Chargaff, E., *Experientia*, **6**, 201 (1950).
481. Watson, J. D., and Crick, F. H. C., *Nature*, **171**, 737, 964 (1953).
482. Sinsheimer, R. L., *J. Mol. Biol.*, **1**, 43 (1959).
483. Chargaff, E., Zamenhof, S., and Green, C., *Nature*, **165**, 756 (1950).
484. Wyatt, G. R., *Biochem. J.*, **48**, 584 (1951).
485. Mead, C. G., and Fox, A. S., *Federation Proc.*, **20**, 353 (1961).
486. Zamenhof, S., and Chargaff, E., *J. Biol. Chem.*, **187**, 1 (1950).
487. Belozersky, A. N., *Nukleoproteidy i Nucleinovye Kisloty Rasteny i ikh Biologicheskie Znachenie* p. 28 (*Moscow, Izdatel, Akad. Nauk S.S.S.R.* (1959).
488. Uryson, S. O., and Belozersky, A. N., *Doklady Akad. Nauk S.S.S.R.*, **132**, 708 (1960).
489. Lunan, K. D., and Sinsheimer, R. L., *Virology*, **2**, 455 (1956).
490. Sinsheimer, R. L., *J. Mol. Biol.* **1**, 43 (1959).
491. Chargaff, E., Zamenhof, S., Brawerman, G., and Kerin, L., *J. Am. Chem. Soc.*, **72**, 3825 (1950).
492. Smith, J. D., and Wyatt, G. R., *Biochem. J.*, **49**, 144 (1951).
493. Gandelman, B., Zamenhof, S., and Chargaff, E., *Biochim. et Biophys. Acta*, **9**, 399 (1952).
494. Spirin, A. S., Belozersky, A. N., Kudlay, D. B., Shavronskaya, A. G., and Mitereva, V. G., *Biokhimiya*, **23**, 154 (1958).
495. Lee, K. Y., Wahl, R., and Barbu, E., *Ann. Inst. Pasteur*, **91**, 212 (1956).
496. Belozersky, A. N., and Spirin, A. S., *Izvestia Akademia Nauk* (*Biological Series*), **25**, 64 (1960).
497. Rolfe, R., and Meselson, M., *Proc. Natl. Acad. Sci. U.S.A.*, **45**, 1039 (1959).
498. Sueoka, N., Marmur, J., and Doty, P., *Nature*, **183**, 1429 (1959).
499. Miescher, F., *Hoppe-Seylers Med.-chem. Untersuchungen*, **4**, 441 (1871).
500. Kossel, A., *Z. physiol. Chem.*, **8**, 511 (1884).
501. Lilienfeld, L., *Z. physiol. Chem.*, **18**, 473 (1894).

502. Vendrely, R., Knobloch, Q., and Matsudaira, H., *Nature*, **181**, 343 (1958).
503. Chargaff, E., and Saidel, H. F., *J. Biol. Chem.*, **177**, 417 (1949).
504. Davison, P. F., and Butler, J. A. V., *Biochim. et Biophys. Acta*, **21**, 568 (1956).
505. Crampton, C. F., and Chargaff, E., *J. Biol. Chem.*, **226**, 157 (1957).
506. Crampton, C. F., and Scheer, J. F., *J. Biol. Chem.*, **227**, 495 (1957).
507. Zubay, G., and Doty, P., *J. Mol. Biol.*, **1**, 1 (1959).
508. Emery, A. J., and Lesko, S. A., *Federation Proc.*, **19**, 305 (1960).
509. Sakar, N. K., and Dounce, A. L., *Arch. Biochem. Biophys.*, **92**, 321 (1961).
510. Nemchinskaya, V. L., *Biokhimiya*, **15**, 478 (1950).
511. Klamerth, O., *Biochem. Z.*, **328**, 443 (1957).
512. Klamerth, O., *Z. Naturforsch.*, **12b**, 186 (1957).
513. Emmerson, P., Scholes, G., Thomson, D. H., Ward, J. F., and Weiss, J., *Nature*, **187**, 319 (1960).
514. Peacocke, A. R., and Preston, B. N., *Nature*, **192**, 228 (1961).
515. Alexander, P., *Nature*, **169**, 226 (1952); *Biochim. et Biophys. Acta*, **10**, 595 (1953).
516. Hammarsten, E., *Biochem. Z.*, **144**, 383 (1924).
517. Spitnik, P., Lipshitz, R., and Chargaff, E., *J. Biol. Chem.*, **215**, 765 (1955).
518. Belozersky, A. N., and Bazhilina, G. D., *Biokhimiya*, **9**, 134 (1944).
519. Ohlmeyer, P., *Biochim. et Biophys. Acta*, **4**, 229 (1950).
520. Greenstein, J. P., and Hoyer, M. L., *J. Biol. Chem.*, **182**, 457 (1950).
521. Zubay, G., and Doty, P., *Biochim. et Biophys. Atca*, **23**, 213 (1957).
522. Diskina, B. S., and Spitkovsky, D. M., *Biofizika*, **3**, 633 (1958).
523. Oparin, A. I., Deborin, G. A., and Baranova, V. Z., *Doklady Akad. Nauk. S.S.S.R.*, **116**, 270 (1957).
524. Hofstee, B. H. J., *Biochim. et Biophys. Acta*, **44**, 194 (1960).
525. Monty, K. J., and Dounce, A. L., *J. Gen. Physiol.*, **41**, 595 (1958).
526. Ames, B. N., Dubin, D. T., and Rosenthal, S. M., *Science*, **127**, 814 (1958).
527. Kay, D., *Biochem. J.*, **73**, 149 (1959).
528. Ames, B. N., and Dubin, D. T., *J. Biol. Chem.*, **235**, 769 (1960).
529. Fraser, D., and Mahler, H. R., *J. Am. Chem. Soc.*, **80**, 6456 (1958).
530. Tabor, H., *Biochem. Biophys. Research Communs.*, **4**, 228 (1961).
531. Keister, D. L., *Federation Proc.*, **17**, 84 (1958).
532. Frisch-Niggemeyer, W., and Hoffmann-Ostenhof, O., *Biokhimiya*, **22**, 404 (1957).
533. Mahler, H. R., Mehrotra, B. D., and Sharp, C. W., *Biochem. Biophys. Research Communs.*, **4**, 79 (1961).
534. Mahler, H. R., and Mehrotra, B. D., *Biochim. et Biophys. Acta*, **55**, 252 (1962).
535. Hammarsten, E., *Biochem. Z.*, **144**, 383 (1924).
536. Stern, K. G., and Steinberg, M. A., *Biochim. et Biophys. Acta*, **11**, 553 (1953).
537. Zubay, G., and Doty, P., *Biochim. et Biophys. Acta*, **29**, 47 (1958).
538. Cavalieri, L. F., *J. Am. Chem. Soc.*, **74**, 1242 (1952).
539. Zubay, G., *Biochim. et Biophys. Acta*, **32**, 233 (1959).
540. Shack, J., and Bynum, B. S., *Nature*, **184**, 535 (1959).
541. Shack, J., Jenkins, R. J., and Thompsett, J. M., *J. Biol. Chem.*, **198**, 85 (1952); **203**, 373 (1953).
542. Pour-El, A., and Dekker, C. A., *Abstracts 137th Am. Chem. Soc. Meeting*, 13C (1960).

543. Dove, W. F., and Yamane, T., *Biochem. Biophys. Research Communs.* **3**, 608 (1960).

544. Eissinger, J., Shulman, R. G., and Blumberg, W. E., *Nature*, **192**, 963 (1961).

545. Stevens, V. L., and Duggan, E. L., *J. Am. Chem. Soc.*, **79**, 5703 (1957).

546. Kirby, K. S., *Biochem. J.*, **66**, 495 (1957); **70**, 260 (1958).

547. Fraenkel-Conrat, H., Ward, W. H., Snell, N. S., and Ducay, E. D., *J. Am. Chem. Soc.*, **72**, 3826 (1950).

548. Fraenkel-Conrat, H., Snell, N. S., and Ducay, E. D., *Arch. Biochem. Biophys.*, **39**, 80 (1952).

549. Fredericq, E., *Biochim. et Biophys. Acta*, **55**, 300 (1962).

550. Kirby, K. S., *Biochim. et Biophys. Acta*, **55**, 382 (1962).

551. Mandell, J. D., and Hershey, A. D., *Anal. Biochem.*, **1**, 66 (1960).

552. Philipson, L., *J. Gen. Physiol.*, **44**, 899 (1961).

553. Takai, M., Kondo, N., and Osawa, S., *Biochim. et Biophys. Acta*, **55**, 416 (1962).

554. Gilham, P. T., *J. Am. Chem. Soc.*, **84**, 687 (1962).

555. Kaltreider, H. B., and Scott, J. F., *Biochim. et Biophys. Acta*, **55**, 379 (1962).

556. Fraenkel-Conrat, H., and Singer, B., *Biochemistry*, **1**, 120 (1962).

557. Apgar, J., Holley, R. W., and Merrill, S. H., *J. Biol. Chem.*, **237**, 796 (1962).

558. Sueoka, N., and Cheng, T. Y., *J. Mol. Biol.*, **4**, 161 (1962).

559. Rushizky, G. W., and Sober, H. A., *J. Biol. Chem.*, **237**, 834 (1962).

560. Kuno, S., and Lehman, I. R., *J. Biol. Chem.*, **237**, 1266 (1962).

561. Witzel, H., and Barnard, E. A., *Biochem. Biophys. Research Communs.*, **7**, 289, 295 (1962).

562. Bautz, E. K. F., and Hall, B. D., *Proc. Natl. Acad. Sci. U.S.A.*, **48**, 400 (1962).

563. Gilham, P. T., *J. Am. Chem. Soc.*, **84**, 1311 (1962).

564. Ralph, R. K., Young, R. J., and Khorana, H. G., *J. Am. Chem. Soc.*, **84**, 1490 (1962).

565. Pfau, C. J., and McCrea, J. F., *Nature*, **194**, 894 (1962).

566. Zubay, G., *J. Mol. Biol.*, **4**, 347 (1962).

567. Rushizky, G. W., Sober, H. A., and Knight, C. A., *Biochim. et Biophys. Acta*, **61**, 56 (1962).

568. Sueoka, N., and Yamane, T., *Proc. Natl. Acad. Sci. U.S.A.*, **48**, 1454 (1962).

569. Tomlinson, E. V., and Tener, G. M., *J. Am. Chem. Soc.*, **84**, 2644 (1962).

570. Bolton, E. T., and McCarthy, B. J., *Proc. Natl. Acad. Sci. U.S.A.*, **48**, 1390 (1962).

571. Levin, D. H., *Biochim. et Biophys. Acta*, **61**, 75 (1962).

572. Whitfeld, P. R., *J. Biol. Chem.*, **237**, 2865 (1962).

573. Radding, C. M., and Kornberg, A., *J. Biol. Chem.*, **237**, 2877 (1962).

574. Habermann, V., *Biochim. et Biophys. Acta*, **55**, 999 (1962).

575. Marmur, J., and Cordes, S., Symposium on Informational Macromolecules, Rutgers University, Sept. 1962.

Chapter 7

SYNTHESIS OF POLYNUCLEOTIDES

Chemical synthesis of nucleic acids (using the term in a biologically significant sense) has yet to be achieved, but ultimately will be achieved given precise structural determinations of the natural polymers. Methods for the polymerisation of mononucleotides have already proved successful for the synthesis of oligonucleotides and small polynucleotides, with considerable control of nucleotide sequence.

CLASSICAL APPROACHES

The first synthetic dinucleoside esters of phosphoric acid were prepared by the more or less classical methods of organic chemistry. Treatment of 2',3'-O-benzylideneuridine (then thought to be the 3',5'-O-benzylidene derivative) with phenyl phosphorodichloridate followed by removal of protecting groups yielded di(uridine-5') phosphate.[1] A similar nucleotide derivative, adenosine-5' uridine-5' phosphate (adenylyl-5' : 5'-uridine), was obtained from the reaction of the silver salt of 2',3'-O-isopropylideneadenosine-5' benzyl phosphate with 2',3'-O-isopropylidene-5'-iodo-5'-deoxyuridine, protecting groups being removed from the intermediate neutral tri-ester by mild acidic hydrolysis.[2] Both diesters were resistant to alkaline hydrolysis.

Phenyl phosphorodichloridate has also been used for the synthesis of dinucleoside phosphate derivatives of the aminonucleoside, 6-dimethylamino-9-β-D-3'-amino-3'-deoxyribofuranosylpurine, from puromycin. Selective acetylation of the 3'-amino group gave the acetamidonucleoside which was treated with phenyl phosphorodichloridate and the product subjected to mild alkaline hydrolysis to give a mixture of the di(acetamidonucleoside-5') phosphate and 6-dimethylamino-9-β-D-3'-acetamido-3'-deoxyribofuranosylpurine-5' phenyl phosphate. These were readily separated by ion exchange chromatography. Further treatment of the latter compound with diphenyl phosphorochloridate gave a tetra-esterified pyrophosphate intermediate which on reaction with the free aminonucleoside in the presence of base gave a good yield of the 3'–5' linked dinucleoside phosphate, spontaneous hydrolysis of the phenyl group from the fully esterified phosphoramidate derivative occurring at pH 9. Protection of the free 5' hydroxyl group was not necessary since completely selective nucleophilic attack by the amino group at the nucleotide phosphorus atom with liberation of diphenyl phosphate could be expected.[3] Successful application of a fully esteri-

400

fied pyrophosphate intermediate in this case may be ascribed to the use of dioxan (as solvent) and tri-n-butylamine (as a hindered tertiary base); under such conditions disproportionation (to give symmetrical pyrophosphate derivatives) was not observed. Also of importance is the ease with which amino groups are phosphorylated compared with hydroxyl groups. It may be noted further that, owing to the greatly disparate reactivity of secondary and primary hydroxyl groups under the conditions employed, protection of the 2'-hydroxyl group was unnecessary in the initial phosphorylation (at the 5' position) of the acetamidonucleoside.

R = 3'-Acetamidonucleoside

In addition to the large hypochromic effects shown by both di-nucleoside phosphates, other properties are of interest. Thus, although the acetamidonucleoside-5' phenyl phosphate was readily converted into the 5' phosphate by the action of rattlesnake venom diesterase (the resultant nucleotide was resistant to the monoesterase present in the crude venom), the di-(acetamidonucleoside-5') phosphate was unaffected, as was the 3'–5' linked dinucleoside phosphate.[3] As expected, the 5'–5' linked diester was resistant to mild acidic or alkaline hydrolysis while the other was readily degraded by dilute acid to the aminoside and nucleotide (presumably the 5' phosphate) but was resistant to the action of alkali, in contrast with normal 3'–5' linked diribonucleoside phosphates (compare also the properties of esters of ethanolamine phosphate).[4, 5] Treatment of the free aminonucleoside with diphenyl phosphorochloridate or tetrabenzyl pyrophosphate gave intermediates with similar properties.

Nucleoside-5' benzyl phosphites were convenient intermediates in other approaches to the synthesis of relatively simple nucleotide esters.[6] Conversion into the nucleoside-5' benzyl phosphorochloridate followed by treatment with a suitably protected nucleoside in the presence of base gave the di-(nucleoside-5') phosphate. Higher yields of adenylyl-5' : 5'-uridine were obtained by the use of mixed anhydrides prepared from the protected nucleoside-5' benzyl phosphorochloridate and diphenyl phosphoric acid or trifluoracetic acid. In a further variation of this approach, mixed anhydrides from diphenyl phosphorochloridate and the nucleoside-5' phosphite (obtained by anionic debenzylation of protected nucleoside-5' benzyl phosphites) were used to prepare di-(nucleoside-5') phosphites by reaction with 2',3'-di-O-acetyl or 2',3'-O-isopropylidene nucleosides. Oxidation of the dinucleoside phosphite by treatment with N-chlorosuccinimide (to give the phosphorochloridate) followed by hydrolysis, and removal of nucleoside protecting groups gave the di-(nucleoside-5') phosphate.

However, it was not until 1955 that the first synthesis of a dinucleotide containing a 3'–5' internucleotide linkage identical with that occurring in the nucleic acids was achieved.[7] Partial deacetylation of 3',5'-di-O-acetylthymidine gave a mixture of 3'-O-acetylthymidine (identified by comparison with the acetate obtained via 5'-O-tritylthymidine) and 5'-O-acetylthymidine. Treatment of 3'-O-acetylthymidine with 5'-O-acetylthymidine-3' benzyl phosphorochloridate (from the nucleoside benzyl phosphite) gave the fully protected dinucleoside phosphate from which the benzyl group was removed by hydrogenolysis. Deacetylation with alkali then gave thymidylyl-5' : 3'-thymidine (thymidine-3' thymidine-5' phosphate). An analogous procedure yielded the dinucleotide thymidylyl-5' : 3'-thymidine-5' phosphate, which was isolated as a crystalline calcium salt. Phosphorylation of 3'-O-acetylthymidine with dibenzyl phosphorochloridate followed by deacetylation gave thymidine-5' dibenzyl phosphate which

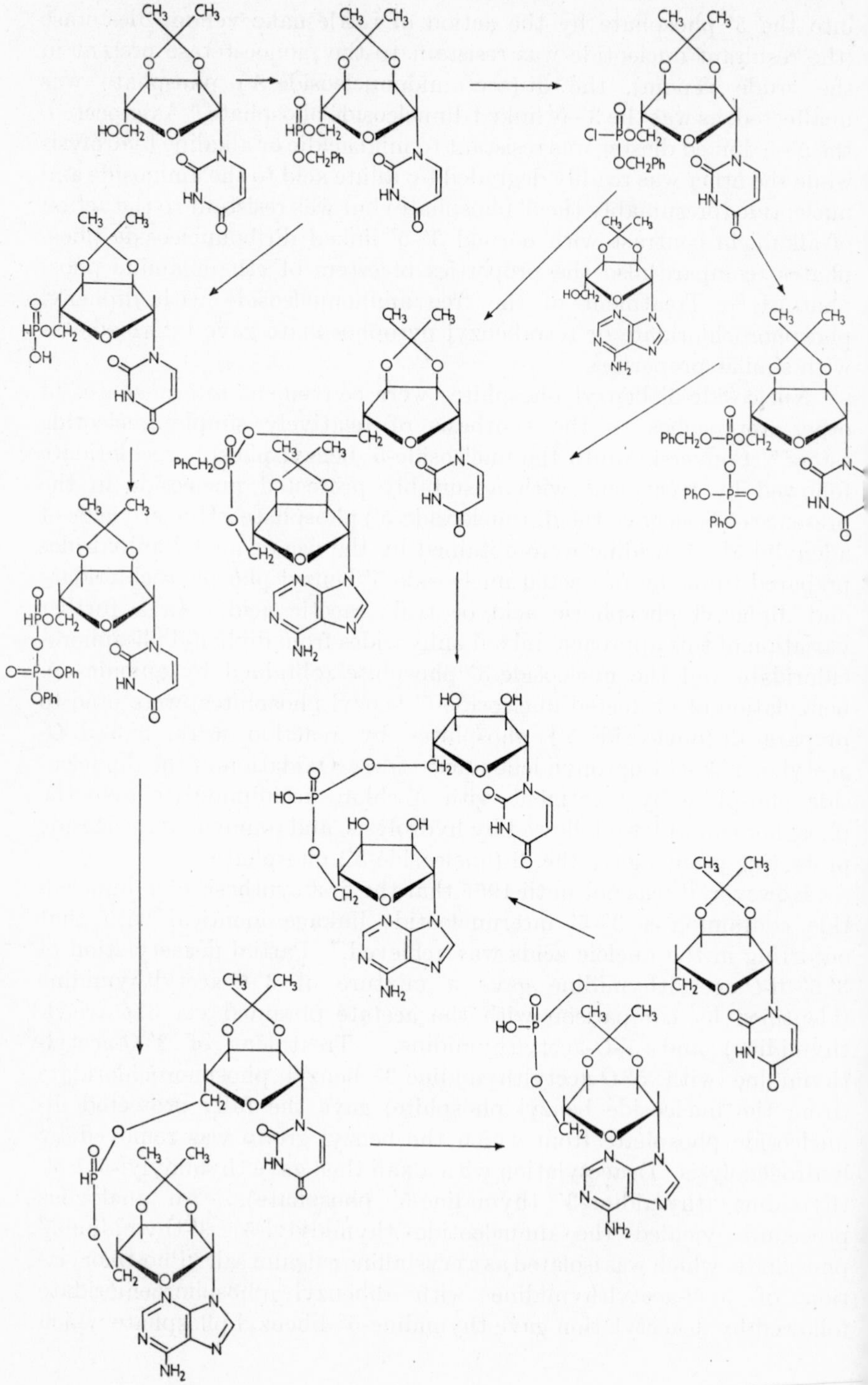

was converted into thymidine-3′ benzyl phosphite 5′ dibenzyl phosphate by treatment with O-benzyl phosphorous di-O-phenyl phosphoric anhydride. Chlorination gave the phosphorochloridate which with 3′-O-acetylthymidine in the presence of base yielded the protected dinucleotide. Acidic hydrolysis followed by treatment with alkali removed two of the three benzyl groups and the acetyl group. Catalytic

hydrogenolysis of the monobenzyl derivative then gave the dinucleotide.[7]

Despite the complications resulting from the *cis* α-glycol group in

ribonucleosides, the method was successfully extended to the synthesis
of adenosine-2' uridine-5' phosphate.[8] Transacetylation in a mixture of
2',3',5'-tri-O-acetyladenosine and 5'-O-acetyladenosine (obtained
directly by partial deacetylation of the tri-acetate) gave a good yield

of 3′,5′-di-O-acetyladenosine. This was converted in the usual way into the 2′-benzyl phosphorochloridate which was brought into reaction with 2′,3′-di-O-acetyluridine. Hydrogenolysis of the benzyl group followed by very mild alkaline treatment gave a mixture of products from which adenylyl-2′ : 5′-uridine (adenosine-2′ uridine-5′ phosphate) was isolated by ion exchange chromatography. Unlike the alkali-stable di-(nucleoside-5′) phosphates previously described, this diester showed many of the properties characteristic of ribonucleic acids. Alkaline hydrolysis yielded uridine and a mixture of adenosine-2′ and -3′ phosphates; enzymic hydrolysis with snake venom diesterase gave adenosine and uridine-5′ phosphate; and periodate oxidation followed by incubation at pH 10 gave uracil and adenosine-2′ phosphate.[8]

DICYCLOHEXYLCARBODI-IMIDE

Although these first successful attempts demonstrated the feasibility of oligonucleotide synthesis, disadvantages were apparent and it was clear that simpler and more effective methods would be required for the synthesis of polynucleotides. An early observation indicated that treatment of a solution of pyridinium uridine-5′ phosphate in dimethylformamide with a large excess of dicyclohexylcarbodi-imide gave rise to materials that were probably of higher molecular weight than the expected dinucleoside pyrophosphate.[9] Further work showed that the reaction of thymidine-5′ phosphate with either toluene-p-sulphonyl chloride, or preferably dicyclohexylcarbodi-imide, in anhydrous pyridine yielded a number of polymeric products.[10] Fractionation of the complex mixture on cellulose anion exchange columns showed the presence of two major series of compounds; these were identified as linear oligodeoxynucleotides (with 3′–5′ internucleotide linkages) containing a terminal 5′ monoesterified phosphate residue, and a related series of cyclic oligonucleotides derived from the linear compounds by phosphorylation of the terminal 3′ hydroxyl group by the 5′ phosphate group at the other end. The extent of intramolecular cyclisation decreased with increase in chain length and only a small amount of the cyclic pentanucleotide was formed relative to the linear pentathymidylic acid. Members of both series up to the pentanucleotide were isolated in a relatively pure condition and characterised by chemical and enzymic methods. Low yields were obtained, partly owing to the formation of unidentified nucleotide derivatives, but chromatographic methods suggested the presence of polymers containing up to eleven nucleotide units. Snake venom diesterase rapidly degraded the linear polymers to thymidine-5′ phosphate whereas treatment with prostate monoesterase (to remove the terminal 5′ phosphate) and then with spleen diesterase gave thymidine-3′ phosphate and the terminal thymidine unit. Chain lengths were determined from the ratio of total phosphate to phosphate released by monoesterase, and from the relative amounts of mononucleotide and nucleoside formed by diesterase (venom or spleen) hydrolysis of the resultant oligonucleotide lacking a terminal phosphate residue. However, in view of the fact that even purified venom diesterase may contain pyrophosphatase,[11] unequivocal demonstration of the purity, homogeneity and structure of the higher oligonucleotides is clearly desirable.

The general structure of the cyclic oligodeoxynucleotides was indicated by the absence of monoesterified phosphate end groups in the di-, tri-, tetra- and penta-thymidylic acids examined. Confirmation was afforded by the ready conversion of linear dithymidylic and trithymidylic acid into the corresponding cyclic oligodeoxynucleotides by treatment with dicyclohexylcarbodi-imide in pyridine. Venom diesterase caused complete degradation to thymidine-5′ phosphate, though with the cyclic dinucleotide hydrolysis was much slower than with the linear compound. In contrast with P^1,P^2-dithymidine-5′ pyrophosphate the cyclic dinucleotide was resistant to the action of 0·1 N hydrochloric acid at 100°. However, more vigorous acidic hydrolysis yielded thymidine-3′,5′ diphosphate, thymine and some inorganic phosphate. Similarly, acidic hydrolysis of the higher cyclic oligodeoxynucleotides gave linear oligothymidylic acids possessing terminal monoesterified phosphate residues at both the 3′ and 5′ hydroxyl groups but with one less thymidine unit, that is, $(\text{thymidine})_n(\text{phosphate})_n$ was converted into $(\text{thymidine})_{n-1}(\text{phosphate})_n$. In each case the initial step involved cleavage of a thymine glycosyl linkage followed by phosphate elimination from the non-glycosylated deoxyribose unit, as in the acidic hydrolysis of deoxyribonucleic acids.

In like manner, polymerisation of thymidine-3′ phosphate (after initial conversion into P^1,P^2-dithymidine-3′ pyrophosphate) by treatment with an excess of dicyclohexylcarbodi-imide in anhydrous pyridine gave a complex mixture of products.[12] Even lower yields of the linear thymidine oligonucleotides (up to pentanucleotide) bearing 3′ phosphate end groups were obtained, together with the homologous series of cyclic oligonucleotides formed from the linear compounds by phosphorylation of the 5′-hydroxyl group at one end by the 3′-phosphate residue at the other. Two other series of nucleotide components were observed, one of which consisted of polymers containing P^1,P^2-dithymidine-3′ pyrophosphate linkages in addition to the 3′–5′ internucleotide linkage. Selective hydrolysis of the pyrophosphate linkage could be achieved by mild acidic treatment to give the nucleotide or oligonucleotide components flanking the pyrophosphate linkage. Members of the other series of homologous products were tentatively

Pyridinium and pyrophosphate derivatives

identified as oligonucleotides containing a 5'-deoxy-5'-quaternary pyridinium derivative of the terminal nucleoside.[12]

Some improvement was obtained by polymerisation of thymidine-5' phosphate (3 parts) in the presence of 3'-O-acetylthymidine-5' phosphate (1 part) as chain terminator, in an attempt to reduce the proportion of cyclic oligonucleotides. Prolonged treatment (6 days) of the mixture with dicyclohexylcarbodi-imide in pyridine at room temperature followed by alkaline hydrolysis of acetyl groups from the initial product again gave a complex mixture of compounds, the major one being cyclic dinucleotide. Linear polymers containing from two to eleven nucleotides (in a total yield of about 50%) were partially purified and characterised (but not isolated in solid form) by means of extensive and repeated column chromatography.[13] Numerous unidentified by-products were also observed. The dangers of assuming purity and homogeneity in single peaks from chromatography on cellulose anion exchangers were indicated, since paper chromatography of several such

fractions indicated five or more compounds, while rechromatography of the original decanucleotide peak gave a chromatographic profile indicating the presence of some ten minor products in addition to the decanucleotide. In a similar fashion, copolymerisation of $N^6,3'-O$-diacetyldeoxycytidine-5' phosphate with thymidine-5' phosphate yielded an extremely complex mixture of products some of which were linear oligothymidylic acids bearing a deoxycytidine-5' phosphate residue at one end.

Owing to interference by the 6-amino group, deoxycytidine-5' phosphate could not be polymerised directly. A rather circuitous method of protection was therefore devised, whereby the nucleotide was fully acylated using excess of anisyl chloride (p-methoxybenzoyl chloride), and the product treated with alkali under carefully controlled conditions. Preferential cleavage of the O-anisyl groups (alcoholic and phosphoryl) gave N^6-anisyldeoxycytidine-5' phosphate. An alternate route to protected deoxycytidine-5' phosphate derivatives of this type lies in acylation of 3'-O-tetrahydropyranyl-2'-deoxycytidine-5' phosphate followed by mild acidic hydrolysis to remove the tetrahydropyranyl group. Polymerisation of a mixture of N^6-anisyldeoxycytidine-5' phosphate and N^6,3'-O-diacetyldeoxycytidine-5' phosphate gave a crude product which was treated with concentrated ammonia to remove the acyl groups. Chromatography gave partial purification of linear oligodeoxycytidylic acids from di- to octanucleotide but again further processing was necessary in order to obtain relatively homogeneous compounds, none of which was isolated as a pure substance in the chemical sense. Rechromatography of material treated with monoesterase to remove the terminal phosphate group showed that the amount of impurities in the major peaks increased with increase in chain length of the oligonucleotides. In addition to cyclic oligonucleotides, pyrophosphate derivatives and smaller amounts of pyridinium compounds and phosphoryl ureas were tentatively identified.[14]

Similar results were obtained on treatment of a mixture of N,3'-O-diacetyl-(or dibenzoyl)-deoxyadenosine-5' phosphate and N-benzoyl-deoxyadenosine-5' phosphate with dicyclohexylcarbodi-imide, except that none of the cyclic dinucleotide was isolated and instead the cyclic trinucleotide was a major product. The complexity of the mixture of products was further increased by inadvertent partial removal of terminal monoesterified phosphate residues.[15]

The mechanisms of the reactions involved have not been fully elucidated as yet. It is likely however that metaphosphate intermediates result from the initially formed imidoyl phosphate derivatives (presumably all the mononucleotide is so converted when an excess of dicyclohexylcarbodi-imide is used under anhydrous conditions). Further reaction of nucleoside-5' monomeric metaphosphate with pyridine to give active phosphoramidates, or conversion into trimetaphosphates or polyphosphates might be expected. Reaction of P^1,P^2-dinucleoside pyrophosphates (either preformed or as initial products) with dicyclohexylcarbodi-imide could also yield monomeric metaphosphate derivatives from the imidoyl phosphate adduct. Similar mechanisms for the action of toluene-p-sulphonyl chloride (or other strong acid anhydrides) have been advanced;[16] these probably also apply to the action of enol phosphates on thymidylic acid, an intermediate tri-esterified pyrophosphate being formed initially.[17]

Further studies on the mechanism of diester formation using dicyclohexylcarbodi-imide have been reported.[18] It was concluded from somewhat non-definitive results on the phosphorylation of protected thymidine derivatives by various monoesterified phosphates that the size of the organic residue in the phosphomonester component has a *marked* effect. It was originally claimed that *direct* activation of nucleotides (resulting in polymerisation) is achieved by means of dicyclohexylcarbodi-imide; at the same time it was supposed that a symmetrical diesterified pyrophosphate was formed initially. More recently it is claimed that the initial phosphorylating agent is a tri-alkyl trimetaphosphate. Treatment of 3'-O-acetylthymidine-5' phosphate or

$$R'-N=C=N-R' + RO-\overset{\overset{O}{\|}}{\underset{OH}{P}}-OH \longrightarrow \text{[pyridinium intermediate]} \text{ or } \text{[isourea intermediate]}$$

$$R'HNCONHR'$$
$$+$$

$$RO-\overset{\overset{O}{\|}}{P}-O^- \longleftarrow RO-\overset{\overset{O}{\|}}{P} \longrightarrow \text{[trimetaphosphate]}$$
$$\underset{N^+}{}$$

$$\downarrow R''OH$$

$$RO-\overset{\overset{O}{\|}}{\underset{OH}{P}}-OR''$$

$$RO-\overset{\overset{O}{\|}}{\underset{OH}{P}}-OH + ArSO_2Cl \longrightarrow RO-\overset{\overset{O}{\|}}{\underset{OH}{P}}-OSO_2Ar$$

$$\downarrow$$

$$RO-\overset{\overset{O}{\|}}{\underset{O}{P}} + HOSO_2Ar$$

P^1,P^2-di-3'-O-acetylthymidine-5' pyrophosphate with excess of dicyclohexylcarbodi-imide in pyridine for a brief period gave a high yield of P^1,P^2,P^3-tri-(3'-O-acetylthymidine-5') triphosphate, presumed to be a breakdown product of the analogous trimetaphosphate derivative; use of the isolated triphosphate (with dicyclohexylcarbodi-imide) to phosphorylate a protected nucleoside was not reported. The results, while of some interest, in no way invalidate the concept of " monomeric metaphosphate " as an *initial* phosphorylating intermediate despite the meretricious conclusion that was drawn.[18] Direct one-step formation of tri-alkyl trimetaphosphates from mono-alkyl phosphate is quite unlikely, but they could well arise from an initially produced monomeric metaphosphate under anhydrous conditions. In any case the solvent (pyridine) undoubtedly plays an important role.

Although claimed as a general method " in which the phospho-monester grouping is activated directly "[10] it is clear that the reaction, even with the simplest nucleotides (with respect to functional groups that could cause interference) is quite complex. Cleavage of pyro-phosphate linkages by treatment of the crude product with acetic anhydride in pyridine simplifies chromatography of the mixture.[44]

Considerably greater success was achieved by this approach in the stepwise synthesis of small oligodeoxynucleotides, using suitably protected nucleotide and nucleoside derivatives.[19] Thus treatment of a mixture of thymidine-5' phosphate and excess of 5'-O-tritylthymidine with toluene-p-sulphonyl chloride followed by acidic hydrolysis of the trityl group gave a mixture of thymidylyl-5' : 3'-thymidine (thymi-dine-5' thymidine-3' phosphate) and other products arising from polymerisation of the unprotected nucleotide. A more controlled synthesis of this dinucleoside phosphate was achieved by the reaction of 3'-O-acetylthymidine-5' phosphate and excess of dicyclohexylcarbodi-imide on the 5'-O-trityl nucleoside.[20] Deacetylation and detritylation of the crude product yielded a mixture containing thymidylyl-5' : 3'-thymidine, thymidine-5' phosphate, thymidine, and P^1,P^2-dithymi-dine-5' pyrophosphate, from which the required compound was separated by paper chromatography. In like manner, treatment of 5'-O-tritylthymidine with N^6,3'-O-diacetyldeoxycytidine-5' phosphate (prepared by acetylation of the free nucleotide) and dicyclohexyl-carbodi-imide yielded deoxycytidylyl-5' : 3'-thymidine. The analogous deoxyadenylyl-5' : 3'-thymidine was prepared from N^6,3'-O-diacetyl-deoxyadenosine-5' phosphate and 5'-O-acetylthymidine since the instability of the purine glycosyl linkage precluded use of the usual acidic methods for removal of the trityl group.[20] Other di-deoxy-nucleoside phosphates have been prepared by a somewhat laborious approach employing fully protected (including the heterocyclic base) deoxynucleoside and deoxynucleotide derivatives.[21]

Synthesis of a dinucleotide was achieved by an approach similar to that used in the original synthesis of thymidylyl-5' : 3'-thymidine-5' phosphate, using 3'-O-acetylthymidine-5' phosphate to phosphorylate thymidine-5' dibenzyl phosphate followed by removal of protecting groups from the product. Replacement of the acetylated thymidine nucleotide by N,3'-O-diacetyldeoxyadenosine-5' phosphate gave the corresponding dinucleotide, deoxyadenylyl-5' : 3'-thymidine-5' phos-phate. Alternative procedures were also developed in which a pro-tected dinucleoside phosphate was phosphorylated at the sole free sugar hydroxyl group. Mild acidic treatment of 3'-O-acetylthymidylyl-5' : 3'-(5'-O-trityl)-thymidine removed the trityl group, and phosphorylation of the resultant 3'-O-acetylthymidylyl-5' : 3'-thymidine with dibenzyl phosphorochloridate followed by treatment with alkali and hydrogenolytic removal of benzyl groups gave thymidylyl-5' : 3'-thymidine-5' phosphate. For the synthesis of the isomeric dinucleotide containing a terminal 3' monoesterified phosphate, the same fully protected intermediate was treated with alkali to give thymidylyl-5' : 3'-(5'-O-trityl)-thymidine. Phosphorylation and removal of protecting

groups then yielded thymidylyl-3' : 5'-thymidine-3' phosphate. More efficient methods for the phosphorylation of dinucleoside phosphates with dicyclohexylcarbodi-imide and β-cyanoethyl phosphate have since been developed.[22]

As with the polymerisation of thymidine-5' phosphate, these syntheses presumably involve metaphosphate intermediates. Although described as a general method for the " specific " synthesis of the 3'–5' internucleotide linkage, application to the stepwise synthesis of oligodeoxynucleotides has in fact been markedly restricted[23] by the necessity of extensive protection of functional groups. Nevertheless, the approach has been successfully extended to the synthesis of two tri-deoxynucleoside diphosphates which, like the dimers, were isolated in a relatively pure condition by paper chromatographic methods. The reaction of 3'-O-acetylthymidine-5' phosphate with thymidylyl-5' : 3'-(5'-O-trityl)-thymidine in the presence of dicyclohexylcarbodi-imide followed by mild alkaline, and then acidic, treatment of the product gave thymidylyl-5' : 3'-thymidylyl-5' : 3'-thymidine. Similarly, deoxycytidylyl-5' : 3'-deoxyadenylyl-5' : 3'-thymidine was obtained from N^6,3'-O-diacetyldeoxycytidine-5' phosphate and deoxyadenylyl-5' : 3'-(5'-O-trityl) thymidine. In this latter case, reactions possibly involving the adenine amino group were encountered, and removal of protecting groups without extensive concomitant degradation was achieved with some difficulty.[23] Similar procedures, employing " phosphorylation " of thymidine-3' cyanoethyl phosphate or a protected oligodeoxynucleotide with β-cyanoethyl phosphate, 5'-O-tritylthymidine-3' phosphate, or

0*

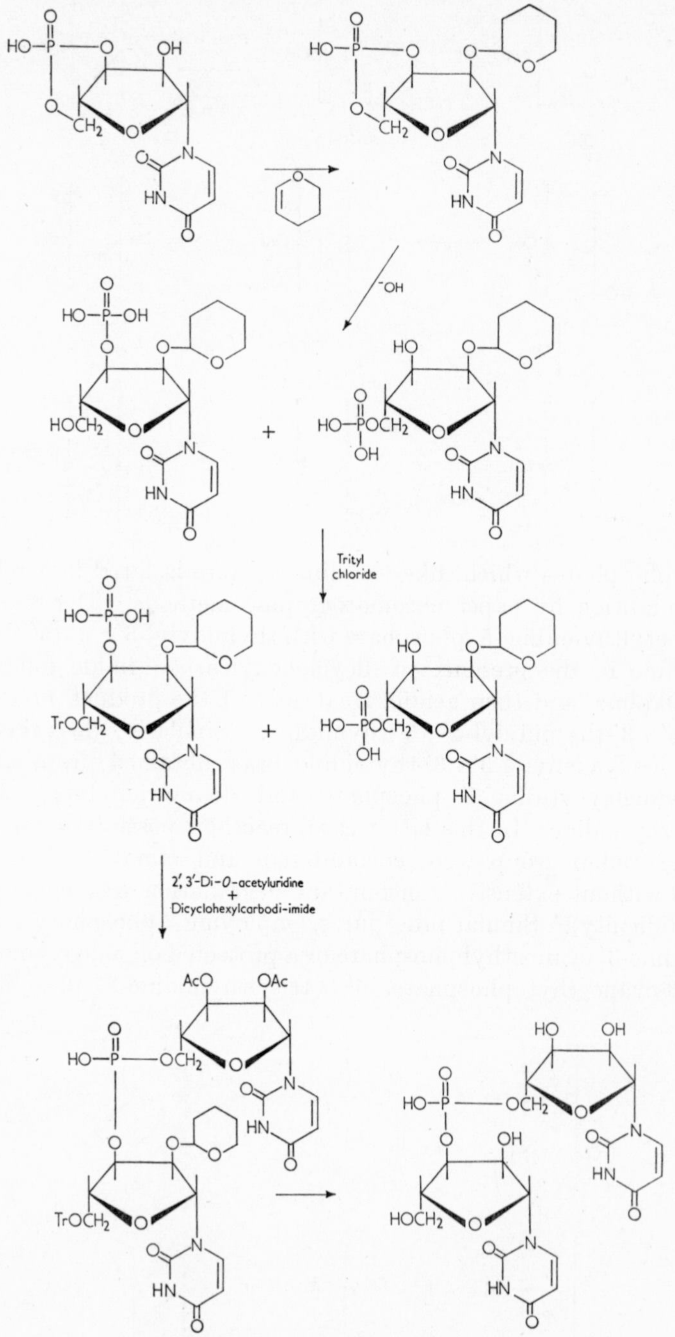

⁻OH
Trityl chloride
2′, 3′-Di-O-acetyluridine
+
Dicyclohexylcarbodi-imide

5'-O-tritylthymidylyl-3' : 5'-thymidine-3' phosphate and dicyclohexyl-carbodi-imide gave di-, tri-, and tetrathymidylic acids containing a terminal 3'-phosphate group.[46]

Oligoribonucleotides have also been prepared by means of dicyclo-hexylcarbodi-imide. Use of suitably protected uridine derivatives resulted in the synthesis of uridylyl-5' : 3'-uridine.[24, 45] Uridine-3',5' cyclic phosphate was treated with dihydropyran to give the 2'-O-tetrahydropyranyl derivative. Alkaline hydrolysis of the cyclic phosphate then gave a mixture of the 2'-O-tetrahydropyranyl ethers of uridine-3' phosphate and uridine-5' phosphate. Tritylation (not entirely specific for the primary hydroxyl group) of the mixture gave 2'-O-tetrahydropyranyl-5'-O-trityluridine-3' phosphate, which was separated from the unchanged 5' phosphate derivative, and treated with 2',3'-di-O-acetyluridine and dicyclohexylcarbodi-imide. Removal of the acetyl groups by alkaline hydrolysis, and of the trityl and tetra-hydropyranyl groups by treatment with aqueous acetic acid, then gave uridylyl-3' : 5'-uridine in low overall yield.[24] In an improved version a 5'-O-di-p-methoxyphenyl-phenylmethyl protecting group (consider-ably less stable to acid than the triphenylmethyl ether) was employed.[45] The method has been extended to the synthesis of uridylyl-3' : 5'-adenosine from $N,N,2',3'$-O-tetrabenzoyl-adenosine (protection of the heterocyclic base is desirable).[45] More directly, the protected mononucleotide can be obtained from the nucleoside-3' phosphate by treatment with dihydropyran to give a 2',5'-di-O-tetrahydropyranyl derivative.[25] It may be noted that presence of the 2'-O-tetrahydropyranyl group renders the intermediate diester stable to alkali, and hence rather vigorous conditions can be used for re-moval of the benzoyl groups.

A more economic approach involving specific opening of a 2',3' cyclic phosphate to a 3'-phosphate has been used for the synthesis of 4-azauridylyl-5' : 3'-uridine.[26, 47] Hydrolysis of 5'-O-acetyluridine-2',3' cyclic phosphate with ribonuclease gave the 3' phosphate which with dihydropyran yielded 5'-O-acetyl-2'-O-tetrahydropyranyluridine-3' phosphate. Treatment of this protected nucleotide with 2',3'-O-benzylidene-4-azauridine and dicyclohexylcarbodi-imide gave the protected dinucleoside phosphate from which uridylyl-3' : 5'-azauridine was obtained by deacetylation and hydrogenolytic removal of tetrahydropyran and benzylidene groups.

MIXED ANHYDRIDES

When the nucleotide contains an unprotected *cis* hydroxyl group adjacent to the phosphate residue the dicyclohexylcarbodi-imide approach cannot be employed owing to the ready formation of cyclic phosphates which, being phosphate diesters, can no longer be converted into metaphosphate intermediates. However, the ribonucleotides can be polymerised easily and quantitatively by means of a modified fully

esterified mixed anhydride approach.[27] Inconveniences attending the use and removal of protecting groups in the ribonucleotide series are avoided by conversion of the nucleoside-2'(3') phosphate into the 2',3' cyclic phosphate, in which only the 5' hydroxyl group is free. Preliminary work with glycerol-2 (or 1) phosphate showed that polyglycerophosphoric acid was readily obtained on treating the monomer with diphenyl phosphorochloridate or tetraphenyl pyrophosphate.[28] The polymerisation process involves initial formation of P^1-glycerol-2 (or 1) P^2-diphenyl pyrophosphate which is rapidly converted into glycerol-1,2 cyclic phosphate; intramolecular phosphorylation is effected by the weaker of the acids forming the anhydride, as is usual with pyrophosphate derivatives. Further reaction of the cyclic phosphate with more diphenyl phosphorochloridate then gives a second transient unsymmetrical anhydride, P^1-glycerol-1,2 cyclic P^2-diphenyl pyrophosphate, which rapidly polymerises by intermolecular phosphorylation of the free hydroxyl group with liberation of diphenyl phosphate.

Final cleavage of bonds in the polymeric phosphate triester to form the diester occurs spontaneously in aqueous solution, and can occur in three ways leading to 1 : 3 interglycerol phosphate linkages, 2 : 3 linkages or degradation of the polymer. (In this case, the product appears to contain 1 : 3 linkages mainly). The hydrolysis of uridine-3' dimethyl phosphate at all pH's (presumably via the methyl cyclic phosphate) to monoesters of uridine-2' and uridine-3' phosphate with only a trace of uridine-2',3' cyclic phosphate[29] indicates that degradation should be slight, and indeed this is so.

Similarly, treatment of adenosine-2'(3') phosphate with diphenyl phosphorochloridate gave first the nucleoside-2',3' cyclic phosphate.[30] Subsequent polymerisation then gave polyadenylic acids of various chain lengths ranging from dinucleotide to polynucleotides containing up to some fifteen monomer units. The method was readily extended to the synthesis of polymers of guanosine-2'(3') phosphate, uridine-2'(3') phosphate,[31] and pseudouridine-2'(3') phosphate.[32] In addition, a number of polymers derived from nucleotide analogues including N^1-methyluridylic acid, 5-chlorouridylic acid, 5-bromouridylic acid, and 5-iodouridylic acid have been prepared.[33]

With cytidine-2'(3') phosphate, polymeric material was also formed, but chemical, enzymic, and spectroscopic examination showed that it did not possess internucleotide linkages analogous to those in the natural nucleic acids (that is, phosphodiester groups linking a secondary sugar hydroxyl group of one nucleoside and the primary hydroxyl group of another). The polymer was quite resistant to alkaline treatment and to enzymic hydrolysis by the common diesterases and it is likely that the general structure involves phosphoramidate internucleotide linkages between the 2' (or 3') phosphate groups and the 6-amino group of an adjacent cytosine residue. Selective acetylation of the amino function in cytidine-2',3' cyclic phosphate and treatment of the product with diphenyl phosphorochloridate gave polynucleotides (with the orthodox type of linkage) from which the acetyl groups were removed by mild alkaline hydrolysis to give oligocytidylic acids of various chain lengths.[32] It may be noted that the intermediate acetyl cyclic phosphate mixed anhydride that is presumably formed initially on treating cytidine-2',3' cyclic phosphate with acetic anhydride acts solely as an acylating agent, in contrast with deoxycytidyl-5′-yl acetate where displacement of the more stable anion (acetate) in pyridine renders the compound subject to nucleophilic attack at the phosphorus atom. Essentially, the difference between the two types of compound lies in the pK values of the phosphoryl dissociations concerned (approximately 1 and 6·5 respectively). Nevertheless, and

despite misguided statements to the contrary,[14] it is likely that selective acetylation of the amino group in deoxycytidine-5′ phosphate can be achieved under appropriate reaction conditions (hindered tertiary base and dioxan as solvent instead of pyridine).

Owing to stereochemical considerations, formation of cyclic dinucleotides via a 2′,3′-cyclic phosphate tri-esterified intermediate is extremely unlikely, and to a lesser extent this is true of cyclic tri- and tetra-nucleotides. In addition, very concentrated solutions are used for polymerisation, thus reducing still further the possibility of cyclic oligonucleotide formation. Such compounds have not been detected, even under dilute polymerisation conditions, and they can form a very small proportion only of the total product, if present at all.

Partial fractionation of the synthetic polymers was achieved by dialysis against water, and against various salt solutions. After dialysis in 2-M sodium chloride solution, the residue consisted of material with an average chain length of 10–12 nucleotides as determined by hydrolysis with venom diesterase to nucleosides and terminal nucleoside-3′,5′ diphosphate, or by dephosphorylation (prostate monoesterase) of the polymers after acidic treatment to open the 2′,3′ cyclic phosphate group at the chain end. Using suitably dilute solutions for the polymerisation reaction, products containing relatively large amounts of the smaller oligonucleotides were obtained. These small oligonucleotides (up to pentanucleotide) were shown to be members of a homologous series of linear polymers containing nucleosides combined through 2′–5′ and 3′–5′ phosphodiester linkages, and ending with a 2′,3′ cyclic phosphate group. (Such oligonucleotides are hydrolysed by rattlesnake venom much more readily than are the analogous compounds containing a terminal 2′ or 3′ monoesterified phosphate group). Removal of this terminal phosphate gave the corresponding series represented by (nucleoside)$_n$ (phosphate)$_{n-1}$, members of which on alkaline hydrolysis yielded nucleoside-2′(3′) phosphate and terminal nucleoside. The general properties of higher molecular weight fractions likewise indicated that they were entirely composed of linear polymers with a general structure analogous to that of biosynthetic polynucleotides and nucleic acids except that some 50% of the internucleotide linkages were 2′–5′, the remainder being 3′–5′.[31] Further fractionation of the higher homologues could be achieved by the use of cellulose anion exchange materials, but less efficiently than with the smaller oligonucleotides.[32]

The polymerisation method is also applicable to the synthesis of polymers with specific head and tail nucleoside or nucleotide residues. Treatment of uridine-2′(or 3′),5′ diphosphate with tetraphenyl pyrophosphate (or diphenyl phosphorochloridate) yielded P^1-uridine-(2′,3′ cyclic phosphate)-5′ P^2-diphenyl pyrophosphate. This was copolymerised with adenylic acid in the usual way, the uridine derivative acting as a chain terminator. Mild alkaline treatment cleaved the terminal triesterified pyrophosphate to give polyadenylic acid containing uridine-5′ phosphate at one end, and adenosine-2′(3′) phosphate at the other. In like manner, polymerisation of adenylic acid in the presence of 2′,3′-di-O-acetyluridine followed by removal of the acetyl groups by selective alkaline hydrolysis gave polyadenylic acid containing a terminal uridine unit. Polymerisation of adenylic acid in the presence of both uridine derivatives gave material with terminal uridine and uridine-5′ phosphate units, that is, poly-(nucleoside-5′ phosphate).[31]

Other polymers containing specific head or tail units that have been prepared include polyadenylic acids carrying a head cytidylic acid residue (using $N^6,5'$-O-diacetylcytidine-$2',3'$ cyclic phosphate)[34] and polyadenylic acid with thymidine at the tail ends (using $3'$-O-acetylthymidine as chain terminator).[31]

In addition to homopolymers of the five major ribonucleotides, several copolymers were synthesised, including a copolymer of all five

nucleotides. Polymerisation of mixtures of adenylic and uridylic acids in various proportions gave the corresponding copolymers containing a more or less random distribution of adenine and uracil, whereas partial polymerisation of adenylic and uridylic acids separately (to an average chain length of approximately 3 mononucleotide units) followed by copolymerisation of the mixture of oligonucleotides, gave polynucleotides with tracts of purines and pyrimidines.[31] Yet a third form of copolymer of adenylic and uridylic acids was obtained by polymerising the dinucleotide adenylyl-$3'$: $5'$-uridine-$3'$ phosphate (after cyclisation of the terminal monoesterified phosphate to the $2'$: $3'$

cyclic phosphate by treatment with ethyl chloroformate) to give oligonucleotides with a defined arrangement of alternating adenylic and uridylic acids.[32]

Similar polymerisation of guanylyl-3' : 5'-cytidine-3' phosphate (G3'P5'C3'P) and of adenylyl-3' : 5'-adenylyl-3' : 5'-cytidine-3' phosphate (A3'P5'A3'P5'C3'P) after preliminary protection of the cytosine 6-amino group by selective acetylation, gave the corresponding polymers containing a defined, repeating order of bases.[32]

The method was readily extended to the stepwise synthesis of oligonucleotides containing a number of different bases in a defined order. Uridine-2' (or-3') phosphate was converted into the cyclic phosphate by the action of ethyl chloroformate and base in aqueous solution, a more

convenient procedure than treatment with diphenyl phosphorochloridate under anhydrous conditions since no subsequent polymerisation occurs. The anhydrous nucleotide was then acetylated and the resultant 5'-O-acetyluridine-2',3' cyclic phosphate treated with diphenyl phosphorochloridate and base in the presence of 2',3'-di-O-acetyladenosine. "Phosphorylation" of the free 5' hydroxyl group of the protected nucleoside by the intermediate P^1-5'-O-acetyluridine-2',3' cyclic P^2-diphenyl pyrophosphate gave a good yield of the protected dinucleoside phosphate from which the acetyl groups were removed selectively by mild alkaline hydrolysis, to give a mixture of uridylyl-2' : 5'-adenosine and uridylyl-3' : 5'-adenosine. Similar reactions between various nucleotide and nucleoside derivatives gave a number of dinucleoside phosphates including ApA, UpA, ApU, UpU, CpU, CpA, GpA and 5'-deoxy-5'-bromouridylyl-2'(3') : 5'-adenosine,[32, 35] where p represents a phosphate linkage from the 3'- (or 2'-) hydroxyl group of the nucleoside on the left, to the 5' hydroxyl group of that on the right, and A, C, G, and U represent the appropriate nucleosides. Isomeric pairs of dinucleoside phosphates (2'–5' and 3'–5' linked) were separated by anion exchange chromatography. Approximately 50% of the material in each case was 3'–5' linked, the remainder being 2'–5'.[32] Many of these dinucleoside phosphates were obtained in crystalline form.

For the synthesis of trinucleoside diphosphates, advantage was taken of the greatly disparate reactivities of the primary and secondary hydroxyl groups in ribonucleosides and their derivatives. Treatment of adenylyl-3' : 5'-uridine with 5'-O-acetylguanosine-2',3' cyclic phosphate and diphenyl phosphorochloridate followed by removal of the acetyl group gave guanylyladenylyluridine (GpApU). In like manner GpUpA, UpGpA, CpUpA and CpApU were prepared from the appropriate acetylated nucleoside-2',3' cyclic phosphate and dinucleoside phosphate.

Repetition of this process using an excess of $N^6,5'$-O-diacetyl-cytidine-$2',3'$ cyclic phosphate on GpApU and subsequent removal of the acetyl groups give cytidylylguanylyladenylyluridine (CpGpApU), and in the same way CpGpUpA and CpUpGpA were synthesised in good yield from the respective trinucleoside diphosphates and mononucleotides.[32] All of these compounds were purified by anion exchange chromatography, and isolated in solid form as the free acid.

In an alternate approach to the stepwise synthesis of oligonucleotides containing specific base sequences, dinucleotides were used to " phos-

phorylate " nucleoside and nucleotide derivatives. Adenylyl-$3'$: $5'$-cytidine-$3'$ phosphate was treated with ethyl chloroformate to give a dinucleotide containing a terminal $2',3'$ cyclic phosphate group. This compound was fully acetylated and the product treated with diphenyl phosphorochloridate and $2',3'$-di-O-acetyluridine to give the protected trinucleoside diphosphate. Removal of acetyl groups then gave adenylylcytidylyluridine (ApCpU). In the same way GpCpU and ApUpU were obtained from $2',3'$-di-O-acetyluridine and guanylyl-$3'$: $5'$-cytidine-$3'$ phosphate (G3′P5′C3′P) or adenylyl-$3'$: $5'$-uridine-$3'$ phosphate (A3′P5′U3′P) respectively, and similar treatment of $2',3'$-di-O-acetyladenosine gave ApCpA, GpCpA and ApUpA.

Extension to the synthesis of tetramers was equally successful, and again selective phosphorylation of the primary hydroxyl group in unprotected dinucleoside phosphates was achieved. Thus treatment of uridylyl-2'(3') : 5'-adenosine with the mixed anhydride derived from acetylated guanylyl-3' : 5'-cytidine-2',3' cyclic phosphate and diphenyl phosphorochloridate gave a product from which acetyl groups were removed, and the resultant guanylylcytidylyluridylyladenosine (GpCpUpA) isolated as the free acid. Similar reactions of GpCp with ApU and of ApUp with GpC yielded GpCpApU and ApUpGpC respectively.[32]

It may be noted that acetylation of dinucleotides does not lead to extensive cleavage of the internucleotide linkage. This is readily explicable in terms of the properties of acetyl anhydrides of dialkyl (or

diaryl) phosphates. Such compounds will almost invariably act solely as acylating agents, and not as phosphorylating agents, particularly under the conditions employed (presence of hindered tertiary base and absence of pyridine catalysis) owing to displacement of the more stable phosphate anion (pK $\sim$ 1 compared with the carboxyl pK $\sim$ 4·5). The additive properties of the carbonyl group accentuate this acylating action. Similarly, the specific action of ethyl chloroformate on the dinucleotides to yield undegraded material possessing a terminal 2',3' cyclic phosphate group is a result of the selectivity of nucleophilic attack by secondary phosphoryl dissociations (pK $\sim$ 6) compared with primary dissociating groups (pK $\sim$ 1) on the reagent. Again, this can be explained in terms of the stability of the anions concerned, which in this case reflects nucleophilic character. Thus ethyl carbonate anhydrides of nucleoside-5' phosphates are readily obtained quantitatively under mild conditions; di-(ethyl carbonate) nucleotide anhydrides have not been reported as yet.

The nature of the degradation products obtained by hydrolysis of the synthetic oligmers with alkali, venom diesterase, and pancreatic ribonuclease fully confirmed the assigned structures and base sequences.

The chemical and biochemical properties of the synthetic homopolymers (and copolymers) were likewise completely in accord with the structures assigned. Mild acidic treatment opened the terminal cyclic phosphate to give oligo- and poly-nucleotides with tail units containing a 2' (or 3') phosphate; more vigorous acidic hydrolysis gave either purines and/or pyrimidine nucleoside-2' and -3' phosphates, depending

on the polymer. Treatment with alkali caused complete breakdown to mononucleotides, and terminal nucleoside-2' (or -3'),5' diphosphate or nucleoside where these were present, polyguanylic acid showing marked resistance to alkaline hydrolysis compared with polyuridylic acid. All the polynucleotides and higher oligonucleotides gave precipitates with protamine sulphate in aqueous solution. Prostatic monoesterase removed the terminal phosphate from acid-treated homopolymers, to give a homologous series of related oligonucleotides. Dinucleotides with a terminal 2' or 3' phosphate group were quite resistant to the mixture of monoesterase and diesterase present in rattlesnake (*Crotalus atrox*) venom. Trinucleotides were slowly attacked, and higher oligonucleotides containing a terminal 2',3' cyclic phosphate residue were more rapidly degraded to the nucleoside and terminal nucleoside diphosphate. Hydrolysis of oligoribonucleotides containing a terminal 2',3' cyclic phosphate group (but not those with a 3' phosphomonoester end group) by venom diesterase has also been observed[36] with material obtained by degradation of RNA. When the polymer lacked a terminal 2' or 3' phosphate (for example, UpUpUpU and CpUpA) then degradation to nucleosides was considerably faster. Whereas polyadenylic and polyguanylic acids were unaffected by pancreatic ribonuclease, the pyrimidine compounds (polycytidylic, polyuridylic and polypseudouridylic acids) were broken down to mixture of nucleoside-3' phosphate and di-, tri- and tetra-nucleotides containing 2'–5' linkages exclusively. It may be noted that both the overall shape and relative arrangement of functional groups characteristic of uridylic acid (of possible significance for hydrogen bonding to the enzyme) are maintained in polypseudouridylic acid.

Similarly, polyadenylic acid was cleaved by spleen diesterase (or by Takadiastase Ribonuclease T2) to a mixture of adenosine-3' phosphate and enzyme-resistant oligonucleotides containing 2'–5' internucleotide

linkages exclusively. The synthetic homopolymers stimulated enzymic polymerisation of nucleoside-5' pyrophosphates by polynucleotide phosphorylase. Lacking a free 3'-hydroxyl group for esterification, they were not incorporated into the biosynthetic polymers, as were the normal oligo-(nucleoside-5' phosphate) primers and oligonucleotides devoid of terminal monoesterified phosphate. Biological properties include the inhibition of tissues in culture (mouse bone marrow, embryonic mouse skin, and mouse sarcomas 76 and 180) by a number of the synthetic polymers; the high activity of oligoguanylic acids, particularly those with a chain length of approximately six nucleotides, in inducing Streptolysin S formation in *Streptococci;* and the promotion of dipeptide synthesis by polymers of longer chain length in an enzymic system utilising nucleoside-5' triphosphates and amino acids.

Synthesis of oligoribonucleotides carrying a terminal 5' phosphate group was readily achieved by the use of nucleoside-2'(3'),5' diphosphates. Treatment of cytidine-2'(3'),5' diphosphate with ethyl chloroformate gave the nucleoside-2',3' cyclic phosphate 5' phosphate ethyl carbonate anhydride which, after acetylation of the 6-amino group (to prevent phosphoramidate formation), was treated with diphenyl phosphorochloridate and 2',3'-di-O-acetyladenosine. Removal of protecting groups from the product under mild conditions then gave a mixture of the isomeric dinucleotides adenylyl-5' : 2'-cytidine-5' phosphate (P5'C2'P5'A) and adenylyl-5' : 3'-cytidine-5' phosphate (P5'C3'P5'A). In similar fashion, adenylyladenosine-5' phosphate P5'A2'(3')P5'A, and adenylyluridine-5' phosphate P5'U2'(3')P5'A were prepared from the corresponding nucleotide derivatives.[37]

Further treatment of these dinucleotides (isolated in solid form as the free acids) with dibenzyl phosphorochloridate gave intermediate P^1-dibenzyl P^2-dinucleotide-5' pyrophosphates which on hydrogenolysis yielded dinucleotide derivatives containing a terminal 5' pyrophosphate residue. These compounds are of possible interest in connection with the action of polynucleotide phosphorylase. In an alternate approach, the dibenzyl derivative (or the P^1-diphenyl P^2-dinucleotide-5' pyrophosphate, prepared by the action of diphenyl phosphorochloridate) was treated with phosphoric acid to effect nucleophilic displacement of dibenzyl (or diphenyl) phosphate. It may be noted that, under the conditions employed, the phosphorochloridates react with secondary phosphoryl groups only (otherwise cleavage of the internucleotide linkage would occur), and that in the final anion exchange procedure a stronger anion is again replaced by a less stable anion. Conversion of the dinucleotide into the unprotected pyrophosphate thus involves two nucleophilic displacements with liberation of the more stable anion of the anhydride (Cl⁻ then diphenyl phosphate) in each case.[37] Preferential reaction of secondary phosphoryl groups only has been discussed previously in connection with the action of ethyl chloroformate; again specificity is a result of the considerable difference in stability of primary and secondary phosphoryl anions.

The structures of the dinucleotides containing a terminal 5'-pyrophosphate group were fully confirmed by alkaline hydrolysis, or by enzymic hydrolysis with crude snake venom diesterase, to give the expected products. Treatment with ribonuclease (pancreatic or taka-diastase where appropriate) gave nucleoside and nucleoside-(3' phosphate)-5' pyrophosphate, the structures of the latter components being verified by comparison with authentic synthetic specimens.

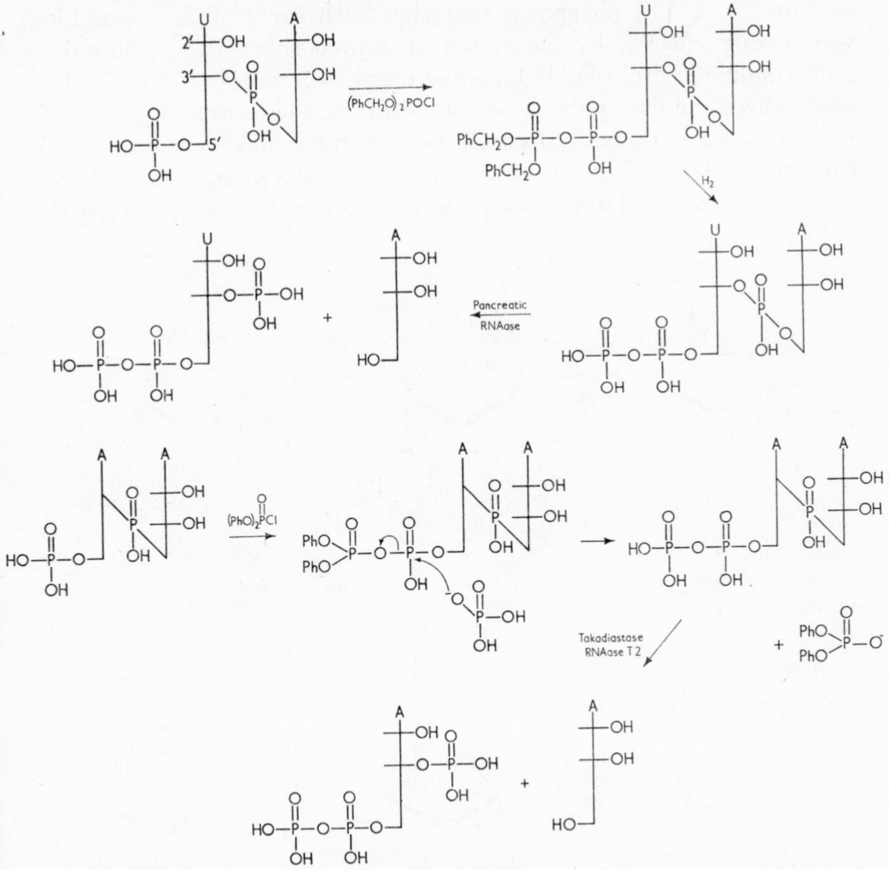

(PhCH₂O)₂POCl

Pancreatic RNAase

H₂

(PhO)₂PCl

Takadiastase RNAase T2

ANALOGUES

In addition to polymers of the naturally occurring nucleotides, a variety of oligoribonucleotide analogues, including poly 4-azauridylic acid,[38] have been prepared by the mixed anhydride method. Halogenation of uridine-2′ (3′) phosphate gave the respective 5-chloro, 5-bromo and 5-iodo derivatives. Conversion into the cyclic phosphate by treatment with ethyl chloroformate followed by polymerisation in the usual manner gave the corresponding polynucleotides.[33] Likewise, poly N^1-methyluridylic acid was readily obtained from N^1-methyluridylic acid, prepared by the action of diazomethane on uridylic acid followed by hydrolysis of phosphate methyl ester groups.[33, 39]

Under suitable conditions, treatment of uridine-2′,3′ cyclic phosphate with methanesulphonyl chloride (or ethanesulphonyl chloride) gives the 5′-O-sulphonyluridine-2′3′ cyclic phosphate which possesses the usual properties of 5′-O-sulphonyl nucleosides. Conversion into 5′-

thio-uridine-2′ (3′) phosphate (together with some of the disulphide) was readily effected by the action of sodium thioacetate followed by mild alkaline hydrolysis. Polymerisation then gave poly 5′-thio-uridylic acid which, unlike poly N^1-methyluridylic acid, was degraded by ribonuclease.[35] Enzymic hydrolysis with rattlesnake venom gave 5′-thiouridine and uridine-2′ (3′) phosphate 5′-thiophosphate, both the 5′-monoesterase and diesterase present in the crude venom being active

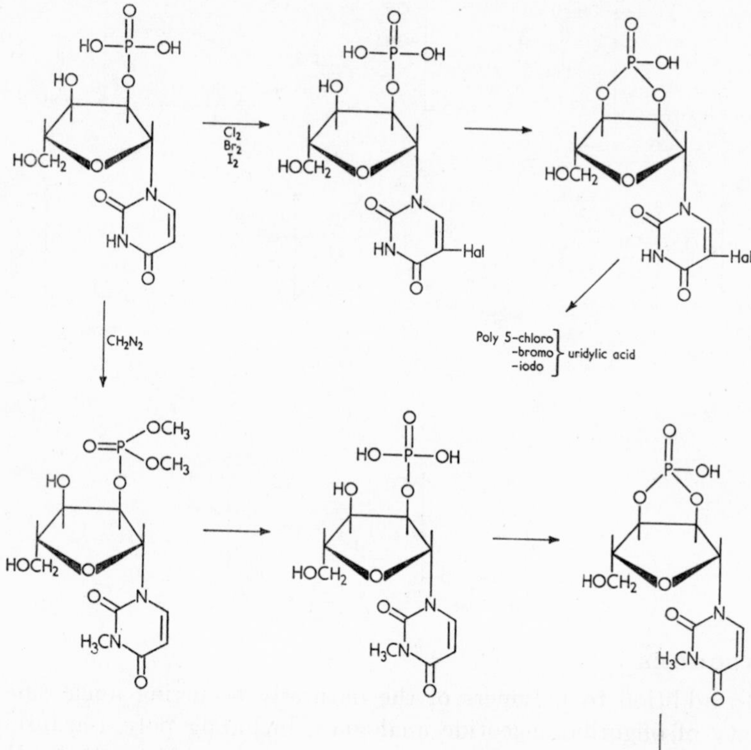

Cl₂ Br₂ I₂

CH₂N₂

Poly S-chloro -bromo -iodo } uridylic acid

Poly N^1-methyluridylic acid

for the 5′-thio derivatives. By treatment with lithium bromide, 5′-O-methanesulphonyluridine-2′,3′ cyclic phosphate was converted into 5′-bromo-5′-deoxyuridine-2′,3′ cyclic phosphate. This, on reaction with 2′,3′-di-O-acetyladenosine and diphenyl phosphorochloridate, followed be removal of protecting groups from the product, gave 5′-bromo-5′-deoxyuridylyl-3′ : 5′-adenosine and the 2′ : 5′ isomer, the former being degraded by ribonuclease.[35]

Treatment of adenosine-2′,3′ cyclic phosphate with methanesulphonyl chloride gave the unstable covalent 5′-O-methanesulphonyl

derivative which on heating was converted into $N^3,5'$-cycloadenosine-
$2',3'$ cyclic phosphate.   Oligoadenylic acids containing a terminal
cycloadenosine residue were prepared in the same way from corres-

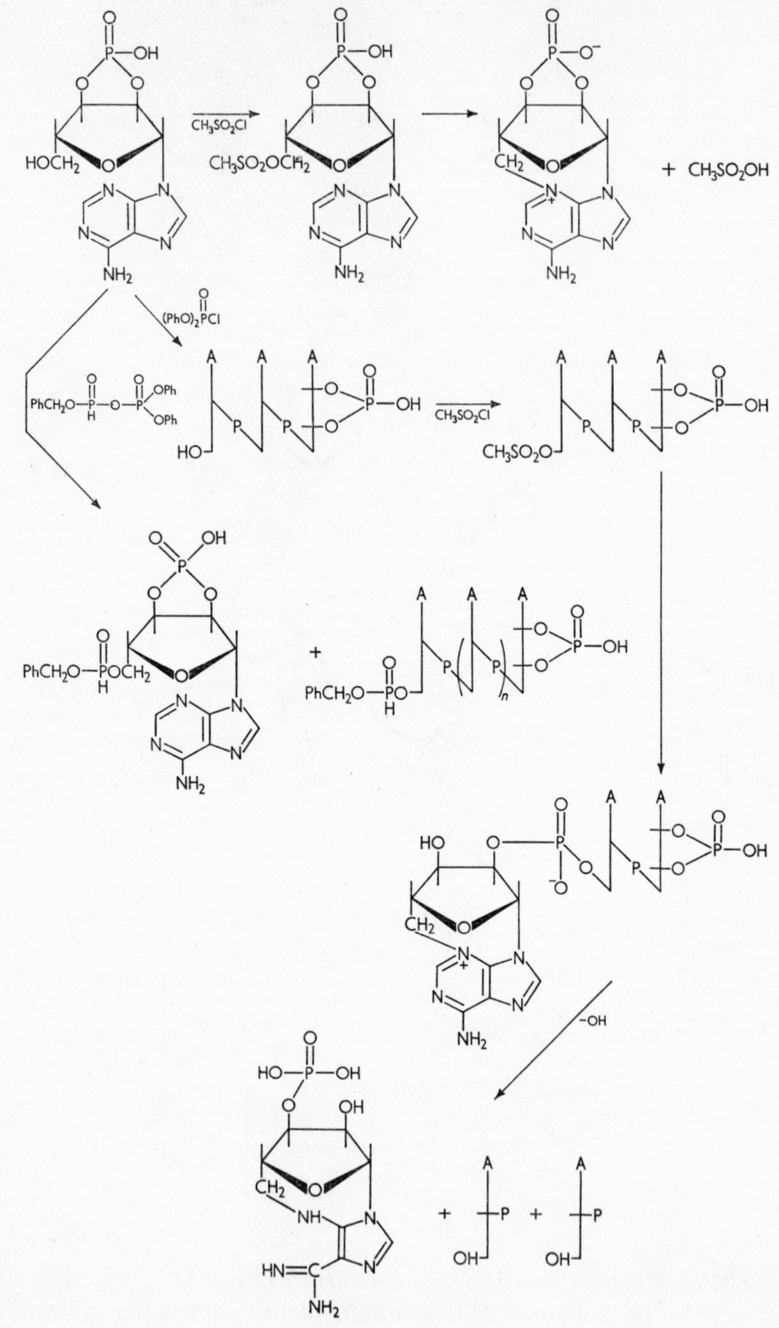
CH3SO2Cl
HOCH2
CH3SO2OCH2
CH2
+ CH3SO2OH
NH2
(PhO)2PCl
PhCH2O—P—O—P(OPh)2
HO
CH3SO2O
PhCH2O—POCH2
PhCH2O—PO
-OH
HO—P—OH
OH
HN=C
NH2

ponding oligonucleotides. On alkaline hydrolysis these were degraded to adenosine-2'(3') phosphate and an imidazole derivative derived from the terminal cyclonucleoside.[31, 34]

Terminally modified polymers of adenylic acid were also formed by the action of O-benzyl phosphorous di-O-phenyl phosphoric anhydride on adenosine-2',3' cyclic phosphate. While some 50% of the material was converted into adenosine-(3',3' cyclic phosphate) 5'-benzyl phosphite,[40] the remainder was isolated as oligoadenylic acids containing a terminal 5'-benzyl phosphite group.[31]

MECHANISM

Although polymerisation of nucleoside-2',3' cyclic phosphates by the action of diphenyl phosphorochloridate provides a clean, rapid, and widely applicable method for the synthesis of oligo- and small poly-ribonucleotides, obvious restrictions yet remain. Thus the products contain a mixture of 2'-5' and 3'-5' internucleotide linkages in approximately equal proportions. Hydrolysis of the intermediate polymeric triester to diester under a variety of solvent and pH conditions had little effect on this ratio, though a similar preparation of benzyl esters of uridylic acid (from uridine-2',3' cyclic phosphate, diphenyl phosphorochloridate, and an excess of benzyl alcohol) gave some 75% of uridine-3' benzyl phosphate and 25% of the 2' isomer.[31] As yet, a direct specific synthesis of the 3'-5' inter-ribonucleotide linkage in the absence of suitable protection of the 2'-hydroxyl group is not available, and use of protecting groups imposes considerable limitations. With respect to the synthesis of polynucleotides of high molecular weight, both the fully esterified mixed anhydride method and the less efficient carbodi-imide approach seem to offer little hope. The chemical synthesis of polynucleotide chains comparable in length with those prepared enzymically will probably require a completely novel approach, perhaps quite unrelated to the more orthodox dogmas of organic chemistry (but see p. 441).

Mechanisms involved in the action of acid anhydrides on nucleoside-2',3' cyclic phosphates were examined further in an investigation of the effect of different anhydrides in dioxan solution in the presence of tri-n-butylamine (that is, a hindered tertiary base), and in pyridine solution.[33] All three possible reactions[41] indicated by cleavage of the an-hydride intermediate at the bonds marked a, b and c can occur, depending on the anhydride and reaction conditions. Nucleophilic attack by the 5' hydroxyl group resulting in cleavage of bonds a or c yields polynucleotide material; cleavage of bond b results in non-polymeric esterification of the 5' hydroxyl group.

Quantitative polymerisation of uridine-2',3' cyclic phosphate occurs

$$X = -\overset{\displaystyle O}{\underset{\displaystyle \|}{P}}\diagup\!\!\!\!\!\overset{OPh}{\diagdown OPh}$$

$$-\overset{\displaystyle O}{\underset{\displaystyle \|}{P}}\diagup\!\!\!\!\!\overset{OCH_2-CH=CH_2}{\diagdown OCH_2-CH=CH_2}$$

$$-\overset{O}{\underset{\|}{C}}\!\!-\!\!\bigcirc \qquad -\overset{O}{\underset{\|}{C}}\!-CH_3$$

$$-SO_2CH_3$$

on treatment with an acid anhydride from a group that includes diphenyl phosphorochloridate, tetraphenyl pyrophosphate, tetra *p*-bromophenyl pyrophosphate, phenyl phosphorodichloridate, and toluene-*p*-sulphonyl chloride, whether the reaction is conducted in pyridine or dioxan. It is reasonable to assume that these reagents all act by mechanism *a*, that is, intermolecular nucleophilic attack by a 5'-hydroxyl group at the nucleotide phosphorus atom with rear displacement of the more stable anion (stronger acid) of the intermediate nucleotide anhydride.

The anhydride must not be too strong, however, since treatment with tetra-*p*-nitrophenyl pyrophosphate does not cause polymerisation, possibly owing to rapid attack by nucleoside cyclic phosphate at the intermediate P^1-nucleoside-2',3' cyclic P^2-di-*p*-nitrophenyl pyrophosphate to give a P^1,P^2-di(nucleoside-2',3' cyclic) pyrophosphate. Such products would be very weak polymerising intermediates, but would be hydrolysed to nucleoside-2',3' cyclic phosphate. (This is probably the mechanism of chain termination in the general polymerisation reactions using diphenyl phosphorochloridate). In common with the anion exchange reactions described previously (p. 221), it appears that for efficient chemical use the reactivity of the intermediate anhydride must not be too small, or too large, and in fact lies between fairly sharply defined limits in terms of the relative stabilities of the anions of the components of the anhydride.

$R' = -CH_2CH=CH_2$

When the intermediate anhydride contains an acid that is not significantly stronger than the cyclic phosphate, as in the case of treatment with tetrabenzyl pyrophosphate, tetra-allyl pyrophosphate, or P^1,P^2-dibenzyl P^1,P^2-diphenyl pyrophosphate, then phosphorylation of the 5' hydroxyl group ensues by mechanism b, that is, nucleophilic attack at the non-nucleotide phosphorus atom of the intermediate anhydride. As may be expected, the reaction is markedly slower than in the case of the stronger anhydrides, and occurs to a significant extent in pyridine only. Since little, if any, reaction occurs in dioxan (in the presence of tri-n-butylamine) the pyridine catalysed reaction probably involves formation of a pyridinium complex.

With benzyl phosphorous diphenyl phosphoric anhydride, the

R=Nucleoside-(2',3' cyclic phosphate)-5'

nucleoside-(2',3' cyclic phosphate)-5' benzyl phosphite was readily formed, both in pyridine and in dioxan solution, via the intermediate nucleoside-2',3' cyclic phosphoric benzyl phosphorous anhydride.   In this case (and possibly in others) the nature of the nucleotide is of some importance since with uridine-2',3' cyclic phosphate only a trace of dinucleotide was formed, whereas with the adenine derivative considerable polymerisation (by mechanism *a*) occurred in addition to " phos-

phitylation " of the 5' hydroxyl group. This may be related to the slightly different acidic strengths of the two nucleoside-2',3' cyclic phosphates, and the stabilities of their anions compared with that of benzyl phosphorous acid.

Carboxylic acid anhydrides of nucleoside-2',3' cyclic phosphates act as acylating agents, that is, nucleophilic attack occurs at the carbonyl group, with displacement of the more stable cyclic phosphate anion (the stronger acid). Thus 5'-*O*-(3,5-dinitrobenzoyl)-uridine-2',3' cyclic phosphate was obtained by the action of 3,5-dinitrobenzoyl chloride on uridine-2',3' cyclic phosphate, in dioxan or in pyridine, acylation being assisted by the additive properties of the carbonyl group. In the same way, acetic anhydride yielded the 5'-O-acetyl derivative.

With benzoyl chloride however, the third mechanism of cleavage at bond c may be invoked, since despite the additive properties of the carbonyl group, considerable polymerisation occurs with this reagent in dioxan solution. Reaction therefore probably involves direct inter-molecular nucleophilic attack by a 5'-hydroxyl group at the phosphorus

R = Nucleoside-(2',3'cyclic phosphate)-5'

atom to give an intermediate oligo(nucleotide–benzoyl anhydride) which is then hydrolysed to oligonucleotide. The same reagent in pyridine effects benzoylation of uridine-2',3' cyclic phosphate (together with some polymerisation), that is, mechanism b is also operative. Treatment of adenosine-2',3' cyclic phosphate with benzoyl chloride gave mainly oligonucleotide material in both solvents. Steric aspects of the conformation of the benzoyl–cyclic phosphate anhydride may be of importance with respect to successful attack at the phosphorus atom.

An even stronger solvent directive effect, but with reverse results, was observed with a group of anhydride reagents that includes methane-sulphonyl chloride and ethanesulphonyl chloride. In dioxan, only the

$5'$-O-alkanesulphonyluridine-$2'$,$3'$ cyclic phosphate was obtained (mechanism b), whereas in pyridine both reagents caused extensive polymerisation.

The nature of the products from fully esterified nucleotide anhydrides of the type described is thus a function of the components of the anhydride and in particular of the non-nucleotide moiety (though differences among the nucleotides are apparent), and the nature of the solvent (presumably the dielectric properties of the environment affects the electronic distribution in the anhydride), and of the presence or absence of base catalysis.[33] In some respects the chemical control and direction of the course of the reactions is at least reminiscent of the enzymic control that is evident in a number of biochemical reactions involving anhydrides of nucleoside-$5'$ phosphates. Further analogies are to be found in the chemical synthesis of nucleotide coenzymes by nucleophilic anion exchange.

ETHYL POLYPHOSPHATE

Recently the use of ethyl polyphosphate (obtained by dissolving phosphorus pentoxide in ethyl ether) for polymerisation of mononucleotides to high molecular weight materials has been described.[42, 43] The nucleotides ($2'$, $3'$ or $5'$ phosphates; or $2'$,$3'$ cyclic phosphates) are simply mixed with the viscous polyphosphate ester and maintained at a temperature of 50–60°; addition of pyridine catalyses polymerisation. After dialysis of the reaction product, non-dialysable polynucleotides are obtained in 10–20% yield. Molecular weights, determined by sedimentation and viscosity measurements, are of the order 2–5×10^4, indicating chain lengths of approximately 100 nucleotides. Preliminary evidence indicated that with the ribonucleotides the naturally occurring $3'$-$5'$ linkage is predominantly formed. The method is also applicable to the polymerisation of deoxynucleotides.

Of considerable interest is the fact that the reagent (which can also be used for the synthesis of nucleosides and mononucleotides) is effective for the replacement of heterocyclic bases in apurinic acid. Thus treatment of apurinic acid from calf thymus DNA with ethyl polyphosphate and adenine gave material in which the gaps were filled completely by adenine, no free aldehydo groups being detectable. Reconstituted DNA was degraded by deoxyribonuclease and snake venom phosphodiesterase, and after hydrolysis deoxyadenosine was found in the required amount. The reconstitution could be carried out either under anhydrous conditions (in dimethylformamide) or in aqueous solution.[43]

Although other approaches to the synthesis of specific compounds may be superior to the use of ethyl polyphosphate, the versatility of this reagent is outstanding. In addition to the synthesis of nucleosides, nucleotides, and polynucleotides the reagent is useful for polypeptide synthesis and for the preparation of linear polysaccharides including poly β-(1 → 4)-D-glucose and even unstable polysaccharides such as poly α-(1 → 5)-D-ribose.[42, 43, 48] Again, small amounts of water do not interfere with polymerisation. All these reactions are of considerable interest in connection with theories of the chemical origin of life.

REFERENCES

1. Gulland, J. M., and Smith, H., *J. Chem. Soc.*, 1532 (1948).
2. Elmore, D. T., and Todd, A. R., *J. Chem. Soc.*, 3681 (1952).
3. Michelson, A. M., *Biochim. et Biophys. Acta*, **55**, 841 (1962).
4. Durant, G. J., Turnbull, J. H., and Wilson, W., *Chem. and Ind. (London)*, 157 (1958).
5. Riley, G., Turnbull, J. H., and Wilson, W., *J. Chem. Soc.*, 1373 (1957).
6. Hall, R. H., Todd, A. R., and Webb, R. F., *J. Chem. Soc.*, 3291 (1957).
7. Michelson, A. M., and Todd, A. R., *J. Chem. Soc.*, 2632 (1955).
8. Michelson, A. M., Szabo, L., and Todd, A. R., *J. Chem. Soc.*, 1546 (1956).
9. Christie, S. M. H., Elmore, D. T., Kenner, G. W., Todd, A. R., and Weymouth, F. J., *J. Chem. Soc.*, 2947 (1953).
10. Tener, G. M., Khorana, H. G., Markham, R., and Pol, E. H., *J. Am. Chem. Soc.*, **80**, 6223 (1958).
11. Okazaki, R., *Biochim. et Biophys. Acta*, **44**, 478 (1960).
12. Turner, A. F., and Khorana, H. G., *J. Am. Chem. Soc.*, **81**, 4651 (1959).
13. Khorana, H. G., and Vizsolyi, J. P., *J. Am. Chem. Soc.*, **83**, 675 (1961).
14. Khorana, H. G., Turner, A. F., and Vizsolyi, J. P., *J. Am. Chem. Soc.*, **83**, 686 (1961).
15. Ralph, R. K., and Khorana, H. G., *J. Am. Chem. Soc.*, **83**, 2926 (1961).
16. Todd, A. R., *Proc. Natl. Acad. Sci. U.S.A.*, **45**, 1389 (1959).
17. Cramer, F., and Wittmann, R., *Angew. Chem.*, **72**, 628 (1960).
18. Weimann, G., and Khorana, H. G., *Chem. and Ind. (London)*, 271 (1962).
19. Khorana, H. G., Razzell, W. E., Gilham, P. T., Tener, G. M., and Pol, E. H., *J. Am. Chem. Soc.*, **79**, 1002 (1957).
20. Gilham, P. T., and Khorana, H. G., *J. Am. Chem. Soc.*, **80**, 6212 (1958).
21. Schaller, H., and Khorana, H. G., *Chem. and Ind. (London)*, 699 (1962).
22. Tener, G. M., *J. Am. Chem. Soc.*, **83**, 159 (1961).
23. Gilham, P. T., and Khorana, H. G., *J. Am. Chem. Soc.*, **81**, 4647 (1959).
24. Smith, M., and Khorana, H. G., *J. Am. Chem. Soc.*, **81**, 2911 (1959).
25. Rammler, D. H., and Khorana, H. G., *J. Am. Chem. Soc.*, **84**, 3112 (1962).
26. Smrt, J., Beranek, J., and Šorm, F., *Collection Czechoslov. Chem. Communs.*, **25**, 2459 (1960).
27. Michelson, A. M., *Nature*, **181**, 303 (1958).
28. Michelson, A. M., *Chem. and Ind. (London)*, 1147 (1958).
29. Brown, D. M., Magrath, D. I., and Todd, A. R., *J. Chem. Soc.*, 4396 (1955).
30. Michelson, A. M., *Chem. and Ind. (London)*, 70 (1958).
31. Michelson, A. M., *J. Chem. Soc.*, 1371 (1959).
32. Michelson, A. M., *J. Chem. Soc.*, 3655 (1959).
33. Letters, R., and Michelson, A. M., *J. Chem. Soc.*, 71 (1962).
34. Michelson, A. M., unpublished work.

35. Michelson, A. M., *J. Chem. Soc.*, 979 (1962).
36. Cohn, W. E., and Volkin, E., *J. Biol. Chem.*, **203**, 319 (1953).
37. Michelson, A. M., Strasbourg Meeting on RNA and Polyphosphates, July, 1961.
38. Beranek, J., and Smrt, J., *Collection Czechoslov. Chem. Communs.*, **25**, 2029 (1960).
39. Szer, W., and Shugar, D., *Acta Biochim. Polon.*, **7**, 491 (1960).
40. Michelson, A. M., *J. Chem. Soc.*, 2055 (1958).
41. Michelson, A. M., *Nature*, **181**, 375 (1958).
42. Schramm, G., Grotsch, H., and Pollmann, W., *Angew. Chem.*, **73**, 619 (1961).
43. Schramm, G., Strasbourg Meeting on RNA and Polyphosphates, July, 1961.
44. Khorana, H. G., Vizsolyi, J. P., and Ralph, R. K., *J. Am. Chem. Soc.*, **84**, 414 (1962).
45. Smith, M., Rammler, D. H., Goldberg, I. H., and Khorana, H. G., *J. Am. Chem. Soc.*, **84**, 430 (1962).
46. Weimann, G., and Khorana, H. G., *J. Am. Chem. Soc.*, **84**, 419 (1962).
47. Smrt, J., and Sorm, F., *Coll. Czech. Chem. Communs.*, **27**, 73 (1962).
48. Schramm, G., Grotsch, H., and Pollmann, N., *Angew. Chem.*, **74**, 53 (1961).

Chapter 8

PHYSICAL CHEMISTRY OF NUCLEIC ACIDS

The physical chemistry of nucleic acids is essentially the description and interpretation of a number of properties that are manifested by virtue of the secondary structures of the polymers. Primary structure, that is, the nature and organisation of the covalent bonds in the molecule, has been, and will continue to be, elucidated mainly by the characteristic methods of biochemistry and organic chemistry. Secondary structural aspects are concerned with the size, shape, and conformation of the macromolecule, and are susceptible to examination by X-ray analytical techniques, as well as the less specialised methods of physical chemistry. To some extent, the purely morphological details of tertiary structure lie within the range of modern electron microscope techniques. These details include the relation of nucleic acid to protein in nucleoproteins, the arrangement of aggregates of polynucleotide strands and the packing of subunits in viruses and nucleoprotein particles. At an even higher level, such as the distribution of nucleic acids in chromosomes, it is doubtful whether the term molecule (or even macromolecule) retains much relevant meaning with respect to indication of distinct entities.

Many of the physical properties formerly assumed to be associated solely with relatively high molecular weight nucleic acids are now known to be exhibited by oligonucleotides and small polynucleotides.[1] Despite the historical distortion involved and the occasional repetition which must ensue, the subject will be treated first in terms of oligonucleotides of known structure. Discussion of the properties of high molecular weight enzymically synthesised polymers will then follow, and finally the nucleic acids themselves will be examined. It is hoped that in this way at least some of the confusions which have arisen from time to time will be avoided, and that heresies will be kept to a minimum.

Physical Properties of Oligonucleotides

Present knowledge of the physical chemistry of oligonucleotides and small polynucleotides has resulted mainly from studies of ribonucleotide materials prepared by chemical synthesis.[2, 3] In addition to synthetic oligoribonucleotides containing 3′–5′ internucleotide linkages as in the naturally occurring nucleic acids, the isomeric 2′–5′ linked derivatives have proved of considerable value for the interpretation and delineation

444

of a number of properties characteristic of oligonucleotides in general.[4] One of the more striking of these properties is the effect of polymerisation on the ultraviolet absorption of the purine and pyrimidine bases.

HYPERCHROMIC EFFECT

Degradation of nucleic acids is accompanied by an increase in ultraviolet absorption, normally measured in the region of the absorption maximum (260 mμ). This hyperchromic effect has been observed frequently[5-16] and it may be concluded that all recorded values of molar absorptivities for intact nucleic acids are lower than the summation of the absorptivities of the component mononucleotides.[17] Since nucleic acids are ill defined, the absorptivity is normally expressed with respect to molar quantities of phosphate,[18] the figure then representing an average molar absorption per nucleotide. Typical values for the increase in absorption on total alkaline or enzymic hydrolysis of ribonucleic acids to mononucleotides range from 24–45%. Somewhat smaller hyperchromic effects (approximately 15%) are shown on partial degradation by treatment with pancreatic ribonuclease. For convenience, hyperchromicity (that is, the percentage increase in ultraviolet absorption at the wavelength maximum on degradation or denaturation) is generally used rather than expression of the results as hypochromicity (percentage decrease in absorption) accompanying polymerisation or hydrogen bonding. Undenatured deoxynucleic acids and certain high molecular weight enzymically synthesised ribonucleotide homopolymers can show extremely large hyperchromicities (up to 60–70%) on total degradation.

Contrary to the view that hypochromicity does not result from the union of a few mononucleotides, several di-deoxynucleotides were found to possess absorptivities lower than those of the constituents[15, 19, 20] by some 5–10%. In agreement with these results hyperchromic effects were also observed on degradation of a wide range of oligoribonucleotides. Representative alkaline hyperchromicities given in Tables 8-I and 8-II indicate that the effect, which can be quite large even in dinucleotides, rapidly reaches a limiting value at chain lengths of 5–6 nucleotides in a given homologous series[21] and is a function, not only of the composition of the entire molecule, but also of the order of the bases.[22]

Considerable variation of hyperchromicity with pH was also observed and again the results (Table 8-II) indicate that, as with the hyperehromic effect itself, the effect of pH on the ultraviolet absorption of oligonucleotides and small polynucleotides relative to the absorption of the component mononucleotides at the same pH is a composite of many different curves, characteristic not only of the nucleotide composi-

TABLE 8-I. *Alkaline hyperchromicities* (%)

Compound	Average chain length	Hyper-chromicity	Compound	Hyper-chromicity
Polyadenylic	7·7	31·8	UpGpA	6·8
Polyadenylic	13·6	36·7	GpApU	11·3
Polycytidylic	9·8	15·9	GpUpA	5·3
Polyguanylic	12·5	0	CpApU	12·5
Polyuridylic	6·6	6·5	CpUpA	7·5
Polyuridylic	11·9	8·6	CpUpGpA	7·7
Polyuridylic	6·2	10·5	CpGpApU	12·9
Poly ACGU	12·5	14·3	CpGpUpA	6·2
Dicytidylic	—	8·7	GpCpApU	12·3
Tricytidylic	—	13·9	GpCpUpA	6·6
Tetracytidylic	—	15·3	ApUpGpC	8·6

All the above polymers contain mixed 2′–5′ and 3′–5′ linkages.

Compound	Hyperchromicity	Compound	Hyperchromicity
A3′P5′A3′P5′C3′P	22·5	C2′P5′C	10·8
A3′P5′A3′P5′C	23·3	C3′P5′C	7·4
G3′P5′C3′P	3·8	G2′P5′A	5·0
G3′P5′C	3·0	G3′P5′A	3·3
U2′P5′A	5·2	A2′P5′A	18·4
U3′P5′A	3·2	A3′P5′A	13·3
A2′P5′U	12·8	C2′P5′A	9·7
A3′P5′U	4·1	C3′P5′A	10·2
A5′P5′U	10·3	A3′P5′C	7·6

tion but also of the distribution of bases. In particular, the hyper-chromicity of dinucleotides containing aminopurines or aminopyrimidines is considerably reduced in acidic solutions, but is virtually the same under neutral or alkaline conditions, whereas dinucleotides containing 6-keto groups (the " acidic " nucleosides) show a marked reduction of the hyperchromic effect at alkaline pHs when the purine or pyrimidine base is fully ionised, relative to the effect in neutral or acidic solutions.

It may also be noted that hyperchromicity is not restricted to 3′–5′ internucleotide linked polymers, but is a property shown by di-nucleoside-5′ phosphates (i.e. 5′–5′ phosphodiesters) as well as 2′–5′ linked isomers. Indeed significant hypochromic effects (of the order 15–40%) are shown by $\alpha\omega$-di-9-purinyl ethanes and hexanes,[23] particularly the

TABLE 8-II. *Variation of hyperchromicity with pH*

Compound	0·01 N HCl	pH 7	0·2 N NaOH
A2′P5′U	12·3	10·0	12·8
A3′P5′U	—	—	4·1
A5′P5′U	13·6	—	10·3
P^1-Adenosine-5′ P^2-uridine-5′ pyrophosphate	9·0	12·6	6·7
N3′P5′N3′Ac*	11·2	22·5	24·5
Ac3′N5′P5′N3′Ac*	11·9	33·1	39·3
P^1,P^2-Di-adenosine-5′ pyrophosphate	13.6	33·9	33·9
Diadenylic acid (mixed 2′–5′ and 3′–5′ linkages)	0	—	15·1
Triadenylic acid (mixed 2′–5′ and 3′–5′ linkages)	6·8	—	22·8
Tetra-adenylic acid (mixed 2′–5′ and 3′–5′ linkages)	13·2	—	30·7
Penta-adenylic acid (mixed 2′–5′ and 3′–5′ linkages)	16·4	—	32·9
Polyadenylic acid (average chain length 13·6)	22·9	—	36·7
Polyguanylic acid (average chain length 12·5)	18·0	23·0	0
Poly [adenylic (2)-guanylic (1)] acid (average chain length 6·2)	14·7	36·7	19·0
Poly N′-methyluridylic acid (average chain length 5·9)	16·5	19·2	8·5
P^1-Adenosine-5′ P^2-oestrone pyrophosphate	—	~ 25	($\epsilon_{max} = 12{,}600$; calculated = 16,000)

* N = 6-dimethylamino-9-β-D-(3′-amino-3′-deoxyribofuranosyl)-purine.

former, compared with the 9-methyl (or ribosyl) derivatives. The purine bases include purine, adenine, 6-dimethylaminopurine, and 6-dimethylamino-8-azapurine, and again the departure from additivity of the absorptivity of the component bases is considerably less in acidic (pH 1) than in neutral or alkaline solution, even with αω-di-9-purinyl hexane.

A reduction in ϵ_{max} values is also evident in P^1,P^2-di-nucleoside-5′ pyrophosphates.[24] The pyrophosphate linkage considerably increases the flexibility necessary for closest approach and maximum overlap of the bases and it is not surprising that hyperchromic values for P^1,P^2-di-adenosine-5′ pyrophosphate are considerably greater than those for the isomeric di-adenylic acids. A 20% decrease from the calculated ϵ value for P^1-adenosine P^2-oestrone pyrophosphate has also been

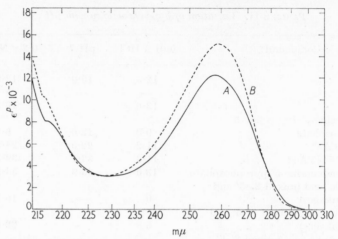

FIG. 8-1. Action of alkali on triadenylic acid. A, in 0·2N NaOH, polymer; B, products.[21]

observed,[25] presumably the result of interaction between the adenine nucleus and benzene ring of the steroid. With respect to dinucleoside phosphates and higher oligonucleotides, in general the 2′–5′ isomers show greater hyperchromic effects than the 3′–5′ derivatives; the effect of base order is demonstrated by the relative hyperchromicities of A2′P5′U and the isomeric U2′P5′A. Though less marked, the latter

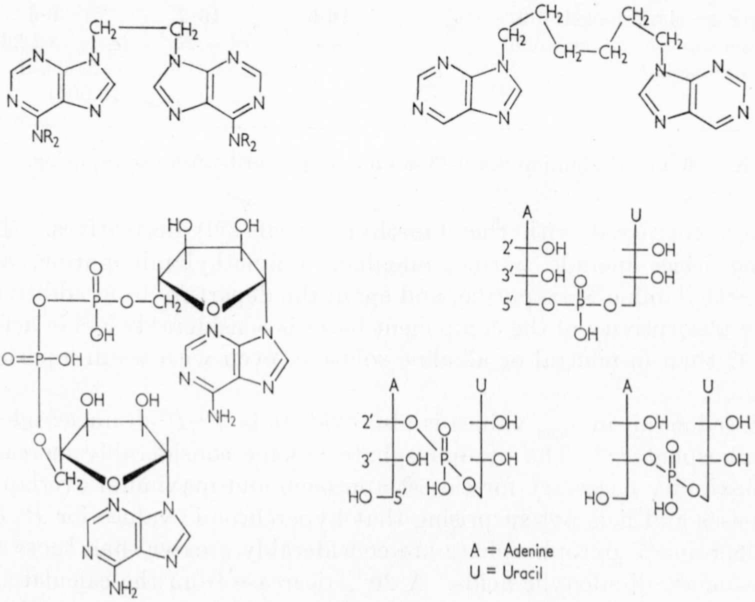

A = Adenine
U = Uracil

FIG. 8-2.

type of variation is also evident in 3'-5' linked oligonucleotides of identical base composition, but differing in base sequence.

Since large hyperchromic effects are shown by dinucleoside phosphates derived from 6-dimethylaminopurine (larger in fact than those shown by the analogous adenine derivatives)[24] at all pHs, it is unlikely that hydrogen bonding plays a significant role in the hypochromicity of oligonucleotides, particularly as the effect is not sensitive to increases in temperature up to 90°C. Ice-like lattices of water molecules, while perhaps significant in connection with the macromolecular structure of high molecular weight deoxynucleic acids, hardly seem reasonable when applied to dinucleoside phosphates. Further, the disappearance of hypochromicity in dinucleotides such as A3'P5'U and A3'P5'C3'P on

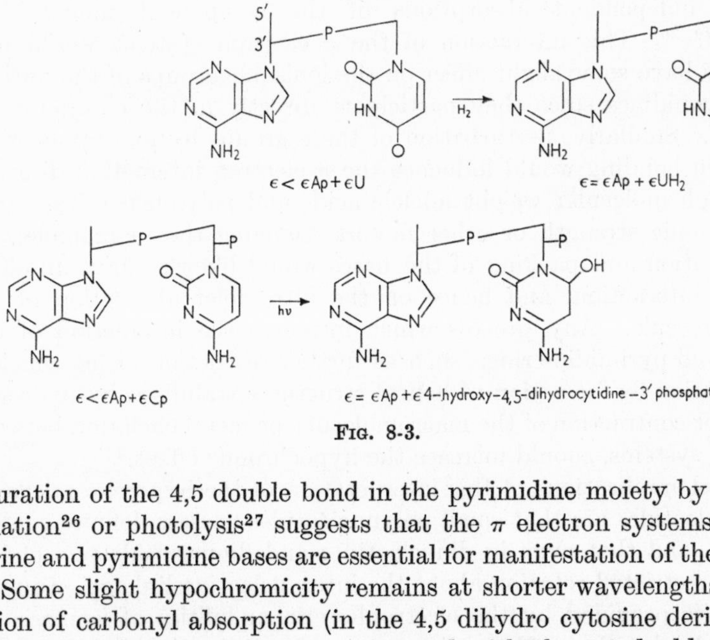

FIG. 8-3.

saturation of the 4,5 double bond in the pyrimidine moiety by hydrogenation[26] or photolysis[27] suggests that the π electron systems of the purine and pyrimidine bases are essential for manifestation of the effect.

Some slight hypochromicity remains at shorter wavelengths in the region of carbonyl absorption (in the 4,5 dihydro cytosine derivatives the 2-carbonyl group remains conjugated with the 1,6 double bond), but loss of aromatic character in such derivatives gives intermediates for which the absorption at the maximum is essentially additive in terms of the component nucleotides.[27] Similarly, saturation of the uracil 4,5 double bond in GpUpA gives a product that shows no hypochromicity, but the dihydro or photolysed product from the isomeric UpGpA still shows a lowered absorptivity resulting from the adjacent purine residues.[28] In the case of the photolysed derivatives, reversal of the reaction (thermal reactivation) results in complete recovery of hypochromicity. Although loss of aromatic character in the pyrimidine ring systems has a marked effect on the dissociation constants (conversion of cytosine into dihydrocytosine shifts the pK of the amino group from 4·6 to greater than 6, and in dihydrouracil the pK of the –NH—CO– group is greater than 11) the 4,5-dihydro pyrimidines exist predominantly in forms that would permit hydrogen bonding.[26]

While other explanations have been offered, the most plausible interpretation of these results is that even in relatively small polynucleotides the purine and/or pyrimidine bases are stacked in layers above each other to some extent, and that interaction of π electrons of adjacent rings not only stabilises this conformation, but also causes an essentially new electronic species with an ultraviolet absorption characteristic of the entire molecule, rather than a simple summation of the independent absorptions of the component mononucleotides.[2, 29, 30] This interaction of the π electron systems would presumably have some slight effect on the ionisable groups of the purines and pyrimidines since they participate directly in the chromophoric systems. Similarly, perturbation of these groups by ionisation or by hydrogen bonding would influence the π electron interaction directly. With high molecular weight nucleic acids and polynucleotides, variation of ionic strength or other factors changing the macromolecular conformation and packing of the bases would likewise have an effect on this interaction, and hence on the ultraviolet absorption of the total molecule. Any process which increases the interaction of the purine and pyrimidine rings, such as further restriction of internucleotide rotation by formation of helical structures stabilised by hydrogen bonds, or contraction of the macromolecule, or metal chelation between the ring systems, should increase the hypochromic effect.[4]

Direct implications of this interpetation of the hyperchromicity of oligonucleotides are that small polynucleotides possess definite conformations, and that even in dinucleotides and dinucleoside phosphates there is restricted rotation about the internucleotide linkage. Support for this is provided by the electrophoretic mobilities of isomeric dinucleoside phosphates.[22] In all cases examined, the 2'–5' linked derivatives show a greater mobility than the 3'–5' isomers (paralleling the hyperchromicities) suggesting that the former are more compact than the latter as a result of stronger interaction between the bases. This is particularly noticeable, since in other respects the 3'–5' compounds behave as stronger acids.

The hyperchromicity of a given oligonucleotide is thus a measure of the interaction between the bases, and this is dependent on the overlap and interplanar distance As may be expected, these factors are not identical in isomeric dinucleoside phosphates such as

A3'P5'C and C3'P5'A, since the direction of the linkage controls the displacement necessary for closest approach of the purine and pyrimidine bases. Similarly, the stereochemistry of 2'–5' isomers, such as A2'P5'U, will in general permit a closer approach and greater overlap of the bases than in the corresponding 3'–5' linked compounds, such as A3'P5'U. In addition to stacking of the bases, the interplanar interaction in larger oligonucleotides and polynucleotides may also result in a helical twist along the sugar phosphate axis, assuming closest approach and maximum overlap of the π electron systems. This may well provide a measure of stability for double helical structures, even in the absence of inter-strand complementary hydrogen bonding, and thus account for the reversible titration of deoxynucleic acids at or below 0°, compared with the hysteresis (indicating denaturation) noted at higher temperatures.[31, 32] Some further restriction of rotation of the base about the glycosyl linkage might also be expected in polyribonucleotides that contain pyrimidine nucleosides, as a result of hydrogen bonding between pyrimidine C2 carbonyl groups and sugar 2' hydroxyl groups. This would be absent in the corresponding polydeoxynucleotides which should therefore show a greater freedom of conformational change. A direct comparison of polycytidylic and polydeoxycytidylic acid would be of interest. (See relative stabilities of complexes of the two polymers with polydeoxyguanylic acid, p. 473.)

The effect of ionisation of the purine and pyrimidine bases on the hypochromic effect has been mentioned previously. While to some extent these changes are a result of alteration of the π electron systems, it is likely that a major cause is the increased lateral displacement or interplanar separation of the bases due to repulsion by similarly charged purines or pyrimidines. Further, in any polynucleotide two opposing effects are presumably present: strain set up by the charged phosphate groups leading to separation, balanced by the interaction of the purine and pyrimidine bases. The position of this balance, in terms of the precise stereochemical structure of the molecule will undoubtedly be greatly influenced by the degree of ionisation of the phosphate residues (effect of pH, ionic strength and nature of cations present) as well as the state of the bases. Since the energy (ΔE) of Van der Waal's interaction for non-polar molecules is an inverse function of the distance between the molecules (r_{AB}) to the sixth power as given in an approximation[33] to London's general equation

$$\Delta E = \frac{- 3\alpha_A\alpha_B(I_A)(I_B)}{2r_{AB}^{6}(I_A + I_B)}$$

α_A and α_B are polarisabilities of the molecules
I_A and I_B are approximately equal to the
ionisation potentials of the molecules

it is clear that very small differences in the interplanar distances will markedly affect the interaction.

In addition to the hypochromicity shown by oligonucleotides at the absorption maximum, small but significant hyperchromic effects are found at longer wavelengths (280–300 mμ), even in di- and tri-nucleotides.[21] (See p. 539 for a more detailed discussion of hypochromism.)

As well as changing the ultraviolet absorption, primary interactions in oligonucleotides cause an increased positive optical rotation of 10–30%. This may be compared with an up to tenfold increase in deoxynucleic acids resulting from the rigorously organised secondary structure.[34]

INTERACTION WITH DYES

Confirmatory evidence that oligonucleotides possess definite conformations involving the stacking of purine and pyrimidine bases is provided by the action of such polymers on the visible absorption spectra of a number of dyes. The binding of certain planar basic dyes and aminoacridines by nucleic acids has been studied extensively.[35–51] Basic dyes that exhibit metachromasy on interaction with poly-electrolytes are characterised by their failure to obey Beer's Law in aqueous solution. This spectroscopic deviation results from aggregation of the dye molecules in concentrated solutions. Aggregation in such cases has long been held to occur by the stacking of the planar aromatic molecules one above the other, the micelle being held together by London dispersion forces among the π electron systems, with consequent change in the visible absorption spectra. Binding of such dyes by nucleic acids causes similar effects in dilute solution. A direct parallel of the metachromasy of the dyes (due to stacking) with the hypochromicity of oligonucleotides is supported by observations[52, 53] indicating that the forces operating between the rings of the neighbouring ions of dye aggregates in concentrated solutions of the dyestuff have an equilibrium distance of 3–4 Å. The negative visible dichroism of dyed fibres of deoxynucleic acid (using Toluidine Blue) suggests that the planar absorbing groups of the dye lie roughly at right angles to the fibre length in such cases.[54] Phosphoryl dissociating groups of polynucleotide chains are generally regarded as the major binding sites for the interaction of basic dye molecules,[37, 55] and the metachromasy induced in Toluidine Blue by calf thymus deoxynucleo-histone has been cited as evidence that the uncombined phosphate groups in the nucleoprotein occur in sequences[36] (possibly a result of the removal of protein subunits). Rosaniline, Thionine, and Acridine Orange have been commonly used for dye interaction studies, in addition to Toluidine Blue. Acridine Orange also exhibits a marked self-quenching of the fluorescence as a result of stacking of the dye molecules, either by concentration effects or by interaction with polyanions.[41]

Effects similar to, but not identical with, those observed using nucleic acids were shown by the action of synthetic oligonucleotides (average chain length approximately 6 nucleotides) on the absorption spectra of Rosaniline, Toluidine Blue, and Acridine Orange.[21, 22] Equimolar amounts of dye and polymer phosphate were used to avoid isolated, " monomeric " bindings which would presumably arise in the presence of a large excess of polymer.[56] Low ionic buffer strengths were also employed, since the binding constants for dye–nucleic acid

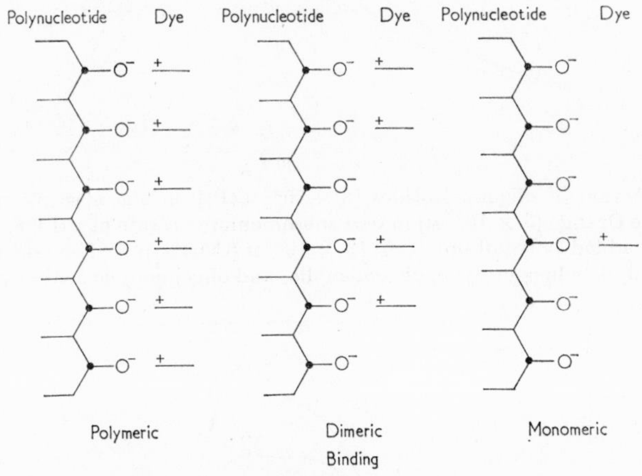

FIG. 8-4.

complexes are lowered by excess cations, particularly divalent cations. (The latter are some thirty times more effective than the monovalent ions and probably act in a purely competitive manner).[57] In all cases the effects of the synthetic polymers on the absorption of the dye were smaller than those observed with degraded ribonucleic acid specimens of comparable chain length. A plausible explanation for this lies in the mixed 2'–5' and 3'–5' internucleotide linkages of the synthetic materials, resulting in an arrangement of phosphate groups along the chain less uniform than in the natural polynucleotides. Hence, even with complete occupation of sites, extensive metachromasy would result only at tracts of 2'–5' or of 3'–5' linkages. Overall, the appearance thus represents " dimeric " rather than " polymeric " binding. As shown, the nature of the purine or pyrimidine base in the polynucleotide chain has a profound effect on the induced metachromasy of the dye. Whether this is an indication of secondary stereospecific requirements for effective binding, or a reflection of the extent of ordered conformation in the various homopolymers is not yet known. The effectiveness of homopolymers of comparable chain lengths is in the ascending order poly U < poly C < poly A < poly G. This order is also observed for polynucleotide-

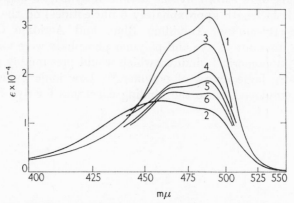

Fig. 8-5. Action of oligonucleotides [3×10^{-5}M (P)] on the absorption spectrum of Acridine Orange (3×10^{-5}M) in 0·01 M-ammonium acetate at pH 6·8. 1, Dye alone; 2, with added polyglutamic acid [3×10^{-5}M (COOH)]; 3, 4, 5 and 6, with added oligouridylic, oligocytidylic, oligoadenylic, and oligoguanylic acid respectively. [21, 22]

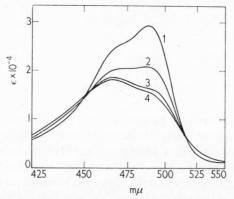

Fig. 8-6. Effect of chain length of oligonucleotide on interaction with Acridine Orange 1, Dye alone; 2, 3 and 4 with added oligoguanylic acids of approximate chain length 4, 6 and 10 respectively. [124]

induced quenching of the fluorescence of Acridine Orange, using the same synthetic polynucleotide specimens. The influence of chain length of the polymer on interaction with dyes is of interest. Significant interaction appears to occur at chain lengths of 8 to 10 nucleotides; with homogeneous material (exclusively 2′–5′ or 3′–5′ linked) effective dye-binding probably occurs at lower chain lengths (4 to 5 nucleotides).

Similar effects have been observed with apurinic acid, which contains relatively short stretches (up to 10 nucleotides) of polypyrimidine deoxynucleotides, and a wide variety of basic dyes.[58]

Polyglycerophosphate (average chain length 12·1 glycerophosphate units) in which a regular spacing of phosphate residues would not be expected, was quite without effect on the dyes under the general conditions used.[21] However, marked interaction of Acridine Orange and α-poly-L-glutamic acid (random conformation), comparable with the metachromasy induced by polyguanylic acid, was observed.[1] To some extent, the dye molecules are presumably stacked at carboxyl binding sites which are suitably located at 3–4 Å intervals.

OTHER PROPERTIES

Interaction of mercuric chloride with oligonucleotides has also been observed. Whereas negligible changes in the ultraviolet absorption spectra occurred on addition of mercuric chloride to adenylyl-3' : 5'-adenosine (A3'P5'A), the synthetic polyadenylic acids showed an increasing degree of interaction with increase in chain length, as evidenced by the bathochromic shift of the λ_{max} and decrease in absorptivity approximately 15%).[59] Direct interaction of mercuric ion with the heterocyclic bases is involved. With deoxynucleic acid a marked decrease in intrinsic viscosity is observed in addition to the spectral changes.[60]

Polymerisation can also affect the apparent pK values of the bases. No significant changes were observed with oligouridylic acid or oligocytidylic acid, but spectrophotometric titrations of oligo-guanylic acid indicated that the apparent pK of 2·3 for the mononucleotide was shifted to 2·6 for polymer with an average chain length of 5·4 nucleotides, and in the alkaline region shifts from 9·3 to 10·8 (for polymers with an average chain length 5·4 units) and to 11·2 (for polyguanylic acid with an average chain length of 12·5 units) were noted. A similar shift of the guanine –NH—CO– dissociation (to 10·2) was observed[22] on polymerisation of the dinucleotide G3'P5'C3'P. While differences might be expected as a result of local (intrastrand) charge effects (and have indeed been observed with respect to the cytosine amino dissociation between cytidine-2' and -3' phosphate,[61] between isomeric 2'–5' and 3'–5' dinucleoside phosphates,[22] and between dinucleoside phosphates and dinucleotides)[22] such effects are small, or virtually absent, as in oligocytidylic acids. The effects of π electron interaction of the bases on pK values are presumably equally small and the possibility arises that such shifts, previously observed in deoxynucleic acids,[62, 63] are primarily the result of hydrogen bonding within the strand or between distinct oligonucleotide chains, even in virtually salt-free solutions. (Compare the increase in acidic pK value when high molecular weight polyuridylic acid forms a hydrogen bonded double helical complex with polyadenylic acid, p. 467.) Thermally induced hyperchromic effects (approximately 20% increase in absorption at 260 mμ between 19° and 80° in neutral salt solution) indicative of hydrogen-bonded (random or otherwise) structures have been observed with the chemically synthesised polyguanylic acid. Somewhat smaller increases in absorption also occur on heating salt-free solutions of short chain polyguanylic acids, and in this case moderate or high ionic strength does not appear to be necessary for effective hydrogen bonding.[24] Related studies of the variation of optical rotation with temperature would be of interest.*

In addition, an increased domain electrostatic potential may result from organisation of the charged phosphate groups in a secondary structure maintained by hydrogen bonds (interstrand charge effects). The effect of ionic strength on the absorptivity and pK values of polyguanylic acid (average chain length 8 nucleotides) suggests that this is so. Solutions of the polymer in 1 M sodium chloride (or in 0·1 M magnesium sulphate) at neutrality possessed an ϵ_{max}^{P} some 6·5% less than that obtained in salt free solution.[24] Apparent pK values in water were 2·7 and 11·6 (determined spectrophotometrically) but in 0·01 M magnesium sulphate the basic dissociation was reduced to 2·2, and in 1 M sodium chloride the acidic dissociation was lowered from 11·6 to 10·2. This reversal of the shifts in pK values is presumably a consequence of the reduced electrostatic potential of ionised phosphate groups (see p. 508).

COMPLEMENTARY HYDROGEN BONDING

Although interaction between chemically synthesised polyadenylic and polyuridylic acids was not observed, partial interaction between polycytidylic and polyguanylic acids (both of average chain length $\sim$ 10 nucleotides) was indicated by countercurrent distribution, and by paper electrophoresis of the homopolymers and their mixture.[22] This interaction (accompanied by a small decrease in ultraviolet absorption) is presumably similar to that occurring with high molecular weight enzymically synthesised polymers.[64] It is likewise a further demonstration of restricted rotation about the internucleotide linkage in oligonucleotides, as well as providing some evidence that hydrogen bonding between cytosine and guanine residues is stronger than that between adenine and uracil. These synthetic materials contained mixed 2'–5' and 3'–5' linkages and complete interaction, even for material of longer

---

* Recent studies with tri- and tetra-deoxyguanylic acid also indicate facile aggregation in confirmation of the above results; sedimentation coefficients of 8–12 are reported.[401]

chain lengths, would not be expected since variation in interplanar distances would considerably reduce effective hydrogen bonding.* Subsequent work showed that hydrogen bonding between high molecular weight polyuridylic acid (chain length ~ 200 nucleotides) and oligoadenylic acids (chain lengths 2–20) containing the natural 3'–5' internucleotide linkage exclusively could be observed readily under suitable conditions.[65, 66] The stability of the complexes increased markedly with the oligonucleotide chain length, the dissociation temperatures (as indicated by measurements of ultraviolet absorption and optical rotation) for di-, tri-, tetra-, penta-, and deca-adenylic acids being approximately 10°, 18°, 30°, 38° and 55° respectively.[65] A maximum decrease in absorptivity (35%) was obtained at base ratios of U : A = 2 : 1, indicating formation of a complex similar to the triple stranded helical complex containing two polyuridylic acid chains and one polyadenylic acid (see p. 463). Under suitable conditions, double stranded complexes (maximum hypochromicity 25%) could also be obtained. Similar interaction was observed between high molecular weight polyadenylic acid and oligouridylic acids of biochemical origin,[66] and between polyadenylic acid and chemically synthesised oligothymidylic acids of dubious chain length and structure.[67]

Although formation of the last complex has been claimed as a demonstration of the possibility of information transfer from DNA to RNA, a more significant pairing is that between polymers of deoxyadenylic acid and uridylic acid (owing to the hydrogen bonding between the 2-keto and 2'-hydroxyl groups in the pyrimidine ribonucleotides). That such complexes can exist was demonstrated by studies of hydrogen bonding between tri-deoxyadenylic acid and polyuridylic acid.[68] A triple-stranded complex containing two polyuridylic acid chains is formed. The hypochromic effect (32%) is comparable with that obtained with the corresponding complex containing tri-riboadenylic acid but the dissociation temperature is somewhat higher (23° against 17°). An even greater thermal stability differential (18°) defines the margin by which the hybrid complex polyribocytidylic acid–polydeoxyguanylic acid is more stable than the double helical structure formed from polydeoxycytidylic acid and polydeoxyguanylic acid.[69] Identification of such hybrid complexes supports the concept that they act as intermediates in the transfer of information from DNA to the site of protein biosynthesis.

* More recent work has shown that hexa-deoxyadenylic acid forms a defined complex with dodeca-thymidylic acid at 0° in 1 M sodium chloride. The stoichiometry indicates a double stranded structure containing equivalent amounts of thymine and adenine (drop in absorptivity is 11% at 259 mμ) with a melting temperature approximately 16° in 1 M NaCl. No evidence of complex formation between hexa-thymidylic acid and hexa-deoxyadenylic acid was obtained.[399]

It has also been found that chemically synthesised oligoadenylic acids containing 2′–5′ internucleotide linkages form complexes with enzymically synthesised polyuridylic acid.[68, 70] In 10^{-3} M magnesium chloride a triple-stranded complex (containing two polyuridylic acid chains) is formed with triadenylic acid containing 2′–5′ linkages exclusively (prepared from the chemical polymer by enzymic hydrolysis) as indicated by the maximum induced hypochromic effect (35%) in mixing curves.[68] However, the melting temperature (13·7°) is significantly lower than that of the corresponding complex from polyuridylic acid and the isomeric natural 3′–5′ linked triadenylic acid ($T_m = 23°$ under identical ionic conditions). Since the stability of the interaction is dependent on stereochemical factors this difference is in accord with the postulate that the interplanar spacings, or other structural factors, are influenced by the nature (2′–5′ or 3′–5′) of the internucleotide linkage. Additional results suggest that tetra-adenylic acid containing random 2′–5′ and 3′–5′ linkages forms both di- and tri-stranded complexes with polyuridylic acid. This work indicates a possible procedure for fractionation of mixtures of 2′–5′ and 3′–5′ linked oligonucleotides by preferential complex formation with enzymically synthesised polymers. Using excess of the mixture relative to the high molecular weight material containing 3′–5′ linkages exclusively, removal of the complex by centrifugation would probably leave a supernatant containing material considerably enriched in 2′–5′ internucleotide linkages.

Reduction in bonding stability also results from non-complementary end groups. Thus polyuridylic acid forms double and triple stranded complexes with pApApApU, pApApApApU, and pApApApApUp but these are less stable than those formed by corresponding oligonucleotides devoid of terminal uridine residues. The stoichiometry of the reaction suggests that the unbonded uridylate " fringes " are bent sufficiently out of position so that locations on the polyuridylic acid chains are not blocked for complementary binding.[68]

Specific bonding of relatively short polydeoxynucleotide chains to high molecular weight strands is indicated by the recovery of transforming activity from sonicated transforming DNA (with essentially zero activity) by renaturation with undegraded wild type DNA.[71]

A lowering of the melting temperature of polyadenylic acid in the presence of uridine or thymidine, suggesting specific interaction, has been reported.[34] However, later work has indicated that hydrogen bonds are not involved; various aromatic compounds (including purines and pyrimidines) are effective, and the decrease in stability may result from " hydrophobic " interactions, or intercalation.[389]

ULTRAVIOLET IRRADIATION

Independent evidence of interaction between adjacent heterocyclic rings in oligonucleotides is suggested by the increased sensitivity of thymine oligonucleotides[27] and of oligouridylic acids[72] to ultraviolet irradiation relative to the mononucleotides. As with the momomers, reversible photochemical transformations involving addition of water to the 4,5 double bond can occur with the pyrimidine nucleotides when these are present in polynucleotide chains.[27]

An interesting effect of ultraviolet irradiation of dried films of oligo-uridylic acid (average chain length approximately 6 nucleotides), deoxynucleic, and apurinic acid is the formation of water insoluble fibres, up to 7–8 mm. $\times$ 200 μ in size. Such fibres are not obtained from polyadenylic or polyguanylic acid, and they presumably result from photochemically induced 4(5)–4(5) cross linking between individual oligonucleotide chains to give an extensive polymer lattice.[73, 74] Such cross linking occurs on ultraviolet irradiation of frozen solutions[75, 76] of

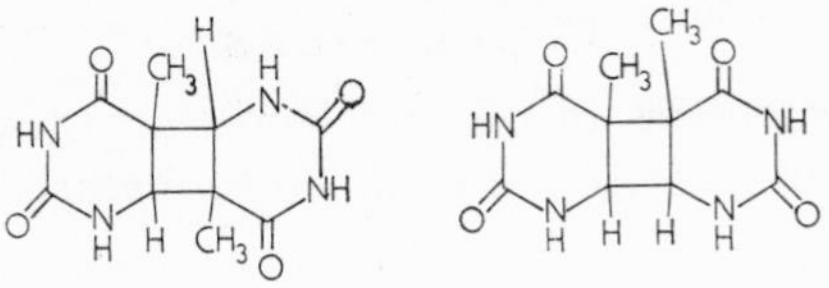

FIG. 8-7.

thymine to give a dimer;[75] further irradiation of the thawed solution causes fast reversion to thymine.[77]

Various structures have been proposed for the thymine dimer.[78] Four isomers are actually possible as a result of cis or trans arrangements of the heterocyclic systems about the cyclobutane ring. Irradiation of a frozen aqueous solution of 1,3-dimethylthymine gives two separable dimers, one of which is identical with that obtained by exhaustive methylation of the single dimer obtained from thymine.[79] Nuclear magnetic resonance spectra do not distinguish between the isomers, as the protons attached to C4 of the pyrimidine rings are in an equivalent magnetic environment regardless of the isomer and hence no spin-spin splitting would be expected even when the C4 positions are adjacent.[79] Irradiation of a mixture of thymine and uracil gives the mixed dimer.[75]

Frozen solutions of thymine were used for irradiation studies in an attempt to approach the " solid state " characteristics of thymine residues in undenatured DNA. However, it should be remembered that successful dimer formation is to a large extent the result of stacking of the heterocyclic rings in crystals of thymine monohydrate. With other pyrimidine bases it could well be that such a crystal structure is not formed. Irradiation of aqueous solutions of DNA causes irreversible hydrogen bond cleavage, and also results in formation of heat-stable linkages between the two complementary polynucleotide strands.[80] Such " denaturation-resistant " cross-links prevent strand separation, as shown by density gradient centrifugation and by decreased degradation on hydrolysis with *E. coli* phosphodiesterase.

Cross linking of the two strands of DNA by the action of nitrous acid,* and with the bifunctional alkylating agent, bis-(β-chloroethyl)-methylamine, has also been described.[81] Such covalent cross-linking results in completely reversible denaturation properties in the product, even with heterogeneous mammalian DNA. It is likely that cross-linked centres in the double stranded structures act as nuclei (by constraining contiguous base pairs) for the renaturation process. Since cross-linking of the complementary strands of DNA by the action of nitrous acid prevents complete separation, such a mechanism may account (apart from deamination of residues containing amino groups) for the mutagenic activity, particularly the highly lethal nature, of nitrous acid.[81]

CONCLUSIONS

The general properties of oligonucleotides suggest that secondary structural characteristics are not confined to material of relatively high

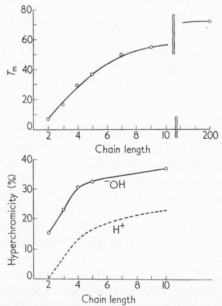

FIG. 8-8. Effect of chain length of oligoadenylic acids on thermal dissociation temperature of complexes with high molecular weight polyuridylic acid.[65] Effect of chain length on hyperchromicity of oligoadenylic acids in acid and in alkali.[21]

    * Compare[412] with the action of nitrous acid on 5-aminouridine (p. 27).

molecular weight.* Restricted rotation about the internucleotide linkage is evident even at the dinucleotide level, and at chain lengths of about 7–10 nucleotides, specific favoured conformations begin to appear since many of the physical properties either begin or reach a limit at this level. (It is of interest that the critical size for helix formation in synthetic polypeptides, though dependent on the nature of the peptide, the solvent, and temperature, is some 7–9 amino acids for peptides of γ-methyl-L-glutamate in dimethylformamide at 25°).[82]

A second level of organisation occurs when virtually complete restriction of movement of the bases (relative to that possible in oligonucleotides) is effected by formation of helical structures. The hypochromic effects associated with this second level of organisation are dependent on the integrity of the structure and hence can vary with change in environmental factors such as temperature and ionic strength, in contrast with the hypochromicity of oligonucleotides, while much greater increases in ultraviolet absorption occur at the pH extremes owing to disruption of the structure.

Physical Chemistry of Enzymically Synthesised Polynucleotides

With the discovery of polyribonucleotide phosphorylase, a variety of polyribonucleotides became available for physical examination. Such enzymically synthesised polymers (of molecular weight 10^5–10^6) have proved extremely useful for the observation, in simplified systems, of a number of properties closely related to those shown by nucleic acids. While this work has greatly increased knowledge of the characteristic physical properties of polynucleotides in general, considerable assistance was derived from earlier studies on the nucleic acids themselves and from the concept of hydrogen bonded base pairs developed for DNA.

INTERACTION BETWEEN POLYNUCLEOTIDE CHAINS

When equimolar quantities (with respect to mononucleotide content) of polyuridylic and polyadenylic acids are mixed in dilute aqueous solution at neutral pH a complex with electrophoretic properties different from those of the homopolymers is formed.[83] Fibres drawn from this material show strong negative birefringence, and give an X-ray diffraction pattern very similar to that of DNA.[84] Detailed X-ray examination has shown that a double helical structure is formed from chains of the two polymers by means of hydrogen bonds between the adenine and uracil residues. As in DNA, there are some ten base pairs per turn of the helix, the helical pitch being 34 Å, and the nucleotides are stacked so that the plane of the bases is approximately normal to the axis of the chain.

* This is possibly significant for speculations on the chemical origin of life. Interplanar interactions can also play a considerable role in the stability of double helical structures, as indicated by the essentially identical thermal dissociation temperatures of DNA and fully deuterated DNA in water or in deuterium oxide.[415, 416].

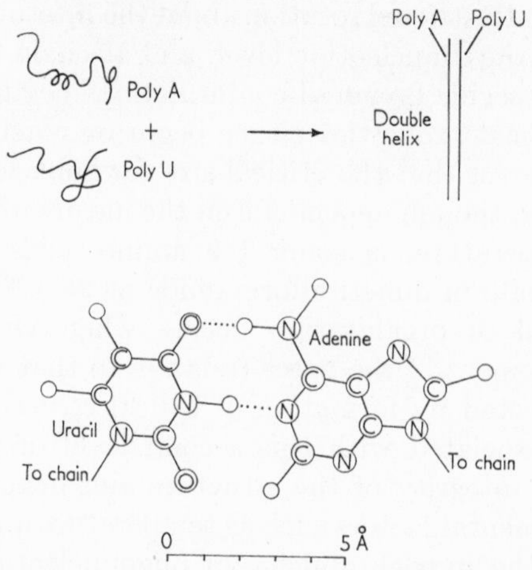

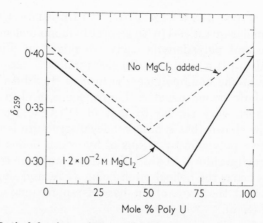

FIG. 8-9. Hydrogen bonding in the polyadenylic-polyuridylic acid complex.[84]

The interaction of polyadenylic and polyuridylic acids can be followed by the hypochromic effects resulting (indirectly) from hydrogen bonding between complementary chains.[85, 86] Under suitable conditions of low cation concentration a minimum ultraviolet absorption is shown by mixtures containing equimolar concentrations of the two polymers, that is, when the number of adenine residues equals the number of uracil residues, suggesting that a new species with precise stoichiometry is formed. A study of the ultracentrifugal characteristics of the two homopolymers, and of the complex, showed formation of a new aggregate possessing a considerably greater sedimentation constant than either of the two components.

FIG. 8-10. Optical density at 259 mμ of mixtures of polyadenylic acid and polyuridylic acid.[85]

A high equilibrium constant for the interaction is indicated by the sharpness of the drop in optical density, which shows reaction of more than 95% of the residues.[87] This suggests that the interaction is reversible, and indeed the effects of temperature variation show that this is so. The complexes are regarded as long chains of overlapping polyadenylic and polyuridylic acid molecules in the form of a double helix in which very few gaps or non-hydrogen bonded regions are left.[87]

In the presence of divalent cations, particularly magnesium, a second complex between polyuridylic and polyadenylic acids is readily formed.[88] Again, the variation of optical density with molar ratio of the two polymers shows a sharp minimum, indicating a stable complex. However, this minimum occurs at a ratio of uracil : adenine equal to 2 : 1 and the complex is three-stranded, with a sedimentation constant some 50% greater than that of the two-stranded complex. The third strand of polyuridylic acid probably fills the deep helical groove of the two-stranded aggregate, displacing water molecules from this site, and thus having little effect on the frictional forces or shape factors of the complex. It is likely that the second uracil residue in each triplet of bases is attached to the original adenine–uracil pair by means of hydrogen bonds from O^6 and N^1 of the uracil to the 6-amino group and N^7 of the adenine residue. X-ray diffraction photographs of such triple-stranded complexes have been obtained, but full analysis is not yet available.[89]

Kinetic studies on formation of the three-stranded complex from a mixture of two-stranded polyadenylic–polyuridylic aggregate and polyuridylic acid have shown that the reaction is second order for divalent cations, that is, two cations are present for each triplet of bases. Although cations such as magnesium or manganese are remarkably effective, they are not unique since the three-stranded complex is also formed in solutions of sodium chloride that are of sufficiently high molarity. It is likely that the major role played by cations lies in reduction of the electrostatic repulsion among negatively charged phosphate groups in the three polynucleotide chains. The greater efficiency of divalent cations relative to monovalent is probably a consequence of the different dissociation constants of the metal-phosphate salts.

Similar evidence has indicated the formation of two and three-stranded complexes from polyadenylic and polyinosinic acids,[90] and a two-stranded complex from polyinosinic and polycytidylic acids.[91, 92] Analogous two and three-stranded aggregates are formed from poly-ribothymidylic acid and polyadenylic acid,[89] and complexes from poly-guanylic and polycytidylic acids have been reported.[93]

In addition to this variety of hetero-stranded complexes, some of the homopolymers undergo self-aggregation under suitable conditions. In neutral solution polyadenylic acid possesses a randomly coiled, single chain conformation as shown by the absence of significant flow birefringence and the rise in viscosity that is observed when the ionic strength is lowered.[94] However, in solutions of low ionic strength more acidic than pH 6·5 there is a sharp change to an ordered conformation, reflected by a decrease in ultraviolet absorption, increase in particle weight, and appearance of very marked negative birefringence of flow.[94, 95] The changes in sedimentation constant, viscosity, and light

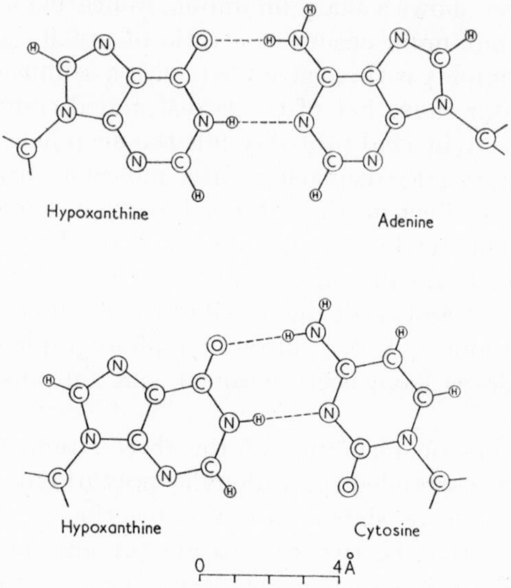

Fig. 8-11. Hydrogen bonding in polyadenylic-polyinosinic acid[90] and polycytidylic-polyinosinic acid complexes.[91, 92]

scattering are paralleled by the titration curve, and the evidence indicates that on protonation of the adenine residues a relatively rigid, interrupted double helical aggregate is formed, composed of various numbers of polyadenylic acid molecules. Since the adenine amino groups react readily with formaldehyde when the polymer is in the randomly coiled state, but not when the protonated complex is formed, it is likely that aggregation is a result of hydrogen bond pairing of adenine bases. Confirmation is afforded by transition of the ordered structure to a random coil over a narrow temperature range (at approximately 90° in 0·15 M salt at acidic pH), similar to the behaviour of deoxynucleic acid, which is accounted for by co-operative breakdown of hydrogen bonds.[94] Helical structure is also lost at very low pH, presumably the result of protonation at N^7 leading to disruption of a hydrogen bond.[96]

X-ray diffraction photographs[97-99] of solutions of polyadenylic acid at acidic pH, or of fibres of the complex, show a strong meridional reflection at 3·8 Å and a layer line spacing at 15·4 Å. These results are in agreement with a model for the acid-form of polyadenylic acid in which the ribose phosphate chains are parallel to each other (unlike the anti-parallel system in DNA) and located on the outside of the molecule, with the bases hydrogen bonded from N^7 of the imidazole ring to the 6-amino group of the opposing adenine. In accord with this, the complex is resistant to nitrous acid.[100] Each pair of bases is related to the next by a translation of 3·8 Å units and a rotation of 45°, there being approximately eight base pairs per turn of the helix. In addition, the phosphate group is pulled towards the axis of the aggregate by a hydrogen bond

Random coil   Interrupted helix

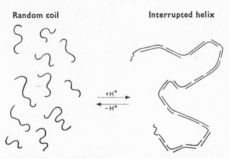

$+H^+$

$-H^+$

FIG. 8-12. Helix-coil transition in polyadenylic acid.[94]

from one of the phosphate oxygen atoms to the amino group of the adenine residue in the opposite chain. This has the effect of tilting the adenine bases to give an interplanar stacking distance of 3·8 Å rather than 3·4 Å commonly found in the hetero complexes. It may be noted that protonation (at N^1) of the adenine ring occurs at pH 6·5 (the limiting pH for stability of the complex) and some internal stabilisation of the double helical structure, indicated by the high thermal dissociation temperature of the complex, is afforded by electrostatic forces between the positively charged adenine residues and the negatively charged phosphates in opposing chains giving an " inner salt " effect.[99]

Solutions of polyinosinic acid can also be converted from random coil into organised helical conformations, and vice versa. At low salt concentration, or extremes of pH, the sedimentation constant of polyinosinic acid is low. However, at high ionic concentrations the sedimentation constant is considerably increased and the ultraviolet absorption is markedly decreased. X-ray diffraction photographs of oriented fibres (these are negatively birefringent) drawn from the polymer aggregate indicate a helical diffraction pattern caused by a multiple-stranded structure.[101] A two-chain model does not fit the diffraction data (which include a first layer line at a spacing of 9·8 Å units in contrast with the more common 30–40 Å spacings, while the

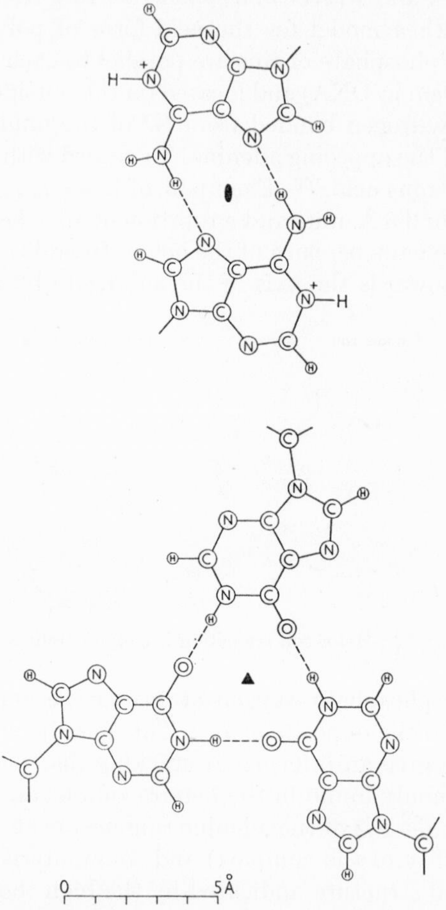

FIG. 8-13. Hydrogen bonds in the acid-form of polyadenylic acid,[99] and in the three stranded model of polyinosinic acid.[101]

second layer line appears at 5·2 Å, and the third intense meridional layer line at 3·4 Å) but a reasonable fit is obtained with a three-stranded model in which the three strands are parallel to each other with an angle between successive residues of 41·6°. The three hypoxanthine residues are organised around a three-fold rotation axis, and are hydrogen bonded in a cyclic manner such that the 6-keto oxygen of the purine ring is hydrogen bonded to N[1] of an adjacent purine. Interaction of

polyinosinic acid with polyadenylic acid occurs only when the former is
in the single-chain random coil form. All the organised helical structures mentioned are formed reversibly; the stability is often dependent
on ionic strength, and the pH range is governed by requirements for
specific tautomeric forms.

Studies of the quantitative infrared spectra of the polynucleotides,
and the complexes which they form, in deuterium oxide solution
suggest that the tautomeric form of the purine or pyrimidine base is
the same as that of the mononucleotide in each case, and that on interaction there is no tautomeric shift. However, upon formation of the
polyadenylic–polyuridylic and polycytidylic–polyinosinic complexes,
there is a decrease in intensity and shift to higher frequencies of certain
bands in the infrared spectra. In particular, the 1630 cm^{-1} band
decreases in intensity in two stranded complexes of polyuridylic and
polyadenylic acid, and disappears as a separate peak in the three
stranded complex two polyuridylic-one polyadenylic (or tetra-adenylic
acid). At elevated temperatures (above the thermal denaturation
point) a fully developed peak at 1625 cm^{-1} again appears.[102] These
changes are considered to result indirectly from hydrogen bonding
between polynucleotide chains causing a displacement of water molecules and hence a decrease in the local dielectric constant.[102] Similar
differences between the infrared spectra of the mononucleotide and of
the homopolymer derived therefrom have also been noted, and presumably result from stacking of the purine or pyrimidine bases.[103] (See
also p. 476).

The rise in ultraviolet absorption on heating solutions of the two-
and three-stranded hetero complexes, and the two-stranded acid-form
of polyadenylic acid, is rapid at a critical temperature (in the range 50
to 90°), indicating disruption of an organised structure in which
cleavage of a few hydrogen bonds reduces the stability of neighbouring
hydrogen bond base pairs. A direct measure of the relative stability of
" bond energies " shown by different types of base pairing is available
from a study of the critical " melting " temperatures for the various
helical complexes.[104] Such information can also be determined from
studies of the variation of optical rotation with temperature.

The helical complexes show a resistance to enzymic phosphorolysis,[83] relative to degradation of the less-organised or random coiled
structures extant under certain conditions. A further effect of hydrogen
bonding is evident in the considerable shifts in apparent pK values of
the bases which occur. Thus titration of the equimolar polyadenylic-
polyuridylic acid complex clearly indicates dissociation of the complex
at pH 10·4 (accompanied by collapse of the organised secondary
structure on dissociation of the proton involved in the hydrogen bond).

In polyuridylic acid itself dissociation of the –NHCO– group occurs at pH 9·7. With the triple-stranded complex (polyadenylic–two polyuridylic) dissociation occurs in two distinct steps, at pH 10·1 and pH 10·4, suggesting that the second polyuridylic acid strand is held less tightly than the first.[105] The anomalous titration behaviour of polyadenylic acid involving a very abrupt uptake of protons at pH 6·5 has been mentioned previously. The free mononucleotide shows a related pK approximately 3·8.

Other properties of the individual homopolymers are of interest. Except for polyuridylic acid, considerably larger hyperchromic effects on degradation to mononucleotide are shown by the high molecular weight polymers, compared with analogous oligonucleotide materials.

TABLE 8-III.

	Approximate hyperchromicity (%) at pH 7
Polyadenylic acid[83]	54
Polycytidylic acid[83]	40
Polyguanylic acid[93]	32
Polyinosinic acid[83]	62
Polyribothymidylic acid[106]	40
Polyuridylic acid[83]	5 (a higher figure of 16% has also been reported)[107]

Since much of the hypochromicity of these homopolymers (except for polyuridylic acid) is temperature sensitive, it is likely that considerable non-organised hydrogen bonding exists in the single-stranded structures.[83] The random nature of this hydrogen bonding is indicated by the variation of ultraviolet absorption with temperature. Unlike the relatively sharp transitions shown by helical complexes of two or more strands, the increase in absorption is gradual and almost constant over a 60° range for polyadenylic acid at pH 7. This behaviour reflects the cleavage of a series of independent bonds rather than co-operative transition.[105] An irregular partially hydrogen bonded single-chain structure with a significant amount of helical order is also indicated for polyadenylic acid by the size of the optical rotation (a measure of organised helical structure) which, while smaller than that of two-stranded helical aggregates such as deoxynucleic acid, polyadenylic-polyuridylic acid, and the acid-form of polyadenylic acid, is larger than that of random coiled non-hydrogen bonded single chains such as polyuridylic acid.[108, 109]

Spectra of the homopolymers (except for polyuridylic acid) show characteristic changes in concentrated urea solutions, indicative of partial cleavage of relatively weak, more or less random, hydrogen bonding. Ultraviolet absorption is also a function of ionic strength, and this may well be related in some cases to repression of the effective ionisation of phosphoryl groups by formation of ion pairs, with contraction of the polynucleotide chain due to a decrease in the electrostatic repulsion between charged phosphate groups.[83, 110] This presumably affects the direct interplanar interactions and may well result in variation in the strength of hydrogen bonding also. In some cases

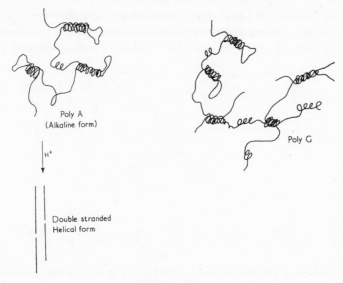

Fig. 8-14.

too, such as polyinosinic acid, increase in ionic strength leads to the formation of multiple-stranded complexes, with consequent decrease in ultraviolet absorption. It may be noted that even in salt-free solution, polyinosinic acid possesses an absorptivity that is increased by addition of urea (but is decreased by addition of salts). This suggests that in this case (as with chemically synthesised oligo- and polyguanylic acids) hydrogen bonded secondary structures (random or otherwise) can be formed effectively in the absence of a moderate ionic environment. Enzymically synthesised polyguanylic acid is highly aggregated in neutral solution,[93] and indeed this is evident even in chemically synthesised polyguanylic acids of chain length approximately 10 nucleotides, as shown by the countercurrent distribution behaviour and large shift in pKs.[22]

Evidence of a helical structure for polyuridylic acid at reduced temperatures has been obtained.[111] Thus in dilute salt solution at 2° a large hypochromic effect is observed, the absorption dropping to some 70% of that shown by the polymer at 23°. A small hypsochromic shift of the absorption maximum also occurs, together with a massive increase in the optical rotation (from $[\alpha]_D = 11°$ at 23°C to $[\alpha]_D = 290°$ at 0·5°C). The transition temperature as determined by the midpoint (that is, at the maximum rate of change with temperature) for changes in ultraviolet absorption and optical rotation is 5·8°C.

INTERACTION WITH DYES

The interaction of basic dyes, particularly Acridine Orange, with enzymically synthesised polynucleotides has been studied.[112] In general, the aggregation of the dyes and the resultant effects on the visible

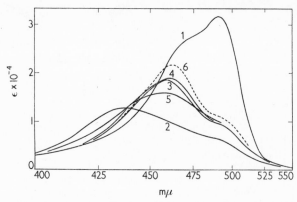

FIG. 8-15. Action of polynucleotides [3 × 10⁻⁵ M (P)] on the absorption spectrum of Acridine Orange (3 × 10⁻⁵ M) in 0·01 M ammonium acetate at pH 6·8. 1, Dye alone; 2, 3, 4, 5 and 6, with added polyuridylic, poly-5-chlorouridylic, poly-5-bromouridylic, poly-5-iodouridylic, and polyadenylic acid respectively. All polymers are high molecular weight, enzymically synthesised products.[125]

absorption spectra can be related to the ratio of available binding sites to dye molecules, and the ionic strength of the medium. As may be expected, an increase in temperature decreases the binding, and presumably an estimate of the relative binding constants for various dyes and homopolymers could be obtained from a comparison of the dissociation temperatures obtained under standard conditions.

Recent work on the effect of combination of small amounts of acridines (Proflavine, Acridine Orange, or acridine) on undenatured DNA in solution has shown that significant structural alterations can occur.[113] Viscosity is markedly enhanced, and there is a diminution of the sedimentation coefficient, contrary to what might be expected from simple aggregation of dye molecules. X-ray diffraction patterns of fibres of the Proflavine-DNA complex suggest considerable modification of the double helical structure and, at least with some acridines, strong binding occurs by intercalation between adjacent nucleotide pair layers by extension and unwinding of the deoxyribose phosphate backbone. The effects are fully reversible, and insertion of the planar acridine, with approximately the same area as purine–pyrimidine base pairs in the double helical DNA, provides a possible explanation of the mutagenic activity of certain acridines.[113] Small angle X-ray scattering studies of Proflavine–DNA complexes indicate that variations of mass per unit length of the rods and of radius of gyration around the axis, as functions of Proflavine concentration, agree with a mechanism of intercalation.[114] This type of strong binding, in which up to one dye molecule is bound per two to five base pairs, is probably also significant in the interaction of dyes with helical complexes formed from enzymically synthesised polyribonucleotides.

An anomalous rotatory dispersion has also been observed for Acridine Orange bound to native double helical DNA. The magnitude of the optical activity that is shown by such complexes (but not by Acridine Orange bound to heat-denatured random coil DNA) depends on the ratio of dye to nucleotide, and a maximum Cotton effect (with λ_{max} 515 mμ) occurs at one dye molecule per four nucleotides (two base pairs).[115] At higher dye ratios this is replaced by a second Cotton effect (λ_{max} 450 mμ) that increases up to the maximum dye binding (1 : 1).

The decrease in ultraviolet absorption which accompanies interaction of polyadenylic acid with polyuridylic acid can be used as a measure of the binding of cations to the polynucleotides, since the interaction is highly dependent on the ionic composition of the solution. Using this approach, strong interaction of magnesium ions and of polyamines, but not of amino acids, has been observed.[116] Conductometric titration showed that the binding of divalent cations by polyadenylic–polyuridylic acid ceases when one equivalent of cation is added per phosphate residue. On addition of polylysine a stoichiometrically well-defined complex is formed; in the course of the reaction the polylysine displaces an equivalent amount of divalent cation.[117]

HETEROPOLYMERS

The physical properties of copolymers of adenylic and uridylic acids have been examined.[118, 119] Titration indicates a marked displacement of the uracil pK, and at neutrality the copolymers show large hypochromic effects. Heating, or treatment with formaldehyde, results in an increase in ultraviolet absorption and change in titration behaviour, and it is likely that considerable hydrogen bonding exists between adenine and uracil residues. Since no change in molecular weight is indicated by viscosity or sedimentation measurements this hydrogen bonding is probably intramolecular.[118] The physical properties suggest that the copolymers possess a compact, highly coiled structure in solution.[120] However, organised helical regions are present and reach a maximum when the copolymer contains approximately equal amounts of adenine and uracil residues, as judged by the optical rotation of the materials and the hyperchromic effect on titration to a pH at which most of the uracil bases are ionised (presumably leading to cleavage of hydrogen bonds and loss of organised structure). Generally, such copolymers probably possess structures similar to those proposed for ribonucleic acids.

Maximum interaction between polyadenylic acid or polyuridylic acid and copolymers containing different amounts of the two nucleotides occurs when the two-stranded complexes contain equimolar complementary and homopolymer residues; non-complementary bases or bases or base sequences are probably accommodated as loops out of the helix.[121] The number of mismatchings that can be tolerated in a DNA-like double helix is quite large (30–40%), and the results suggested a possible model for RNA consisting of short helical regions with looped out material, to give a tertiary structure of possible biological significance.

Similar studies on copolmers of adenylic acid and inosinic or cytidylic acid have been reported.[122] Progressive introduction of inosinic residues into the polyadenylic acid chain results in disappearance of the characteristic structural transition at acidic pH, a fall in helical content as measured by ultraviolet hypochromism and optical rotation, and lowering of the dissociation temperature of the complex formed with polyuridylic acid. Copolymers of adenylic and cytidylic acid appear to show considerably less decline in helical content with increasing proportions of cytidylic acid. Optical rotation and thermal dependence of hypochromism suggest a significant helical content also for copolymers of cytidylic and inosinic acids.[123] In contrast, copoly (uridylic plus inosinic acid) appears to be essentially amorphous.

Unlike polyuridylic acid, the methylated analogue poly N^1-methyluridylic acid (enzymically prepared from N^1-methyluridine-5' pyrophosphate) exhibits no secondary structure under any conditions, nor does it form any complexes with polyadenylic acid.[70] The material shows a 10% hyperchromic effect which cannot be a result of internal hydrogen bonding. Copolymers of uridylic and N^1-methyluridylic acid show secondary structure characteristics and complexing abilities with adenylic acid which are dependent on the ratio of uracil to N^1-

methyluracil in the chain. Again the results suggested that the methyl-uridylic residues form " loops " from organised complementary helical structures. Ribonuclease hydrolysis products of the copolymer were in accord (qualitatively and quantitatively) with the resistance to the enzyme shown by esters of N^1-methyluridine-3′ phosphate.[70]

Hybrid polyribonucleotide–polydeoxyribonucleotide complexes have also been described. Thermal denaturation of double stranded enzymically synthesised polydeoxycytidylic–polydeoxyguanylic acid in the presence of polyribocytidylic acid, followed by renaturation, results in displacement of the polydeoxycytidylic chain and formation of the considerably more stable hybrid complex polyribocytidylic–polydeoxyguanylic acid.[69] Apart from possessing a considerably higher (by 18°) dissociation temperature, the new complex has a characteristic density (1·86), higher than that of the original complex (1·80), as determined by centrifugation to equilibrium in a density gradient. Moreover, the complex is resistant to hydrolysis by ribonuclease, deoxyribonuclease, or a mixture of the two enzymes.

Physical Chemistry of Nucleic Acids

Concepts of the precise physical attributes of nucleic acids and interpretation of these properties in terms of molecular shape and conformation have undergone numerous changes during the past ninety years. Recent advances have clarified many aspects of secondary structure, particularly for deoxynucleic acids.

Macromolecular Structure of Deoxynucleic Acid

Given the covalent primary structure of nucleic acids as polymers of mononucleotides, the precise stereochemical arrangements are susceptible to analysis by X-ray methods. Early X-ray diffraction photographs of oriented fibres of deoxynucleic acid showed a strong meridional reflection at 3·4 Å, and it was concluded that the structural characteristic responsible for this lay in the stacking of flat nucleotides roughly at right angles to the fibre axis.[126, 127] In addition, it was clear that the molecule had longer periodicities along its length. The high negative flow birefringence of solutions of DNA also indicated that the molecule was long and thin,[128] with the absorbing groups oriented normal to the long axis. Confirmation of this was afforded by the ultraviolet dichroism (variation of absorption with the direction of the electric vector of the radiation, relative to the plane or axis of the absorbing system) of DNA films oriented by stretching.[129] Electro-metric titration of deoxynucleic acids showed that whereas the phosphate groups were titratable in normal fashion, the amino and –NHCO– dissociations of the heterocyclic bases did not behave normally, and were apparently masked, unless the nucleic acid was " denatured " by excessive acidic or alkaline conditions. The idea of hydrogen bonds between these groups in the purine and pyrimidine bases was therefore introduced,[130] and DNA was pictured as aggregates of polynucleotide chains joined by such hydrogen bonds.[131] In accord with this, the variation of viscosity (and of flow birefringence) with pH indicated a disaggregation of micelles into smaller molecular units at pH limits ($< 5\cdot6$ and $> 10\cdot9$) closely associated with the liberation of amino and –NHCO– groups. At these critical pH values the viscosity fell sharply to a very low value relative to that shown by neutral solutions of DNA.

X-Ray examination of the crystal structure of cytidine then showed that the heterocyclic and sugar rings were not in fact coplanar, but almost perpendicular.[132] Suitably modified single strand structures for DNA were advanced in which the planes of the sugar rings were approximately parallel to the long axis of the polynucleotide.[133] A helical structure involving three intertwined strands with the phosphate groups centrally located and the purine and pyrimidine residues projecting radially was considered,[134] but found to be contrary to much of the information available. Improved X-ray photographs, and examination of sodium deoxynucleate fibres under different humidity conditions showed two distinct conformations, one (at 75% relative humidity) giving a well defined oriented crystalline pattern and the other (at higher humidities) giving an X-ray diffraction pattern characteristic of helical structures but showing a lower degree of crystallinity.[135] In both the crystalline and semi-crystalline forms (which are reversible) the phosphate groups are accessible to water and hence must lie on the outside of the structure.

Watson and Crick[136] then proposed (1953) a structure for DNA that accommodated the molar relationships between adenine and thymine, and between guanine and cytosine, shown in the analytical results from many different deoxynucleic acids,[137, 138] and was compatible with the basic features of the available X-ray diffraction patterns.[139–141] This structure consists of two right handed helical polynucleotide chains (each coiled about the same axis) containing ten nucleotides per turn, with a pitch of 34 Å and a diameter of 20 Å. The sequence of internucleotide linkages in the two chains run in opposite directions (that is, $3' \rightarrow 5'$ and $5' \rightarrow 3'$), but each purine or pyrimidine base lies normal to the helix axis and is joined by hydrogen bonds to a specific complementary base in the opposing chain, namely adenine to thymine, and guanine to cytosine. The bases are on the inside of the double helix, the phosphate groups are on the outside, and because of the specific spatial fit involved (purine to pyrimidine in all cases) complete stereochemical regularity is obtained along the fibre axis.

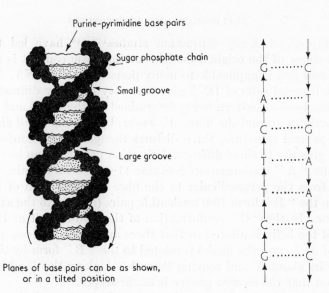

Purine-pyrimidine base pairs

Sugar phosphate chain

Small groove

Large groove

Planes of base pairs can be as shown,
or in a tilted position

G········C
A········T
C········G
T········A
T········A
C········G
G········C

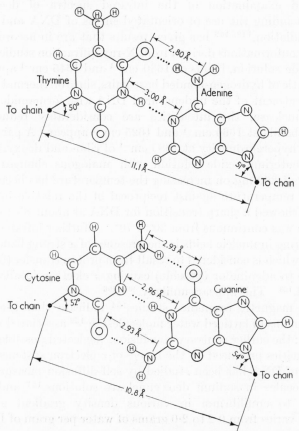

Thymine

To chain 50°

2.80 Å

3.00 Å

Adenine

11.1 Å

51°

To chain

Cytosine

To chain 52°

2.93 Å

2.96 Å

2.93 Å

Guanine

54°

To chain

10.8 Å

FIG. 8-16. Macromolecular structure of DNA double helix.[136, 139]

More refined X-ray diffraction studies[142-146] have led to slight modifications of the original model, but the basic concept is now well established and is applicable to many preparations of DNA. Fibres of the alkali metal salts of DNA give a variety of X-ray diffraction patterns, the type of pattern being determined by the metal and the relative humidity around the fibre. However, by making small alterations in the general structure, three distinct though related conformations (which give rise to three different diffraction patterns) can be obtained. Thus the " A " conformation contains 11·0 nucleotide pairs (inclined at 20° from the perpendicular to the fibre axis) per turn of the helix while in the " B " form 10·0 nucleotide pairs (normal to the axis) occur per turn. In the " C " conformation of the lithium salt of DNA, the pitch of the helix is altered so that there are about 9·3 base pairs in a pitch of 31 Å, and the model is related to the " B " form by tilting the base pairs about 6° and moving them 1·5 Å along the dyad in such a direction that the narrow groove is made deeper.[146]

Detailed examination of the infrared spectra of deoxynucleic acids,[147] including the use of orientated sheets of DNA and polarised infrared radiation,[148, 149] has given results that are in accord with the molecular conformations derived from X-ray diffraction studies. In deuterium oxide solution, bands at 1680 cm^{-1} and 1645 cm^{-1} appear to be characteristic of hydrogen-bonded base pairs, since on thermal denaturation, or treatment of the undenatured DNA with formamide, alkali, or deoxyribonuclease, the intensities are considerably reduced,[150-152] while new bands at 1660 cm^{-1} and 1625 cm^{-1} appear. A parallelism of changes in hyperchromicity at 1685 cm^{-1} of ribo- and deoxyribonucleic acids in deuterium oxide solution with analogous changes in hypochromicity at 260 mμ on increasing the temperature has been noted.[153] Profiles of temperature against reciprocal of the relative intensity at 1685 cm^{-1} showed a sharp transition for DNA at about 85°; with RNA the change was continuous from 30 to 70°. A further infrared criterion of base pairing in nucleic acids is the presence of a strong band at about 1710 cm^{-1} which is considered to result from proton transfer (from uracil or guanine to adenine or cytosine) causing π electron localisation in a $C=N$ bond.[153] This appears unlikely.[405, 406]

Proton magnetic resonance studies[154] indicate that there are no ice-like domains of latticed water molecules[155, 156] associated with DNA in solution; the earlier contrary conclusions neglected possible magnetic inhomogeneities produced by the layers of π electron systems. The net hydration of DNA has been studied by self-diffusion measurements of water molecules in sodium deoxynucleate solutions,[157] and by sedimentation to equilibrium in various density gradient systems.[158] Hydration varies from 0·2 to 2·0 grams of water per gram of DNA (that is, from about 3 to 50 molecules of water per nucleotide) depending on the solvent.[158] In dilute salt solutions, DNA appears to be extensively hydrated. Deuteration rates of lithium and sodium DNA are extremely fast (less than two minutes for completion) and hence the hydrogen atoms involved in hydrogen bonding between the bases are completely accessible to protons, and possibly to water molecules.[149]

X-ray diffraction patterns strictly comparable with those of DNA have not been obtained with ribonucleic acid preparations, but this does not exclude possible helical (single or double stranded) structures for these polymers, and indeed recent work suggests that a considerable amount of organised helical structure can be present. (See p. 533.) It may also be noted that not all deoxynucleic acids exist in a complementary double helical form, since undenatured preparations that are single stranded (for example, the DNA from bacteriophage ϕX174)[159] have been described. Marked morphological differences between double helical deoxynucleic acids and ribonucleic acids have been observed by electron microscopical techniques.[160, 161] Deoxynucleic acid from a number of sources formed smooth strands about 20 Å in diameter and many microns long; heat-denatured material gave amorphous patches. Ribonucleic acids appeared as nodose filaments in which the molecule is probably coiled up on itself.

MOLECULAR WEIGHT

The molecular weights of nucleic acids can be estimated by a variety of methods such as sedimentation in the ultracentrifuge, diffusion, intrinsic viscosity, and light scattering.[162] Both the sedimentation and diffusion constants vary with concentration and, coupled with the undoubted heterogeneity[163, 164] of many preparations of nucleic acids, a precisely determined molecular weight with any real meaning is somewhat rare. With deoxynucleic acids of high molecular weight, sedimentation and viscosity measurements give results some two or three times higher than those obtained from light scattering, possibly because of the failure of light scattering theory when applied to very long rods.[165] Typical molecular weight values for deoxynucleic acid preparations are 4–8 × 10⁶ though much higher figures have been recorded. Indeed, autoradiographic estimates of the minimum length of E. coli DNA liberated by extremely mild lysis of the cell suggest that the material exists as a single entity approximately 400 μ long, indicating a molecular weight of 10^9 or more.[400]

In addition to the normal difficulties inherent in the methods employed, the significance of the estimated molecular weights and their relation to in vivo chain lengths cannot easily be defined owing to the ready cleavage of extremely high molecular weight chains. Thus, essentially unidisperse DNA was obtained by passing a solution of the polymer through an atomiser. No denaturation occurred but the molecular weight decreased, and the distribution of sedimentation coefficients was narrowed.[166, 167] Other studies of the effect of hydro-dynamic shear on DNA further showed that fragmentation by double chain scission, leaving the helical structure intact, readily occurred under stirring conditions commonly used for the isolation of deoxynucleic acids.[168–170] The rupturing force causing scission of the double helix has been determined by subjecting DNA (labelled with ^{32}P) from T2 bacteriophage to controlled hydrodynamic shearing forces. Stress produced by flow gradient at critical shear was found to be approximately 11×10^{-4} dynes. Calculation shows that this is compatible with the bond strengths involved (approximately $9–18 \times 10^{-4}$ dynes to break both chains at the same time).[171] The longer the molecule, the more fragile the integrity with respect to manipulations such as stirring or pipetting. Similar degradation occurs on sonic[172–174] treatment of deoxynucleic acid. The molecular weight of deoxynucleic acid *in vivo* may therefore be considerably higher, particularly if protein bridges between DNA subunits occur.[175] On the other hand, there is some evidence that aggregation of calf thymus DNA is readily induced by close packing, as in pellets obtained by high speed centrifugation, and various reported molecular weights of 6, 12 or 18×10^6 may represent aggregates, perhaps artifacts, of a basic subunit of molecular weight $1–2 \times 10^6$ as determined by light scattering.[176]

The nature of this basic subunit with respect to deoxynucleic acid isolated from *Escherichia coli* has been questioned recently.[177] As extracted and deproteinised the nucleic acid had a molecular weight of 11×10^6 (light scattering). Heating the material in caesium chloride solution reduced the molecular weight to $5\cdot6 \times 10^6$, while treatment with chymotrypsin (or chloroform–octanol mixtures) gave polymer of molecular weight $2\cdot4 \times 10^6$ that had a normal sigmoid optical density–temperature curve with a midpoint at 92°. Heating this latter nucleic acid in caesium chloride ($7\cdot7$ molal) reduced the molecular weight to $1\cdot3 \times 10^6$, but gave double-stranded material as shown by the kinetics of enzymic (deoxyribonuclease II) degradation. In the absence of caesium chloride treatment, four-stranded material was indicated by the same approach and it was therefore suggested that the unit DNA of *Escherichia coli* is a dimer of two double helices laterally bonded together, each double helix being conserved intact in cell division. Protein linkages, as in the aggregate of molecular weight 11×10^6, are unaffected by heating in caesium chloride, this treatment rupturing the dimer bonds between pairs of double helical structures.[177]

Further evidence of multi-stranded DNA was obtained by examination of the decay in molecular weight by X-irradiation as a function of the X-ray dose, using light scattering to determine molecular weight.[178] As a result of non-random attacks, low values, constituting a minimum estimate, are obtained for the numbers of strands. These were $n = 1·5$ for calf thymus DNA, $n = 1·6$ for sea urchin sperm DNA, but for *Pneumococcus* DNA a figure of $3·2$ was obtained. (Kinetics of degradation by deoxyribonuclease II gave $n = 4·2$ for the same nucleic acid.)[179] The results support conclusions that DNA from non-proliferating sources is in the form of double helices whereas that from proliferating sources consists of linked pairs of double helices.[178, 180] Presence of four-stranded structures in DNA from *Pneumococcus* is strongly suggested by electron microscopic studies,[181] both by the morphology of the particles and by comparison of weight–average molecular weight ($1·6 \times 10^6$ by light scattering) with weight–average length (4300 Å). The latter approach gives an average mass per Å equal to 370, approximately twice that expected (208) for a double helical structure. Electron micrographs also indicate that the two double helices are not intertwined, but lie side by side.[181]

Additional support for this concept was obtained by a study of DNA isolated from synchronised cultures of a thymine-requiring mutant of *Escherichia coli* at various times. At first the DNA was four stranded and indistinguishable from log phase *E. coli* DNA, but at the beginning of DNA synthesis the molecular weight was halved, and the DNA was two stranded and possessed the properties of undenatured double helical DNA isolated from non-proliferating sources. It was concluded that replication of the parental four-stranded complex is semiconservative, but that replication of the double helix is conservative.[182]

Enzymic degradation of DNA into subunits has also been reported. Both calf thymus DNA (molecular weight $6·5 \times 10^6$) and DNA from chicken erythrocytes (molecular weight $8·0 \times 10^6$) were degraded by erythrocyte extracts to subunits of molecular weight $5·5 \times 10^5$. No dialysable products were formed and no significant changes in the absorptivity at 260 mμ were detected.[183] Light scattering studies indicated that the subunits were monodisperse rods with a molecular weight per unit length (Å) of 200 ± 20, in good agreement with the double helix model. The subunits therefore possess a much higher degree of molecular asymmetry than the original DNA (which is subject to a gentle coiling clearly absent from the subunits) and a possible site of the enzymic action may be the flexible joints (protein or non-mated base sequences) in a DNA superstructure. The kinetics of enzymic degradation suggested single-strand cleavage to these subunits (without a time lag) which then showed double-strand behaviour.[184]

The molecular weight of bacteriophage T2 DNA has been examined extensively. Sedimentation velocity and other properties of material isolated without mechanical breakage (avoidance of rapid stirring, pipettes or other causes of hydrodynamic shear) indicated[185] a molecular weight of $50-120 \times 10^6$. Comparison of autoradiographs from ^{32}P labelled bacteriophage or the DNA from the virus, showed that all the DNA in each particle is present as one structural entity,[186] in the form of unbranched rods, some 52μ long, indicating[187] a molecular weight 110×10^6. Further extension of such " molecular autoradiographic " methods provided a most elegant method for the determination of molecular weight.[188] The DNA molecules were embedded in a radiation-sensitive emulsion; emitted β-particles resulting from the decay of ^{32}P produced tracks that, emanating from a point source, gave stars. Counts of the average number of tracks per star gave the number of ^{32}P atoms per particle and hence, from the specific activity of the phosphate used, the total phosphorus content per DNA molecule could be calculated. In this way it was shown that bacteriophage T2 contains a single molecule of DNA,* the sodium salt of which has a molecular weight $130-160 \times 10^6$.

Controlled stirring of solutions of this DNA at different speeds gave first and second breakage products with an average molecular weight one-half and one-quarter of the original. Comparison of molecular weights determined by the method described above, and by sedimentation and viscosity characteristics, indicated that the latter approach gave results that were too low by a factor of two.[188]

A small deoxynucleic acid component of crystalline cytochrome b_2 has been isolated.[189, 190] The molecular weight is only some 10,000 (that is, approximately thirty nucleotides) and the material may provide a suitable beginning for the determination of nucleotide sequence in naturally occurring deoxynucleic acids. Various properties of the DNA (melting curve, effect of ionic strength on ultraviolet absorption, reactivity with formaldehyde and with E. coli diesterase, precipitation with plumbous ions) show that it is single stranded.[390]

As with the deoxynucleic acids, the ribonucleic acids have had a somewhat varied molecular weight history. The best defined ribonucleic acid is probably that from tobacco mosaic virus; it has a molecular weight of $1.94 \pm 0.16 \times 10^6$ as determined from light scattering, sedimentation and viscosity measurements.[191] In the absence of a decrease in molecular weight there is no change in infectivity accompanying expansion and contraction of the molecule by thermal treatment or changes in ionic strength. Turnip yellow mosaic virus (a spherical virus) also contains a high molecular weight RNA (approximately 2.3×10^6),[404] and many isolated cellular ribonucleic acids have molecular weights[192] of $1-2 \times 10^6$. Two main components of cellular

*T3 bacteriophage also contains a single piece of unbranched DNA, but with a molecular weight (determined by electron microscopy)[411] of 49×10^6.

RNA have been isolated repeatedly, one being this high molecular weight material, the other having a molecular weight of $3-7 \times 10^5$. Even lower molecular weights have been reported for the " soluble ", or transfer, ribonucleic acids which contain only 60–100 nucleotides.

ELECTROMETRIC TITRATION OF NUCLEIC ACIDS

DEOXYNUCLEIC ACIDS

The early titration results[193, 194] and the interpretations derived therefrom may be disregarded in the main, since grossly degraded nucleic acids were used, though some indication of the virtual absence of secondary phosphoryl dissociations (pK 6 to 7) was obtained.[195, 196]

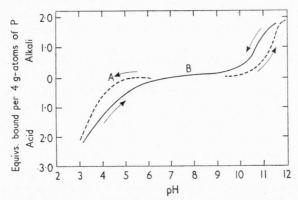

FIG. 8-17. Titration of herring sperm DNA at 25° ($\mu = 0.05$). A, Forward titration; B, back-titration.[204]

Forward and backward titration curves of undenatured deoxynucleic acid are not identical, subsequent back titration from high or low pH's (pH 12 or 2·5) giving curves that are displaced towards neutral pH under normal titration conditions.[197–200]   These hysteresis effects resulting from very mild acidic or alkaline treatment of deoxynucleic acid are ascribed to the disorganisation of hydrogen bonding in the macromolecule.[200–202]   However, at low temperatures ($- 0.75°$) titration of dissociating groups, that is, the –CO—NH– and –NH$_2$ groups or ring nitrogens of the purine and pyrimidine bases, becomes fully reversible.[203–205]   Although previously held not to be coincident,[200, 202] the backward titration curves of denatured DNA from high or low pH are fully reversible when non-continuous titration methods are used.[201, 203–205]

While titration of DNA from neutrality to pH 2·6 and back at 25° leads to irreversible collapse of the hydrogen bonded double helical structure, as evidenced by the hysteresis, titration to intermediate pH values gives a number of backward titration curves from which the proportion of broken hydrogen bonds can be calculated.[206] If only 10 to 15% of the hydrogen bonds are broken these reform on return to neutrality, but cleavage of 75% or more of the hydrogen bonds results in an unstable structure which rapidly collapses to the disorganised denatured form. Thermal denaturation can also be followed by the progressive displacement of the forward titration curves over pH 7 to 3. Rapid irreversible cleavage of hydrogen bonds occurs above 75°, and coincident with the displacement of the titration curve of the denatured material there is an increase in the ultraviolet absorption which shows a linear relation with the number of hydrogen bonds broken.[207, 208] Ionic strength has an effect on the reversible electrometric titration of both undenatured and denatured sodium deoxynucleates, the entire curves being displaced to lower pH values with increase in salt concentration.[201]

The effect of ionic strength on the apparent dissociation constants of the heterocyclic bases in DNA is readily followed by spectrophotometric titration.[208–210] In 0·01 M sodium chloride, titration of DNA with acid results in an abrupt and irreversible increase in ultraviolet absorption at pH 3·3, but in 0·1 M sodium chloride this does not occur until pH 2·4. This increase in absorption is associated with protonation of guanine residues.[209, 210] It may be noted that there is a considerable shift in apparent pK values of the bases when present in DNA, relative to those shown by the mononucleotides.[200, 209] The dependence of this shift on the ionic strength of the medium is shown in Table 8-IV.[209]

TABLE 8-IV.

DNA in		Apparent pK values			Mono-nucleotide
		H_2O	0·01 M NaCl	0·1 M NaCl	
Cytosine	base dissociation	6·0	5·2	3·8	4·2
Guanine	base dissociation	4·0	3·7	2·7	2·4
Guanine	—NH—CO— group	11·6	< 11·6	< 11·6	9·3
Thymine	—NH—CO— group	11·6	< 11·6	< 11·6	9·4

As indicated by the displacement of electrometric titration curves on denaturation, the pK values for the bases in denatured DNA more nearly resemble those of the mononucleotides, but are likewise a function of the ionic strength. Dialysis of solutions of DNA against water lowers the pH to 2·6, and is accompanied by denaturation.[211] Dilution[212, 213] or reduction of the ionic strength[210, 214] (by dialysis or other methods) at pH 6·5 (but not at pH 8) also results in denaturation owing to the shift in pK values at low ionic strength.[210] From the variation of pK values with ionic concentration it has been concluded that internal field effects due to the proximity of neighbouring charged phosphate groups in hydrogen bonded structures (possibly aggregates of double helices) raise the pKs of the amino groups present, so that at

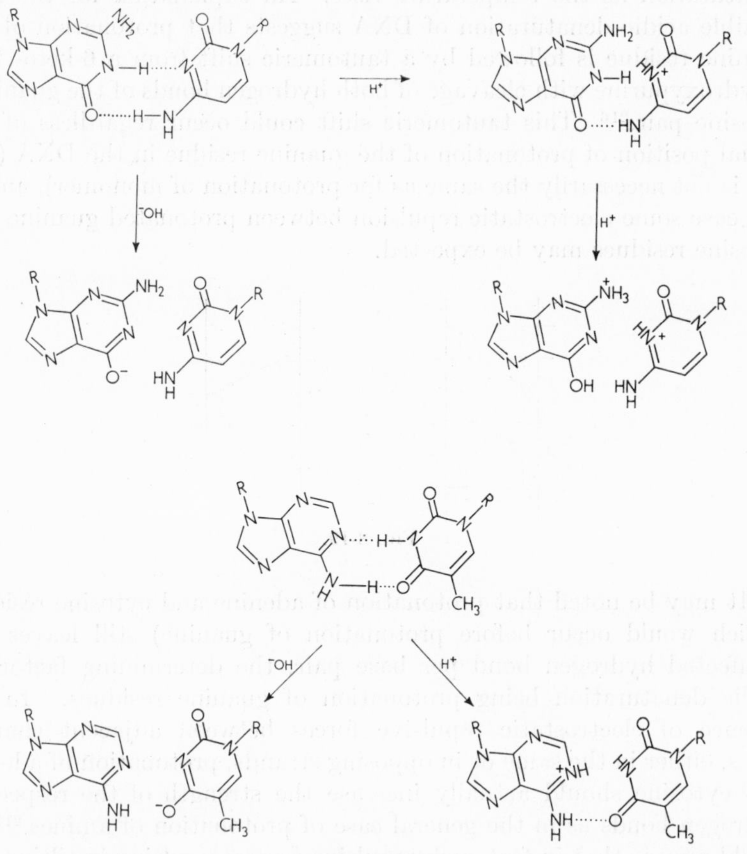

FIG. 8-18.

low ionic strength protonation of these groups and subsequent collapse of the hydrogen bonds occurs readily.[209, 210] At high ionic strength this field effect is probably considerably reduced by shielding of the phorphoryl dissociations. Dissolution of the nucleic acid in strong (6 M) urea (an agent normally regarded as conducive to the rupture of hydrogen bonds) raises the pH at which acidic denaturation occurs at any given temperature.[208]

Since irreversible effects as a result of acidification occur almost entirely in the pH region associated with protonation of the guanine residues, it is clear that protonation of adenine or cytosine residues (possibly at the N^1 position)[208, 215] does not necessarily lead to separation of the two strands. As may be expected, ionisation of the basic groups and thermal effects operate jointly in denaturation,[201, 208] so that fewer equivalents of acid are necessary to initiate denaturation as the temperature rises. An explanation for the irreversible acidic denaturation of DNA suggests that protonation of the guanine residue is followed by a tautomeric shift from a 6-keto- to a 6-hydroxypurine with cleavage of both hydrogen bonds of the guanine–cytosine pair.[216] This tautomeric shift could occur regardless of the actual position of protonation of the guanine residue in the DNA (and this is not necessarily the same as for protonation of monomer), and in any case some electrostatic repulsion between protonated guanine and cytosine residues may be expected.

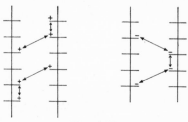

FIG. 8-19.

It may be noted that protonation of adenine and cytosine residues (which would occur before protonation of guanine) still leaves one unaffected hydrogen bond per base pair, the determining factor for acidic denaturation being protonation of guanine residues. In the absence of electrostatic repulsive forces between adjacent charged bases, either in the same or in opposing strands, protonation of adenine and cytosine should actually increase the strength of the respective hydrogen bonds as in the general case of protonation of amines.[217] It would appear that in fact such repulsive forces, resulting in tilting and lateral dislocation of the bases, play an important part in the process of acidic or alkaline denaturation (cf. properties of synthetic oligonucleotides).

Removal of a proton from the guanine and thymine residues under alkaline conditions results in the cleavage of only one hydrogen bond directly. However, it is likely that the tautomeric shift involved in ionisation of the 6-keto groups causes complete rupture. In addition, the increased electrostatic repulsion among the charged phosphate groups at alkaline pH probably weakens the helical structure.

Denaturation of DNA by mild acidic or alkaline treatment is thus in accord with the general structure involving hydrogen bonded complementary helices proposed by Watson and Crick. Some hydrogen bonds can be broken reversibly before onset of denaturation (that is, collapse of the double helix) which begins when a critical number of these bonds are cleaved, the number depending on the temperature, ionic strength, and solvent.[208] The solution properties of the polymers indicate a substantial contraction of the molecule on lowering[211] the pH to 2·6, and a similar transition[218] is observed at pH 11·7 to 11·9. Deoxynucleic acid denatured in this way is regarded as consisting of randomly coiled highly flexible chains containing a number of non-periodic hydrogen bonds (unbroken or re-formed), but with considerable rotational freedom in long sections of the chains. Undenatured DNA is highly extended and relatively rigid (though subject to some gentle coiling in a random fashion) as a result of the organised structure.[218] With alkali-denatured DNA reduction of the ionic strength of the medium is accompanied by a very large molecular expansion, presumably because of repulsion among the highly charged phosphate groups. In contrast, the conformation of native DNA is relatively unaltered by changes in the ionic strength of the medium (within limits).[218]

RIBONUCLEIC ACIDS

Electrometric titration has also indicated the presence of hydrogen bonds in a bacterial ribonucleic acid, since a hysteresis effect on forward and backward titration was observed.[219] No appreciable number of secondary phosphoryl dissociations was apparent. Early interpretations[220] of the titration of yeast ribonucleic acid reflecting the presence of three amino groups, two –NH—CO– groups, one secondary and three primary phosphoryl dissociations, are of historical interest only.

SOLUTION PROPERTIES OF DEOXYNUCLEIC ACID

VISCOSITY

The decrease in viscosity of neutral solutions of sodium deoxynucleate on addition of salts[221-223] may be a consequence of screening of the charged phosphate groups, permitting an increased coiling of the molecule; in addition there is possibly a small general contraction of the double helix. In solutions at very low ionic strength the macromolecule is fully stretched as a result of repulsion among the dissociated phosphoryl residues.[224] Alternate views have been advanced, based on viscosity measurements at very low shear rates[225] (permitting extrapolation to zero shear) and on studies of the variation of streaming birefringence[226] with ionic strength. The results suggested that the macromolecule does not contract on addition of salt, the variation of viscosity being due to electrostatic interaction between nucleate ions, and this is reduced by higher concentrations of cations.[225] However, many of these early studies are vitiated owing to the use of DNA that was at least partly denatured by dissolution at some stage in salt-free media. Light scattering studies,[227, 228] dichroism measurements[210] and examination of the intrinsic viscosity of undenatured material in 10^{-3}M and in 0·2 M sodium chloride[210] confirm that DNA is deformable, but the contraction in length on increase in ionic strength is rather small and not comparable with the behaviour of a typical polyelectrolyte, or of denatured DNA. Indeed, changes in hydration of the DNA double helix at different ionic strengths could well account for many of the observations. The viscosity curves also show that concentration dependent interactions are greater at the lower ionic strengths. Residual interactions are still present with 1 M sodium chloride as solvent however, and probably result from hydrodynamic factors relating to the flexibility of the structure. Denaturation of DNA (by acid, alkali, or heat) is accompanied by a ten-fold lowering of the intrinsic viscosity, and an approximately three-fold reduction in radius of gyration (from 2600 Å to 900 Å) without significant change in the molecular weight (light scattering).[218] Dependence of the reduced specific viscosity of denatured DNA on ionic strength is much greater than in the case of undenatured material.[218] The radius of gyration is also substantially increased at lower ionic strengths. In many respects, the results are best explained on the basis of a gently coiled double helical structure for undenatured DNA since contraction of the double strands will be limited (owing to the nature of the structure), but this contraction could endow the molecule with greater rigidity (thus increasing flow birefringence) while having little effect on the average length of the macromolecule owing to the decrease in coiling. Considerably greater deformation would be expected in denatured DNA. Gentle coiling of undenatured DNA is further suggested from a consideration of the length of the molecule in solution. This is probably some 6000 to 8000 Å as determined from streaming birefringence[229] and light scattering measurements.[228, 230, 231] Since a completely rigid double helix of molecular weight 8×10^6 would have dimensions of 40,000 Å $\times$ 20 Å it is clear that some degree of random coiling occurs in aqueous solution, to give a much less asymmetric particle.[227, 230]

FLOW DICHROISM

The absorption of polarised ultraviolet light by the purine and pyrimidine ring systems is greatest when the electric vector is in the plane of the ring, and least when it is perpendicular to the plane of the system. Dichroism is expressed as the absorptivity with the electric vector parallel to the structure minus that with the vector perpendicular to it, and can thus be positive or negative depending on the relation of the absorbing system to the molecular structure. The ratio of the two absorptivities is known as the dichroic ratio. Thymus deoxynucleic acid oriented by stretching has a negative ultraviolet dichroism,[129] and dichroic ratios of 1·7–4·7 have been obtained for oriented films obtained by shearing a viscous gel.[232] The humidity (and hence hydration of the specimen) has a marked effect on the dichroism of DNA, higher dichroic ratios being obtained with increasing humidity up to 93%. This dependence can be correlated with the different conformations of the DNA helical structure shown by X-ray analysis, and thus

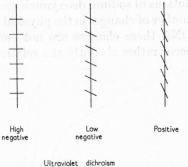

High   Low   Positive
negative   negative

Ultraviolet   dichroism

Fig. 8-20.

reflects a rotation of the planes of the purine and pyrimidine rings along the axis of the helix. Maximum dichroism is shown when the planes are normal to this axis; tilting of the bases reduces the dichroism.[233]

Orientation of the DNA macromolecule (this is of course essential for measurement of dichroism) can also be obtained in solution by streaming. Flow dichroism of undenatured DNA is directly related to the angle between the absorbing planes and the flow lines when the molecules are completely oriented.[234, 235] Measurements of absorptivity of solutions of DNA randomly oriented (at rest) and oriented by flow, using light of wavelength 260 mμ polarised in the direction parallel to the flow lines show that dichroism is dependent on the ionic strength of the solution, being higher in 10^{-3} M sodium chloride than in 0·2 M solution. The results suggest that the gentle coiling of undenatured DNA is reduced at low ionic strengths (due to repulsion between charged phosphate groups unshielded by counterions), and increased at higher ionic strengths, though a change in the angle of the bases to the axis of the molecule could also be involved. No flow dichroism is observed in denatured DNA, as may be expected from a random coil structure which would prevent orientation by streaming. The decrease in dichroism as denaturation proceeds, for example in acidic denaturation, parallels but precedes the rise of optical density and is thus more sensitive to the early stages. These probably involve an increase in coiling of the double helix on addition of a few protons to the basic deoxynucleosides, since distortion of the planar stacking would presumably be reflected in immediate changes in ultraviolet absorption. Viscosity measurements also indicate an increased flexibility in the initial stages of denaturation, before any increase in ultraviolet absorption occurs.

THERMAL DENATURATION

Exposure of solutions of sodium deoxynucleate to elevated temperatures results in a number of changes in the physical properties. However, for undenatured DNA these changes are not continuous with rise in temperature, but occur rather abruptly at a relatively high temperature

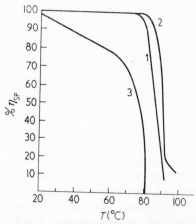

FIG. 8-21. Effect of thermal treatment (1 hr) on the viscosity of DNA. 1, Human DNA; 2, ox DNA; both in buffer ; 3, ox DNA in distilled water. Specific viscosities (measured at 23°) are expressed as a percentage of the maximum viscosity.[236]

In the region 75–95°) specific for the nucleic acid.[236]   Thus, heating solutions of human DNA (in buffer solution) for one hour has little effect on the viscosity of the solution (measured after cooling) until a temperature of 81° is reached. Abover this, a rapid decrease in viscosity occurs with a midpoint at 86°. Similar treatment of ox DNA causes the same drastic drop in viscosity with a midpoint at 89°. Stability of the DNA as indicated by the drop in viscosity on heating is markedly dependent on the ionic strength of the medium, and in salt free solution the change is continuous from room temperature, rather than abrupt, in accord with the protective action of ions against collapse of the double helix.

A more detailed examination[237] of the thermal denaturation of DNA showed that the change in viscosity behaviour occurred rapidly at the specific " melting " temperature, and was accompanied by a large decrease in mean end to end length, but no change in molecular weight according to light scattering studies. (Prolonged heating, particularly in slightly acidic solutions of low ionic strength causes cleavage of covalent bonds and hence a reduction in molecular weight.) Denaturing agents such as 8 M urea have no effect at room temperature, but lower the temperature range in which the changes occur by 10–20°. Within the temperature transition region, the viscosity reaches its final value after about 15 minutes heating. Since the process was not significantly reversible (under the conditions studied), it was held that denaturation is an all or none process, that is, weakening of any part of the structure facilitates further rapid collapse and there are no intermediate states in a partially denatured DNA specimen. It was further concluded that the changes at elevated temperatures result from the " melting out " of regions of hydrogen bonded structure[237, 243] in the DNA double helix, and that this breakdown of the organised native structure is co-operative as in the case of alkaline or acidic denaturation.[237] Failure to observe complete dissociation of the complementary strands may be ascribed to random hydrogen bonds formed on cooling the solution, particularly under the concentration conditions employed.

The most convenient method by which the thermal transition from native to denatured DNA can be followed employs the change in ultra-violet absorption on proceeding from a helical to a random coil structure.[238] The profile and magnitude of the increase differs if measured after cooling to room temperature rather than at the ambient elevated temperature owing to re-formation of hydrogen bonds (giving rise to short organised helical regions) on lowering the temperature. This process is particularly reversible at higher ionic strength which (as in the viscosity determined denaturation) shifts the " melting " temperature to higher values. Magnesium ions (and other divalent cations such as Ca^{++}, Ba^{++}, Mn^{++}, Co^{++}, Ni^{++} and Zn^{++}) are considerably more effective than monovalent cations. In contrast, cupric ions decrease the thermal stability of double helical DNA (for example, presence of Mg^{++} can raise the dissociation temperature of a particular DNA from 63° to 80°, whereas Cu^{++} ions effect a lowering to 42°) and in addition no decrease in ultraviolet absorption occurs on cooling the solution of DNA.[391] These effects presumably arise from co-ordination

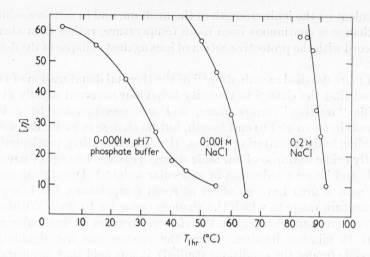

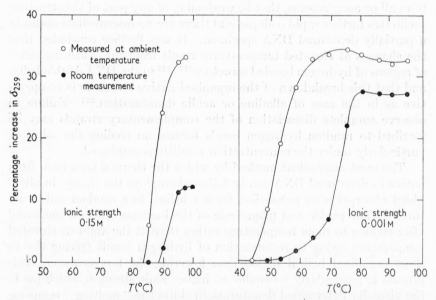

F$_{IG}$. 8-22. (*Above*) Variation of intrinsic viscosity of salmon sperm DNA measured at 25° after the solution has been heated for one hour at the temperature and ionic strength indicated.[23] (*Below*) Variation in optical density at 259 mμ of calf thymus DNA as a function of temperature.[238]

of Cu^{++} with the electron donor groups in the bases, thus destroying hydrogen bonds and preventing their re-formation, as with denaturation in the presence of formaldehyde. (See also p. 384 for the stabilising effect of diamines and polyamines on the secondary structure of deoxynucleic acids). The optical density–temperature profile of denatured DNA determined through several cycles is essentially reversible, the increase in ultraviolet absorption being continuous from 25 to 100°. This is indicative of a low degree of organisation involving short helical regions (differing in length and composition) virtually isolated by sections that are either non-bonded single strands, or essentially mismatched randomly bound chain segments.

While relatively sharp, the temperature transition region of DNA is broader than may be expected for long, perfectly formed, helical structures. Within this region, only completely denatured or native structures are found as shown by electron microscopy.[239] Again, within this region the drop in viscosity rapidly reaches a limiting value and a further decrease occurs only on increasing the temperature, suggesting a distribution of specific denaturation temperatures. A reasonable explanation for this is that the two types of base pairs provide an unequal contribution to the stability of the helix. Thermal denaturation would then depend on the relative composition of either whole double helical structures, or large segments thereof. The melting temperatures (that is, the midpoint temperature of the temperature–optical density profile) of a number of deoxynucleic acids differing in base composition were found to be directly proportional to the guanine–cytosine content of the nucleic acid[240] when determined under standard conditions (0·15 M sodium chloride in 0·015 M sodium citrate). Linear correlation of melting temperature with guanine–cytosine content is remarkably accurate, and determination of this temperature provides a useful estimate* of the molar ratios of the heterocyclic bases in a given DNA.[241, 242] Extrapolation of the results for deoxynucleic acids containing from 38% to 67% guanine–cytosine (T_m range from 84° to 96°) gives an estimate of the melting temperatures for double helical structures containing either base pair exclusively. For adenine–thymine this is 69° and for guanine–cytosine the figure is 110°. Enzymically synthesised copoly(deoxyadenylic–thymidylic acid) in which each strand has an alternating adenine–thymine sequence, has a melting temperature of 65° and a limiting low transition width, while for the polydeoxyguanylic–polydeoxycytidylic acid complex $T_m = 104°$. The small differences from the extrapolated figures are probably due to slightly different helix dimensions when both base pairs need not be accommodated. (In these cases thermal denaturation is completely reversible).

Considerable spread in the dispersion of guanine–cytosine content was observed in calf thymus DNA, as shown by the larger transition width. Fractionation of a partially denatured specimen (held at a temperature causing 80% of the total possible transition) by precipita-

*Molar percentage of guanine plus cytosine is given by the equation[413]

$$T_m = 69·3 + 0·41 (GC)$$

for solutions of the DNA in 0·2 M Na⁺.

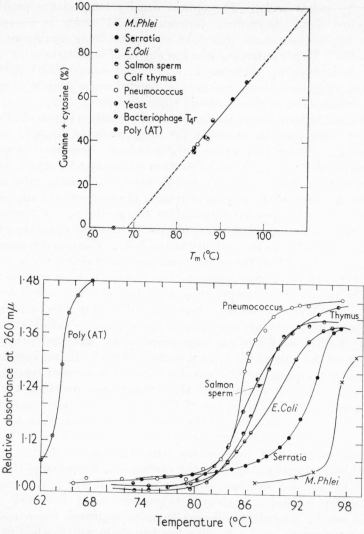

FIG. 8-23. Relation of guanine-cytosine content to denaturation temperature (T_m) for various deoxynucleic acids in 0·15 M NaCl + 0·015 M citrate, determined by change in absorptivity at 260 mμ.[240]

tion with streptomycin gave material with a melting curve displaced significantly higher than the original. This also provides a simple means of partial fractionation of the molecular species in DNA preparations. A relatively small dispersion in the distribution of guanine and cytosine composition was observed in bacterial deoxynucleic acids and, considering the broad range of mean composition of such deoxynucleic acids, it would appear that there is essentially no overlap in the composition of DNA molecules of many bacteria.[240] A narrow range of composition is not confined to bacterial species. The shape of the thermal profiles of DNA from ten normal, and malignant mouse tissues indicated that the dispersion of composition was considerably less than that evident in salmon sperm DNA or calf thymus DNA, and was in fact comparable with bacterial DNA, including absence of overlap.[244]

The low heterogeneity with respect to composition (but not necessarily sequence) of bacterial deoxynucleic acids is also evident in buoyant density determinations using density gradient ultracentrifugation.[245, 246] Again a linear relation between density and guanine–

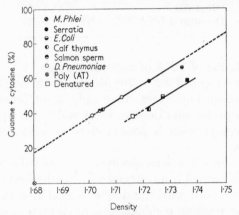

FIG. 8-24. Relation of guanine–cytosine content to density for various deoxynucleic acids.[245]

cytosine content was found on examination of a number of deoxynucleic acids. Extrapolation of the results indicated that an adenine–thymine polydeoxynucleotide double helix should have a density of 1·662 and for the corresponding guanine–cytosine material the density would be 1·764. Between these extremes, density determinations of undenatured DNA give an accurate estimate* of the base composition.[241] The corresponding denatured deoxynucleic acids show buoyant densities some 0·015 units greater. While heterogeneity in two mammalian deoxynucleic acids was indicated by increased band widths, the bacterial nucleic acids showed a narrow range of composition (half width of 3 to 5 mole % of guanine–cytosine against 11·0% for calf thymus DNA), and the spread in composition of bacteriophage DNA was too narrow to be measured. Preferential thermal denaturation of calf thymus DNA (low guanine–cytosine content) gave a fraction of undenatured material with a higher density than the original DNA from which it was isolated.[245]

*Molar percentage of guanine plus cytosine is given by the equation[414]
$$\rho = 1\cdot660 + 0\cdot098 \text{ (GC)}$$
where ρ is the buoyant density in cesium chloride. Unlike the melting temperature, buoyant density is affected by the presence of glucosidic and other residues.

Centrifugation to equilibrium in a density gradient of cesium chloride is an extremely sensitive method for characterising bacterial nucleic acids labelled with ^{15}N (bacteria grown with ^{15}NH$_4$Cl as nitrogen source), or deuterium (bacteria grown in D$_2$O), or both. Representative figures are those for DNA from *Escherichia coli*.[247]

	Buoyant density
Normal DNA	1·709
^{15}N	1·725
^{2}H	1·736
^{15}N + ^{2}H	1·752
Denatured DNA, ^{15}N + ^{2}H	1·767

Sonic degradation of DNA of molecular weight 8×10^6 to material with a molecular weight of $6·2 \times 10^5$ (double chain scission rather than cleavage of hydrogen bonds) produced only slight broadening of both the temperature profile and density band width. It appears that the distribution of composition is preserved to at least one tenth of the original molecule.

The temperature–ultraviolet absorption profiles of the multistranded helical complexes formed from enzymically synthesised polyribonucleotides are fully in accord with the double helical structure for DNA.[238] A number of the possible combinations have been examined, and all show the relatively sharp transition characteristic of a co-operative process for thermal denaturation. Under the same conditions (0·15 M sodium chloride) used for thermal denaturation of the deoxynucleic acids the double stranded complex from polyadenylic acid and polyuridylic acid has a $T_m = 61°$. Again ionic strength has a profound effect on the temperature of thermal denaturation; in 1 M sodium chloride the midpoint temperature for the polyadenylic–polyuridylic acid complex is raised to approximately 82°.

A theoretical study of the electronic structure of purine–pyrimidine pairs in DNA, using the molecular orbital method, indicated significant quantitative differences in a number of their electronic properties.[248] Calculation showed that both the total resonance energy, and the particular part of it representing stabilisation as a result of hydrogen bond formation, should be greater in the guanine–cytosine pair than in the adenine–thymine pair. The distribution of electrical charges in the base pairs further suggested that definition of the position of protonation of the basic deoxynucleosides in DNA by extrapolation from experimental studies of the monomers may not be valid, since the relative proton affinity of the various heterocyclic nitrogens could be modified as a result of hydrogen bonding. Axial interactions among the stacked bases will presumably have some effect also. In general, the results obtained by examination of the electronic submolecular structure of nucleic acids using the theoretical procedures of quantum chemistry (molecular orbital methods) are in accord with the essential chemical and physico-chemical properties of the polymers.[249]

It has been concluded from crystal structure data for purines and pyrimidines that cytosine and guanine should form three hydrogen bonds, the third bridging the guanine 2-amino group and the 2-keto function of cytosine.[250] To some extent this is confirmed by the greater stability of guanine–cytosine hydrogen bonding relative to that between adenine and thymine, but an examination of the reaction of nitrous acid with native, and denatured, DNA followed by hydrolysis to the free bases for estimation suggests otherwise.[251] Inhibition of the reaction of adenine and cytosine 6-amino groups with nitrous acid was observed in native thymus DNA compared with heat denatured polymer, presumably as a result of hydrogen bonding (though stereochemical factors may be important), but no such effect was observed with the guanine amino group. Titration evidence also suggests that the guanine amino group is not involved, but again the evidence is not decisive.[197, 202] Oscillographic polarography of highly polymerised DNA shows a reaction of the guanine 2-amino group but not of cytosine residues.[252] In apurinic acid, however, the cytosine gives an oscillopolarographic indentation.

Thermal denaturation of DNA also affects the chromatographic behaviour on cellulose anion exchange materials.[253, 254] The protective action of salt is noticeable, as well as an indication that all the molecules in a specimen of DNA do not behave in a uniform manner, some being more resistant than others.

Although reversibility of thermal denaturation may be regarded as negligible under conditions of rapid cooling at low ionic strength, there is some re-formation of helical regions on lowering the temperature at higher ionic strength. Since the high viscosity of undenatured DNA is not restored, these regions are presumably short compared with the length of the strands. However, under conditions of slow cooling, base pairing over most of the length can be attained and the material is essentially renatured as shown by restoration of the density, hydrodynamic properties, ultraviolet absorption–temperature profile and transforming activity.[255, 256] In addition to homologous renaturation of bacterial DNA, hybrid double helices can be obtained by slow cooling in the presence of heterologous DNA strands from closely related bacteria (but not from genetically unrelated bacteria). It would thus seem that at the denaturation temperature complete separation of the poly-deoxynucleotide strands does in fact occur, and would be apparent in molecular weight determinations at such elevated temperatures. However, on cooling, considerable partial mating of complementary strands can occur, particularly when the concentration of DNA is high. Renaturation under slow cooling conditions can result in up to 75% reconstitution in helical form, as indicated by sedimentation rate, intrinsic viscosity, and drop in density. Thus undenatured DNA from *Diplococcus pneumoniae* has a density of 1·700. Thermally denatured material cooled rapidly has a density of 1·716, but if cooling is slow, then a recovered density of 1·704 is obtained. The renatured DNA can hardly be distinguished from native DNA by electron microscopy.

Clearly the more uniform the DNA specimen (as shown for instance by the narrowness of the density profile in gradient centrifugation) the more readily will renaturation be attained, since the concentration of complementary strands after denaturation is highest in a completely homogeneous DNA. Renaturation of bacteriophage DNA, and to a lesser extent, bacterial DNA may thus be highly successful, but is unlikely with any mammalian DNA (such as that from calf thymus) that exhibits a wide range of compositional heterogeneity. (See also p. 514 for a more detailed discussion of denaturation and renaturation.)

Two mechanisms of inactivation of transforming DNA by heat must be distinguished.[257, 258] One is rapid at a critical temperature (5 minutes is sufficient) that is characteristic not only of the bacterial DNA examined, but also of the genetic marker. This process corresponds to the helix–random coil transition, and collapse of the organised structure results in a loss of 93–98% of the activity. Studies with pneumococcal transforming DNA containing a number of drug resistance markers have shown that whereas genetically linked markers have the same inactivation temperature, different markers can have relatively widely separated (by about 4°) inactivation temperatures. The inactivation–temperature profiles are extremely sharp with a spread of only ± 0·2° compared with the ultraviolet absorption–temperature profiles which show a spread of ± 2°. The difference in inactivation temperatures (e.g. 88° for micrococcin resistance, 90° for sulphonamide, streptomycin and canavanine and 91° for amethopterin in 0·15 M sodium chloride; it may be noted that at 88° there is no detectable loss of activity of the more stable markers) is probably due not only to heterogeneities in the content of guanine–cytosine pairs in the marker DNA, but also to distributional heterogeneity. Long sequences of guanine or cytosine, with corresponding stretches of adenine or thymine, are probably more stable than alternating adenine–thymine and guanine–cytosine arrangements, even though the overall composition of the marker or the DNA may be the same. Light scattering measurements show a drop in the effective molecular length from 9000 Å to less than 1000 Å, but no change in molecular weight (approximately 4×10^6) on thermal inactivation.[257, 258] However, this is probably a consequence of random aggregation.

In addition to this critical inactivation process, loss of transforming activity can occur by prolonged heating at subcritical temperatures. Whereas the collapse temperature is different for different markers in the same sample, the dependence of the subcritical process on temperature is nearly the same for all markers, providing the collapse process does not intrude. This second inactivation behaves as a single hit process, and is a first order reaction that probably proceeds only at those base pairs that are non-hydrogen bonded as a result of thermal excitation; hence the rate increases anomalously rapidly with temperature in the region just below the critical temperature.[257] The process is greatly accelerated at pH 5·4 and the larger the genetic region the greater the sensitivity to this subcritical thermal inactivation.[258] Glycosyl cleavage of purine deoxynucleosides is almost certainly involved.[257, 258] From the known rate of cleavage of purine deoxynucleosides the size of the streptomycin resistance marker has been estimated as approximately 430 base pairs.[257] (Compare with an independent estimate, p. 556.)

OPTICAL ROTATION

The optical activity of undenatured deoxynucleic acids is markedly greater than that of the component mononucleotides.[259] Specific rotations (arising from the sugar moieties) of the monomers lie within the range $+ 50°$ to $- 50°$ with an average value approximately $0°$ for equimolar quantities of the major nucleotides. For deoxynucleic acids, $[\alpha]_D$ lies between $+ 100°$ and $+ 150°$ or, expressed as a molar rotation based on phosphate, an approximate figure of $[M_p]_D = + 42,000°$ is typical. While some variation might be expected simply as a result of esterification of mononucleotide phosphate, values for the specific rotation of di- and oligonucleotides suggest that this is small.[260, 261] For example the corresponding value of $[M_p]_D$ for thymidylyl-5′ : 3′-thymidine-5′ phosphate is $+ 2800°$ in neutral solution. However, with helical structures a substantial contribution to the total optical activity may arise from unique and uncompensated interactions that such conformations of single-handedness make possible. Destruction of the organised helical structure should thus result in a drop in the optical activity of the material.[238] This was found to be the case. Further, the variation of optical rotation of DNA as a function of temperature was directly comparable with the temperature–ultraviolet absorption pro-

files previously described. For calf thymus DNA, $[\alpha]_D$ falls from
$+ 126°$ at room temperature to $+ 28°$ at $92°$, the midpoint of the change
giving a thermal denaturation temperature very close to that determined
by change in ultraviolet absorption.

The close correlation of the two profiles provides additional evidence
that the organised hydrogen bonding in deoxynucleic acids is such that
helical structures are formed, since the optical rotation is sensitive to
conformation rather than simply to hydrogen bonds. Hydrogen
bonding of the bases may be assumed to have a negligible direct effect

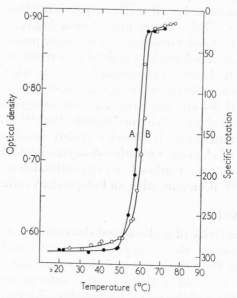

FIG. 8-25. Variation of specific rotation (A) and optical density (B) with temperature
for solutions of the double helical complex polyadenylic–polyuridylic acid in 0·15 M
NaCl + 0·015 M citrate, pH 7.[238]

on the specific rotation, although the optical activity of the mononucleotides is dependent on the nature of the base. Similar congruent
changes in optical density and specific rotation (from $+ 300°$ to $+ 25°$)
were observed on thermal treatment of the double-stranded polyadenylic–polyuridylic acid complex, indicating a direct correlation of
cleavage of hydrogen bonds with the helix–random coil transition.[238]
Restoration of the optical rotation presumably occurs to a large extent
on renaturation of thermally denatured DNA. As with ultraviolet
dichroism, changes in optical rotation are a more sensitive criterion of
interference with ordered secondary structure than are changes in
ultraviolet absorption.[34]

COUNTER-ION ACTIVITY

A sharp irreversible increase in the activity of sodium ions occurs on thermal denaturation of DNA. This change in the degree of binding of the cations over a very narrow range of temperature coincides with similar changes in optical density and optical rotation. It has been explained in terms of a decrease of charge density of the DNA macro-ion upon denaturation, owing to the presence of short sequences of " stretched " conformations in the random coil. This leads to an increase in contour length (but decrease in radius of gyration) of the molecule accompanying the helix–coil transition of DNA.[262]

ULTRAVIOLET ABSORPTION SPECTRA OF DEOXYNUCLEIC ACIDS

The ultraviolet absorption of nucleic acids is dependent on a number of factors, not least of which is the nature of the pretreatment. Present methods for the isolation of ribonucleic and deoxyribonucleic acids avoid most of the conditions leading to denaturation, such as high or low pH, low ionic strength, or high temperatures, all of which can cause irreversible changes in the absorption spectra.[263–267] For so-called native DNA the absorptivity (ϵ_{max}) with respect to phosphate (that is, an average value per nucleotide) lies between 6000 and 6500 in 10^{-3} (or higher) M sodium chloride at neutrality. In salt-free solution, extensive denaturation occurs even at pH 7, and between pH 6·5 and 7·5 there are large changes in the ultraviolet absorptivity,[265] presumably the consequence of shifted pK values which result in protonation of the adenine and cytosine residues in this pH region. Since the absorptivity of a corresponding mixture of mononucleotides would be approximately $\epsilon_{max} = 10,500$ considerable hypochromic effects are associated with the structural characteristics of DNA. Essentially, the variation of ultraviolet absorption of polynucleotides as a result of changes in pH, temperature, and ionic strength reflects the major or minor conformational changes (apparent in other physical properties) which increase or decrease the hypochromic effect.

EFFECT OF TEMPERATURE

As previously mentioned, increase in temperature of solutions of undenatured DNA leads to a " melting out " of tracts of hydrogen bonded base pairs. Thermal denaturation is a co-operative breakdown of the organised structure over a small temperature range.[264] For most deoxynucleic acids the critical melting temperature is above 75° in normal solution conditions.[240] Below this temperature the absorptivity is virtually constant over the range 0° to the " melting " temperature

(T_m), ultraviolet absorption being measured at the ambient temperature.[267] Further, the absorptivity is also independent of the ionic strength (10^{-3} M to 1 M sodium chloride) over this temperature range, though with a decrease in ionic strength the critical melting temperature is lowered. At or above this temperature there is a large increase in absorption and the ϵ_{max} rises to some 90% (from 60–65%) of that calculated for the mononucleotide content. The size of the hyperchromic effect on thermal denaturation (measured at the elevated temperature) is also a function of the guanine–cytosine content of the nucleic acid.[240] The increase varies from 44% (for DNA containing 38% of guanine plus cytosine) to 34% (for DNA containing 67% guanine plus cytosine). Thermal denaturation of the enzymically synthesised copoly deoxyadenylic–thymidylic acid (double stranded with alternating adenine and thymine in each strand) results in a 52% increase in ultraviolet absorption at the maximum. Extrapolation of these figures suggests that a poly deoxycytidylic–deoxyguanylic acid helical complex would show a 25% increase on denaturation.* Thus, the formation of organised structures involving adenine and thymine residues is considerably more effective in lowering the ultraviolet absorptivity than is bonding between guanine and cytosine residues, though greater thermal stability is shown by the latter pair.

On cooling, the absorptivity decreases to a lower value, the final ϵ_{max} being dependent on the rate of cooling and ionic strength. Complete reversibility is not normally attained, and the final thermally denatured DNA generally has an absorptivity 70–80% (rather than 60%) of the calculated value, that is, ϵ_{max} is approximately[264, 266] 7500 to 8500. Because of this increase in absorptivity on thermal denaturation, critical denaturation temperature profiles can also be obtained by heating solutions of DNA for one hour, followed by cooling to room temperature and determination of the absorption, though clearly this is a less refined approach.[264] Nevertheless, the early work, in which this technique was employed, did indicate that deoxynucleic acids from different sources (calf thymus, frog and starfish testes) possessed different sensitivities to heat, and that increasing salt concentrations (from 10^{-2} M to M sodium chloride) exerted an increasing protective effect against denaturation at 100°. The constancy of absorptivity with temperature for native DNA up to the denaturation temperature was also apparent.[264]

In contrast, the absorptivity of thermally denatured DNA (which contains re-formed hydrogen bonded base pairs, random or otherwise) is strongly and continuously dependent on temperature[267] from 0° to 100°. Increase in temperature gives an increased ϵ_{max} value measured at the ambient temperature. Further, at each temperature ϵ_{max} is

*The experimentally determined figure [410] is approximately 23%.

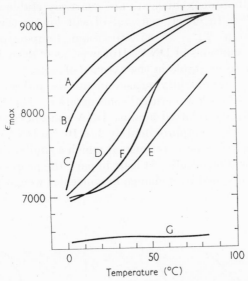

Fig. 8-26. Variation of ϵ_{max} for denatured DNA at different temperatures and salt concentration. A, in water; B, in 0·001 M NaCl; C, in 0·01 M NaCl; D, in 0·1 M NaCl; E, in 1 M NaCl; F, in 0·001 M MgCl$_2$. G, undenatured DNA in 0·01 M or 0·1 M NaCl.[267]

dependent on salt concentration, and the nature of the cations present. Increase in salt concentration lowers the absorptivity, and divalent cations such as magnesium are some 100 times as effective as monovalent cations in terms of molar concentration.

EFFECTS OF SALTS

As stated above, the absorptivity of undenatured DNA is independent of ionic concentration in the region 1 M to 10⁻³ M sodium chloride. In solutions of lower ionic strength than 10⁻³ M, or in salt-free water at pH 6·7, an increase in ϵ_{max} to about 8000–8800 occurs at room temperature, indicative of denaturation.[264-266] The change is irreversible in that the back spectrophotometric salt titration curve is not coincident with the forward one, and the extinction coefficient is not lowered to that of the undenatured DNA.[264] As with acidic, alkaline, or thermal denaturation, water denaturation does not necessarily result in a significant change in molecular weight.[265]

At low ionic concentrations the extent of the increase in absorptivity is also a function of the concentration of the DNA. This is probably a result of the contribution of counterions to the ionic strength, and to traces of salt in the DNA preparation, since the lower the concentration of the DNA the greater the increase in optical density. Concentrated solutions of sodium deoxynucleate are relatively stable in the absence of added salt.[265] In effect, removal of salt lowers the denaturation temperature from $T_m = 75\text{--}85°$ to room temperature for dilute (10^{-4} M or less) solutions of DNA. However, at $0°$ even dilute solutions of DNA appear to be stable in the absence of salts.

Conductivity and mobility measurements also indicate denaturation of DNA on dilution below a critical concentration. The discontinuity in specific conductivity (plotted against DNA concentration) appears at the same concentration (approximately 2×10^{-4} M DNA with respect to phosphate for salt-free preparations) at which a similar discontinuity in ultraviolet absorption occurs. At least in part, the process is irreversible and is not accompanied by a change in molecular weight as determined

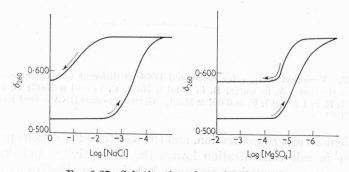

Fig. 8-27. Salt titration of star-fish DNA.[264]

by light scattering.[268] No change in molecular weight (when measured at high ionic strength) occurs on denaturation by acidic, alkaline, or thermal treatment, or by reduction of the ionic strength, and it is possible that unwinding of the collapsed double strands of denatured DNA does not occur rapidly under the conditions used, although such a process is energetically feasible. Formation of non-specific hydrogen bonds would tend to restrict complete separation of single strands; random aggregation may also be a significant factor.

The dilution effects were shown to be a reflection of true denaturation, rather than a reversible disaggregation of micelles containing a number of double helical units, by a comparison of the variation of specific conductivity against concentration (above and below the critical concentration) for "native" and thermally denatured DNA.[268] However, two discontinuities were observed in other studies of the influence of counterion association on the conformational stability of DNA in solution. In the absence of added salt both the activity coefficient of the sodium ions (determined with a membrane electrode) and the specific conductivity showed two discontinuities (at approximately 2×10^{-4} M_p DNA and 4×10^{-4} M_p DNA) when plotted against DNA concentration. The results were tentatively interpreted in terms of aggregates of double helical structures present in concentrated solutions; dilution to the higher critical value caused dissociation into isolated double helical structures.[269]

The destruction of hydrogen bonds can be ascribed[265] to a shift in the pK values (to approximately 7) of those nucleosides containing an amino group, permitting protonation at pH 6·7. In accord with this concept denaturation does not occur if DNA is dissolved in salt-free water at pH 8, as shown by the extinction coefficient ($\epsilon_{max} = 6300$) and by viscosity and dichroism measurements.[265] Acidic titration of this solution gives two sharp increases in ultraviolet absorptivity, one at pH 7 and the other at pH 5·0 to 4·5, indicative of macromolecular structural changes. Like acidic denaturation, water denaturation therefore involves addition of protons to DNA.

An explanation for this shift in pK values has been briefly mentioned previously. At high ionic strength the counterions in the vicinity of the charged phosphate groups provide effective shielding, so that little electrostatic effect is exerted and there are no significant local variations in sodium ion concentration or in the domain electric field. All the basic (and –NH—CO–) dissociating groups are thus subject to fields of constant electrostatic potential throughout the length of the structure. This stage (basic pK values $\sim 4\cdot5$) is attained in 10^{-3} M sodium chloride, that is, greater than the counterion concentration of deoxynucleate solutions vulnerable to water denaturation; sodium deoxynucleate in greater concentration than 10^{-3} M does not denature unless dialysis is used to reduce the pH to 2·6. At ionic strengths higher than 10^{-3} M the increased screening of phosphate groups is uniform and asymptotic, and progressively larger amounts of salt are required to produce shifts to lower pK values. However, at lower ionic strengths diffusion of counterions away from the peripheral phosphate groups of the double helix leaves regions of net charge where unshielded phosphate groups can exert a strong field. An increase in the number and size of such regions with decreasing ionic concentration may be expected. This nonuniform charge distribution, which is enhanced by the almost rigid nature of the double helical structure preventing a separation of neighbouring charged phosphate groups either along a strand or in opposing strands, is capable of raising the pK values of the amino-containing nucleosides to 7. In addition to the effects of protonation on hydrogen bond strength, weakening of the helical structure by increased electrostatic repulsions that arise as the shielding by counterions is reduced may be expected to assist partial separation of the two strands and eventual collapse of the structure. The greater shielding effect of divalent counterions such as magnesium, compared with sodium ions, is in accord with these interpretations. Whereas denaturation of dilute solutions of DNA (approximately 10^{-4} M with respect to phosphate), as evidenced by a rise in ϵ_{max}, begins on reduction of the ionic strength to 10^{-3} M in sodium chloride, the same effect is observed in magnesium sulphate only on reduction to 10^{-5} M. Considerably greater protection against water denaturation is thus afforded by such divalent cations. Again however, in the region of ionic strength in which DNA remains undenatured, that is from 10^{-5} M to higher molarity, magnesium sulphate has no effect on the ultraviolet absorption of undenatured DNA.[264]

Very high salt concentrations (2–8 M) also cause an increase in the absorptivity of undenatured DNA, an increase that is approximately linear with salt concentration.[270] However, in this case the hyperchromic effect is entirely reversed on removal of the excess of salt. Salt hyperchromicity is most pronounced in sodium bromide solutions and to a lesser extent in solutions of other alkali halides, but is completely absent in lithium chloride solutions (and indeed, above 6 M this salt induces a hypochromic effect). The increase in absorption (approximately 12%) in very strong salt solution is accompanied by a decrease in specific rotation (from 110° to 65°) indicative of considerable reduction in the helical character responsible for the high positive rotation of undenatured DNA.[270] Possible explanations for these reversible effects are that a limited number of hydrogen bonds are broken, such as those between adenine and thymine, resulting in collapsed regions of the double helix which can re-form on removal of the salt owing to the stable guanine–cytosine segments, or simply that untwisting of the double helix without cleavage of hydrogen bonds occurs. Such an increase in helical pitch towards a linear conformation (increase in number of base pairs per turn) could result in a smaller specific rotation, while the changed electrostatic environment of the purine and pyrimidine bases together with changes in the angle of the base pairs to the helix axis and a possible increase in interplanar distance could well result in an increase in ultraviolet absorption (that is, a reduction of the hypochromicity). X-Ray diffraction studies have shown that the precise structure of DNA fibres is highly dependent on the relative humidity, that is, hydration (and on the alkali metal forming the salt); similar changes in pitch and base-pair inclination might well occur under different solution conditions, particularly those that affect the hydration of DNA to greater or lesser extent (and this would certainly be expected in concentrated sodium bromide solution). Removal of the electrostatic repulsion of the phosphate groups due to greatly increased ion-pair formation would result in greater flexibility, and permit considerably more random coiling of the macromolecule than is normally present. This might explain the drop in viscosity which is also observed, though again, decrease in hydration of the DNA could well account for this effect too.

The effect of monovalent anions in high concentration on the stability of the DNA double helix has been examined in detail.[398] At neutral pH the thermal dissociation temperature is lowered by as much as 60° in the presence of 4 to 7 M salt, the " chaotropic " series being in the order

$$CCl_3COO^- \gg CNS^- > CF_3COO^- > ClO_4^-$$
$$> I^- > CH_3COO^- > Br^-, Cl^-, HCOO^-.$$

The dependence of thermal stability of DNA on base composition is increased in 7·2 M sodium perchlorate (compared with buffered 0·15 M NaCl) and indeed the normal narrow transitions of viral deoxynucleic acids are noticeably broadened. Rapid reversibility of partial denaturation can be demonstrated and it is likely that under such conditions the thermal transition of helix to random coil in each molecular species occurs over a relatively wide range of temperature, due in part to intramolecular heterogeneity in base composition and sequence. These general " denaturing " agents are described as " hydrophobic bond " breakers, acting by virtue of their effect on the structure of water,[398] presumably by altering the net hydration of the macromolecule.

The ultraviolet absorption of denatured DNA is markedly affected by the ionic strength of the medium at any given temperature. Increasing concentrations of sodium chloride lower the ϵ_{max} value over the range 10^{-3}–$1·0$ M (for heat denatured DNA) at room temperature; at 0° the effective range is shifted to lower ionic strengths (10^{-5}–10^{-2} M). Divalent cations such as magnesium, calcium, or barium are some 100 to 1000 times as effective as monovalent ions.[267, 271] The maximum effect on absorptivity occurs at about 0·7 equivalents of divalent cation per phosphate group. Conductivity studies also indicate much stronger binding of such cations relative to monovalent ions. Nevertheless, binding of divalent cations is reversible, and can be inhibited by an excess of sodium ions.[261] Thus thermally denatured calf thymus DNA (5×10^{-5} M with respect to phosphate) in 4×10^{-5} M Mg^{++} solution has an $\epsilon_{260} = 7300$ but on addition of sodium chloride to 10^{-2} M Na^+ the ϵ_{260} rises to 8600. Increase in sodium ion concentration to 10^{-1} M reduces the absorptivity in the normal manner to $\epsilon_{260} = 7800$. At pH 12 ionic strength (up to M sodium chloride) has no effect on the absorptivity of denatured DNA.[271] All hydrogen bonds are presumably broken at this pH, and the molecule is completely free of organised secondary structure.

Whereas 6 M urea has no effect on the absorptivity of native DNA in salt solution at room temperature (but does lower the melting temperature), a considerable rise in absorption occurs with denatured DNA, suggesting the disruption of weak, non-specific hydrogen bonds,[272] or of relatively short organised regions.

The decrease in absorptivity with increase in ionic strength at neutrality is probably the result of increased molecular organisation (hydrogen-bonded structure) following a decrease of net charge on the DNA, divalent cations being particularly effective. It may be noted that salts (up to 1 M sodium chloride) have no effect on the absorptivity of short-chain chemically synthesised polyadenylic, polycytidylic, or polyuridylic acid (random 2′–5′ and 3′–5′ linkages and of average chain length approximately 9 nucleotides).[261] However, with chemically synthesised polyguanylic acid, which even at short chain lengths readily forms hydrogen bonded aggregates, the absorptivity is less in salt solutions than in pure water. (In 0·1 M NaCl 2·5% less, in 1 M NaCl 6·5% less, in 0·1 M MgSO$_4$ 6% less.) In this case the ionic strength also has a marked effect on the pK values (11·65 in water, 10·3 in M NaCl; 2·70 in water, 2·2 in 0·01 M MgSO$_4$). Denatured DNA may therefore be regarded as consisting of chains of polydeoxynucleotides containing, and probably united by, hydrogen bonded (specific or otherwise) regions with a continuous series of melting temperatures from 0° to 100°. Thermal rupture of these random hydrogen bonds and of different lengths of organised regions of different stability is non-cooperative, and thus gives a continuous increase in ultraviolet absorption with increase in temperature.

EFFECT OF PH

Variation of the ultraviolet absorption of oligonucleotides relative to that of the component nucleotides (that is, changes in hypochromicity) on ionisation of the bases has been discussed previously. Considerably greater changes occur with undenatured deoxynucleic acids at the pH extremes, and it is clear that the major part of the hyperchromic effect is associated with collapse of the double helical structure as a result of cleavage of hydrogen bonds. Forward and backward spectrophotometric titrations are not coincident, the hysteresis effect being due to irreversible denaturation in alkaline or acidic solution. Again, the ionic strength of the medium strongly influences the pH at which the sharp rise in absorptivity occurs, shifts of the apparent pKs to lower values occurring with increase in ionic strength.[263, 265, 266] Divalent cations such as magnesium or barium produce the same effect at considerably lower ionic concentration. Approximate $pH_{\frac{1}{2}}$ values (pH of the midpoint of the absorptivity change) for acidic titration of calf thymus DNA in various concentrations of sodium chloride are given in Table 8-V.

TABLE 8-V.

Molarity of sodium chloride	$pH_{\frac{1}{2}}$
0 (H$_2$O)	7·2
10^{-3}	4·7
10^{-2}	4·1
0·2	3·1
1	2·8

Further studies of the spectrophotometric acid-titration of DNA (calf thymus) have indicated that changes in the spectra before denaturation (that is, before the rapid rise in absorptivity resulting from loss of organised structure) which occur at pH 2·59 at 0° and at 3·32 at 30° are due to protonation of cytosine residues.[273] The conclusion was drawn that the structure is stable at 0° when each adenine and cytosine residue is protonated, and hence up to this point titration is reversible, but that denaturation occurs (in aggreement with earlier observations) on protonation of the guanine residues. Controlled changes in pH or

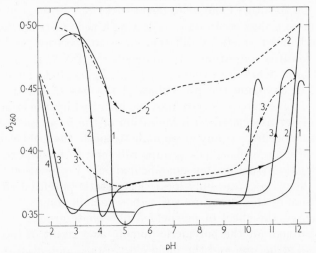

FIG. 8-28. Spectrophotometric titration of calf thymus DNA. Heavy lines, forward titration from pH 7; broken lines, back titration. 1, in 0·001 M NaCl; 2, in 0·01 M NaCl; 3, in 1 M NaCl; 4, in 4·5 M LiCl.[261]

temperature resulted in partial denaturation, indicative of the heterogeneity of the DNA.[273]   However, estimation of the width of pH of
denaturation, coupled with a study of the variation of $pH_{\frac{1}{2}}$ (the pH at
which denaturation is 50% complete) of nucleic acids containing different contents of guanine–cytosine, suggested that acid-denaturation at
high ionic strength, although sharp, is not an all-or-none process.
Compositional heterogeneity alone did not appear to account for the
breadth of the acid-denaturation transition.[274]   As may be expected,
at lower temperatures a higher degree of protonation is required for
denaturation, causing the curves to be shifted to lower pH values.
Thus, at 30° the pH of half denaturation is 3·07 (calf thymus DNA,
$\mu = 0·1$ M); at 0° this is lowered to pH 2·25.   Increase in the content of
guanine–cytosine also lowers the pH of denaturation, but the shift is
relatively small.[274]

Denatured (acid, alkali, or heat) deoxynucleic acid behaves quite
differently on spectrophotometric titration.   The increase in absorptivity is much less, occurs over a wider range of pH, and both the acidic
and alkaline ionisations are shifted to pHs nearer 7 compared with
those of undenatured DNA in the same ionic environment.   Titration is
essentially reversible, as are the backward curves from pH 2·5 or pH 12
after titration (and denaturation) of undenatured DNA at room temperature.

The abnormal steepness and asymmetrical shape of the forward
titration curves of undenatured DNA is presumably due to simultaneous
breaking of many hydrogen bonds resulting in gross conformational
changes.   On the other hand, with denatured DNA cleavage of hydrogen
bonds is more or less continuous, reflecting a wide distribution of short
hydrogen bonded tracts of different base composition and different
stability towards ionisation.   In undenatured DNA, the structure is
such that local field effects due to unshielded phosphate ionisations are
dominant in changing the pK values of the bases, and the effect of
increasing ionic strength is to reduce the pH at which the large increase
in absorptivity associated with ionisation of the bases and collapse of
the structure occurs.   At any given ionic strength, the local electrostatic
potential of ionised phosphate groups will tend to be uniformly distributed along the structure, but not smeared out.   Protonation of some of
the bases likewise causes only local electrostatic potential effects and,
until collapse of the structure, pK values remain constant.   With denatured DNA, the effect of unshielded phosphate groups is uniformly
smeared throughout the polymeric domain as a result of the compact
random coil structure, and the main electrostatic potential is independent of charge location and is constant throughout the molecule.[275]
The effect of protonation of some of the bases (or ionisation of –NH—

CO– groups) is likewise smeared throughout the molecule, causing the pK values to be a continuous function of the pH (since the domain electrostatic potential is a continuous function of the protonation or ionisation) and sharp spectroscopic changes no longer occur. Increasing ionic concentration reduces the domain electrostatic potential, and hence pK values.

NON-AQUEOUS SOLUTIONS OF DNA

Salts of polynucleotides with long chain amines such as tri-n-octylamine are soluble in a variety of organic solvents including ethanol, dioxan, and dimethylformamide.[261] Quaternary ammonium salts of DNA and RNA prepared from cetyl trimethylammonium bromide[276] are insoluble in water but soluble in dimethyl formamide or ethanol.[277] In general at least one alkyl chain of the amine must be longer than C_{12} to attain a measure of solubility in non-aqueous solvents for the salt. Addition of concentrated solutions of sodium chloride to the ethanolic quaternary ammonium nucleate gives a precipitate of the sodium nucleate.[277, 278] Dissolution in ethanol, and recovery of the sodium salt of tobacco mosaic virus RNA in this way does not destroy infectivity,[279] nor is biological activity of amino acid acceptor RNA lost.[318]

Sodium deoxynucleate itself is soluble in formamide, and dimethyl sulphoxide,[261, 280] neither of which are entirely satisfactory as solvents. Dissolution of DNA (or RNA) in formamide or dimethyl sulphoxide results in denaturation. Loss of secondary structure is indicated by the low specific rotation (which is independent of temperature) of nucleic acids in these solvents, and by the similarity of optical and hydrodynamic properties of recovered material with those of heat denatured material.[281] Change from an organised structure to a random coil conformation is also suggested by the opposite signs of simple rotatory dispersion curves of nucleic acids (but not of mononucleotides) when dissolved in aqueous and organic systems.[281, 282] Denaturation by formamide at a given ionic strength and temperature occurs at a critical concentration (approximately 60% by volume) of formamide, as followed by loss in transforming activity of pneumococcal DNA. Removal of the formamide by dialysis does not result in renaturation; a subsequent thermal treatment (at temperatures below the melting temperature) is required for recovery of biological activity.[283] Strand separation of $^{14}N-^{15}N$ labelled hybrid *E. coli* DNA as a result of dissolution in formamide has been demonstrated by density gradient centrifugation. Solvent denaturation occurs at a much lower fraction of dimethylformamide in aqueous solution than with formamide.[284, 402]

Ethanolic solutions of sodium deoxynucleate are readily prepared by dialysis of aqueous solutions against increasing concentrations of ethanol.[285] A marked increase in sedimentation rate and a three-fold decrease in the radius of gyration of the macromolecule occurs rather sharply at approximately 65% ethanol but no significant change in the molecular weight (light scattering) occurs. Solutions of DNA in 95% ethanol have an equivalent conductivity approximately 1% of that of aqueous solutions, presumably mainly as a result of greater ion pair formation between sodium ions and phosphate groups.[286] Zero net charge in solutions of low dielectric constant is also indicated by the dialysis of single-stranded DNA from the virus ϕX174 in aqueous dimethylformamide or 2-methoxyethanol;[287] under normal aqueous conditions polynucleotides of chain length greater than ten nucleotides are non-dialysable even in strong salt solutions.

The physical properties of solutions of DNA in ethanol and in methanol (prepared by gradient dialysis) have been investigated in some detail.[288] Macromolecular and optical criteria (increased sedimentation velocity, lowered viscosity and radius of gyration, and high ultraviolet absorption) indicate denaturation. Although disruption of the secondary structure is apparently complete as judged by macromolecular and optical criteria, methanol denaturation is rapidly and readily reversible by water. An irreversible thermal transition also occurs in methanol-rich solvents, but again water appears to cause renaturation. Thus two forms of " denatured " DNA are possible in methanol solutions, each of which appears to differ from material denatured in aqueous solution.[284] Whereas denaturation by many organic solvents (including dimethylformamide) is largely reversed by water in the presence of electrolytes, denaturation by dimethyl sulphoxide is irreversible.[402]

In the presence of electrolytes, addition of ethanol (or methanol) to an aqueous solution of DNA lowers the thermal denaturation temperature.[288] The decrease in stability of the DNA double helix in ethanol, methanol, formamide, dimethylformamide[402] and other non-aqueous solvents (similar results with ethylene glycol and glycerol have been reported)[289] is considered to support the concept that a major contribution to the stability of the helix in aqueous solution lies in " hydrophobic interactions " between the relatively non-polar residues of the macromolecule. Such " interactions " are primarily a consequence of the greater stability inherent in a solution containing the maximum number of solvent–solvent interactions.[288] A hydrated counterion between two charged phosphates has also been suggested since ethanol would be expected to destroy any crystal lattice of the shell of hydration.[290]

However, while DNA is undoubtedly solvated by hydrogen bonded water molecules in aqueous solution, there is no real evidence of sheaths of ice-like lattices of water (above 0°) of an organisation sufficient to confer a stability that is presumably extant up to the melting temperature (85–95°). Although hydration plays some part, as evidenced by the increased susceptibility of DNA to denaturation in 6–8 M urea (urea does not denature DNA but can " denature " synthetic polymers in which hydrogen bonding is not possible, suggesting interference with a hydration lattice)[291] other sources of the rigidity of the double helical structure may well lie in the direct interaction between the heterocyclic bases in the same strand along the axis together with the hydrogen bond vector perpendicular (or tilted 10–20°) to the axis. Repulsion among unshielded ionised phosphate groups along the axis provides an additional reason for the low flexibility of native DNA in aqueous solution. Virtually complete removal of this stretching force by ion pair formation in non-aqueous solution, with possibly considerable tilting of the bases and alteration of the pitch of the double helix, could well lead to greatly increased flexibility, if not collapse, of the macromolecule. Apart from this, the other factors mentioned will undoubtedly be influenced by solvents possessing a dielectric constant differing greatly from that of water. Thus both the hydrogen bond strength and the π electron interaction between the bases will be affected considerably by solvents with a low dielectric constant, independently of any stability effect due to interference with a water lattice. The ready reversibility of the " denaturation " process in methanol suggests that strand separation does not in fact occur, and that the physical effects merely reflect a greatly increased coiling. A naïve correlation of hyperchromicity with cleavage of hydrogen bonds (based on the mistaken belief that hydrogen bonding per se lowers absorptivity) is quite unwarranted. Since the ultraviolet absorptivity will be altered in any case as a result of the effect of environmental dielectric constant on π electron interaction, it may well be that the material remains extensively hydrogen bonded, but the double helix is " untwisted " to a large extent, to give a much more flexible " linear " double strand susceptible to random coiling. Information on the properties of mononucleotides and oligonucleotides (tri-n-butylammonium salts) in non-aqueous solution is clearly desirable.

Ethanolic solutions of thermally denatured DNA are readily obtained by the slow addition of hot ethanol to an aqueous solution of the sodium deoxynucleate maintained above the thermal denaturation temperature.[261] The high absorptivities of such solutions ($\epsilon_{260}^{P} = 9800$ for denatured calf thymus DNA in 98% ethanol) suggest that no organised structures are present, though restricted rotation about internucleotide linkages may still be evident. On dissolution of the material in water the ϵ_{260}^{P} is lowered to 8650; in 0·1 M sodium chloride a value of 7800 is obtained.

Methanolic solutions of enzymically‾synthesised polyadenylic acid have been prepared. Such solutions also show a large increase in the sedimentation constant, decrease in intrinsic viscosity, drop in optical rotation and increase in ultraviolet absorption as shown in Table 8-VI.[292] A residual hypochromicity of approximately 10% may be noted for methanolic solutions of " denatured " polyadenylic acid, suggesting that some stacking of the adenine residues is still present, but again values of ϵ_{max} for the monomer in methanol would be desirable for comparison.

TABLE 8-VI.

Polyadenylic acid in	Water (0·001 M NaOAc)	Methanol (0·001 M NaOAc)
Sedimentation coefficient	6·9	50
Intrinsic viscosity	16·8	0·26
Optical rotation $[\alpha]_D$	+ 100°	− 25°
ϵ_{260}^{P} at 20°	9500	13,600
ϵ_{260}^{P} at 50°	12,400	13,600

ϵ_{260} for adenylic acid in water = 15,000

NATIVE SINGLE-STRANDED DNA

While most isolated deoxynucleic acids possess a complementary double-stranded helical structure, in some instances, for example, vaccinia virus[293] and bacteriophage S13,[294] the nucleic acid occurs naturally in a single stranded conformation. The first such case was discovered in an examination[287] of the properties of DNA from the bacteriophage ϕX174. This virus has a particle weight of $6·2 \times 10^6$ and contains 25% by weight of DNA of molecular weight $1·7 \times 10^6$, indicating one molecule per virus.[295] The DNA obtained by phenolic extraction of the virus does not have a complementary nucleotide composition, it is precipitated by plumbous ions, and it reacts with formaldehyde indicating that blocking of the purine and pyrimidine 6-amino groups by a strongly hydrogen bonded structure is absent. Further, the ultraviolet absorption is dependent on temperature in the range 20° to 60° and on the ionic strength of the medium in the range 10^{-3} to 1 M. The absorptivity of the DNA in 0·2 M sodium chloride (ϵ_{max} = 8000) is considerably higher than that of undenatured double helical DNA, and the properties in general resemble those of such DNA after thermal denaturation.[287] Light scattering studies indicated that the DNA from bacteriophage ϕX174 was highly flexible and that the conformation was strongly dependent upon the ionic strength of the solution. In 0·02 M sodium chloride at 37° the radius of gyration was found to be 1140 Å, but in 0·2 M saline this dropped to 440 Å. Magnesium ions were even more effective in causing this contraction. On degradation of the polymer with pancreatic deoxyribonuclease, the weight-average molecular weight decreased in accord with the function expected for a single-stranded molecule.

This last approach, kinetic examination of the enzymic degradation of polynucleotides, is of general application for the determination of multi-stranded structures.[296, 297] The basis lies in the cleavage of a single strand at each catalysed hydrolysis whereas a two-stranded structure requires at least two such breaks. Assuming that a lag phase in drop in molecular weight is not the result of a preliminary rupture of hydrogen bonds in particular segments, the kinetics of degradation can indicate single, di-, tri-, or higher-stranded structures. Results with calf thymus DNA and pancreatic deoxyribonuclease further indicated that the minimum number of nucleotides which must be present between breaks in the two chains to prevent scission of the double strand is no more than six. Conversely, it is clear that enzymic cleavage of each strand must occur within 6 nucleotides of each other for variation in molecular weight.

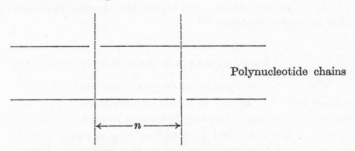

Polynucleotide chains

n = 6 or more nucleotides : double strand is stable
at room temperature.
n < 6 nucleotides : fission.

Resistance to enzymic attack by double stranded structures is also evidenced with a phosphodiesterase from *Escherichia coli*. Only slight activity is observed with intact double-stranded DNA, but heat denatured material, and the DNA from bacteriophage ϕX174, are rapidly hydrolysed to deoxynucleoside-5′ phosphates.[298]

The occurrence of single-stranded DNA in preparations from mammalian sources has been examined, using precipitation with lead ion as a test. Whereas native double helical DNA does not form an insoluble lead complex, denatured (heat, acid, or alkali) DNA readily gives a granular precipitate with plumbous ions.[299] Lead deoxynucleate gels were obtained from native DNA by centrifugation; regenerated DNA from this gel showed considerable single strand character.[300] Single-stranded DNA can also be separated from double helical material (and from RNA) by electrophoresis.[301]

A method which distinguishes between single and double stranded polynucleotides *in vivo* uses the greater sensitivity to ultraviolet light of the pyrimidines, relative to the purine bases. Experimentally, the action spectra for inactivation of the bacteriophages ϕX174 (containing single-stranded DNA) and T2 (containing double-stranded DNA) were found to be significantly different in that the first was closely similar to the ultraviolet absorption of a mixture of deoxycytidine and thymidine with a minimum at 240 mμ, whereas T2 bacteriophage showed an action spectrum with a minimum at 230 mμ, as in the ultraviolet absorption spectrum of DNA.[302] A possible theoretical interpretation of this suggests that in the double helical structure transfer of an absorbed quantum from a purine to a pyrimidine results in approximately equal efficiencies for all absorbed quanta, whether by purine or pyrimidine, giving an action spectrum resembling the ultraviolet absorption spectrum of the DNA, rather than that of the pyrimidine components.[302] Similar work on the action spectra of transforming DNA (from *Hemophilus influenzae*) above, and below, the thermal denaturation temperature has been reported.[303]

DENATURATION AND RENATURATION

The solution properties of deoxynucleic acid are in full accord with a double helical structure in which comparative rigidity is maintained by the lateral hydrogen bonding of base pairs and by π electron interactions among the purine and pyrimidine ring systems stacked above each other. Under normal conditions the hydration lattice of hydrogen bonded water molecules probably makes a significant, but not overwhelming contribution to the stability. Flexibility of the structure is very small (in comparison with the random coil structure of other polyelectrolytes) but some gentle coiling is evident. The extent of this is probably dependent on the magnitude of the electrostatic repulsions among the phosphate groups, that is, on the degree of counterion shielding provided by the environment. One might therefore expect complexes of DNA with polybasic amines such as polylysine or spermine (prepared under conditions of dilution such that cross linking and aggregation does not occur) to show increased flexibility, leading to more intensive coiling and a smaller radius of gyration, as with the deoxyribonucleohistones.

Denaturation of DNA usually refers to collapse of the organised secondary structure resulting from cleavage of the hydrogen bonds. This can be achieved by increase in temperature, by treatment with acid or alkali, or by dilution of the ionic (including counterion) concentration below a critical value. Simultaneous cleavage of a number of hydrogen bonds is probably required to initiate denaturation of DNA, but subsequently the process is co-operative, that is, collapse of the weaker regions of the double helix (for thermal denaturation this would be sequences composed predominantly of adenine and thymine residues) reduces the stability of adjacent regions and leads to a rapidly increasing progressive disruption. Thus variation in degree of denaturation of a given preparation is a reflection of the compositional (and possibly sequential) heterogeneity of the DNA species, and at the molecular level denaturation is an all or none process giving a mixture of fully denatured, and undenatured molecules. Such a process is enhanced by the reversibility of hydrogen bond formation which, if the critical point resulting in collapse of the total structure has not been reached, results in re-formation of the secondary structure of relatively short disrupted regions on removal of the denaturing conditions.

Nevertheless, considering the length of the DNA helix, partial denaturation may well be possible if the nucleotide sequence consists of fairly extensive regions of guanine–cytosine pairs and corresponding stretches that are predominantly adenine–thymine base pairs. Electron micrographs of DNA denatured by dilution[304] suggest that this is indeed so. Undenatured DNA appears as long rather straight threads whereas the denatured nucleic acid forms amorphous blotches. Occasionally, however, remnants of threads attached to terminal or central blotches can be seen[160, 304] suggesting that the progressive collapse has been arrested at particularly resistant regions of the chain.

Although denaturation is a collapse of the helical structures to a random coil conformation consequent on cleavage of hydrogen bonds, reduction of the molecular weight to one half, corresponding to separation of the two chains, does not always occur. However, it must be remembered that estimations of molecular weight are seldom performed under the operating denaturing conditions (high temperature, the pH extremes, or DNA and ionic concentrations less than 10^{-4} M). An explanation for the lack of change in molecular weight is possibly to be found in the rapid collapse of the structure once the critical denaturation point has been reached. This could result in small segments of hydrogen bonded sequences being " trapped " in the random coil structure, and thus protected from further cleavage. From the properties of chemically and enzymically synthesised oligonucleotides, it is clear that regions of only 3 to 6 hydrogen bonded base pairs would be sufficient to prevent dissociation of the two strands. Under conditions such that the denatured DNA is highly extended (low ionic strength) dissociation is possible. Recent work has indicated that thermal denaturation of DNA in 0·2 M salt solution results in an uncontrolled amount of intermolecular association as well as a large variety of conformations among DNA strands. However, in 0·01 M salt and at low concentrations of nucleic acid (less than 0·1 gram per litre) denatured DNA behaves as single chains.[305] Molecular weight measurements of *E. coli* DNA before, and after, denaturation under these conditions indicate a decrease from $10·5 \times 10^6$ to 5×10^6.

A somewhat different approach has also shown that under thermal denaturing conditions DNA is single stranded. The kinetics of thermal degradation of DNA (at 95°) and RNA (at 80°) were examined using viscosity measurements to follow the degradation.[306] For Lettre–Ehrlich tumour RNA the slope of the curve (0·86) indicated single strands; for DNA the slope was 1·1 for the first 30 minutes and thereafter less, but at no time was it consistent with a double stranded structure at 95°. It may be noted that the kinetics of enzymic degradation of heat denatured DNA can be misleading, since double helical structures (either from a single strand or from different strands) re-formed on cooling may be sufficiently stable to result in an apparent two stranded kinetics of degradation by deoxyribonuclease.

On reversal of the denaturation conditions, considerable re-formation of hydrogen bonds occurs. In concentrated solutions of DNA this probably results in cross linking and aggregation, and hence gel formation. At lower concentrations it is likely that some reorganisation occurs even under rapid cooling, and in addition to random hydrogen bonds, helical regions of complementary base pairs are formed as a result of local exploration of the most stable conformation, since sections of each strand will have sufficient freedom of movement relative to the other. Denatured DNA possesses a significant thermal hyperchromicity suggestive of such reorganisation. The sodium salt of heat denatured DNA gives a diffuse B-type X-ray diffraction pattern, but the intensity of the pattern shows that a large part of the helical structure has reformed, though in an irregular manner.[307] Many types of hydrogen bonding may be expected in denatured DNA, but the main base pairs are probably those involving hydrogen bonds between 6-amino and 6-keto groups, that is, cytosine–thymine and adenine–guanine in addition to the specific adenine–thymine and guanine–cytosine combinations.

Conditions for optimal renaturation of heat denatured DNA have been established.[308] Concentration of sodium ions should be above 0·4 M and the temperature about 25° below the "melting" or dissociation temperature. Since the helix–coil transition is reproducible (with respect to physical properties and thermal inactivation of biological markers) the same secondary structure is formed by annealing, and non-specific hydrogen bonding is not involved to any significant extent. Completeness of renaturation increases with the molecular weight of the DNA and, as may be expected, is markedly affected by the homogeneity of the specimen. Re-formation of secondary structure is in a decreasing order for DNA from bacteriophage > small bacteria > bacteria > mammalian sources, an order that reflects the variation in numbers of different DNA molecules and spread in base composition characterising each source.[308] As shown by fractionation of renatured transforming DNA by density gradient centrifugation, renaturation is not an all or none process, but varying extents of double helix re-formation are possible.[309] This is mainly a consequence of random fission of covalent linkages in the polynucleotide strand during the heat treatment. Under the standard conditions of heat denaturation and subsequent annealing, it can be calculated that approximately three scissions would occur on average in each strand of DNA with a molecular weight 10^7. Hence the renaturation process involves complementary strands differing in length by one quarter to one half, resulting in 20 to 30% non-renaturation.[310] Indeed, electron micrographs show frequent blobs at one or both ends of renatured chains, consistent with protrusion of a single-stranded chain end.

The entire process of strand separation and recombination, and formation of hybrid DNA molecules with each of the strands coming from a different source, has been subjected to detailed examination.[310] Use of ^{14}N–^{15}N half labelled biological "hybrid" DNA (in which ^{15}N is present in one strand only), coupled with equilibrium centrifugation in a density gradient, showed that the kinetics of separation into single stranded subunits (followed by disappearance of the hybrid band, or appearance of the two bands of single-stranded material, all components possessing a characteristic density) corresponded closely to calculations[311] for unwinding of a double helix of comparable length in which no bonds hold the strands together. At 100° in 0·15 M sodium chloride containing 0·015 M sodium citrate, strand separation is complete in about 60 seconds. Also in accord with theoretical prediction,[312] this time increases with increase in the viscosity of the solution, using either concentrated sucrose solutions or higher concentrations of DNA. Renaturation of bacterial DNA (in approximately 0·3 M sodium chloride containing 0·03 M sodium citrate) is essentially complete in about three hours at 68°. It is likely that renaturation of more homogeneous bacteriophage DNA is considerably more rapid.

Existence of protruding single stranded material in renatured DNA has been mentioned. Removal of these unmatched single chain ends is essential for the study of non-biological hybrid formation since such unpaired protrusions lead to aggregation in a random sense. This is readily avoided by digestion of the product with *Escherichia coli* phosphodiesterase (selective attack on single stranded DNA), a process that also reduces the remaining minor differences (such as density) between renatured and native DNA. When a mixture of heavy isotope (^{15}N and ^{2}H) fully labelled bacterial DNA and normal DNA was taken through the denaturation–renaturation cycle (thermal dissociation, followed by annealing and then treatment with diesterase), three bands were observed on density gradient centrifugation in caesium chloride solution, corresponding to heavy renatured, hybrid, and light renatured DNA. As expected for random pairing, the amount of hybrid was double that of the heavy or the light compound. Hence strands which unite in renaturation are not the same strands that were united in native DNA, but are complementary strands originating in different cells.[310] The same proportions of heavy, hybrid, and light DNA were obtained when biologically hybrid $^{1}H + ^{14}N : ^{2}H + ^{15}N$ DNA was taken through a denaturation and renaturation cycle. With respect to hybrid formation with deoxynucleic acids from different bacteria (readily followed by using a normal DNA from one source and a heavy DNA from the other), this is only possible when the two samples have a similar overall base composition. This in itself does not necessarily lead to hybrids, owing to an additional requirement for considerable similarity in base sequence. Parallelism between genetic compatibility and formation of DNA hybrids *in vitro* led to the proposal that organisms yielding DNA capable of forming hybrid molecules are genetically and taxonomically related.[310]

All methods examined (heat, formamide, acidic or alkaline conditions, or concentrated urea at 50–70°) for denaturation of biologically hybrid ^{14}N–^{15}N DNA gave two density bands (for example, native ^{14}N–^{15}N DNA of density 1·717 gives a light ^{14}N band density 1·717, and a heavy ^{15}N band density 1·740; increase in density on change in conformation also occurs) indicative of strand separation. However, contrary to the results with methanol and ethanol, withdrawal of the hydrogen bond breaking agent does not produce renaturation, and this is only possible by a thermal treatment. It is probable that the decreased Brownian motion of chain segments at room temperature is insufficient to provide the mobility required for the exploration necessary to create "nuclei", considerable regions of the molecule being frozen in mismatched pairings,[310] or more likely, by short matching segments in the wrong strand or location. ("Renaturation" of polyribonucleotide complexes, e.g. polyadenylic–polyuridylic acid, is very rapid at room temperature.)

Reversibility of DNA denaturation can be divided into a slow process which necessitates overcoming relatively large kinetic barriers after complete denaturation, and a rapid renaturation around residual " nuclei " of the original conformation. It is claimed that the latter can occur after partial denaturation involving up to 95% disordering of the base pairs.[313] These nuclei, possibly stretches of 10–20 guanine–cytosine pairs, form only a small fraction of the purine–pyrimidine base pairs; the additional stability relative to the rest of the secondary structure varies with the source of the DNA. At temperatures near the beginning of thermal melting of the double helix, fluctuations of unbonded sections occur. The fraction of such disordered sections increases rapidly with temperature just below the critical temperature.[257, 314] This can be followed readily by heating the DNA in the presence of formaldehyde,[314, 315] (hydroxymethylation of the basic nucleosides is preceded by hydrogen bond cleavage) which causes a lowering of the thermal transition temperature by about 10°. The lowering can be attributed at least in part, to interference with the equilibrium between native and denatured DNA by hydroxymethylation of amino groups.[314] (See also p. 521.) Thus at temperatures where essentially no hyperchromic effects are observed, the reaction of DNA with formaldehyde can be demonstrated spectrophotometrically, by viscosity–temperature profiles, and by change in antigenic activity (antigenic properties are dependent on the proportion of non-hydrogen bonded bases). Electron microscopy of material treated in this way shows " puddles " of denatured polynucleotide segments attached to structurally intact linear strands.[316] Dialysis of the hydroxymethylated DNA in buffer at pH 8·5 restores the lowered ultraviolet absorption characteristic of undenatured DNA, that is, removal of the hydroxymethyl groups permits renaturation. Renaturation can also be demonstrated immunochemically; approximately 30% of the antigenic activity remains, indicating some permanent damage, but this is not observable spectrophotometrically.[314]

Similar immunological studies on the thermal denaturation and renaturation of T4 bacteriophage DNA have been reported.[317] At least in part, the glucosidic hydroxymethylcytosine residues are responsible for antibody formation. These determinant groups are available in the denatured DNA, but not in the native or renatured material. Using this approach, studies of renaturation showed that the process was bimolecular, dependent on ionic strength, and possessed a temperature optimum at 55°. Heterologous renaturation with T2 and T6 DNA was also demonstrated.[317]

Hydrogen bonding in denatured DNA is effectively prevented by formaldehyde[395-397] and the molecule is stabilised in a relatively uncoiled state; this results in decreased resistance to enzymic degradation and more efficient antigen-antibody aggregation.[396] Electron microscopy of denatured DNA after treatment with formaldehyde shows long thin fibrils with a diameter considerably less than that of native DNA.[397] Rather striking pictures have been obtained of denatured DNA treated with the diazonium salt of 8-amino-1,3,6-naphthalene trisulphonic acid (coupling is probably at C8 of guanine residues) followed by staining with uranyl acetate in dilute formaldehyde. The marker is plainly visible in electron micrographs, and the technique offers a possible approach to the determination of base sequence in nucleic acids by electron microscopy.[397]

Secondary Structure of Ribonucleic Acids

Whereas most deoxynucleic acids possess a helical structure formed from two complementary strands, the ribonucleic acids show physical properties characteristic of single stranded polynucleotides. A complementary composition in which the molar proportions of uracil to adenine and of guanine to cytosine equal unity is seldom found, though in a less specific sense, the sum of the 6-amino nucleosides is often equal to that of the 6-keto nucleosides. Nevertheless, considerable secondary structure is apparent in ribonucleic acids though the conformations involved appear to be less stable than in the case of deoxynucleic acid. Generalisations are even more dangerous in the case of the ribonucleic acids, and it is perhaps prudent to distinguish at least three main classes at this time. These are the viral ribonucleic acids of high molecular weight (approximately 2×10^6), microsomal ribonucleic acids (including informational " messenger " RNA) also of high molecular weight ($1-2 \times 10^6$ and 6×10^5), and the so-called " soluble " amino acid acceptor and transfer ribonucleic acids which are considerably smaller, with a molecular weight of approximately 25,000, that is, about 75 nucleotides. All possess physical properties which in many respects, but not all, are directly comparable with those of denatured deoxynucleic acid. Rather extravagant extrapolation from physical aspects such as hypochromic effects and changes in optical rotation has been used to calculate the percentage of helical structure in preparations of ribonucleic acid under different conditions. Until considerably more is known of the precise conformations involved, and the effects such conformations have on physical properties (as is now fairly well known for complementary double helical structures such as DNA), the accuracy of these calculations may be regarded as somewhat less than has occasionally been implied.

TOBACCO MOSAIC VIRUS RIBONUCLEIC ACID

As one of the few nucleic acid preparations that may reasonably be considered homogeneous, the ribonucleic acid isolated from tobacco mosaic virus by mild procedures[319, 320] has been studied extensively. The infectivity of such preparations and the ready loss of infectivity provide criteria for the integrity or otherwise of the nucleic acid relative to that present in the intact virus. Infectivity also indicates that, certainly in this case, variation of secondary structure in the absence of degradation has little effect on biological activity.

Hydrodynamically, the viral RNA behaves as homologous randomly coiled chains[321] of molecular weight approximately 2×10^6, with a radius of gyration (determined from light scattering and viscosity measurements) of some 400 Å in 0·1 M sodium phosphate buffer at pH 6·8. Rearrangement into a more compact conformation (increased sedimentation coefficient and decreased viscosity) occurs slowly at room temperature and more rapidly at elevated temperatures. Thermal treatment also results in loss of infectivity, probably by hydrolysis of phosphodiester linkages.[322] Objections have been raised[321, 323] against covalent bond cleavage, but the physical methods employed were by no means sensitive enough to follow liberation of a terminal nucleotide or other relatively small residue. Up to 50° there is no change in the viscosity of infective RNA in 0·1 M buffer, but between 50° and 60° there is a marked rise in viscosity. This rise is accentuated in 6 M urea which also lowers (and sharpens) the transition temperature to 40°. The increase in viscosity is accompanied by a decrease in sedimentation constant, suggesting an uncoiling of the random coil structure with a sharp increase in the asymmetry of the molecules at high temperatures.[324]

Hydrogen bonded structures were indicated from studies of the rate of reaction of formaldehyde with the amino groups of the polynucleotide at different temperatures.[238, 325] As a result of strong hydrogen bonding, undenatured DNA is not affected by mild treatment with formaldehyde.[325] Similarly, with tobacco mosaic virus ribonucleic acid there is only a slow reaction at 25°. However, at 45° there is a 19 fold increase in rate indicative of the unmasking of amino groups. Kinetic studies showed that the action of formaldehyde on polynucleotides involves two steps, first denaturation and then reaction with the free amino groups.[326] In accord with the postulated first step the thermal dissociation temperature of polyinosinic acid is lowered some 18° in the presence of approximately 1% formaldehyde. (Apart from any purely physical effects, attack by formaldehyde at N^1 of the purine base would also decrease stability; this is possibly the initial reaction with adenine residues.) Results with tobacco mosaic virus RNA were held to identify hydrogen bonding with the existence of helical regions, and to show some 60% helical content in the nucleic acid under the conditions studied. Each of the amino groups, including that of guanine, appears to be involved in this hydrogen bonding.[326] Exaltation of the normal increase in rate of enzymic digestion (by ribonuclease or polynucleotide phosphorylase) with rise in temperature has also been observed, and this correlates well with absorptivity increases at the elevated temperature, indicative of the breakdown of organised structures following cleavage of hydrogen bonds.[238, 327]

The temperature–ultraviolet absorptivity profile of tobacco mosaic virus RNA is different from that of undenatured DNA. Despite the homogeneity of the RNA, the melting temperature is not sharply defined, increase in absorptivity (up to 32%) occurring over a wide range (from room temperature to 90° in media containing $0 \cdot 1$ M or less sodium ions). Increase in ionic strength lowers the absorptivity, that is, retards the transition,[321, 328, 329] but even in salt free solution there is some hypochromicity (relative to the thermal maximum of absorptivity) at room temperature.[321] Magnesium ions are some 25,000 times as effective as sodium ions in changing the melting temperature, a maximum hypochromic effect being obtained with one magnesium ion per three phosphate residues.[321] Addition of 6 M urea shifts the transition curve to a lower temperature by about 25° causing an increase in ultraviolet absorption at room temperature[329] and maximum absorptivity is reached[238, 330] at 70°.

Although magnesium ions are much more effective than sodium ions in reducing the absorptivity of the ribonucleic acid, the actual binding of Mg^{++} by the phosphate groups is reversible, and can be inhibited by a sufficiently large excess of sodium ions. This results in a profile with a lower midpoint temperature for a solution of the ribonucleic acid that contains 10^{-3} M Mg^{++} and $1 \cdot 5 \times 10^{-2}$ M Na^+ compared with a solution containing the magnesium ions (10^{-3} M) only, despite the higher total ionic concentration in the former case. However, even in high concentrations of sodium chloride such that addition of magnesium ions has no effect on the actual melting temperature, the thermal transition region is narrowed considerably.[321] A similar inhibitory effect by sodium ions has been observed with thermally denatured calf thymus DNA.[261]

Since the absorptivity of tobacco mosaic virus RNA is dependent on the ionic concentration at room temperature, correlation of hypochromicity and sedimentation constant is possible. A ninefold increase of the sedimentation coefficient was observed when the sodium ion concentration was changed from 2×10^{-4} M to $1 \cdot 5 \times 10^{-1}$ M and, significantly,

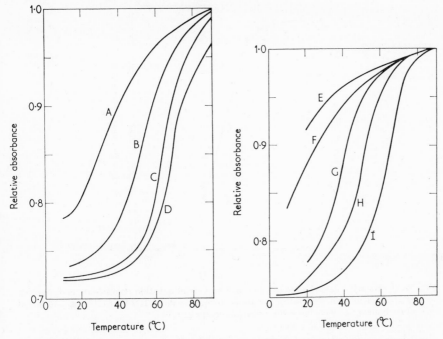

FIG. 8-29. Effect of magnesium and sodium ions on the ultraviolet absorption–temperature profile of RNA from tobacco mosaic virus. A, 10^{-6}M Mg^{++}; B, 10^{-5}M Mg^{++}; C, 10^{-4}M Mg^{++}; D, 10^{-3}M Mg^{++}; E, 6×10^{-5}M Na^{+}; F, 17×10^{-5}M Na^{+}; G, 34×10^{-3}M Na^{+}; H, 15×10^{-2}M Na^{+}; I, 1·4M Na^{+}. RNA concentration ~ 15 μg/ml.[321]

this increase closely paralleled the increase in hypochromicity (that is, the reduction in ultraviolet absorption). Although part of the molecular contraction undoubtedly reflects the general behaviour of polyelectrolytes, the transition is too large and occurs over too narrow a range of ionic strength to be explicable in terms of electrostatic repulsion alone.[321] The distribution of sedimentation coefficients was equally sharp at various ionic concentrations, in accord with the concept of homogeneous molecular species.

Spectrophotometric titration of the RNA differs from that of undenatured DNA but closely resembles that for denatured DNA.[329] Even under optimum conditions for hydrogen bonding, the absorptivity of the viral nucleic acid is not reduced below $\epsilon_{max} = 7500$ to 7800 compared with ϵ values of 6500 for native DNA. (Apart from dependent structural considerations, base composition will affect absorptivity directly owing to the different ϵ values of the monomers; the latter effects are probably small for most, but not all, nucleic acids.)

As with denatured DNA, but in contrast with native DNA, all of

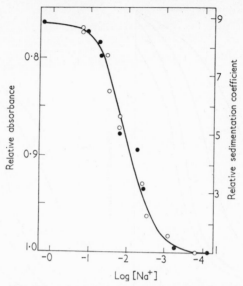

FIG. 8-30. Relative absorbance (at 258 mμ) and sedimentation coefficients as functions of sodium ion concentration for tobacco mosaic virus RNA at 21°. ●—Relative absorbance; O—relative sedimentation coefficient.[321]

the changes in physical behaviour (reflecting macromolecular transitions) that have been described are fully reversible and, in the absence of actual degradation of the primary structure, have little effect on infectivity. The physical properties indicate hydrogen bonded structures of varying stability, so that cleavage of the hydrogen bonds is not a co-operative process. Tobacco mosaic virus ribonucleic acid thus appears to consist of single flexible chains which, under appropriate environmental conditions, coil into compact hydrogen bonded particles lacking, however, any unique conformation. That this hydrogen

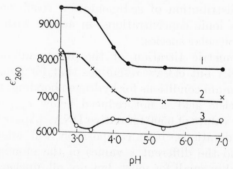

FIG. 8-31. Spectrophotometric titration of tobacco mosaic virus RNA (1); denatured DNA (2); and undenatured DNA (3); all with $\mu = 0·1$.[329]

bonding results in, or is paralleled by, a considerable degree of helical conformation[238, 321, 330] has been established in studies of the changes in optical rotation accompanying certain treatments. The specific rotation of the viral RNA falls from $[\alpha]_D = + 180°$ and $[\alpha]_{546m\mu} = + 220°$ to $[\alpha]_D = 20°$ and $[\alpha]_{546m\mu} < + 30°$ on enzymic degradation,[331, 332] suggesting destruction of a helical conformation. Also significant, is the fact that limited degradation by ribonuclease to an extent corresponding to one break per twenty nucleotides results in a low specific rotation and a 15% increase in ultraviolet absorption.[332]

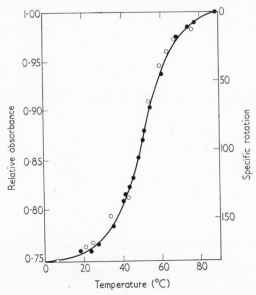

FIG. 8-32. Relative absorbance (at 258 mμ)—●, and specific rotation (at 589 mμ)—○, as functions of temperature for tobacco mosaic virus RNA in 0·1 M sodium phosphate.[321]

Comparison of the absorptivity–temperature and optical rotation–temperature profiles[330] showed that the two could be brought into coincidence using suitable ordinate scales.[238, 321] Thus, as with DNA, variations of optical rotation and absorptivity with temperature are strong indications of helical conformations maintained by hydrogen bonds. That these are weak is further suggested by the action of 6 M urea, which decreases optical rotation[330] as well as increasing absorptivity. Calculations based on a comparison with the optical properties of the double helical polyadenylic–polyuridylic acid complex (which shows a 51% increase in absorptivity and a change in rotation from $[\alpha]_D = + 300°$ to $[\alpha]_D = + 25°$ on heating; the analogous polycytidylic-polyguanylic acid complex probably possesses approximately 25% thermal hyperchromicity) and on the hyperchromicity and optical rotation relative to the maximum thermal effects, have been used to derive an estimate of 60% helical structure (in 0·1 M sodium phosphate) for tobacco mosaic virus ribonucleic acid. (Some of these calculations do not appear to be applicable to undenatured calf thymus deoxynucleic acid.) Even more precise claims[321] of a 21·5% helical content for tobacco mosaic virus RNA in 10^{-4} M Na^+ have been made.

Tobacco mosaic virus ribonucleic acid possesses a spectrum of

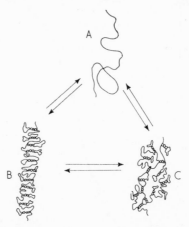

Fig. 8-33. Possible conformations and transitions of tobacco mosaic virus RNA. A, Random coil in absence of salt or at high temperatures; B, compact rod at low temperatures and low ionic strength; C, compact coil at low temperatures and high ionic strength.[334]

conformations, each of which is characterised by a definite sedimentation coefficient, specific rotation, and absorptivity. Changes in these properties resulting from altered environmental conditions are quite reversible, and reflect transitions among various degrees of hydrogen bonded helical structure present in the molecule. Neither completely random nor completely organised conformations appear to be attained at room temperature. The precise form of the helical regions is probably analogous to the complementary double helical complexes, with specific hydrogen bonding between anti-parallel parts of the chain. Electron microscopical examination[333] of tobacco mosaic virus RNA under various conditions has given results that are in agreement with a reversible helix-coil transformation. From water, the nucleic acid appeared as globules or clumps of globules, but from salt solutions, irregularly contoured rod-like particles averaging about 1200 Å by approximately

30 Å could be seen. Long narrow strands up to 50,000 Å long by approximately 10 Å were also observed.

Some evidence of tertiary structure in tobacco mosaic virus RNA at low ionic strength (0·01 M) has been obtained from electric ultraviolet dichroism measurements.[334] At room temperature the sign of dichroism is positive (opposite to that of native DNA). Under these conditions the macromolecule is not a random coil, since the dichroic ratio (+ 1·2) suggests a mainly parallel orientation of the planes of the base rings (these are presumably normal to the length of the strand) with respect to the long axis of the compact particle. The results are accommodated in a model in which successive double helical regions united by non-organised single strand sections are piled to form a rodlike structure. Increase in temperature causes first a disappearance of dichroism (at 40°) followed by appearance of negative dichroism (− 1·1 at 50°). This thermal inversion of the sign of dichroism is reversible. Electron microscopy has given results that are in accord with the different conformations and their transitions.[335]

MICROSOMAL RIBONUCLEIC ACID

The solution properties of high molecular weight ribonucleic acid isolated from yeast,[336] *Escherichia coli*,[337, 338] and calf liver microsomal particles[339] closely resemble those of tobacco mosaic virus. Significant amounts of hydrogen bonded helical structure were indicated for the yeast RNA by the variation in absorptivity and optical rotation resulting from changes in ionic strength or addition of urea.[336] A more detailed physical examination of the high molecular weight RNA from *E. coli* also indicated a coiled single strand molecule, with at least a partly organised structure involving hydrogen bonds. Whereas solutions of native DNA possess viscosity characteristics that are relatively independent of the ionic strength (above the denaturation concentration) owing to the insensitivity of the double helical structure to counterion induced expansion or contraction, there is a marked decrease in the viscosity of the RNA from *E. coli* with increase in ionic strength, in the region 10^{-3} M to 10^{-2} M sodium chloride, suggesting a flexible structure capable of considerable expansion at low ionic strengths as a result of increased electrostatic repulsion among the unscreened phosphate groups. Again, magnesium ions are considerably more effective than sodium ions in reducing the viscosity, as in the case of denatured DNA.

A contractile model is also indicated by the disappearance of flow birefringence with increase in ionic strength. The sign of birefringence of the RNA in water is positive (in contrast with DNA which shows negative flow birefringence) but in 0·2 M sodium chloride the rather small birefringence is completely abolished (cf. effect of salt on viscosity).

Potentiometric titration is essentially reversible, though a small but significant hysteresis loop in the complete titration curve between pH 2·8 and pH 10·8 occurs.[337, 340] At 0·4° this hysteresis is considerably enhanced; at 38·5° a single curve is followed on all occasions after the first treatment with acid, but hysteresis is again found[338] on subsequent titration at 0·4°. This suggests that on titration with acid or alkali at 38·5° a transition to a more random form occurs, but on cooling to 0·4° the " ordered " conformation is re-formed.

In accord with a rather weakly hydrogen bonded structure, the ultraviolet absorption of the RNA is markedly dependent on ionic strength ($\epsilon^P = 8700$ in water, 8160 in 10^{-3} M NaCl and 7450 in 0·2 M

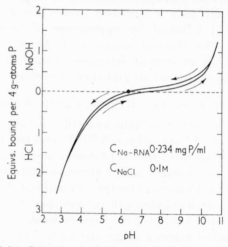

FIG. 8-34. Potentiometric titration of microsomal RNA.[337]

NaCl),[337] and in 8 M urea a considerable hyperchromic effect ($\sim 26\%$) is observed.[341] Increase in absorptivity with rise in temperature[342] is more or less continuous from 25° to 75°, with a maximum thermal hyperchromic effect of 31%. However, the total hyperchromicity on alkaline degradation of the RNA is some 59% (ϵ_{260} in 1·0 M phosphate pH 7·1 = 7290; ϵ_{260} of the hydrolysis products under the same conditions = 11,600), the same increase being observed on complete phosphorolysis with polynucleotide phosphorylase.[337] These figures indicate that in some nucleic acids " residual " hyperchromicity, not attributable to specific secondary structure, can be considerable.

As in the case of DNA, examination of the infrared spectra of ribosomal RNA from *E. coli* suggests that in deuterium oxide solution a band at 1680 cm⁻¹ (or for the undeuterated base residues at 1710 cm⁻¹) is a criterion of base pairing (possibly the result of concentration of π electrons at the hydrogen bonded portions) since this band is weakened when the RNA is heated, or degraded with ribonuclease.[343] The X-Ray diffraction pattern* of RNA from ribosomes of *E. coli* closely resembles that of disoriented double helical DNA in the B-conformation, suggesting that a large part of the RNA has a similar double helical structure.[342] Electron microscopy indicates three principal conformations (dependent on the environment) similar to those observed with tobacco mosaic virus RNA. Although indications of the two main

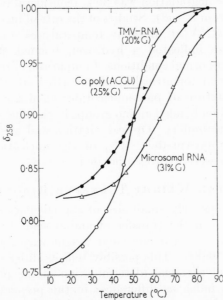

FIG. 8-35. Variation in absorbance (at 258 mμ) with temperature for solutions of tobacco mosaic virus RNA, calf liver microsomal RNA, and enzymically synthesised co-poly (ACGU) in 0·1 M phosphate buffer at pH 7. Molar percentages of guanine content are given.[238]

molecular weights were present, no evidence of smaller " subunits " was obtained.[335]

Physical characteristics of ribonucleic acid from microsomal particles of calf liver (phenol procedure) have also been examined in some detail.[339] As with high molecular weight RNA from *E. coli*, two major components were obtained. These were relatively homogeneous and clearly resolved on sedimentation, with approximate molecular weights of 1·3 × 10⁶ and 6 × 10⁵ respectively. Heating solutions of the ribonucleic acids caused degradation to " subunits " (molecular weight approximately 1·2 × 10⁵) which gave a single, relatively narrow sedimenting peak suggesting specific dissociation of the high molecular

*Recent small-angle X-Ray scattering studies indicate that high molecular weight RNA is composed of short double helical rods (50–150Å long) joined by small flexible regions.[420]

weight RNA, though cleavage of covalent bonds cannot be excluded. Indeed, no conclusive evidence of the pre-existence of subunits has been presented. The temperature–absorptivity profile was similar to that previously described for tobacco mosaic virus RNA, and again 6 M urea induced a hyperchromic effect at all temperatures. Changes in absorptivity were quite reversible suggesting re-formation of hydrogen bonded secondary structures. Thermal hyperchromicity amounted to some 27%; the total increase in ultraviolet absorption (at 258 mμ) on complete alkaline degradation was 39% (considerably lower than that shown by RNA from *E. coli*). Studies of the rate of reaction of formaldehyde with the RNA at different temperatures and different ionic strengths likewise indicated a hydrogen bonded structure for the nucleic acid under normal conditions. Comparison of the rate of reaction (followed spectrophotometrically) of the RNA at 25° with the rate found with a mixture of mononucleotides gave a rough estimate of some 60% hydrogen bonded amino groups in the nucleic acid (in 0·05 M sodium phosphate buffer). Optical rotation and absorptivity studies indicated that approximately 40% of the nucleotides in calf liver microsomal RNA were hydrogen bonded.

Low Molecular Weight Transfer Ribonucleic Acids

Despite the relatively small size of the ribonucleic acids that are biologically active in the transfer of amino acids to the microsomal particles, estimates of their molecular weight vary rather widely from about 18,000 to 50,000. This possibly reflects differences in methods, both physical and chemical (determination of the proportion of end groups)[344, 345] as much as differences in the preparations examined. However, some of the variation is probably the result of aggregation. Although no change in molecular weight occurs on heating dilute solutions of " soluble " RNA from *Escherichia coli* (fully charged with amino acids) followed by rapid cooling, with concentrated solutions the weight average molecular weight is nearly doubled.[346] This suggests that in the one case hydrogen bonding is within the same chain (folded back on itself) but in the other bonding is between different strands. End group analysis of a preparation of " soluble " RNA from the same organism[345] indicated a molecular weight approximately 18,500 but physical methods (diffusion and sedimentation) gave a figure of 35,000. A reasonably accurate value for the " soluble " ribonucleic acids from yeast[347, 348] and from *Escherichia coli*[349] is probably about 25,000 or some 75 nucleotides per polymer chain for single-stranded material.[344] A comparable figure has been found for fractionated soluble RNA from *Escherichia coli*. Alkaline hydrolysis of threonine-active and phenylalanine-active RNA gave adenosine to the extent of 1·5 molar per cent, indicating a chain length of 67 nucleotides.[350] Mammalian (rat liver) soluble RNA has a molecular weight of 27,000 as determined from sedimentation and diffusion coefficients.[351]

Except for the effect of molecular weight on viscosity, sedimentation, and related physical properties,[347-349] the transfer ribonucleic acids are analogous in behaviour to the microsomal nucleic acids, though possessing quite different nucleotide compositions. Variations of extinction coefficient and optical rotation with temperature again suggest a hydrogen bonded structure,[344, 349, 352] and this is confirmed by the low rate of reaction with formaldehyde.[349] A somewhat more stable and more organised conformation than that for microsomal RNA is indicated by the higher melting temperature and sharper transition profile ($T_m = 60°$ approximately in 0·1 M sodium chloride, the rise in absorptivity beginning at about 40°). Increase or decrease in ionic strength raises or lowers the midpoint temperature, and concentrated urea has a marked effect on absorbtivity even at room temperature, due to lowering of the melting temperature.[349] The increase in absorptivity in salt-free water is virtually the same as the thermal maximum (24%). Again, these changes are quite reversible, and indeed no loss in biological activity occurs[344] on heating solutions ($\mu = 0·2$) to 70° at pH 6·8. Although " residual " hypochromicity is often regarded as negligible, particularly with respect to DNA, it may be noted that in the case of soluble RNA from rat liver,[351] structural (heat or 6 M urea treatment) hyperchromicity is approximately 21%, but total hyperchromicity on alkaline hydrolysis is 49%, indicating a considerable effect resulting from stacking of the bases in the absence of hydrogen bonded organised secondary structure. (Compare also the corresponding figures for microsomal RNA from *Escherichia coli*.)

In salt solutions at 25° the " soluble " ribonucleic acids possess a considerable amount of organised hydrogen bonded helical structure, though yet retaining many of the behaviour characteristics of randomly coiled flexible chains. Values of the specific rotation ($[\alpha]_D = + 134°$ in 0·1 M sodium chloride) for RNA from *E. coli* suggest that some 45% of the bases are present in helical structures.[352]

The greater stability of the conformation of low molecular weight RNA from *E. coli* compared with the microsomal nucleic acids has been mentioned. As a result of the higher melting temperature of the former, dependent differences are observed at room temperature since the melting zone of the high, but not of the low, molecular weight ribonucleic acids extends down to this temperature.[352] Thus ionic strength (at room temperature) has little effect on the absorptivity of the " soluble " RNA (up to the point where " water denaturation " occurs), and a similar independence of viscosity on ionic concentration has been observed, in contrast* with the behaviour of microsomal RNA. Of interest, however, is the fact that whereas the specific rotation– and absorptivity–salt concentration profiles are virtually identical for microsomal RNA, a considerable drop in optical rotation occurs with " soluble " RNA on decreasing the concentration of sodium chloride from 10^{-1} M to 10^{-4} M (from $[\alpha]_{405} = +390°$ to $[\alpha]_{405} = +345°$) in the absence of an increase in ultraviolet absorption.[352] The greater sensitivity of optical rotation to changes in secondary structure, compared with ultraviolet absorption, has been mentioned previously. Increased electrostatic repulsions, coupled with changes in hydration, possibly induce a change in helical pitch.

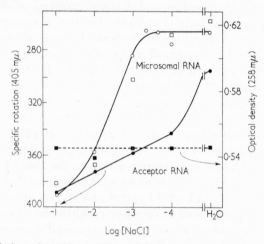

Fig. 8-36. Variation of specific rotation (at 405 mμ) and optical density (at 258 mμ) with sodium chloride concentration for solutions of microsomal RNA (open squares and circles) and low molecular weight amino acid acceptor RNA at 25°. Squares— optical density; Circles—specific rotation.[352]

A sharp drop in optical rotation occurs at salt concentrations less than 10^{-4} M. With the microsomal RNA a similar sharp decrease occurs at 10^{-2} to 10^{-3} M sodium chloride, again indicating a greater conformational stability for soluble RNA. A possible cause of this may lie in the nearer equivalence of guanine and cytosine (and of adenine and uracil) content in the low molecular weight nucleic acid.[352] However, in view of the broadness of the various transition profiles, relative compositional heterogeneities may be significant. The presence of the minor bases in the soluble RNA, and in particular pseudouridine, could also be significant with regard to secondary and tertiary structure.

A biochemical comparison of the conformational stability of different ribonucleic acids is afforded by the relative rates of phosphorolysis

*At least some of the increased stability of transfer RNA appears to be due to the presence of traces of tightly bound polyvalent metal ions.[421]

with polynucleotide phosphorylase. At 37° the rates are in the decreasing order tobacco mosaic virus RNA > high molecular weight (microsomal) RNA > soluble RNA.[327]   Indeed, with the soluble RNA, degradation stops at 20–30% of completion, only a fraction of the polynucleotide chains being phosphorolysed.[353]   In contrast, ability to accept activated amino acids is lost after a minimal degradation of less than 5% with venom diesterase, that is, after removal of terminal groups.[353, 354]   The increased resistance of helical multi-stranded complexes formed from enzymically synthesised polyribonucleotides, relative to the non-helical forms, suggests that the different rates of

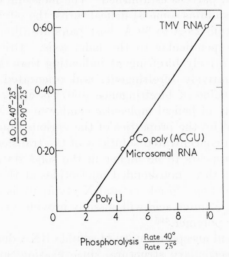

FIG. 8-37. Relation between relative hyperchromicity and temperature dependence of the rate of phosphorolysis for solutions of tobacco mosaic virus RNA, microsomal RNA, and enzymically synthesised polyuridylic acid and co-poly (ACGU).[327]

phosphorolysis of the various nucleic acids are, at least in part, a measure of their organised structural content.[327] The effects of increased temperature on the rates of phosphorolysis differ markedly also, and provide a further indication of relative conformational stability. Thus the increase in rate between 25° and 40° is very marked for tobacco mosaic virus RNA, and much less so for microsomal RNA. That this increase in rate reflects thermal destruction of hydrogen bonded regions of organised structure is indicated by direct correlation of the ratio of phosphorolysis rates at 40° and 25° with the ratio of induced hyperchromic effects in this temperature range to total thermal hyperchromicity (25°–90°).[327]

Recent X-ray diffraction studies on soluble RNA from *Escherichia coli* are in accord with a secondary structure involving a fairly high double helical content.[346] An extensive and relatively precise secondary structure in native RNA has also been indicated by ultraviolet optical rotary dispersion curves.[355] An X-ray diffraction study of crystalline amino acid transfer RNA from yeast (obtained by slow evaporation of an aqueous solution of the sodium salt) has been reported.[403] The pattern obtained is superior to previous results with RNA and shows a striking resemblance to the A type DNA pattern. A folded molecule (probably exactly complementary from end to end except for the three nucleotides forming the bend) with a double helical structure exactly as in DNA is indicated, and in particular the anti-parallel nature of the hydrogen bonded parts is established. The molecule is approximately 100 Å long and contains some $3\frac{1}{2}$ helical turns, the pitch length varying with humidity from 28 Å to 30 Å; base pairs are tilted approximately 20° from the perpendicular to the helix axis. Dried layers of the material are negatively birefringent indicating that the molecules are rod shaped, negatively birefringent, and orientated parallel to the interface. The value of birefringence (0·07) is consistent with fibres composed entirely of helical molecules similar to the A form of DNA. This is confirmed by the properties of the various liquid crystal forms which develop in concentrated solutions of the transfer RNA. Overall helical content appears to be higher in the solid state than in dilute solution, and the three non-bonded nucleotides at the fold may be of significance for coding. Single crystal X-ray analysis of purified RNA specific for a single amino acid will possibly provide a complete primary structure for the polymer.[403]

The amino acid acceptor ability of soluble RNA does not appear to depend on the secondary structure, since heating, and then rapidly cooling, solutions of such RNA does not affect the activity.[344, 346, 351] Specific binding of amino acids may not require the co-operation of the monoesterified phosphate end of the chain, and the nucleotide sequences determining specificity may be quite near the –C—C—A terminal. Neither heating nor treatment with urea causes irreversible destruction of transfer activity of soluble RNA and for this function too, a specific secondary structure appear to be unnecessary,[351] unless a readily reversible unique structure (governed by nucleotide sequence) is assumed. It may be noted that even removal of the amino acids (at pH 10) from soluble RNA may cause a change in secondary structure, since such a process is accompanied by an increase in sedimentation coefficient (from approximately 3·0 to 4·0).[346]

CONFORMATION OF RIBONUCLEIC ACID

The various physical properties of ribonucleic acid indicate a partial helical structure in neutral saline at low temperatures. Since the material is single stranded, and does not contain equimolar quantities of the complementary bases, it was concluded that each polynucleotide chain contains a number of imperfect double helical sections (joined at one end), similar in character to those of deoxynucleic acid, united by flexible regions lacking defined structure.[238] Of the many possible base pairs, the adenine–uracil and guanine–cytosine hydrogen bonded pairs appear to be the most stable and are probably the only arrangements that are mutually conformable in a regular helical structure. Within such a structure all other base pairs are either separated by too great a distance or are sterically intolerable. In accord with the view that the major pairing systems are those mentioned, a linear correlation was found between the thermal stability of a given RNA and the guanine–cytosine content.[356]

Other studies on double helix formation between homopolymers and copolymers of adenylic and uridylic acids indicated that non-complementary bases were readily accommodated in loops out of the helical structure, since optimal base pairing occurred when the number of homopolymer residues was equalled by the number of complementary residues in the copolymer chain.[357] As may be expected, the double helix with looped out nucleotide sequences is weaker than a perfect complementary structure owing to the reduction in length of undisturbed matched sequences, strain induced by the loops in adjacent helical regions, and increased electrostatic repulsive forces in the looped area. Nevertheless, helical structures that are stable at 25° could be obtained with up to 30% of the nucleotides in a polynucleotide strand accommodated as loops. Interaction of oligonucleotides with complementary high molecular weight homopolynucleotides produces helical structures which are stable at 25° when the oligmer is tetranucleotide or larger,[358] and hence relatively short stretches of hydrogen bonded complementary base pairs (with a minimum length of three or four nucleotide pairs) separated by looped-out regions may be envisaged for ribonucleic acids.[359] An alternate estimate of the minimum length of stable hydrogen bonded tracts is available from studies on the degradation of DNA which indicate that a sequence of no more than six nucleotides between two gaps in the double helix is sufficient to prevent scission.[297]

As a result of a lateral mobility permitting exploration of most competitive conformations, single-stranded RNA assumes the most stable conformation consonant with the temperature and ionic strength. In this process, considerably increased base-pairing is made possible by extrusion of residues in the form of loops, the " helical " sections taking the form of U-shaped stretches in which the anti-parallel hydrogen bonded sequences are connected by a minimum of three non-paired nucleotides round the bend.[359] An example of the type of secondary structure pictured for ribonucleic acids is shown.

Such conformations are in accord with estimates of the hydrogen bonded helical content, the large thermal transition zone, and the physical behaviour of RNA. The rather limited expansion of the molecule with decreasing salt concentration at moderate ionic strengths, in contrast with the behaviour of typical polyelectrolytes on the one hand and undenatured DNA on the other (but analogous to denatured DNA), is accommodated by this model, particularly since such expansion is accompanied by loss of some helical structure.

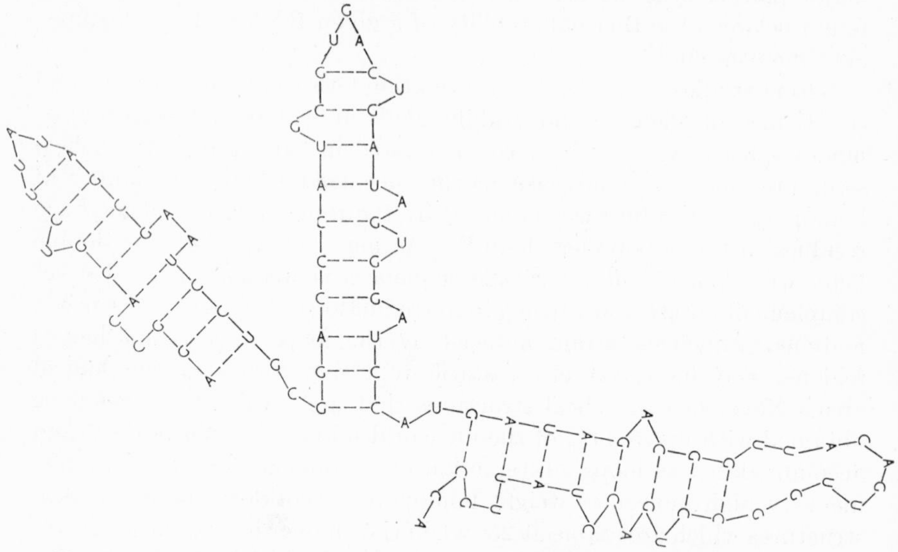

FIG. 8-38. A possible arrangement for secondary structure in ribonucleic acids.[359]

The precise secondary structure of RNA is thus dictated by the nucleotide sequence, and this also determines a tertiary structure of loops of unpaired bases and open chain sections which are held in specific fixed relation to each other. Such "naked" sequences provide potential sites for structural connections and base pairing with other ribonucleic acids at specific locations (for example, between ribosomal or "messenger" and transfer ribonucleic acids), and in general provide new possibilities in coding and information transfer that are not inherent in structureless single strands or perfectly base-paired double helices. The marginal stability at cell temperature of many of the helical regions in the model proposed, leading to momentary opening of base paired sequences as a result of thermal (or other energetic) fluctuation, may be of biological significance also.[359]

Conformation of Nucleic Acids in Nucleoproteins

Little definitive work on the organisation between nucleic acid and protein in nucleoproteins has been reported as yet. In the deoxynucleo-histones and related complexes, the basic protein is more or less wrapped around the DNA, which has the same conformation as in the isolated state.[360, 361, 408, 409] Salt-like linkages between unshielded phosphate ionisations and basic groups of the protein are presumably mainly responsible for the binding, since dissolution in molar sodium chloride causes considerable dissociation.[362] Spectrophotometric titrations of calf thymus nucleohistone are virtually identical with those of the separated undenatured deoxynucleic acid under the same ionic conditions.[363] Stereochemical factors relating the protein subunits to the large groove in the DNA double helix are possibly of importance in providing a measure of specificity. Results obtained from examination of DNA-protamine with polarised infrared show that at high humidity the DNA is in the B conformation (base pairs perpendicular to the helix axis) and the protein is in an extended rather than helical form.[392] In DNA-histone approximately half the protein has an α-helical confirmation.[393] X-Ray analysis of an artificially prepared complex of DNA and copoly L-alanine: L-lysine (in ratio 4 : 1) gives a diffraction pattern consisting mainly of an α-helix pattern superimposed on that due to a B type DNA.[394] It is likely that the alanine rich parts of the polypeptide form α helices while the lysine residues are electrostatically linked to the DNA.

Wide angle X-ray powder diagrams of turnip yellow mosaic virus (containing 40% ribonucleic acid) and of the protein shells indicate that the virus scattering curve is not simply the sum of scattering due to protein and free viral RNA. In this virus it is likely that the ribonucleic acid has a secondary structure (presumably imposed by the protein) which differs from that of the isolated viral nucleic acid.[364] However, X-ray diffraction studies of ribonucleoprotein particles from *Escherichia coli*,[365] yeast, and rat liver[366] suggest that the ribonucleic acid in the particles has a structure similar to that of the extracted RNA.[365, 366] Variation of the diffraction pattern of the particles with changes in humidity resembles results obtained with deoxynucleo-histone, indicating that the nucleic acid and protein possess an appreciable degree of structural independence.

Ultraviolet absorption studies also suggest that the RNA in ribosomal particles has a secondary structure similar to that of the free nucleic acid. The extinction coefficients (with respect to molar phosphate) of both the free ribonucleic acid and the ribonucleoprotein at 255 mμ (absorption due to the protein at this wavelength is negligible) are identical ($\epsilon_{255}^P \sim 8100$), and subject to an increase[339, 365] on raising the temperature to 85°. Further, the hyperchromic effects on degradation of the ribosomal particles and the RNA derived therefrom with alkali, or by enzymic hydrolysis to the nucleoside-3′ phosphates, are identical and amount to a 41% increase in absorptivity at 260 mμ.[341] Thermal treatment of the isolated RNA gives a 29% increase in absorptivity, most of this being reversed on lowering the temperature. The identical hypochromicity of ribosomes and isolated RNA is a strong indication (but does not prove) that the polynucleotide conformation is the same in both cases, and is a defined structure rather than randomly hydrogen bonded.

In an alternate approach, the ultraviolet absorption spectra of various nucleoproteins was examined before and after separation into protein and nucleic acid by treatment with sodium dodecyl sulphate.[367] Suitable corrections were applied for light scattering, and the experimental conditions were such that free nucleic acid would be " undenatured ", that is, hypochromic, and hence any decrease in absorptivity would show that the nucleic acid has a smaller hypochromicity in the intact nucleoprotein, indicating conformational changes on liberation of the nucleic acid. No change in absorptivity occurred on cleavage of DNA type viruses such as bacteriophage T6 and Shope papilloma virus (although the isolated DNA is clearly subject to some sort of packing arrangement inside the virus), and in these cases the secondary structure of the nucleic acid in the virus is presumably the same as that of the isolated material. Similarly, the absorptivity of ribonucleoprotein particles from yeast was virtually the same as that of the degraded particles.[367]

However, cleavage of tobacco mosaic virus into RNA and protein was accompanied by a marked decrease in absorptivity, suggesting that structures maintained by inter-base hydrogen bonding in the isolated RNA are precluded by the packing of protein subunits in the intact virus, as indicated by X-ray diffraction.[368] In the absence of salt, the absorptivity (at 260 mμ) of the degraded virus was almost identical with that of the intact virus. Addition of salt caused an immediate decrease in absorptivity due to formation of hydrogen bonded (random or otherwise) secondary structure in the ribonucleic acid. Heating this solution caused an increase (25%) in absorptivity to that of the intact virus. The spherical bushy stunt virus represents an intermediate case, in that cleavage into protein and nucleic acid caused a slight decrease in absorptivity, but thermal treatment resulted in a 23% increase to a value greater than that of the intact particles. Moreover, a 47% increase in absorptivity occurred on alkaline degradation of the intact virus,[341] and hence the ribonucleic acid, when present in the virus, probably possesses a significantly organised secondary structure. This is increased on removal of the constraint imposed by the packing of protein subunits, suggesting a change to a thermodynamically more stable conformation for the free ribonucleic acid.

The assumption made in this work, that changes in absorptivity do not result from protein–nucleic acid interactions, may not be entirely valid in all cases. Conclusions of the presence or absence of hydrogen bonds between purines and pyrimidines in ribonucleoproteins based on ultraviolet absorption properties are also suspect, since other mechanisms constraining the internucleotide rotation (hence affecting the ultraviolet absorption) may be operative.

Hypochromism

Complete degradation of an undenatured deoxynucleic acid to nucleosides or mononucleotides can result in an increase in ultraviolet absorption at 260 mμ of up to 60–70%. To a lesser extent, all polynucleotides (including apurinic and apyrimidinic acids)[369] and oligonucleotides show a decreased absorptivity relative to the component monomers. At various times the hyperchromic effect on degradation of polynucleotides has been attributed particularly to guanylic acid residues,[370] to guanylic and cytidylic residues,[371] and to polypurine segments.[372] Collapse of an organised hydrogen bonded structure is accompanied by a large hyperchromic effect, but even under conditions of complete denaturation there remains a " residual " hypochromicity of 10–20%. This effect corresponds to the hypochromicity of oligonucleotides, which is not significantly affected by ionic strength or temperature, and is not irreversibly altered by the usual denaturation conditions. That hydrogen bonding is not responsible for this " residual " hypochromicity has been amply demonstrated in studies on synthetic oligonucleotides. (See p. 445.)

Further confirmation is provided by an examination of the ultraviolet absorption spectra of 1-methyl-, 3-methyl-, 9-methyl, and 1,9-dimethylhypoxanthine in acetonitrile and acetonitrile–water mixtures.[373] The results showed that in acetonitrile–water mixtures, water molecules were hydrogen bonded to the carbonyl oxygen at the 6 position of hypoxanthine. The spectral consequences of this hydrogen bonding were a slight bathochromic shift of the maximum and a *hyperchromic* effect, both changes being in the same direction as formation of the enolate anion. Moreover, when the ultraviolet spectrum of the helical complex polycytidylic–polyinosinic acid was examined in detail, it was found that that part of the spectrum arising mainly from cytosine was unchanged upon denaturation, despite the fact that hydrogen bonds involving the amino group as proton donor and N^1 as proton acceptor stabilise the helix, and are absent in the denatured form. It was concluded that hydrogen bonds do not directly account for the hypochromicity of nucleic acids.

Disturbance of tautomeric equilibria as a result of polymerisation has also been postulated as the cause of hypochromicity,[374] but again experimental measurements of the extinction coefficients of methylated hypoxanthines showed that this was not the case,[373] and infrared spectra indicate that the tautomeric form of the base is the same in monomer and polymer.[375]

It is likely that the basic cause of hypochromicity is direct interaction among the heterocyclic bases, and that the effects of hydrogen bonding on absorptivity result primarily from the stacking of nucleotides in an organised structure with virtually complete restriction of movement, relative to that possible in oligonucleotides. That neither hydrogen bonding nor helical structure is necessary even for relatively large effects has been demonstrated with dinucleoside phosphates derived from 6-dimethylaminopurine which show a 35% increase in absorption on

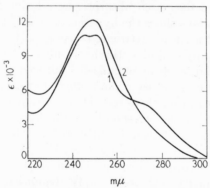

FIG. 8-39. Spectra of 9-methylhypoxanthine in (1) acetonitrile; and (2) in acetonitrile–water.[373]

degradation. While the absorptivity at or near the wavelength maximum is decreased on polymerisation, at longer wavelengths (approximately 280–300 mμ for adenine and uracil derivatives) a small, but significant increase in absorption occurs. This increase is apparent not only in high molecular weight polymers but also in di- and higher oligonucleotides.

In addition, a similar increase in absorption on formation of oligonucleotides often occurs at short wavelengths (200–230 mμ). Even in the region of λ_{max}, hypochromicity shows significant quantitative changes. Indeed, profiles of the change in absorption with wavelength on degradation of various oligonucleotides and small polynucleotides indicate several bands, both positive and negative.[261] It may be noted that maximum hypochromicity, at least in such materials devoid of

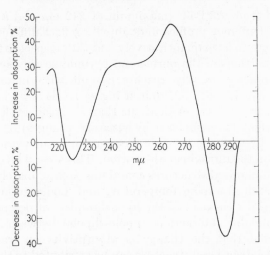

Fig. 8-40. Change in absorption–wavelength profile at alkaline pH for degradation of polyadenylic acid (chain length approximately 10 nucleotides) containing mixed 2'–5' and 3'–5' internucleotide linkages. The short vertical bar indicates the position of λ_{max} for the polymer.[261] Organised secondary structure is absent in alkaline solution, but at acidic pH indications of an acid-form, similar to that obtained with high molecular weight enzymically synthesised polyadenylic acid, have been observed[261, 417] with oligoadenylic acids larger than hexanucleotide.

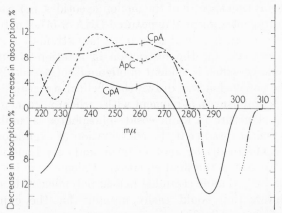

Fig. 8-41. Change in absorption–wavelength profiles at alkaline pH for degradation to monomers of guanylyl-3':5'-adenosine (GpA ——); cytidylyl-3':5'-adenosine (CpA.—.—.); and adenyl-3':5'-cytidine (ApC - - - -). Short vertical bars indicate the position of λ_{max} for the dinucleoside phosphates.[261]

hydrogen bonded secondary structure, is seldom coincident with the wavelength maximum. (This results in a " hypsochromic shift " of the λ_{max}). The nature of the profile is strongly influenced by pH, by base composition, by chain length and by sequence; for example, C3'P5'A (maximum hyperchromicity on degradation at 262 mμ) is readily distinguished from A3'P5'C (maximum at 242 mμ and a second peak at 272 mμ). Different profiles undoubtedly reflect differences in interplanar interaction, both quantitatively and with respect to the particular overlapping portions of the purine and pyrimidine ring systems.[261]

Hypochromicity rapidly reaches a limit with increase in chain length of oligonucleotides. A limit at higher levels of hydrogen bonded helical structures is also evident, in that a considerable decrease in molecular weight (as evidenced by viscosity changes) of undenatured nucleic acids by enzymic or sonic scission can occur without concomitant changes in the ultraviolet absorption. This second level is probably reached with organised structures containing approximately 10 perfectly paired nucleotides at room temperature and moderate ionic strength.

A theoretical treatment of the hypochromism of polynucleotides in terms of coulombic interaction (dipole–dipole) between the different bases suggested that the change in absorptivity on transition from an ordered to a disordered structure can be attributed to the interaction between the dipoles induced in the chromophores by the light.[376] Calculated values for the relative absorption coefficients of undenatured DNA and the component mononucleotides were consistent with experimental observations.* Exact quantitative effects of dipolar interaction could not be determined because of insufficient information about the absorption spectra of the mononucleotides, nor was an examination of the hypochromism of denatured DNA or other polynucleotides feasible. The forces involved appear to be extremely weak, and insufficient to account for the restriction in rotation about the internucleotide linkage which is evident in oligonucleotides at all pH values. However, the conclusion was drawn that helical structure is not necessary for hypochromism, in agreement with earlier experimental observations (helical structure in dinucleoside phosphates is unlikely). Subsequently it was realised that the contribution of excitation resonance was cancelled identically by another term, and only London dispersion force effects appear in the final equation. Calculations by approximation methods for a double stranded helical polynucleotide showed that dispersion interaction could easily account for the experimentally observed hypochromicity.[377]

Approximate quantum mechanical π electron overlap integrals between the parallel bases of DNA at a distance of 3·36 Å also indicate the existence of non-negligible π electron interaction that may well account quantitatively for the anomalous ultraviolet absorption spectrum of oligo- and polynucleotides, and provide an explanation of partial stacking of bases even in non-hydrogen-bonded oligonucleotides.[378] The different overlap integral values beteen the different heterocyclic ring systems show that the electronic distribution and π

*Further elaboration[418] has indicated that G–C polymers should show more hypochromism than A–T polymers. Since this is contrary to experimental fact it was concluded that either the theory or the experimental was incorrect. The latter case could

electron interaction is dependent on the base sequence, in accord with experimental results.[379]

In addition to hypochromism at the absorption maximum in polynucleotides and helical complexes resulting from stacking of $\pi \rightarrow \pi^*$ chromophoric units, a hyperchromic effect is present at longer wavelengths. This increase in absorption (at 280–300 mμ) has been noted for several polynucleotide helical complexes. The effect is additional to a similar hyperchromism previously noted in oligonucleotides,[380] but has nevertheless been ascribed to the alignment of n $\rightarrow \pi^*$ transitions.[381]

Studies of ultraviolet dichroic absorption curves of oriented films of helical polynucleotides also indicated the two types of absorption.[381] Thus for polycytidylic acid, two strong peaks at 270 mμ and 225 mμ ($\pi \rightarrow \pi^*$ bands) were observed when the electric vector was perpendicular to the helix axis (that is, in the plane of the heterocyclic ring systems; the $\pi \rightarrow \pi^*$ transition moments are polarised in-plane). With parallel polarisation (parallel to the helix axis, but perpendicular to the plane of the bases) absorption was much less intense, and a low broad peak was observed, with λ_{max} near 280 mμ. This was assigned to a n $\rightarrow \pi^*$ transition (these absorption bands are intrinsically of lower intensity; transition moments are polarised out of plane).[381] Ultraviolet rotatory dispersion curves of native, and denatured, DNA and RNA, and a mononucleotide mixture, were also consistent with $\pi \rightarrow \pi^*$ transitions (polarised perpendicular to the helix axis) and n $\rightarrow \pi^*$ transitions causing peaks at 257 mμ and 289 mμ respectively.[382, 383]

Assignment of a n $\rightarrow \pi^*$ transition to the hyperchromic band at 280 mμ in helical complexes such as polyadenylic–polyuridylic acid[381] has been seriously questioned as a result of more detailed studies on polarised spectra of oriented streaks of double helical copoly (deoxyadenylic–thymidylic acid).[384] Dichroism was 2·3 at the absorption peak, but closely similar values were obtained over the whole band (2·2 at 250 mμ; 2·3 at 260 mμ; 2·4 at 270 mμ; 2·5 at 280 mμ; and 2·2 at 290 mμ). The shoulder at 280 mμ, far from possessing an inverse dichroism to the main peak, thus appears to result from the same perpendicular polarisation, and most probably also represents a transition in the plane of the bases.[384]

The effect of chain length of the oligomer upon the hypochromism of two stranded helical complexes between polyriboadenylic acid (of high molecular weight) and oligothymidylic acids of alleged chain lengths 2 to 16 nucleotides has been interpeted to indicate the presence of " loose ends " of 2 to 4 thymidylic acid residues.[385] Such two-stranded structures seem to be quite unlike three-stranded complexes containing oligonucleotides in that the latter are virtually rigid, with little or no flexibility; they also appear to differ from double helical complexes

arise as a result of aggregation and stacking of guanine residues even at high temperatures. A more reasonable theoretical approach has been taken in a comprehensive discussion[419] of the theory of hypochromism of both oligonucleotides and helical com-

formed from polyuridylic acid and oligoadenylic acids,[386] possibly as a result of greater interplanar interaction in oligoadenylic acids compared with oligothymidylic acids. However, some reservations must be attached to the "loose end" work owing to the use of chemically synthesised oligothymidylic acids[387] of dubious homogeneity, structure, purity, and chain length.[388]

REFERENCES

1. Michelson, A. M., *Ann. Rev. Biochem.*, **30**, 133 (1961).
2. Michelson, A. M., *Nature*, **182**, 1502 (1958).
3. Michelson, A. M., *Nature*, **181**, 303 (1958).
4. Michelson, A. M., *Acta Biochim. Polon.*, **6**, 335 (1959).
5. Kunitz, M., *J. Biol. Chem.*, **164**, 563 (1946); *J. Gen. Physiol.*, **33**, 349 (1950).
6. Oster, G., and Grimsson, H., *Arch. Biochem. Biophys.*, **24**, 119 (1949).
7. Ogur, M., and Rosen, G., *Arch. Biochem. Biophys.*, **25**, 262 (1950).
8. Tsuboi, K. K., *Biochim. et Biophys. Acta*, **6**, 202 (1950).
9. Magasanik, B., and Chargaff, E., *Biochim. et Biophys. Acta*, **7**, 396 (1951).
10. Little, J. A., and Butler, G. C., *J. Biol. Chem.*, **188**, 695 (1951).
11. Tamm, C., Hodes, M. E., and Chargaff, E., *J. Biol. Chem.*, **195**, 49 (1952).
12. Thomas, R., *Bull. soc. chim. biol.*, **35**, 609 (1953).
13. Mallette, M. F., and Lamanna, C., *Arch. Biochem. Biophys.*, **51**, 217 (1954).
14. Holden, M., and Pirie, N. W., *Biochim. et Biophys. Acta*, **16**, 317 (1955).
15. de Garilhe, M. P., and Laskowski, M., *J. Biol. Chem.*, **223**, 661 (1956).
16. Gierer, A., *Nature*, **179**, 1297 (1957).
17. Beaven, G. H., Holiday, E. R., and Johnson, E. A., in *The Nucleic Acids*, **I**, 517 (Academic Press, New York, 1955).
18. Chargaff, E., and Zamenhof, S., *J. Biol. Chem.*, **173**, 327 (1948).
19. Sinsheimer, R. L., *J. Biol. Chem.*, **208**, 445 (1954).
20. Shapiro, H. S., and Chargaff, E., *Biochim. et Biophys. Acta*, **26**, 596 (1957).
21. Michelson, A. M., *J. Chem. Soc.*, 1371 (1959).
22. Michelson, A. M., *J. Chem. Soc.*, 3655 (1959).
23. Lister, J. H., *J. Chem. Soc.*, 3394 (1960).
24. Michelson, A. M., *Biochim. et Biophys. Acta*, **55**, 841 (1962).
25. Riess, J., and Ourisson, G., *Bull. soc. chim.*, 1243 (1961).
26. Janion, C., and Shugar, D., *Acta Biochim. Polon.*, **7**, 309 (1960).
27. Wierzchowski, K. L., and Shugar, D., *Acta Biochim. Polon.*, **7**, 377 (1960).
28. Wierzchowski, K. L., and Shugar, D., *Photochem. and Photobiol.*, **1**, 21 (1962).
29. Scott, J. F., in *Physical Techniques in Biological Research*, ed. Oster, G., and Pollister, A. W., **1**, 144 (Academic Press, New York, 1955).
30. Laland, S. G., Lee, W. A., Overend, W. G., and Peacocke, A. R., *Biochim. et Biophys. Acta*, **14**, 356 (1954).
31. Peacocke, A. R., *Chem. Soc. Special Publ.*, No. 8, p. 163 (1957).
32. Geiduschek, E. P., *J. Polymer Sci.*, **31**, 67 (1958).
33. Waugh, D. F., *Advances in Protein Chemistry*, **XI**, 325 (1954).
34. Ts'O, P. O. P., Helmkamp, G. K., and Sander, C., *Federation Proc.*, **20**, 352 (1961).
35. Michaelis, L., *Cold Spring Harbor Symp. Quant. Biol.*, **12**, 131 (1947).
36. Davison, P. F., and Butler, J. A. V., *Biochim. et Biophys. Acta*, **21**, 568 (1956).
37. Cavalieri, L. F., and Angelos, A., *J. Am. Chem. Soc.*, **72**, 4686 (1950).

plexes in terms of transverse and longitudinal polarisability (both cause hypochromism). Essentially, the treatment deals with the reduction, to a greater or lesser extent, of energy dissipation by an oscillating dipole as a consequence of the coherent action of radiation coming from other dipoles.

38. Lawley, P. D., *Biochim. et Biophys. Acta*, **19**, 160 (1956).
39. Lawley, P. D., *Biochim. et Biophys. Acta*, **19**, 328 (1956).
40. Weissman, N., Carnes, W. H., Rubin, P. S., and Fisher, J., *J. Am. Chem. Soc.*, **74**, 1423 (1952).
41. Steiner, R. F., and Beers, R. F., *Science*, **127**, 335 (1958).
42. Lawley, P. D., *Biochim. et Biophys. Acta*, **22**, 451 (1956).
43. Irvin, J. L., and Irvin, E. M., *J. Biol. Chem.*, **206**, 39 (1954).
44. de Bruyn, P. P. H., Farr, R. S., Banks, H., and Morthland, F. W., *Exptl. Cell Research*, **4**, 174 (1953).
45. Morthland, F. W., de Bruyn, P. P. H., and Smith, N. H., *Exptl. Cell Research*, **7**, 201 (1954).
46. Peacocke, A. R., and Skerrett, T. N. H., *Trans. Farad. Soc.*, **52**, 361 (1956).
47. Cavalieri, L. F., and Stone, A. L., *J. Am. Chem. Soc.*, **78**, 353 (1956).
48. Cavalieri, L. F., Angelos, A., and Balis, M. E., *J. Am. Chem. Soc.*, **73**, 4902 (1951).
49. Bradley, D. F., and Wolf, M. K., *Proc. Natl. Acad. Sci. U.S.A.*, **45**, 944 (1959).
50. Bradley, D. F., and Felsenfeld, G., *Nature*, **184**, 1920 (1959).
51. Stone, A. L., and Bradley, D. F., *J. Am. Chem. Soc.*, **83**, 3627 (1961).
52. Rabinowitch, E., and Epstein, L. F., *J. Am. Chem. Soc.*, **63**, 69 (1941).
53. Sheppard, S. E., and Geddes, A. L., *J. Am. Chem. Soc.*, **66**, 1995 (1944).
54. White, J. C., and Elmes, P. C., *Nature*, **169**, 151 (1952).
55. Cavalieri, L. F., Kerr, S. E., and Angelos, A., *J. Am. Chem. Soc.*, **73**, 2567 (1951).
56. Lawley, P. D., *Biochim. et Biophys. Acta*, **19**, 328 (1956).
57. Lawley, P. D., *Biochim. et Biophys. Acta*, **19**, 160 (1956).
58. Ademiec, A., and Shugar, D., *Acta Biochim. Polon.*, **6**, 425 (1959).
59. Pour-El, A., and Dekker, C. A., *Abstracts 137th Am. Chem. Soc. Meeting*, 13c (1960).
60. Yamane, T., and Davidson, N., *J. Am. Chem. Soc.*, **83**, 2599 (1961).
61. Cavalieri, L. F., *J. Am. Chem. Soc.*, **75**, 5268 (1953).
62. Lee, W. A., and Peacocke, A. R., *J. Chem. Soc.*, 3361 (1951).
63. Cavalieri, L. F., and Stone, A. L., *J. Am. Chem. Soc.*, **77**, 6499 (1955).
64. Warner, R. C., *J. Biol. Chem.*, **229**, 711 (1957).
65. Lipsett, M. N., Heppel, L. A., and Bradley, D. F., *Biochim. et Biophys. Acta*, **41**, 175 (1960).
66. Lipsett, M. N., *Federation Proc.*, **19**, 316 (1960).
67. Rich, A., *Proc. Natl. Acad. Sci. U.S.A.*, **46**, 1044 (1960).
68. Lipsett, M. N., Heppel, L. A., and Bradley, D. F., *J. Biol. Chem.*, **236**, 857 (1961).
69. Schildkraut, C. L., Marmur, J., Fresco, J. R., and Doty, P., *J. Biol. Chem.*, **236**, PC2 (1961).
70. Szer, W., and Shugar, D., *Acta Biochim. Polon.*, **8**, 235 (1961).
71. Doty, P., *Harvey Lectures*, 1960.
72. Wierzchowski, K. L., and Shugar, D., *Acta Biochim. Polon.*, **6**, 313 (1959).
73. Shugar, D., and Baranowska, J., *Nature*, **185**, 33 (1960).
74. Baranowska, J., and Shugar, D., *Acta Biochim. Polon.*, **7**, 505 (1960).
75. Beukers, R., and Berends, W., *Biochim. et Biophys. Acta*, **41**, 550 (1960).
76. Wang, S. Y., *Nature*, **190**, 690 (1961).
77. Beukers, R., and Berends, W., *Biochim. et Biophys. Acta*, **49**, 181 (1961).
78. Wacker, A., Dellweg, H., and Lodemann, E., *Angew. Chem.*, **73**, 64 (1961).
79. Wulff, D. L., and Fraenkel, G., *Biochim. et Biophys. Acta*, **51**, 332 (1961).

80. Marmur, J., and Grossman, L., *Proc. Natl. Acad. Sci. U.S.A.*, **47**, 778 (1961).
81. Geiduschek, E. P., *Proc. Natl. Acad. Sci.*, *U.S.A.*, **47**, 950 (1961).
82. Goodman, M., Schmitt, E. E., and Yphantis, D., *J. Am. Chem. Soc.*, **82**, 3483 (1960).
83. Warner, R. C., *J. Biol. Chem.*, **229**, 711 (1957).
84. Rich, A., and Davies, D. R., *J. Am. Chem. Soc.*, **78**, 3548 (1956).
85. Felsenfeld, G., and Rich, A., *Biochim. et Biophys. Acta*, **26**, 457 (1957).
86. Steiner, R. F., and Beers, R. F., *Biochim. et Biophys. Acta*, **33**, 470 (1959).
87. Felsenfeld, G., *Biochim. et Biophys. Acta*, **29**, 133 (1958).
88. Felsenfeld, G., Davies, D. R., and Rich, A., *J. Am. Chem. Soc.*, **79**, 2023 (1957).
89. Rich, A., *Reviews of Modern Physics*, **31**, 191 (1959).
90. Rich, A., *Nature*, **181**, 521 (1958).
91. Davies, D. R., and Rich, A., *J. Am. Chem. Soc.*, **80**, 1003 (1958).
92. Davies, D. R., *Nature*, **196**, 1030 (1960).
93. Mii, S., and Warner, R. C., *Federation Proc.*, **19**, 317 (1960).
94. Fresco, J. R., and Doty, P., *J. Am. Chem. Soc.*, **79**, 3928 (1957).
95. Steiner, R. F., and Beers, R. F., *Biochim. et Biophys. Acta*, **32**, 166 (1959).
96. Bryan, R. F., and Tomita, K., *Nature*, **192**, 812 (1961).
97. Fresco, J. R., *J. Mol. Biol.*, **1**, 106 (1959).
98. Rich, A., *Proceedings of the Fourth International Congress of Biochemistry, Vienna, 1958*, IX, 137.
99. Rich, A., Davies, D. R., Crick, F. H. C., and Watson, J. D., *J. Mol. Biol.*, **3**, 71 (1961).
100. Bendich, A., and Rosenkranz, H., unpublished work.
101. Rich, A., *Biochim. et Biophys. Acta*, **29**, 502 (1958).
102. Miles, H. T., *Biochim. et Biophys. Acta*, **45**, 196 (1960).
103. Miles, H. T., *Biochim. et Biophys. Acta*, **30**, 324 (1958); **35**, 274 (1959). *Nature*, **183**, 1814 (1959).
104. Doty, P., *Reviews of Modern Physics*, **31**, 107 (1959).
105. Warner, R. C., and Breslow, E., *Proceedings of the Fourth International Congress of Biochemistry, Vienna, 1958*, **IX**, 157.
106. Griffin, B. E., Todd, A. R., and Rich, A., *Proc. Natl. Acad. Sci. U.S.A.*, **44**, 1123 (1958).
107. Michelson, A. M., Dondon, J., and Grunberg-Manago, M., *Biochim. et Biophys. Acta*, **55**, 529 (1962).
108. Fresco, J. R., *Federation Proc.*, **18**, 904 (1949).
109. Fresco, J. R., and Klemperer, E., *Ann. New York Acad. Sci.*, **81**, 730 (1959).
110. Steiner, R. F., and Beers, R. F., *Biochim. et Biophys. Acta*, **26**, 336 (1957).
111. Lipsett, M. N., *Proc. Natl. Acad. Sci. U.S.A.*, **46**, 445 (1960).
112. Steiner, R. F., and Beers, R. F., *Arch. Biochem. Biophys.*, **81**, 75 (1959).
113. Lerman, L. S., *J. Mol. Biol.*, **3**, 18 (1961).
114. Luzzati, V., Masson, F., and Lerman, L. S., *J. Mol. Biol.*, **3**, 634 (1961).
115. Neville, D. M., and Bradley, D. F., *Biochim. et Biophys. Acta*, **50**, 397 (1961).
116. Felsenfeld, G., and Huang, S., *Biochim. et Biophys. Acta*, **37**, 425 (1960).
117. Felsenfeld, G., and Huang, S., *Biochim. et Biophys. Acta*, **34**, 234 (1959).
118. Breslow, E., and Warner, R. C., *Federation Proc.*, **18**, 775 (1959).
119. Steiner, R. F., *Ann. New York Acad. Sci.*, **81**, 742 (1959).
120. Steiner, R. F., *J. Biol. Chem.*, **235**, 2946 (1960).
121. Fresco, J. R., and Alberts, B. M., *Proc. Natl. Acad. Sci. U.S.A.*, **46**, 311 (1960).

122. Steiner, R. F., *J. Biol. Chem.*, **236**, 842 (1961).
123. Steiner, R. F., *J. Biol. Chem.*, **236**, 3037 (1961).
124. Michelson, A. M., unpublished work.
125. Michelson, A. M., and Grunberg-Manago, M., unpublished work.
126. Astbury, W. T., and Bell, F. O., *Nature*, **141**, 747 (1938).
127. Astbury, W. T., *Symposia Soc. Exptl. Biol.*, **1**, 66 (1947).
128. Signer, R., Caspersson, T., and Hammarsten, E., *Nature*, **141**, 122 (1938).
129. Caspersson, T., *Chromosoma*, **1**, 605 (1940).
130. Gulland, J. M., and Jordan, D. O., *Symposia Soc. Exptl. Biol.*, **1**, 56 (1947).
131. Gulland, J. M., *Cold Spring Harbor Symp. Quant. Biol.*, **12**, 95 (1947).
132. Furberg, S., *Acta Cryst.*, **3**, 325 (1950); *Nature*, **164**, 22 (1949).
133. Furberg, S., *Acta Chem. Scand.*, **6**, 634 (1952).
134. Pauling, L., and Corey, R. B., *Proc. Natl. Acad. Sci. U.S.A.*, **39**, 84 (1953); *Nature*, **171**, 346 (1953).
135. Franklin, R. E., and Gosling, R. G., *Acta Cryst.*, **6**, 673 (1953).
136. Watson, J. D., and Crick, F. H. C., *Nature*, **171**, 737, 964 (1953).
137. Chargaff, E., *Experientia*, **6**, 201 (1950).
138. Wyatt, G. R., *Biochem. J.*, **48**, 584 (1951); *J. Gen. Physiol.*, **36**, 201 (1952).
139. Wilkins, M. H. F., Stokes, A. R., and Wilson, H. R., *Nature*, **171**, 738 (1953).
140. Franklin, R. E., and Gosling, R. G., *Nature*, **171**, 740 (1953).
141. Wilkins, M. H. F., Seeds, W. E., Stokes, A. R., and Wilson, H. R., *Nature*, **172**, 759 (1953).
142. Langridge, R., Seeds, W. E., Wilson, H. R., Hooper, C. S., Wilkins, M. H. F., and Hamilton, L. D., *J. Biophys. Biochem. Cytol.*, **3**, 767 (1957).
143. Marvin, D. A., Spencer, M., Wilkins, M. H. F., and Hamilton, L. D., *Nature*, **182**, 387 (1958).
144. Langridge, R., Wilson, H. R., Hooper, C. W., Wilkins, M. H. F., and Hamilton, L. D., *J. Mol. Biol.*, **2**, 19 (1960).
145. Langridge, R., Marvin, D. A., Seeds, W. E., Wilson, H. R., Hooper, C. W., Wilkins, M. H. F., and Hamilton, L. D., *J. Mol. Biol.*, **2**, 38 (1960).
146. Marvin, D. A., Spencer, M., Wilkins, M. H. F., and Hamilton, L. D., *J. Mol. Biol.*, **3**, 547 (1961).
147. Sutherland, G. B. B. M., and Tsuboi, M., *Proc. Roy. Soc.*, **239A**, 446 (1957).
148. Wilkinson, G. R., Price, W. C., and Bradbury, E. M., *Spectrochemica Acta*, **14**, 284 (1959).
149. Bradbury, E. M., Price, W. C., and Wilkinson, G. R., *J. Mol. Biol.*, **3**, 301 (1961).
150. Blout, E. R., and Lenormant, H., *Biochim. et Biophys. Acta*, **17**, 325 (1955).
151. Shimanouchi, T., Tsuboi, M., Kyogoku, Y., and Watanabe, I., *Biochim. et Biophys. Acta*, **45**, 195 (1960).
152. Kyogoku, Y., Tsuboi, M., Shimanouchi, T., and Watanabe, I., *J. Mol. Biol.*, **3**, 741 (1961).
153. Kyogoku, Y., Tsuboi, M., Shimanouchi, T., and Watanabe, I., *Nature*, **189**, 120 (1961).
154. Balazs, E. A., Bothner-By, A. A., and Gergely, J., *J. Mol. Biol.*, **1**, 147 (1959). See also reference 407.
155. Jacobson, B., *Nature*, **172**, 666 (1953); *J. Am. Chem. Soc.*, **77**, 2919 (1955).
156. Jacobson, B., Anderson, W. A., and Arnold, J. T., *Nature*, **173**, 772 (1954).
157. Wang, J. H., *J. Amer. Chem. Soc.*, **77**, 258 (1955).
158. Hearst, J. E., and Vinograd, J., *Proc. Natl. Acad. Sci. U.S.A.*, **47**, 825, 1005 (1961).

548 NUCLEOSIDES AND NUCLEOTIDES

159. Sinsheimer, R. L., *J. Mol. Biol.*, **1**, 43 (1959).
160. Hall, C. E., and Litt, M., *J. Biophys. Biochem. Cytol.*, **4**, 1 (1958).
161. Hall, C. E., *Proceedings of the IVth International Congress of Biochemistry, Vienna, 1958*, **IX**, 90.
162. Jordan, D. O., *The Nucleic Acids* (ed. E. Chargaff and J. N. Davidson, Academic Press, New York 1955) **I**, 470.
163. Shooter, K. V., and Butler, J. A. V., *Nature*, **177**, 1033 (1956).
164. Rosenkranz, H. S., and Bendich, A., *J. Am. Chem. Soc.*, **81**, 902 (1959).
165. Butler, J. A. V., Laurence, D. J. R., Robins, A. B., and Shooter, K. V., *Nature*, **180**, 1340 (1957).
166. Cavalieri, L. F., *J. Am. Chem. Soc.*, **79**, 5319 (1957).
167. Cavalieri, L. F., and Rosenberg, B. H., *J. Am. Chem. Soc.*, **81**, 5136 (1959).
168. Davidson, P. F., *Proc. Natl. Acad. Sci. U.S.A.*, **45**, 1560 (1959).
169. Rosenkranz, H. S., and Bendich, A., *J. Am. Chem. Soc.*, **82**, 3198 (1960).
170. Hershey, A. D., and Burgi, E., *J. Mol. Biol.*, **2**, 143 (1960).
171. Levinthal, C., and Davison, P. F., *J. Mol. Biol.*, **3**, 674 (1961).
172. Hall, C. E., and Litt, M., *J. Biophys. Biochem. Cytol.*, **4**, 1 (1958).
173. Doty, P., McGill, B. B., and Rice, S. A., *Proc. Natl. Acad. Sci. U.S.A.*, **44**, 432 (1958).
174. Laland, S. G., Overend, W. G., and Stacey, M., *J. Chem. Soc.*, 303 (1952).
175. Davison, P. F., *Nature*, **185**, 918 (1960).
176. Cavalieri, L. F., and Deutsch, J. F., *Federation Proc.*, **19**, 306 (1960).
177. Cavalieri, L. F., Rosenberg, B. H., and Deutsch, J. F., *Biochem. Biophys. Research Communs.*, **1**, 124 (1959).
178. Cavalieri, L. F., Finston, R., and Rosenberg, B. H., *Nature*, **189**, 833 (1961).
179. Cavalieri, L. F., and Rosenberg, B. H., *Biophys. J.*, **1**, 323 (1961).
180. Cavalieri, L. F., and Rosenberg, B. H., *Biophys. J.*, **1**, 317 (1961).
181. Hall, C. E., and Cavalieri, L. F., *J. Biophys. Biochem. Cytol.*, **10**, 347 (1961).
182. Cavalieri, L. F., and Rosenberg, B. H., *Biophys. J.*, **1**, 337 (1961).
183. Bernardi, G., Champagne, M., and Sadron, C., *Nature*, **188**, 228 (1960); *Biochim. et Biophys. Acta*, **49**, 1 (1961).
184. Bernardi, G., and Sadron, C., *Nature*, **191**, 809 (1961).
185. Burgi, E., and Hershey, A. D., *J. Mol. Biol.*, **3**, 458 (1961).
186. Davison, P. F., Freifelder, D., Hede, R., and Levinthal, C., *Proc. Natl. Acad. Sci. U.S.A.*, **47**, 1123 (1961).
187. Cairns, J., *J. Mol. Biol.*, **3**, 756 (1961).
188. Rubenstein, I., Thomas, C. A., and Hershey, A. D., *Proc. Natl. Acad. Sci. U.S.A.*, **47**, 1113 (1961).
189. Montague, M. D., and Morton, R. K., *Nature*, **187**, 916 (1960).
190. Appleby, C. A., and Morton, R. K., *Biochem. J.*, **75**, 258 (1960).
191. Boedtker, H., *Biochim. et Biophys. Acta*, **32**, 519 (1959).
192. Cheng, P-Y., *Proc. Natl. Acad. Sci. U.S.A.*, **45**, 1557 (1959).
193. Steudel, H., *Z. physiol. Chem.*, **77**, 497 (1912).
194. Levene, P. A., and Simms, H. S., *J. Biol. Chem.*, **65**, 519 (1925); **70**, 327 (1926).
195. Hammarsten, E., *Biochem. Z.*, **144**, 383 (1924).
196. Jorpes, E., *Biochem. J.*, **28**, 2102 (1934).
197. Gulland, J. M., Jordan, D. O., and Taylor, H. F. W., *J. Chem. Soc.*, 1131 (1947).
198. Cosgrove, D. J., and Jordan, D. O., *J. Chem. Soc.*, 1413 (1949).
199. Signer, R., and Schwander, H., *Helv. Chim. Acta*, **32**, 853 (1949).
200. Lee, W. A., and Peacocke, A. R., *J. Chem. Soc.*, 3361 (1951).

201. Cox, R. A., and Peacocke, A. R., *J. Chem. Soc.*, 2499 (1956).
202. Jordan, D. O., Mathieson, A. R., and Matty, S., *J. Chem. Soc.*, **154**, 158 (1956).
203. Cox, R. A., and Peacocke, A. R., *J. Chem. Soc.*, 4724 (1957).
204. Peacocke, A. R., and Preston, B. N., *J. Chem. Soc.*, 2783 (1959).
205. Geiduschek, E. P., *J. Polymer Sci.*, **31**, 67 (1958).
206. Cox, R. A., and Peacocke, A. R., *J. Chem. Soc.*, 4117 (1958).
207. Cox, R. A., and Peacocke, A. R., *J. Chem. Soc.*, 2646 (1956).
208. Cavalieri, L. F., and Rosenberg, B. H., *J. Am. Chem. Soc.*, **79**, 5352 (1957).
209. Cavalieri, L. F., and Stone, A. L., *J. Am. Chem. Soc.*, **77**, 6499 (1955).
210. Cavalieri, L. F., Rosoff, M., and Rosenberg, B. H., *J. Am. Chem. Soc.*, **78**, 5239 (1956).
211. Thomas, C. A., and Doty, P., *J. Am. Chem. Soc.*, **78**, 1854 (1956).
212. Thomas, R., *Biochim. et Biophys. Acta*, **14**, 231 (1954).
213. Inman, R. B., and Jordan, D. O., *Biochim. et Biophys. Acta*, **42**, 427 (1960).
214. Duggan, E. L., Stevens, V. L., and Grunbaum, B. W., *J. Am. Chem. Soc.*, **79**, 4859 (1957).
215. Zubay, G., *Biochim. et Biophys. Acta*, **28**, 644 (1958).
216. Cavalieri, L. F., and Rosenberg, B. H., *Biochim. et Biophys. Acta*, **21**, 202 (1956).
217. Pauling, L., *The Nature of the Chemical Bond*, p. 452 (Oxford University Press, 3rd Edition, 1960).
218. Ehrlich, P., and Doty, P., *J. Am. Chem. Soc.*, **80**, 4251 (1958).
219. Cox, R. A., Jones, A. S., Marsh, G. E., and Peacocke, A. R., *Biochim. et Biophys. Acta*, **21**, 576 (1956).
220. Fletcher, W. E., Gulland, J. M., and Jordan, D. O., *J. Chem. Soc.*, 33 (1944).
221. Signer, R., and Schwander, H., *Helv., Chim. Acta*, **32**, 853 (1949).
222. Vallet, G., and Schwander, H., *Helv. Chim. Acta*, **32**, 2508 (1949).
223. Creeth, J. M., Gulland, J. M., and Jordan, D. O., *J. Chem. Soc.*, 1141 (1947).
224. Jordan, D. O., *Trans. Faraday Soc.*, **46**, 792 (1950).
225. Conway, B. E., and Butler, J. A. V., *J. Polymer Sci.*, **12**, 199 (1954).
226. Schwander, H., and Cerf, R., *Helv. Chim. Acta*, **32**, 2356 (1949); **34**, 436 (1951).
227. Reichmann, M. E., Varin, R., and Doty, P., *J. Am. Chem. Soc.*, **74**, 3203 (1952).
228. Rowen, J. W., Eden, M., and Kahler, H., *Biochim. et Biophys. Acta*, **10**, 89 (1953).
229. Schwander, H., *J. chim. phys.*, **47**, 718 (1950).
230. Doty, P. and Bunce, B. H., *J. Am. Chem. Soc.*, **74**, 5029 (1952).
231. Steiner, R. F., *Trans. Faraday. Soc.*, **48**, 1185 (1952).
232. Seeds, W. E., and Wilkins, M. H. F., *Discussions Faraday Soc.*, No. 9, 417 (1950).
233. Wilkins, M. H. F., Gosling, R. G., and Seeds, W. E., *Nature*, **167**, 759 (1951).
234. Cavalieri, L. F., Rosenberg, B. H., and Rosoff, M., *J. Am. Chem. Soc.*, **78**, 5235 (1956).
235. Cavalieri, L. F., Rosoff, M., and Rosenberg, B. H., *J. Am. Chem. Soc.*, **78**, 5239 (1956).
236. Zamenhof, S., Griboff, G., and Marullo, N., *Biochim. et Biophys. Acta*, **13**, 459 (1954).
237. Rice, S. A., and Doty, P., *J. Am. Chem. Soc.*, **79**, 3937 (1957).
238. Doty, P., Boedtker, H., Fresco, J. R., Haselkorn, R., and Litt, M., *Proc. Natl. Acad. Sci. U.S.A.*, **45**, 482 (1959).

239. Hall, C. E., and Litt, M., *J. Biophys. Biochem. Cytol.*, **4,** 1 (1958).
240. Marmur, J. and Doty, P., *Nature*, **183,** 1427 (1959).
241. Watson, J. D., and Littlefield, J. W., *J. Mol. Biol.*, **2,** 161 (1960).
242. Marmur, J., *Biochim. et Biophys. Acta*, **38,** 342 (1960).
243. Laland, S. G., Lee, W. A., Overend, W. G., and Peacocke, A. R., *Biochim. et Biophys. Acta*, **14,** 356 (1954).
244. Kit, S., *Biochem. Biophys. Research Communs.*, **3,** 361 (1960).
245. Sueoka, N., Marmur, J., and Doty, P., *Nature*, **183,** 1429 (1959).
246. Rolfe, R., and Meselson, M., *Proc. Natl. Acad. Sci. U.S.A.*, **45,** 1039 (1959).
247. Marmur, J., and Schildkraut, C. L., *Nature*, **189,** 636 (1961).
248. Pullman, B., and Pullman, A., *Biochim. et Biophys. Acta*, **36,** 343 (1959).
249. Pullman, B., and Pullman, A., *Nature*, **189,** 725 (1961).
250. Pauling, L., and Corey, R. B., *Arch. Biochem. Biophys.*, **65,** 164 (1956).
251. Schuster, H., *Biochem. Biophys. Research Communs.*, **2,** 320 (1960); *Z. Naturforsch.*, **15b,** 298 (1960).
252. Paleček, E., *Nature*, **188,** 656 (1960); *Biochim. et Biophys. Acta*, **51,** 1 (1961).
253. Rosenkranz, H. S., and Bendich, A., *J. Am. Chem. Soc.*, **81,** 6255 (1959).
254. Kit, S., *Nature*, **184,** 36 (1959).
255. Marmur, J., and Lane, D., *Proc. Natl. Acad. Sci. U.S.A.*, **46,** 453 (1960).
256. Doty, P., Marmur, J., Eigner, J., and Schildkraut, C. L., *Proc. Natl. Acad. Sci. U.S.A.*, **46,** (1960).
257. Ginoza, W., and Zimm, B. H., *Proc. Natl. Acad. Sci. U.S.A.*, **47,** 639 (1961).
258. Roger, M., and Hotchkiss, R. D., *Proc. Natl. Acad. Sci. U.S.A.*, **47,** 653 (1961).
259. Tamm, C., Hodes, M. E., and Chargaff, E., *J. Biol. Chem.*, **195,** 49 (1952).
260. Michelson, A. M., and Todd, A. R., *J. Chem. Soc.*, 2632 (1955).
261. Michelson, A. M., unpublished work.
262. Ascoli, F., Botré, C., and Liquori, A. M., *J. Mol. Biol.*, **3,** 202 (1961).
263. Shack, J., and Thompsett, J. M., *J. Biol. Chem.*, **197,** 17 (1952).
264. Thomas, R., *Biochim. et Biophys. Acta*, **14,** 231 (1954).
265. Cavalieri, L. F., Rosoff, M., and Rosenberg, B. H., *J. Am. Chem. Soc.*, **78,** 5239 (1956).
266. Lawley, P. D., *Biochim. et Biophys. Acta*, **21,** 481 (1956).
267. Shack, J., *J. Biol. Chem.*, **233,** 677 (1958).
268. Inman, R. B., and Jordan, D. O., *Biochim. et Biophys. Acta*, **42,** 421, 427 (1960).
269. Ascoli, F., Botré, C., Crescenzi, V., and Mele, A., *Nature*, **184,** 1482 (1959).
270. Emmanuel, C. F., *Biochim. et Biophys. Acta*, **42,** 91 (1960).
271. Shack, J., Jenkins, R. J., and Thompsett, J. M., *J. Biol. Chem.*, **203,** 373 (1953).
272. Spirin, A. S., Gavrilova, L. P., and Belozersky, A. N., *Doklady Akad. Nauk. S.S.S.R.*, **125,** 658 (1959).
273. Dove, W. F., Wallace, F. A., and Davidson, N., *Biochem. Biophys. Research Communs.*, **1,** 312 (1959).
274. Bunville, L. G., and Geiduschek, E. P., *Biochem. Biophys. Research Communs.*, **2,** 287 (1960).
275. Nagasawa, M., and Rice, S. A., *J. Am. Chem. Soc.*, **82,** 5070 (1960).
276. Jones, A. S., *Biochim. et Biophys. Acta*, **10,** 607 (1953).
277. Aubel-Sadron, G., Beck, G., Ebel, J.-P., and Sadron, C., *Biochim. et Biophys. Acta*, **42,** 542 (1960).
278. Aubel-Sadron, G., Beck, G., and Ebel, J.-P., *Biochim. et Biophys. Acta*, **53,** 11 (1961).

279. Hirth, L., Lebeurier, G., Aubel-Sadron, G., Beck, G., Ebel, J.-P., and Horn, P., *Nature*, **188**, 689 (1960). See also reference 318.
280. Helmkamp, G. K., and Ts'O, P. O. P., *Federation Proc.*, **19**, 316 (1960).
281. Helmkamp, G. K., and Ts'O, P. O. P., *J. Am. Chem. Soc.*, **83**, 138 (1961); *Biochim. et Biophys. Acta*, **55**, 601 (1962); Ts'O, P. O. P., Helmkamp, G. K., and Sander, C., *Biochim. et Biophys. Acta*, **55**, 584 (1962).
282. Ts'O, P. O. P., and Helmkamp, G. K., *Tetrahedron*, **13**, 198 (1961).
283. Marmur, J., and Ts'O, P. O. P., *Biochim. et Biophys. Acta*, **51**, 32 (1961).
284. Geiduschek, E. P., and Herskovits, T. T., *Arch. Biochem. Biophys.*, **95**, 114 (1961).
285. Geiduschek, P., and Gray, I., *J. Am. Chem. Soc.*, **78**, 879 (1956).
286. Coates, J. H., and Jordan, D. O., *Biochim. et Biophys. Acta*, **43**, 214 (1960).
287. Sinsheimer, R. L., *J. Mol. Biol.*, **1**, 43 (1959).
288. Herskovits, T. T., Singer, S. J., and Geiduschek, E. P., *Arch. Biochem. Biophys.*, **94**, 99 (1961).
289. Duggan, E. L., *Biochem. Biophys. Research Communs.*, **6**, 93 (1961).
290. Rice, S. A., and Geiduschek, E. P., *Discussions Faraday Soc.*, No. 25, 215 (1958).
291. Klotz, I. M., and Stryker, V. H., *J. Am. Chem. Soc.*, **82**, 5169 (1960).
292. Steiner, R. F., *Nature*, **190**, 340 (1961).
293. Pfau, C. J., and McCrea, J. F., *Biochim. et Biophys. Acta*, **55**, 271 (1962).
294. Tessman, I., *Virology*, **7**, 263 (1959).
295. Sinsheimer, R. L., *J. Mol. Biol.*, **1**, 37 (1959).
296. Dekker, C. A., and Schachman, H. K., *Proc. Natl. Acad. Sci. U.S.A.*, **40**, 894 (1954).
297. Schumaker, V. N., Richards, E. G., and Schachman, H. K., *J. Am. Chem. Soc.*, **78**, 4230 (1956).
298. Lehman, I. R., *J. Biol. Chem.*, **235**, 1479 (1960).
299. Stevens, V. L., and Duggan, E. L., *J. Am. Chem. Soc.*, **79**, 5703 (1957).
300. Korngold, G. C., and Bendich, A., *Abstracts 138th Am. Chem. Soc. Meeting*, 52C (1960).
301. Matsubara, K., and Takagi, Y., *Biochim. et Biophys. Acta*, **55**, 389 (1962).
302. Setlow, R., *Biochim. et Biophys. Acta*, **39**, 180 (1960).
303. Setlow, J. K., and Setlow, R. B., *Proc. Natl. Acad. Sci. U.S.A.*, **47**, 1619 (1961).
304. Inman, R. B., and Jordan, D. O., *Biochim. et Biophys. Acta*, **43**, 206 (1960).
305. Doty, P., Harvey Lectures, 1960.
306. Kit, S., *Biochem. Biophys. Research Communs.*, **3**, 377 (1960).
307. Zubay, G., and Wilkins, M. H. F., *J. Mol. Biol.*, **2**, 105 (1960).
308. Marmur, J., and Doty, P., *J. Mol. Biol.*, **3**, 585 (1961).
309. Rownd, R., Lanyi, J., and Doty, P., *Biochim. et Biophys. Acta*, **53**, 225 (1961).
310. Schildkraut, C. L., Marmur, J., and Doty, P., *J. Mol. Biol.*, **3**, 595 (1961).
311. Kuhn, W., *Experientia*, **13**, 301 (1957).
312. Longuet-Higgins, H. C., and Zimm, B. H., *J. Mol. Biol.*, **2**, 1 (1960).
313. Geiduschek, E. P., *Federation Proc.*, **20**, 353 (1961).
314. Grossman, L., Levine, S. S., and Allison, W. S., *J. Mol. Biol.*, **3**, 47 (1961).
315. Sarkar, N. K., and Dounce, A. L., *Biochim. et Biophys. Acta*, **49**, 160 (1961).
316. Beer, M., and Thomas, C. A., *J. Mol. Biol.*, **3**, 699 (1961).
317. Levine, L., and Murakami, W. T., *Abst. Vth International Biochemical Congress, Moscow*, 1961, 73.
318. Weil, J. H., Ebel, J. P., and Monier, R., *Nature*, **192**, 169 (1961).
319. Gierer, A., and Schramm, G., *Nature*, **177**, 702 (1956).

320. Fraenkel-Conrat, H., Singer, B., and Williams, R. C., *Biochim. et Biophys. Acta,* **25,** 87 (1957).

321. Boedtker, H., *J. Mol. Biol.,* **2,** 171 (1960).

322. Ginoza, W., *Nature,* **181,** 958 (1958).

323. Gavrilova, L. P., Spirin, A. S., and Belozersky, A. N., *Doklady Akad. Nauk. S.S.S.R.,* **124,** 933 (1959).

324. Gavrilova, L. P., Spirin, A. S., and Belozersky, A. N., *Doklady Akad. Nauk. S.S.S.R.,* **126,** 1121 (1959).

325. Fraenkel-Conrat, H., *Biochim. et Biophys. Acta,* **15,** 307 (1954).

326. Haselkorn, R., and Doty, P., *J. Biol. Chem.,* **236,** 2738 (1961).

327. Grunberg-Manago, M., *J. Mol. Biol.,* **1,** 240 (1959).

328. Haschemeyer, E., Singer, B., and Fraenkel-Conrat, H., *Proc. Natl. Acad. Sci. U.S.A.,* **45,** 313 (1959).

329. Spirin, A. S., Gavrilova, L. P., and Belozersky, A. N., *Doklady Akad. Nauk. S.S.S.R.,* **125,** 658 (1959).

330. Spirin, A. S., Gavrilova, L. P., Bresler, S. E., and Mosevitsky, M. I., *Biokhimiya,* **24,** 938 (1959).

331. Gierer, A., *Z. Naturforsch,* **13b,** 477 (1958).

332. Gierer, A., *Nature,* **179,** 1297 (1957).

333. Rice, R. V., *Biochim. et Biophys. Acta,* **53,** 29 (1961).

334. Spirin, A. S., *J. Mol. Biol.,* **2,** 436 (1960).

335. Kisselev, N. A., Gavrilova, L. P., and Spirin, A. S., *J. Mol. Biol.,* **3,** 778 (1961).

336. Hummel, J. P., and Kalnitsky, G., *J. Biol. Chem.,* **234,** 1517 (1959).

337. Littauer, U. Z., and Eisenberg, H., *Biochim. et Biophys. Acta,* **32,** 320 (1959).

338. Cox, R. A., and Littauer, U. Z., *Nature,* **184,** 818 (1959); *Biochim. et Biophys. Acta,* **61,** 197 (1962).

339. Hall, B. D., and Doty, P., *J. Mol. Biol.,* **1,** 111 (1959).

340. Cox, R. A., Jones, A. S., Marsh, G. E., and Peacocke, A. R., *Biochim. et Biophys. Acta,* **21,** 576 (1956).

341. Schlessinger, D., *J. Mol. Biol.,* **2,** 92 (1960).

342. Zubay, G., and Wilkins, M. H. F., *J. Mol. Biol.,* **2,** 105 (1960).

343. Shimanouchi, T., Tsuboi, M., Kyogoku, Y., and Watanabe, I., *Biochim. et Biophys. Acta,* **45,** 195 (1960).

344. Allen, E. H., Glassman, E., and Schweet, R. S., *J. Biol. Chem.,* **235,** 1061 (1960).

345. Zillig, W., Schachtschabel, D., and Krone, W., *Z. physiol. Chem.,* **318,** 100 (1960).

346. Brown, G. L., and Zubay, G., *J. Mol. Biol.,* **2,** 287 (1960).

347. Osawa, S., *Biochem. et Biophys. Acta,* **43,** 110 (1960).

348. Otaka, E., and Osawa, S., *Nature,* **185,** 921 (1960).

349. Tissières, A., *J. Mol. Biol.,* **1,** 365 (1959).

350. Hartmann, G., and Coy, U., *Biochim. et Biophys. Acta,* **47,** 612 (1961).

351. Takanami, M., Okamoto, T., and Watanabe, I., *J. Mol. Biol.,* **3,** 476 (1961).

352. Cox, R. A., and Littauer, U. Z., *J. Mol. Biol.,* **2,** 166 (1960).

353. Singer, M. F., Luborsky, S., Morrison, R. A., and Cantoni, G. L., *Biochim. et Biophys. Acta,* **38,** 568 (1960).

354. Preiss, J., Berg, P., Ofengand, E. J., Bergman, F. H., and Dieckmann, M., *Proc. Natl. Acad. Sci. U.S.A.,* **45,** 319 (1959).

355. Fresco, J. R., Lesk, A. M., Gorn, R., and Doty, P., *J. Am. Chem. Soc.,* **83,** 3155 (1961).

356. Fresco, J. R., and Givelber, H., unpublished work.

357. Fresco, J. R., and Alberts, B. M., *Proc. Natl. Acad. Sci. U.S.A.*, **46**, 311 (1960).

358. Lipsett, M. N., Heppel, L., and Bradley, D. F., *Biochim. et Biophys. Acta*, **41**, 175 (1960).

359. Fresco, J. R., Alberts, B. M., and Doty, P., *Nature*, **188**, 98 (1960).

360. Feighelman, M., Langridge, R., Seeds, W. E., Stokes, A. R., Wilson, H. R., Hooper, C. W., Wilkins, M. H. F., Barclay, R. K., and Hamilton, L. D., *Nature*, **175**, 834 (1955).

361. Wilkins, M. H. F., Zubay, G., and Wilson, H. R., *J. Mol. Biol.*, **1**, 179 (1959).

362. Cohen, S. S., *J. Biol. Chem.*, **158**, 255 (1945).

363. Shack, J., and Thompsett, J. M., *J. Biol. Chem.*, **197**, 17 (1952).

364. Klug, A., and Finch, J. T., *J. Mol. Biol.*, **2**, 201 (1960).

365. Zubay, G., and Wilkins, M. H. F., *J. Mol. Biol.*, **2**, 105 (1960).

366. Klug, A., Holmes, K. C., and Finch, J. T., *J. Mol. Biol.*, **3**, 87 (1961).

367. Bonhoeffer, F., and Schachman, H. K., *Biochem. Biophys. Research Communs.*, **2**, 366 (1960).

368. Franklin, R. E., Caspar, D. L. D., and Klug, A., *Problems and Progress in Plant Pathology* 1908–1958, p. 447 (University of Wisconsin Press 1959).

369. Spirin, A. S., Gavrilova, L. P., and Belozersky, A. N., *Biokhimiya*, **24**, 600 (1959).

370. Magasanik, B., and Chargaff, E., *Biochim. et Biophys. Acta*, **7**, 396 (1951).

371. Mihalyi, E., Bradley, D. F., and Knoller, M. I., *J. Am. Chem. Soc.*, **79**, 6387 (1957).

372. Reddi, K. K., *Biochim. et Biophys. Acta*, **27**, 1 (1958).

373. Haselkorn, R., *Ph.D. Thesis, The Conformational Properties of Synthetic Polynucleotides in Solution*, Harvard University (1959).

374. Beaven, G. H., Holiday, E. R., and Johnson, E. A., in *The Nucleic Acids*, **1**, 525, ed. Chargaff, E., and Davidson, J. N. (Academic Press, New York, 1955).

375. Miles, H. T., *Biochim. et Biophys. Acta*, **30**, 324 (1958).

376. Tinoco, I., *J. Am. Chem. Soc.*, **82**, 4785 (1960).

377. Rhodes, W., *J. Am. Chem. Soc.*, **83**, 3609 (1961).

378. Ladik, J., *Acta Phys. Acad. Sci. Hung.*, **11**, 239 (1960).

379. Michelson, A. M., *J. Chem. Soc.*, 3655 (1959).

380. Michelson, A. M., *J. Chem. Soc.*, 1371 (1959).

381. Rich, A., and Kasha, M., *J. Am. Chem. Soc.*, **82**, 6197 (1960).

382. Fresco, J. R., Lesk, A. M., Gorn, R., and Doty, P., *J. Am. Chem. Soc.*, **83**, 3155 (1961).

383. Fresco, J. R., *Tetrahedron*, **13**, 185 (1961).

384. Gellert, M., *J. Am. Chem. Soc.*, **83**, 4664 (1961).

385. Rich, A., and Tinoco, I., *J. Am. Chem. Soc.*, **82**, 6409 (1960).

386. Lipsett, M. N., Heppel, L. A., and Bradley, D. F., *J. Biol. Chem.*, **236**, 857 (1961).

387. Tener, G. M., Khorana, H. G., Markham, R., and Pol, E. H., *J. Am. Chem. Soc.*, **80**, 6223 (1958).

388. Khorana, H. G., and Vizsolyi, J. P., *J. Am. Chem. Soc.*, **83**, 675 (1961).

389. Ts'o, P. O. P., Helmkamp, G. K., and Sander, C., *Proc. Natl. Acad. Sci. U.S.A.*, **48**, 686 (1962).

390. Pereira, A. S., and Mahler, H. R., *J. Mol. Biol.*, **4**, 211 (1962).

391. Eichhorn, G. L., *Nature*, **194**, 474 (1962).

392. Bradbury, E. M., Price, W. C., and Wilkinson, G. R., *J. Mol. Biol.*, **4**, 39 (1962).
393. Bradbury, E. M., Price, W. C., Wilkinson, G. R., and Zubay, G., *J. Mol. Biol.*, **4**, 50 (1962).
394. Zubay, G., Wilkins, M. H. F., and Blout, E. R., *J. Mol. Biol.*, **4**, 69 (1962).
395. Thomas, C. A., and Berns, K. I., *J. Mol. Biol.*, **4**, 309 (1962).
396. Stollar, D., and Grossman, L., *J. Mol. Biol.*, **4**, 31 (1962).
397. Beer, M., and Moudrianakis, E. N., *Proc. Natl. Acad. Sci. U.S.A.*, **48**, 409 (1962).
398. Hamaguchi, K., and Geiduschek, E. P., *J. Am. Chem. Soc.*, **84**, 1329 (1962).
399. Gilham, P. T., *J. Am. Chem. Soc.*, **84**, 1311 (1962).
400. Cairns, J., *J. Mol. Biol.*, **4**, 407 (1962).
401. Ralph, R. K., Connors, W. J., and Khorana, H. G., *J. Am. Chem. Soc.*, **84**, 2265 (1962).
402. Herskovits, T. T., *Arch. Biochem. Biophys.*, **97**, 474 (1962).
403. Spencer, M., Fuller, W., Wilkins, M. H. F., and Brown, G. L., *Nature*, **194**, 1014 (1962).
404. Haselkorn, R., *J. Mol. Biol.*, **4**, 357 (1962).
405. Miles, H. T., *Nature*, **195**, 459 (1962).
406. Kyogoku, Y., Shimanouchi, T., Tsuboi, M., and Watanabe, I., *Nature*, **195**, 460 (1962).
407. Depireux, J., and Williams, D., *Nature*, **195**, 699 (1962).
408. Murray, K., and Peacocke, A. R., *Biochim. et Biophys. Acta*, **55**, 935 (1962).
409. Bayley, P. M., Preston, B. N., and Peacocke, A. R., *Biochim. et Biophys. Acta*, **55**, 943 (1962).
410. Radding, C. M., Josse, J., and Kornberg, A., *J. Biol. Chem.*, **237**, 2869 (1962).
411. Bendet, I., Schachter, E., and Lauffer, M. A., *J. Mol. Biol.*, **5**, 76 (1962).
412. Krieg, D. R., personal communication.
413. Marmur, J., and Doty, P., *J. Mol. Biol.*, **5**, 109 (1962).
414. Schildkraut, C. L., Marmur, J., and Doty, P., *J. Mol. Biol.*, **4**, 430 (1962).
415. Crespi, H. L., and Katz, J. J., *J. Mol. Biol.*, **4**, 65 (1962).
416. Mahler, H. R., and Mehrotra, B. D., *Biochim. et Biophys. Acta*, **55**, 789 (1962).
417. Singer, M. F., Heppel, L. A., Rushizky, G. W., and Sober, H. A., *Biochim. et Biophys. Acta*, **61**, 474 (1962).
418. de Voe, H., and Tinoco, I., *J. Mol. Biol.*, **4**, 500, 518 (1962).
419. Bolton, H. C., and Weiss, J., *Nature*, **195**, 666 (1962).
420. Luzzati, V., Witz, J., and Timasheff, S. N., Strasbourg Meeting on RNA and Polyphosphates, July 1961.
421. Littauer, U. Z., and Daniel, V., Strasbourg Meeting on RNA and Polyphosphates, July 1961.

Chapter 9

BIOLOGY OF NUCLEIC ACIDS

Although much of the drama of "living molecules" and the "secret of life" written by Sunday journalists bears but a tenuous connection with scientific fact, knowledge of the biological significance of nucleic acids has indeed increased enormously in the past twenty years. Formerly veiled in obscurity, nucleic acids are now accepted as playing key roles in cellular growth, reproduction, and mutation (and hence evolution), and biosynthetic mechanisms that do not involve smaller nucleotide derivatives have become almost a rarity. Nevertheless, the living cell does contain other functional molecular species, and until biologically active nucleoproteins such as the simpler viruses have been successfully cultivated *in vitro* it is perhaps a little premature to identify, too rigorously, such compounds with life itself.

GENETIC ROLE OF NUCLEIC ACIDS

Recognition of the physical reality and chemical nature of the heredity determinants or genes, once a purely abstract concept, has greatly assisted the tremendous expansion in scope and perspectives of modern genetics. Early work by Griffith (1928) demonstrated *in vivo* transformation of pneumococci by the injection into mice of a mixture of living non-capsulated (R) cells of one type and heat-killed capsulated (S) cells of a different type. Living capsulated organisms of the same type as the heat-killed S forms were then recovered from the animals. The new characteristics of the living pneumococci (that is, not only production of a polysaccharide capsule when previously this was lacking, but also type specificity of this capsule) were retained and reproduced by subsequent generations, and indeed, heat-killed transformed cells showed the same "transforming activity" as the original capsulated pneumococci. Further work eliminated the possibility of revival of the dead cells (rather than transformation of the living) since transformation of the R cells could be achieved *in vitro* not only by whole "donor" heat-killed S cells but also by cell-free filterable aqueous extracts therefrom. Finally, in 1944, these extracts were purified sufficiently to allow an almost unequivocal indentification of the material responsible for the effect as deoxyribonucleic acid. No conclusive evidence to the contrary or for the possession of transforming properties by molecular species other than nucleic acids has yet appeared. Many other examples of bacterial transformations by specific deoxy-

* As with chapter 5, extensive documentation has not been attempted.

nucleic acids have been described, covering a range of micro-organisms and metabolic activities.

Inactivation of transforming deoxynucleic acid by treatment with ionising radiation appears to be a one hit process and the length of the critical segment essential for genetic activity is approximately 8% of the intact DNA. Similar studies of survival curves suggest a molecular weight of approximately 300,000 for the minimum unit of DNA with transforming activity for streptomycin resistance in pneumococci. Fractionation of transforming DNA on cellulose anion exchange columns indicates a wide distribution of a particular activity in different molecules, possibly the result of partial degradation.

The biological activity of thermally denatured transforming DNA from streptomycin resistant *Diplococcus pneumoniae* has been examined. Rapid quenching to 0°, at low ionic strength and low concentrations of DNA, of the heated solution of nucleic acid gave material with only 0·2% of residual transforming activity. However, slow cooling at high ionic strength and high concentrations of DNA (conditions conducive to renaturation) yielded material with up to thirty times this activity and it appears that two strands of a double helical structure separate and reform in a specific manner, since addition of an excess of denatured homologous, but not of heterologous, wild type DNA (that is, addition of DNA identical with the transforming material except for the region responsible for streptomycin resistance, possibly involving change in a single nucleotide pair) during cooling further increased the biological activity by a factor of two. Thus only one of the two strands is required to carry information for transformation to streptomycin resistance, but at least partial reformation of complementary strands into helical regions is necessary to satisfy one or more steps in the transformation process. Indeed, density gradient studies show that residual transforming activity in denatured DNA is an intrinsic property of the material, and the loss in activity on denaturation is due to a decreased, but non-zero, efficiency of incorporation. However, material that is incorporated carries out the remaining biological steps as well as undenatured DNA. A possible extension of this work would involve fractionation of partially degraded (e.g. by enzymic hydrolysis) denatured transforming DNA and recombination of different fragments with denatured homologous wild type DNA. Formation of heterozygotes by annealing a mixture of genetically different transforming deoxynucleic acids from different stocks of *Hemophilus influenzae* has also been achieved. Doubly marked transformants were obtained by the action of physical units carrying both genetic markers, but only when the two transforming deoxynucleic acids were mixed, heated above the denaturation temperature, and then slowly cooled.

Even greater detail has been obtained by genetic analysis of a group of *Pneumococci* mutants lacking the enzyme catalysing the conversion of maltose into glucose and oligosaccharides, using DNA-mediated transformations of the different strains. Thermal inactivation of the deoxynucleic acids destroyed most rapidly those transforming factors corresponding to larger genetic regions, whereas factors corresponding to smaller regions were inactivated less rapidly. It was further concluded that genetic properties of markers such as size, linkage, linearity and discreteness are reflections of the actual distribution of determinants within the deoxynucleic acid.

Related to transformation in bacteria, the process known as trans-duction involves changes by heredity determinants carried in an in-

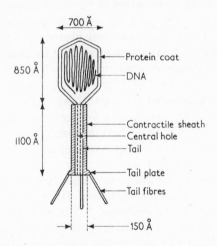

Type T2 coliphage

vading virus rather than by purified preparations of deoxynucleic acid. The bacteriophages themselves provide further evidence for the genetic role of deoxynucleic acids. *Escherichia coli* T*even* phages have received most study, and are structurally quite complex. They consist of a protein shell attached to a hollow cylindrical tail which is surrounded by a sheath that can contract in length with coincident increase in thickness. A number of tail fibres are attached to a small plate at the base of the tail. The tail contains a lytic enzyme that can dissolve the bacterial cell wall, and in addition, phosphatase, calcium ions, and bound adenosine-5′ triphosphate are present. It is likely that the metal ions stimulate hydrolysis of the nucleotide during contraction of the phage tail protein on interaction with the host cell walls during viral invasion. Inside the protein head membrane is a large amount of deoxynucleic acid, together with a small amount of internal protein. Considerable folding of the DNA must occur, since the dimensions of the extended form would be some $6\cdot3 \times 10^4$ mμ by 2 mμ compared with the container dimensions of 95 mμ by 65 mμ. Such folding is probably orientated parallel to the long axis of the phage particle in the case of T2 bacteriophage.

Radioactive tracer experiments have shown that infection of the cells is accomplished by injection of phage DNA (together with the small amounts of internal protein), the head membrane remaining outside as a phage " ghost ". The deoxynucleic acid of T2 bacteriophage appears to consist of one double stranded molecule of molecular weight approximately 130×10^6, forming a single structural entity within the particle. However, the observed distribution of ^{32}P labelled parental nucleic acid from T4 phage among the progeny possibly reflects a division of the nucleic acid into parts that are transferred as larger and smaller fragments. While infection of bacterial cells by a highly purified preparation of bacteriophage deoxyribonucleic acid has not been described, successful infection of bacterial protoplasts (including those from bacteria that are resistant to the bacteriophage) by deoxynucleic acid preparations devoid of viable phage particles has been reported. Recently, bacteriophage transformation (analogous to bacterial transformation) has been achieved by infection of E. coli spheroplasts with a mixture of purified T4 DNA and intact rII mutant of T4. Genetic recombination to give r+ T4 phage demonstrated the biological activity of the purified DNA. Further, infectious DNA has been isolated from SE Polyoma-infected tissue cultures. This preparation (ribonuclease resistant, deoxyribonuclease sensitive) gave rise to tumours in hamsters.

A fascinating picture of subversive activity has been uncovered by American investigators, for the events following host invasion by T*even* phages. The deoxynucleic acids of these bacteriophages contain no cytosine, this being entirely replaced by 5-hydroxymethylcytosine, whereas the bacterial host is free of the latter pyrimidine. Within two to four minutes after infection of E. coli cells by phage T2, there is a rapid synthesis of specific proteins prior to synthesis of viral deoxynucleic acid. Much of this early protein synthesis, if not all, can be identified with an increase in the amount of certain enzymes (probably with similar specificity as enzymes normally present in the host but of different structure) and the *de novo* production of other enzymes that are absent from both the phage and bacterium prior to infection (Table 9-I). Fifteen minutes after infection the cell contains approximately 8300 new molecules of deoxycytidylate hydroxymethylase, an average production rate of some 9 molecules per second for but one of the specific proteins formed.

TABLE 9-I.

Enzyme	Function	
Thymidylate synthetase	dU5′P → T5′P	Increased ~ 7 fold
Thymidylate kinase ⎤	T5′P → T5′PPP	Increased 10–20 fold (New enzyme distinct from that of host)
Deoxyguanylate kinase ⎬ *	dG5′P → dG5′PPP	Increased 10–20 fold (New enzyme distinct from that of host)
Deoxycytidylate kinase ⎦	dC5′PPP → dC5′P dC5′PP → dC5′P	New enzyme (probably single enzyme for both hydrolytic reactions)
Deoxycytidylate hydroxymethylase	dC5′P → 5HMdC5′P	New enzyme
5-Hydroxymethyl-2′ -deoxycytidylate kinase	5HMdC5′P → 5HMdC5′PPP	New enzyme
Glucose transferases	DNA → glucosidic viral DNA (transfer of glucose from UDPG to 5HMC residues in polynucleotide)	New enzymes α-glucosyl transferase β-glucosyl transferase α-glucose-β-glucosyl transferase depending on virus (T2, T4 and T6)
DNA polymerase	Polymerisation	New enzyme, immunologically different from host polymerase.

* Possibly a trifunctional kinase.

Synthesis of new enzymes related to the production of 5-hydroxy-methyl-2′-deoxycytidine-5′ triphosphate does not occur on infection of *E. coli* with the T*odd* phages which do not possess 5-hydroxymethyl-cytosine as a component of the nucleic acid. With T2 infected bacteria, rapid destruction of deoxycytidine-5′ triphosphate both prevents normal bacterial DNA synthesis and provides a suitable substrate for the synthesis of 5-hydroxymethyl-2′-deoxycytidine-5′ phosphate, as hydroxymethylation occurs at the monophosphate level. After synthesis of these enzymes (via initially formed ribonucleic acids) replication of the viral DNA proceeds, as well as synthesis of the phage head membrane and tail proteins. In addition to physical identification of the major part of the phage inoculum as DNA, the stimulation of phage mutation rates by the action of nitrous acid or certain purine or pyrimidine analogues that are readily incorporated into polydeoxy-nucleotide chains again implicates such polymers as the centre of induced mutations, and hence of heredity characteristics in general.

While expression of the genetic properties of most bacterial viruses is a function of their DNA content, in a considerable number of viruses the heredity characteristics are dependent largely, if not entirely, on the high molecular weight ribonucleic acid which they contain. This type, until recently represented mainly by the more easily investigated plant viruses, now includes a number of animal viruses and at least two with a bacterial host, coliphages f2 and MS2. In general they are considerably simpler than the DNA type bacteriophages, and consist of protein and ribonucleic acid in various proportions, though the presence of other components in very small amount cannot be excluded entirely. Particularly striking recent developments include demonstrations that infectivity in the absence of complete virus can be achieved, that this infectivity is associated with the ribonucleic acid rather than the protein, and that with reconstituted ribonucleoproteins using RNA from one strain of tobacco mosaic virus and protein from another, the nature of the disease (that is, the new virus produced) is characteristic of the strain supplying the RNA rather than the protein. First achieved with tobacco mosaic virus, infectious ribonucleic acids have been isolated from a number of other viruses including tomato bushy stunt, turnip yellow mosaic, encephalitis, encephalomyocarditis, equine encephalomyelitis, polio, and foot and mouth disease. With respect to tobacco mosaic virus, which contains a single molecule of ribonucleic acid, only intact nucleic acids of molecular weight approximately 2×10^6 show biological activity. Degradation by ribonuclease to the extent of one cleavage per 6000 nucleotides (the length of the chain) incurs loss of infectivity, and deamination of one in 3000 of the individual bases (adenine $\rightarrow$ hypoxanthine; cytosine $\rightarrow$ uracil) by the action of nitrous acid is mutagenic. Differences in the protein moiety corresponding to the replacement of one amino acid by another have been observed in different strains of tobacco mosaic virus. A wider host range specificity can be shown by infective ribonucleic acids compared with the intact virus (tobacco mosaic at low levels of plant illumination, and polio), and the protein, though non-infectious, plays an important part in the delineation of host range. In the case of tobacco mosaic virus, intensity of illumination plays an undefined role in the susceptibility of *Rhoes discolor* to infection by the intact virus. As with invasion of bacteria by bacteriophages, the mechanism of infection of mammalian cells by animal viruses appears to involve rapid injection of the RNA (without contact with the medium), so that immediately after infection all the infective RNA is present in the cells in a form susceptible to the action of ribonuclease. With foot and mouth disease virus it is likely that the residual protein coat disintegrates into smaller subunits following injection of the RNA.

The geometry of many of these viruses has been developed by electron microscope and X-ray studies. Tobacco mosaic virus is a cylindrical particle 3000 Å × 150 Å with a central channel 40 Å wide, formed by a helical single-stranded ribonucleic acid molecule embedded in a hollow cylinder of protein composed of some 2200 protein subunits (of molecular weight 17,400) each containing 157 amino acids. (The amino acid sequence of this subunit has been resolved). There are some 48 nucleotides per turn of the RNA helix (diameter 80 Å) and 120–130 full turns

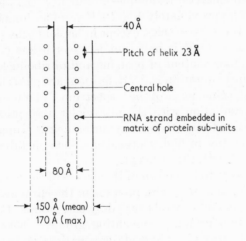

Tobacco mosaic virus

per normal virus length. Since there are approximately 16 protein subunits per helical turn, each subunit is associated with three nucleotides in the polynucleotide chain.

Some viruses show an icosahedral symmetry, for example poliomyelitis virus which is built up of 60 protein subunits each of molecular weight approximately 80,000; others form filamentous helical structures (beet yellow and mumps viruses).

While the viruses so far mentioned consist almost exclusively of nucleic acid (either DNA or RNA) and protein, others of a more complicated nature such as influenza, and avian PPLO-5969 viruses may contain both types of nucleic acid, lipids and polysaccharides. Phage alpha appears to possess unidentified material attached to one strand only of the DNA.

The genetic systems of bacteria and viruses are much less complicated than those present in higher organisms. However, here too the evidence, though indirect, is entirely in favour of deoxynucleic acid as the primary genetic material. (Indeed, the demonstrated absorption of DNA by mammalian cells suggests that reproducible transformation in higher organisms will be achieved ultimately). Thus the chromosomes, long recognised as the essential locality of heredity determinants, are composed largely of deoxyribonucleoprotein, and in specialised cells such as spermatozoa some 50% of the cell is DNA. The composition of the proteins in such cells is quite different from that of the cells resulting from fertilisation and subsequent growth and differentiation, whereas the composition of the DNA remains constant (within the errors of present analytic techniques). Further, the absolute amount of DNA per cell (approximately 4×10^{-12} gram for humans) is the same in all tissues of the same species, except in haploid cells such as spermatozoa where the amount is half (but is nevertheless double stranded DNA). The cellular content of proteins and of ribonucleic acids varies enormously. Since mutation is, by definition, a replicable change in the genetic material, coincidence of the " spectrum " of mutagenic efficiency of ultraviolet irradiation with the ultraviolet absorption spectrum of nucleic acids also indicates that deoxynucleic acid is primarly responsible for genetic properties in higher organisms. The metabolic stability of DNA is in accord with this concept.

Nothing appears to be known of the nature of the covalent organisation (if any) of nucleic acids and proteins in the chromosome, or indeed of the precise form and control exerted by end groups. Convenient (but purely speculative) protein " cementing groups " between chains of nucleic acid could arise via anhydride or ester linkages to the nucleic acid from a protein carboxyl group on the one hand, and phosphoramidate derivatives from the nucleic acid terminal phosphate to a protein amino group on the other.

RELATION OF NUCLEIC ACIDS TO PROTEIN SYNTHESIS

Since chromosomal deoxynucleic acids are now held to carry all the information necessary for cell growth and reproduction, the biosynthetic mechanisms involved in the formation of deoxyribonucleic acids, ribonucleic acids, and proteins, and the mechanisms of information transfer are subject to intensive study, both theoretical and experimental. Little finality can be expressed as yet, and in some ways the major advance has been a development towards the right questions rather than their answers.

Studies *in vivo* have shown that synthesis of ribonucleic acids is extremely active in the nucleus (probably primarily on the chromatin followed by transfer to the nucleolus) and it is generally thought that the nuclear deoxynucleic acid acts as a template for the synthesis of nuclear ribonucleic acids, of which there are not only many different species, but also at least three distinct kinds differing markedly in metabolic activity and solubility characteristics. Much of the ribonucleic acid synthesised in the nucleus may then be transferred to the cytoplasm, though under certain conditions independent synthesis of microsomal ribonucleic acid can occur. There is no mandatory coupling of ribonucleic acid and protein biosynthesis (with respect to the synthesis of cytoplasmic proteins) and the biosynthesis of proteins seems to be regulated by the function and not the formation of specific ribonucleic acids.[1]

Biochemical studies with cell free preparations have elucidated a number of steps in one biosynthetic route to cytoplasmic proteins.[2] By the action of adenosine-5′ triphosphate and specific amino acyl-RNA synthetase enzymes, individual amino acids are converted into an aminoacyl adenylate anhydride which, without liberation from the enzyme, aminoacylates a 2′ or 3′ hydroxyl group of the terminal nucleoside of a specific, low molecular weight (approximately 30,000) " soluble " or " transfer " ribonucleic acid possessing the terminal grouping-C3′P5′C3′P5′A. This RNA-aminoacyl ester then transfers to the microsomal ribonucleoprotein particles, at which loci peptide bond formation and synthesis of proteins with specific amino acid sequences occur. Transfer of the RNA (enzymically catalysed, with guanosine-5′ triphosphate as cofactor) can occur even if no amino acid esterifies the terminal nucleoside, but the integrity of the CCA ending is essential. Although amino-acyl RNA from a particular species can be used with equal success for *in vitro* incorporation of the amino acid into ribosomal particles from a variety of organisms, the peptide-linking (transfer) enzymes show species specificity in that mammalian ribosomes will respond only to the mammalian transfer enzyme and ribosomes from *E. coli* will react only with the *E. coli* transfer enzyme. Thus the transfer enzymes are at least to some degree specific for the corresponding ribosomes but not for the source of the aminoacyl-RNA intermediates. However, this specificity depends on the particular amino acid examined, and in certain cases " cross-reaction " is possible. These results suggest that there is a different transfer enzyme (as well as activating enzyme) for each amino-acyl RNA.

Little is known of the precise mechanism of specificity as yet, but a plausible (and probably incorrect) hypothesis suggests that the microsomal ribonucleic acids (molecular weight $1–2 \times 10^6$) carry the information derived from the nuclear deoxyribonucleic acid in the form of a specific base sequence, and that they act as final templates for amino acid sequence in proteins. Thus each amino acid has a specific small ribonucleic acid carrier, of which a particular stretch is matched in a complementary fashion with a specific base sequence in the microsomal ribonucleic acids. The significance of the presence of the minor nucleotides in " transfer " ribonucleic acids and their relative absence in the microsomal nucleic acids is not yet apparent. Since all the polymers concerned possess secondary and possibly tertiary macromolecular structures to some degree, the mechanics of the operation may not involve any simple complementariness of base pair formation and a " coding system " based on consecutive nucleotides in a linear chain, but rather on the nature of sequences of bases that are spatially adjacent even though separated by 20–40 covalently linked nucleotide residues. Indeed the distribution of a single nucleoside (such as pseudo-uridine, a " bifunctional " hydrogen bonding base) in the transfer RNA could confer specificity both for the enzymically catalysed acylation by an amino acid and for contact with a particular location of the microsomal RNA by creation of two or more " special " areas at specific intervals in the polynucleotide helix. However, this latter speculation is introduced merely to suggest that macromolecular structure and conformation may have more important functions in protein biosynthesis than those now assigned. In any case, whatever the coding system, the macro structure of the microsomal ribonucleoprotein, and in particular the distribution of ribonucleic acid, is clearly of importance.

Some experimental support for the role of ribonucleic acids as templates is provided by *in vivo* studies of the inhibition of protein biosynthesis by the purine analogue 8-azaguanine. Since guanosine-5′ triphosphate is involved in protein biosynthesis (as cofactor for the conversion of aminoacyl ribonucleic acids into protein) a general inhibition of antibody and enzyme formation might be expected, and is observed. However, under conditions such that there is little, if any, suppression of ribonucleic acid synthesis, the analogue being incorporated, the formation of certain enzymes is affected far more than that of others and a reasonable assumption is that the analogue acts by interfering with the activity of substances that are involved in the control of specificity in protein biosynthesis. Differential inhibition of the synthesis of bacterial and bacteriophage protein in induced lysogenic bacteria by such agents as ribonuclease, 2-thiouracil and 8-azaguanine has also been observed. Examination of substituted ribonucleic acids from *Bacillus cereus* indicated that the replacement of guanine in polynucleotides by azaguanine is not random and that the analogue may be concentrated at chain ends.

A direct relation between nucleotide sequence in polynucleotides and amino acid sequence in proteins is suggested by studies on the amino acid composition of chemically evoked mutants of tobacco mosaic virus. Treatment of infective viral RNA with nitrous acid, followed by reconstitution with the extracted protein, and then inoculation gave mutant virus in which certain proline, aspartic and threonine residues were replaced by leucine, alanine and serine.[3, 82]

Further indications of the necessity of preformed ribonucleic acids for protein biosynthesis are provided by studies of the action of chloramphenicol on *Escherichia coli* infected with phage T2 +. Ribonucleic acid is totally absent from this phage but infection induces the formation of new RNA (or a specific change in RNA metabolism possibly involving destruction of a nucleic acid receptor followed by resynthesis) in addition to the synthesis of new proteins before the appearance of phage DNA. Formation of this special RNA is independent of protein synthesis (presumably the ribonucleotide polymerase enzymes are present in the host cell) and indeed no protein synthesis is obtained in the absence of RNA formation after infection. The new RNA has a characteristic nucleotide composition different from that of the normal host cell RNA but analogous to the composition of T2 DNA. This new RNA is probably involved in the synthesis of enzymes (e.g. deoxycytidylate hydroxymethylase) necessary for the formation of new phage DNA. With T*odd* phages, which do not require formation of new specific enzymes to prepare suitable substrates for the deoxynucleotide polymerase, a considerable increase of DNA occurs after infection of the host in the virtual absence of protein synthesis. The induction of enzyme formation by T2 phage may occur by the action of a portion of the injected DNA smaller than that required for replication of the viral nucleic acid, since this induction is not affected by irradiation to an extent that synthesis of viral DNA is strongly impaired.

More recently the role of microsomal RNA as a template for protein synthesis has been questioned, and the original one gene–one ribosome–one protein hypothesis replaced by concepts with rather more experimental foundation.[4, 5] It is now held that the ribosomal RNA is not the intermediate carrier of information from gene to protein but rather that ribosomes (cytoplasmic ribonucleoprotein particles) are nonspecialised structures which receive genetic information in the form of an unstable " messenger " RNA. Extensive use of isotopic labelling, density gradient centrifugation, and manipulative skill in an examination of protein synthesis in *Escherichia coli* infected by T*even* bacteriophage yielded the following conclusions.

After phage infection no new ribosomes can be detected, but a new RNA with a relatively rapid turnover is synthesised. This RNA, which has a base composition corresponding to that of the phage DNA (but different from the host DNA) is added to pre-existing ribosomes from which it can be detached in a caesium chloride gradient by lowering the magnesium ion concentration. Most, and perhaps all, protein synthesis in the infected cell occurs in pre-existing ribosomes. Similarly, in un-infected cells there is an RNA fraction which has a rapid turnover and which can become reversibly attached to the ribosomes. Although the normal messenger RNA and the phage-specific RNA have different compositions (corresponding to the respective deoxynucleic acids) they are physically similar, (but distinct from ribosomal and soluble RNA) heterogeneous in size, and with a minimum molecular weight of 0·25–0·5 × 10⁶. This messenger RNA, though a minor fraction (< 4%) of that total cellular RNA, is not uniformly distributed over all ribosomes, and may be large enough to code for long polypeptide chains. The details of information transfer by messenger RNA have not been elucidated as yet. However, it has been shown unequivocally that information for protein synthesis is not encoded in the base sequence of the ribosomal RNA. Ribosomes are non-specialised structures on which is synthesised the protein dictated by the messenger RNA they happen to contain. No fundamental difference exists between protein synthesis in phage-infected and uninfected bacteria other than the introduction of alien messenger RNA.

Studies on the formation of rabbit haemoglobin *in vitro* using rabbit ribosomes, but unrelated aminoacyl RNA, indicate that in this case the ribosome may directly control the amino acid sequence of the protein which it synthesises. Thus in reticulocytes specificity information appears to be more stable and " rapid turnover " of this information may not be an obligatory feature of all protein synthesis.

In vitro studies of " bacterial " protein synthesis that is dependent on naturally occurring or synthetic polyribonucleotides have been described recently.[6–9, 79] Incorporation of amino acids into protein by cell-free extracts of *Escherichia coli* requires ribosomes and a soluble supernatant fraction (amino-acyl " soluble " RNA intermediates are involved), but in addition a heat stable template RNA must be present. The system needs ATP and is stimulated by a complete mixture of L-amino acids, but is markedly inhibited by puromycin, chloramphenicol, or ribonuclease. Correlation between the amount of amino acid incorporated and the amount of added RNA suggested a stoichiometric rather than a catalytic activity. Low molecular weight amino acid acceptor RNA could not replace the template RNA, but tobacco mosaic virus RNA was highly efficient and activity was also shown by enzymically synthesised polyribonucleotides. For example, polyuridylic acid activated specific incorporation of L-phenylalanine to give poly L-phenylalanine, and copolymers of cytidylic and uridylic acid specifically mediated incorporation of L-proline to give poly L-proline. A considerable number of other amino acids have been defined by specific nucleotide copolymers containing various proportions of two or more bases, and this sytem provides a means of breaking the nucleic acid–protein code in a relatively simple manner.[83-85] The results suggest that this code is degenerate (leucine incorporation is effected by copolymers of uridylic acid and cytidylic or guanylic acid*) and the minimum coding ratio is three nucleotides per amino acid, but may be larger. In this system the amino acid acceptor RNA functions as an adaptor in specifying the polymerisation of amino acids on a template. Thus reduction of cysteinyl-RNA to alanyl-RNA (with Raney Nickel) caused no change in coding properties of the RNA and hence the specific messenger catalysing incorporation of cysteine (poly UG) now effected incorporation of alanine (bound to cysteine-specific RNA).[88]

Addition of purified RNA polymerase (and ribonucleoside-5' triphosphates) to the system has no effect on amino acid incorporation, but addition of DNA from T2 bacteriophage as well causes a four fold increase in rate and up to 20 fold increase in extent of the reaction.[10] However, addition of single stranded DNA (from phage ϕX174 or heat denatured T2 DNA) has no effect, although such material is active as a primer for synthesis of RNA by the polymerase. It is possible that in some way " active " RNA is produced from a double stranded DNA template only. The complete system thus represents synthesis of protein controlled by RNA enzymically synthesised from a DNA template which itself can be enzymically synthesised.

Some evidence exists for alternate pathways of polypeptide synthesis that do not involve formation of aminoacyl adenylates by pyrophosphorolysis of adenosine-5' triphosphate or transfer by " soluble " ribonucleic acids. Other amino acid incorporation enzymes in *Alcaligenes faecalis* fragments have been described.[11, 12] The preparations were free of pyrophosphate exchange " activating enzymes ", but they catalysed exchange of phosphate between homologous ribonucleoside-5' pyrophosphates and nucleoside-5' triphosphates. Thermal inactivation studies suggested the presence of four different specific enzymes each catalysing phosphate exchange in the polyphosphates derived from adenosine, cytidine, guanosine, and uridine respectively. Synthesis of peptides from free amino acids was demonstrated with this sytem; the stoichiometry of the reaction indicated cleavage of one mol of nucleoside-5' triphosphate to nucleoside-5' pyrophosphate and orthophosphate per peptide bond formed. Each of the ribonucleoside-5' triphosphates was active with a rather specific set of L-amino acids. (See also chapter 4, p. 191).

* The two leucine-specific transfer ribonucleic acids giving rise to this degeneracy have been separated by counter-current distribution.[95]

OTHER BIOLOGICAL PROPERTIES
OF ISOLATED POLYNUCLEOTIDES AND NUCLEOPROTEINS

The induction of streptolysin S formation in *Streptococci* by poly-nucleotides is one of the few examples of a relatively specific effect associated with a particular sequence of nucleotides.[89]   Early work showed that streptolysin S potency of *S. pyogenes* was greatly increased by yeast ribonucleic acid and that ribonuclease resistant fractions from the nucleic acid, that is, polypurine segments, were considerably more active, particularly those components rich in guanine (rather than adenine) with a chain length of 5–6 nucleotides.[13, 14]   The activity of enzymically synthesised copolymers of the ribonucleotides was likewise paralleled by the content of guanylic acid.[15]   High activity was shown by oligoguanylic acids prepared by the action of ribonuclease T1 on guanosine-2',3' cyclic phosphate[16] and by chemically synthesised homo-polymers of guanylic acid.[17]   Fractions with a chain length of 4–6 nucleotides were most effective but the reduced activity shown by polyguanylic acids of higher average molecular weight may be a result of differential cell permeability or of the ready aggregation of even small polyguanylic acids.

Stimulation of amylase formation in *B. subtilis* by a ribonucleic acid preparation from the same organism has been observed.[18]   Pretreat-ment of the nucleic acid with ribonuclease did not destroy the stimulatory activity but did render the factor acid-soluble.   Alkaline hydrolysates of the bacterial ribonucleic acid were without effect, and it is likely that in this case also the active factor is a small oligonucleotide.

A so-called " polyribonucleotide coenzyme " of oxidative phos-phorylation by extracts of *Alcaligenes faecalis* has been described.[19]   The material appears to be a tetranucleotide[20] that contains adenine, guanine and uracil in the molar ratio 2 : 1 : 1.   A similar, but non-specific, requirement for anionic polyelectrolytes has been observed in the synthesis of adenosine-5' triphosphate by isolated cell nuclei[21] and in oxidative phosphorylation by mitochondria.[22, 23]

Enzymic activities are closely associated with isolated nucleoproteins. An adenosine-5' triphosphatase activity of deoxyribonucleoproteins from thymus has been observed,[24] and ribonucleoproteins from *E. coli* contain both ribonuclease and deoxyribonuclease in latent forms.[25–29] The enzymes are tightly bound to the nucleoprotein and appear not to be contaminants.   Activity appears after treatments that disrupt the nucleoprotein structure, such as tryptic digestion, or denaturation by the action of heat or concentrated solutions of urea or salts.   The latent ribonuclease is associated almost entirely with the smallest ribo-nucleoprotein complexes (30S) from *E. coli* and not with the larger

50S particles, whereas deoxyribonuclease is held by the still larger 70S particles but is released on dissociation of the ribosomes into smaller particles by reduction of magnesium ion concentration.

Other studies have shown the presence of polynucleotide phosphorylase.[30, 31] In addition, a fraction of the cellular β-galactosidase is ribosome-bound to the extent of one enzyme molecule per cell in non-induced inducible cells. This fraction, which rises to 10–20 molecules per cell in the fully induced and constitutive states, is distinguished from the soluble enzymes by a higher sedimentation coefficient and also differs in response to a specific anti-β-galactosidase serum.[32]

Studies of the composition of the protein from *Escherichia coli* ribosomes indicate two major NH_2 terminal end groups, methionine and alanine. Two classes of basic proteins of average molecular weight 25,000 but with wide compositional differences within each class can be distinguished. The protein thus bears a striking resemblance to calf thymus histone (in which alanine and proline account for 90% of the end groups) and is not a random sample of the total cellular protein but may possibly serve to maintain the ribosomal RNA in a suitable conformation for protein synthesis.[33]

Antiviral properties are shown by helenine, an unstable ribonucleoprotein isolated from *Penicillium funiculosum*.[34, 35]

Both ribonucleoproteins and purified ribonucleic acids cause profound heteromorphic changes in cultures of rat subcutaneous areolar fibroplasts,[36] and other mammalian cells.[37]

Nucleic Acids Containing Base Analogues

Under suitable conditions, extensive *in vivo* incorporation of analogues into the nucleic acids of viruses (including bacteriophage), microorganisms, and mammalian cells in culture can be effected. Examples include the replacement of guanine by 8-azaguanine in ribonucleic acids of *Bacillus cereus* and tobacco mosaic virus,[38, 39] and the replacement of uracil by 2-thiouracil[40, 41] or 5-flourouracil in bacterial[42] and viral[43] ribonucleic acids with little, if any, disturbance of the molar equivalency of 6-amino and 6-keto nucleotides. Incorporation of 2-thiouracil into the RNA of tobacco mosaic virus leads to sterility[44] while substitution with 5-fluorouracil is much less harmful and, as might be expected, the genetically active ribonucleic acids are less sensitive to the extent of replacement of bases by an analogue than they are to the nature of the analogue.[45] Considerable incorporation of thymine analogues such as 4-azathymine,[46] 5-chlorouracil, 5-bromouracil, and 5-iodouracil[47, 48] into the deoxyribonucleic acids of bacteria and bacteriophage is possible. Use of the preformed deoxynucleoside, particularly 5-bromo-2'-deoxyuridine, is even more effective for the replacement of thymine (up to 80%) in the deoxynucleic acids of mammalian cells in culture.[49-51]

While incorporation of certain analogues may well result in " deformed " ribo- and deoxyribonucleic acids which then interfere with growth (protein synthesis) and reproduction, there is evidence that, like substituted ribonucleic acids, some analogue containing deoxynucleic acids can remain biologically active. Thus incorporation of 5-bromouracil into the deoxynucleic acids of *Bacillus subtilis* gave material with transforming activity.[52] Centrifugation of the analogue-containing transforming principle in a caesium chloride gradient gave several fractions (the density of the nucleic acid being a function of the 5-bromouracil content), the transforming properties of which, using indole, methionine, and histidine markers, indicated that the deoxynucleic acid was biologically functional even after extensive replacement of thymine by 5-bromouracil in one or both strands of the double helical structures.[53] While there is no *a priori* reason against retention of activity, such experiments cannot be fully decisive, however, until deoxynucleic acids that are homogeneous not only in composition but also with respect to the location of the analogue, are obtained.

Virtually complete replacement of thymine by 5-bromouracil can be effected in T2 bacteriophage.[54] The mutational effects arising from such incorporation are also obtained with 5-chloro- and 5-iodo-uracil. Incorporation of the halogenouracils into the deoxynucleic acids of bacteria or bacteriophage results in a marked increase in sensitivity of the organism to ultraviolet irradiation (and to heat) together with lower photoreactivation characteristics.[54-56] These effects are not shown by the progeny, and undoubtedly reflect changes in the stability of the DNA itself owing to the properties of the halogenouracils compared with those of thymine. A similar increase in sensitivity towards irradiation by X-rays has been noted.[57, 58] Enhanced sensitivity of *E. coli* to X-ray and ultraviolet irradiation also occurs on incorporation of thioguanine (this base is appreciably more sensitive to ultraviolet irradiation than are the natural purine bases) into DNA.[59] Incorporation of bromouracil apparently results in single strand breaks in the DNA; these points possibly manifest themselves as chromosome breakage on subsequent replication. In accord with this, the effects of 5-bromo-2'-deoxyuridine on mammalian chromosomes include chromatid breakages, secondary constrictions, and lengthening of centromeric regions.[60] Introduction of bromouracil into mammalian DNA increases the thermal stability of the isolated nucleic acid, the dissociation temperature being several degrees higher than for normal DNA in dilute salt solution.[61] In accord with this, enzymically synthesised copoly deoxyadenylic–bromodeoxyuridylic acid has a melting temperature some 10°

higher than copoly deoxyadenylic–thymidylic acid.[62] The increased
stability possibly results from an increase in strength of hydrogen
bonding owing to the greater negativity of the halogeno-substituted
uracil ring relative to thymine. Similar results have been obtained
with complexes from polyadenylic acid and poly-halogenouridylic
acids.

Severe distortion of the sequence characteristics in DNA from
Escherichia coli on incorporation of 5-bromouracil has been claimed.[63]
While " replacement " of approximately one third of the thymine
occurred, in the sense that molar proportions and ratios were not
affected, the nucleotide pattern (as shown by acidic hydrolysis) was
drastically changed. Thus in the substituted nucleic acid twice as many
solitary pyrimidine units, that is, purine–pyrimidine–purine sequences,
were present compared with the normal DNA. The proportions of
pCpCp and pCpTp isolated were also increased and it is clear that
replacement in a specific sense may not occur.* In this connection, it is
perhaps significant that in those deoxynucleic acids containing
5-methylcytosine a greater proportion of the base, relative to cytosine, is
adjacent to purine nucleotides. The results suggest that after selection
of equal numbers of 6-amino and 6-keto nucleosides in specific pairings,
an exclusion principle operates in the determination of sequence.[63]
However, since there is continued synthesis of deoxynucleic acid in
Escherichia coli 15T⁻ treated with 5-bromodeoxyuridine while the cell
count remains constant[64] it is possible that the bulk of the DNA in
which thymine is substituted by 5-bromouracil is either non-functional
or has a metabolic function other than replication. More recent studies
(diphenylamine–formic acid method of degradation) suggest that
incorporation of 5-bromouracil into DNA has a negligible effect on
sequence,[80] in direct contradiction with the earlier results. Nearest
neighbour sequence analysis of enzymically synthesised (DNA polymerase system) 5-bromouracil substituted DNA and of the normal
E. coli DNA used as primer has also shown that the sequence patterns
are indistinguishable.[86]

Many of the nucleotide analogues have been developed mainly with
a view to their possible carcinostatic properties. Since similarities exist
between virus infections and cancer (indeed some cancers appear to be a
consequence of virus-like agents)[65] it is surprising that relatively little
work has been reported on the effect of such analogues on growth of the
more serious animal (including human) viruses. Although difficulties in
the manipulation and control of powerful analogues (which may well be
carcinogenic or mutagenic) doubtless exist, the commercial possibilities
inherent in control of viral diseases would warrant a fairly intensive
search for analogues (particularly of ribonucleotides since the genetic

* It has now been found (by the same methods) that no gross sequence changes occur
on replacement.[94]

apparatus of many of the animal viruses appears to be RNA) effective as antiviral agents. Antiviral activity of 5-fluoro-2′-deoxyuridine, 5-iodo-2′-deoxyuridine and 5-iodo-2′-deoxycytidine against *Herpes simplex* (in rabbits) has been reported.[90, 91]

REPLICATION OF DEOXYNUCLEIC ACID

Definition of the structure of DNA as a hydrogen bonded double helix of complementary chains of purine and pyrimidine deoxynucleotides led directly to a semi-conservative replication theory in which the two chains separate and serve as templates for the synthesis of new complementary chains. The original duplex thus gives rise to two double helical DNA complexes, each identical with the original. Theoretical calculations of " unwinding times " indicate that such a mechanism is feasible. Experimental evidence for a semi-conservative process of DNA replication in *Escherichia coli* (though not necessarily of such a process as outlined above) has been provided by a study of the distribution of ^{15}N labelled DNA, using density gradient (caesium chloride) centrifugation.[66] *Escherichia coli* grown for many generations in a medium containing ^{15}N as the only source of nitrogen were then transferred to the normal ^{14}N medium. After one generation time the bacteria yielded DNA that was half labelled with ^{15}N and formed a band with density characteristics in between those of DNA fully labelled with ^{15}N and DNA containing ^{14}N only, both of which were absent. After two generation times two equal bands were observed, corresponding to half-labelled DNA and unlabelled DNA; subsequent multiplication of the bacteria gave more and more of the unlabelled DNA, the quantity of half-labelled or hybrid DNA remaining essentially constant. Heat denaturation of the nucleic acid yielded material with half the molecular weight of the undenatured material, and denaturation of the half-labelled DNA gave two molecular species, one fully labelled with ^{15}N and the other unlabelled. Similarly, strand separation (by heat denaturation) of DNA from mammalian cells that had grown and divided once in the presence of 5-bromo-2′-deoxyuridine (approximately 50% replacement of thymine) gave two bands on density centrifugation, one essentially free of bromouracil with a density of 1·716 to 1·722 and the other substituted with bromouracil with a density of 1·821 to 1·831 grams per cubic centimetre, confirming that such DNA is hybrid and that in mammalian cells also, replication is semi-conservative.[67]

It has also been suggested that the polymer complex in bacterial DNA may be a laterally bonded dimer of two double helices, each double helix being conserved intact during cell division.[68] Heating in caesium chloride solution breaks the complex into two double-stranded units. The bonding that is broken is much weaker than the hydrogen bonds maintaining the double helix conformation.

Autoradiographic studies of the distribution of incorporated ^{3}H labelled thymidine among the progeny of a thymine-requiring strain of *Escherichia coli* likewise indicated a semi-conservative replication. Distribution was markedly heterogeneous and characterised by the presence of a small number of cells containing most of the label. Exposure of the bacteria to ^{3}H labelled thymidine for less than one division time gave results which suggested the presence of two large DNA containing structures which separate at cell division. These structures may be perpetuated intact for many successive cell divisions, but are subject at random to a finite probability of fragmentation during cell division.

Examination of mutations in T2 and T4 bacteriophages induced by 5-bromodeoxyuridine showed that some of the mutant phages are heterozygous, in that they give rise to mixed clones of mutant and non-mutant progeny, the proportion of heterozygotes being larger (up to 80%) with short exposure periods of the infected *E. coli* to the mutagen. Prolonged exposure led to a reduction in the proportion of heterozygotes, and a plausible interpretation is that mutational heterozygosity of a phage particle resides in a double stranded DNA that contains one mutant and one non-mutant polynucleotide chain. Similar results have been obtained with mutations induced by *in vitro* treatment of phage particles with nitrous acid. Mutagenic effects of nitrous acid appear to be primarily a consequence of the deamination of cytosine (including 5-hydroxymethylcytosine) and/or adenine rather than of guanine, as indicated by a comparison of the change in rates of deamination of the bases (in DNA itself) at pH 4·2 and at pH 5·0 with the change in mutation rate of T2 phage. Whereas a 90 fold difference in rate was found for the 6-amino derivatives compared with an 88 fold change in mutation rate, the difference for guanine was only 35 fold. This again is in accord with the Watson–Crick structure for DNA in which the pairing specificities are determined mainly by 6-keto groups (guanine and thymine) and 6-amino groups (adenine and cytosine). Deamination of adenine to hypoxanthine thus leads to pairing by cytosine rather than thymine on replication, that is, conversion of an original A–T base pair into G–C via HX–C. Similarly, deamination results in a permanent change of a C–G pair in the double helix to T–A. Replication of the strand complementary to that containing the deaminated base is unaffected however and gives " non-mutated " DNA. However, nitrous acid induced mutation of phage ϕX174, the deoxynucleic acid of which is single stranded, does not give rise to mutational heterozygotes. Studies on the r$^-$ mutation in bacteriophage T2 induced by nitrous acid suggest that deamination of any one of the 370 base pairs of the rII region (molecular weight approximately 225,000; compare with estimates of the minimum unit for transforming activity, pp. 497, 556) can cause a mutation.

The basis of the powerful mutational effects shown by certain purine and pyrimidine analogues such as 2-aminopurine and 5-bromouracil (or the deoxynucleosides) has not been unequivocally determined. Again however, a plausible explanation is to be found in concepts of mistaken base-pairing, either during incorporation into the polynucleotide chain or on subsequent replication, with consequent change from a " normal " A–T base pair to G–C (or hydroxymethylcytosine) or vice versa. Similar rare mistaken base pairings resulting from tautomeric shifts in the bases were originally suggested as a possible cause of spontaneous mutations. In accord with this, replication of copoly deoxyadenylic–thymidylic acid with the DNA polymerase system occurs with no detectable incorporation of guanine residues in the presence of deoxyguanosine-5′ triphosphate, whereas on replication of copoly deoxyadenylic–5-bromo-2′-deoxyuridylic acid a significant amount of guanine (one residue per 2000 to 25,000 nucleotides polymerised) is incorporated. However, the sequential arrangement of the incorporated guanine residues is not consistent with current theories of bromouracil mutagenesis. Although guanine should be flanked exclusively by bromouracil (since the polymer contains alternate adenine and bromouracil residues), nearest neighbour analysis showed frequencies of only 41% for bromouracil, with 42% guanine and 17% adenine.[86] The increased thermal stability of complexes of polybromouridylic acid with polyadenylic acid compared with the polyuridylic–polyadenylic acid complex is also contrary to increased ionisation or tautomeric shift hypotheses since a decrease in stability would be expected.

One cause of mutations induced by alkylating agents such as ethyl ethanesulphonate may lie in removal of guanine residues as a result of alkylation at N7 and subsequent cleavage of the glycosyl linkage under very mild conditions. Esterification of the internucleotide phosphate group (to give a tri-ester) is also probably sufficient to initiate the chain of events leading to mutation.[69] A third hypothetical explanation is that alkylation at N7 leads to base pairing (from N1 and the extranuclear 2-amino group) with thymine instead of cytosine (and hence conversion of a G–C pair into an A–T pair) as a result of loss of a proton from N1 at pH 7 to give a zwitterionic derivative.[70]

It is perhaps significant that many of the base analogues that inhibit bacterial growth, but are not readily incorporated into polydeoxynucleotide chains, or if incorporated would not give rise to mistaken base-pairing (e.g. 6-mercaptopurine, 8-azaguanine and 4-azathymine) are not highly mutagenic, suggesting that the effect is direct rather than a result of the general unbalancing of nucleic acid metabolism. Although alteration of a particular nucleotide sequence in the DNA chain may be regarded as mutation, every mutation may not result in an altered gene-controlled product, that is, an altered amino acid sequence in a particular protein. Some regions of the DNA may be primarily concerned with tertiary structure (folding of the double helix or other morphological factors) and hence mutations in structure, devoid of metabolic effects, could occur. Some indications of this may be present in acridine-resistant mutants of bacteriophages.[71]

Despite the simplicity of the Watson–Crick replication hypothesis, other semi-conservative processes may be considered. The complementary pairing of bases in the double helices of DNA results in stability and structural characteristics which in themselves may be

important. It is perhaps relevant that suitably paired double stranded DNA is necessary for transforming activity since this activity is lost on denaturation or partial pairing with heterologous polydeoxynucleotide chains. While this may well be a consequence of absorption requirements or of resistance to enzymic degradation, the possibility arises that in some cases double helical structures are not subject to separation and that *in vivo* replication involves synthesis of a double helical structure directly from an original duplex following separation of aggregated pairs of DNA duplexes. The mutagenic activity of acridines, probably due to intercalation of dye molecules in a double stranded structure (as well as to photodynamic destruction of guanine residues), suggests that the template is possibly an intact double helix. Such processes may be independent of ribonucleic acids or may actually require a re-transfer of information from RNA molecules previously formed from the DNA.*

* It must be noted, however, that most of the available evidence is in accord with the primitive conception.

Precise relationships among deoxynucleic acids, ribonucleic acids and proteins *in vivo* are difficult to evaluate because of the common precursors (amino acids) and nucleotide coenzymes involved. Various studies have indicated that in cell nuclei there is little or no synthesis of RNA at the time of synthesis of DNA, most of the nuclear RNA being synthesised just before and following DNA synthesis. Protein synthesis (perhaps of polymerase enzymes) is continuous. The absence of fresh DNA synthesis has little effect on the synthesis of RNA and protein (the antibiotic mitomycin C is an effective inhibitor of DNA synthesis) but interference with RNA or protein synthesis can have a marked effect on the synthesis of DNA. Evidence suggesting that the synthesis of DNA *in vivo* may be mediated by, or depend on, a ribonucleic acid has been found in the effect of ribonuclease on the incorporation of labelled deoxynucleosides into DNA of cultured cancer cells, and in studies of induced mutagenesis by certain agents. Mutation fixation, that is, the stabilisation of potential mutations, in ultraviolet irradiated *Escherichia coli* was found to be closely dependent on the synthesis of RNA rather than DNA or protein, and it is possible that one effect of ultraviolet light is to modify RNA precursors present at the time of irradiation. Mutation frequency response is increased by pre-irradiation incubation of the bacteria with cytidine and uridine but decreased by addition of these nucleosides (but not by thymine of deoxynucleosides) immediately following irradiation. Since the pyrimidines are readily modified by ultraviolet irradiation (e.g. formation of 4,5-dihydro-4-hydroxy derivatives and 4–5 cross linked dimers) it is possible that synthesis of RNA from such modified precursors followed by replication of DNA from this RNA is the basis of such mutation fixation. Mediation of the mutagenic effect of formaldehyde by ribonucleic acid and by adenosine and its derivatives has been observed in *Drosophila melanogaster* and may again involve intercession of modified RNA. An alternative explanation has been advanced suggesting direct incorporation of methylene linked adenine residues (at the 6-amino group) into polydeoxynucleotide chains, in which case one might reasonably expect deoxyadenosine to be even more effective than the ribose nucleoside in mediating formaldehyde induced mutations.

If indeed RNA is directly involved in the *in vivo* replication of DNA then it should be possible to obtain mutational effects by analogue incorporation not only into DNA, but also into ribonucleic acids.

The evidence for direct intercession of RNA in the replication of DNA is somewhat circumstantial and may ultimately prove misleading. Several attractive hypotheses dealing with this type of replication have been devised and will be discussed in connection with the transfer of information from DNA to RNA, a problem which yet remains whatever the mechanism for replication of the genetic material. Identification of a DNA-polymerase that requires a ribonucleic acid primer has not been reported, but recent work has shown that polynucleotide formation by the action of RNA-polymerases (mammalian, bacterial or plant) is sensitive to deoxyribonuclease, and requires a DNA template primer in addition to all four classical ribonucleoside-5′ triphosphates. With the RNA polymerase from *Escherichia coli*, single stranded DNA (ϕX 174) produces RNA with a complementary base composition. The related double stranded material (prepared by using ϕX 174 DNA as a primer for DNA polymerase) gives RNA with a composition virtually the same as that of the primer, i.e. both strands can act *in vitro* as template primer for the production of new RNA.[72]

Two points that are not accommodated by any simple replication scheme concern the non-random replacement of cytosine by 5-methylcytosine in those deoxynucleic acids that contain this base,[96] and the distribution of α- or β-D-glucosidic and non-glucosidic 5-hydroxymethylcytosine residues in the deoxynucleic acids from T*even* phages.[97] In these cases, base pairing characteristics (the essential *modus operandi* of present day replication schemes) are presumably identical. Specific location of preformed 5-methylcytosine in the polynucleotide chain may result from specificity properties inherent in the polymerase enzyme or from a " linear exclusion factor ". However, since methylation of uracil to thymine (and possibly of other bases) in transfer RNA occurs at the polymer level,[98] it is possible that this is also true of DNA with respect to 5-methylcytosine, in which case other specificity mechanisms can be considered. With deoxynucleic acids that contain glucose bound to 5-hydroxymethylcytosine residues, glucoside formation (by a transfer from uridine diphosphate glucose) occurs after polymer synthesis. Since the hydroxymethyl group is presumably capable of hydrogen bonding to suitably located sites in the macromolecule (e.g. to the imidazole nitrogen in a purine base stacked above or below the pyrimidine) enzymic transfer of glucose to such units may depend on the availability of the hydroxyl group. If this is so, then any specificity in the distribution of glucosidic 5-hydroxymethylcytosine residues relative to non-glucosidic is a function of the nucleotide sequence of the deoxynucleic acid itself. Alternatively, the glucoside transferase may possess a substrate base-sequence specificity.

Hypothetical Mechanisms of Information Transfer from DNA to RNA

Formation of a polyribonucleotide chain (or ribonucleoprotein) along the deep groove of the DNA double helix model has been advanced as a possible means of directly relating nucleotide sequence in DNA to that in certain ribonucleic acids. The product would possibly be analogous to the triple stranded complex formed on addition of polyuridylic acid (but not polyadenylic or polycytidylic acid) to the two stranded poly A–poly U complex. Information transfer is effected by relating specific pairs of bases in the DNA duplex to a particular purine or pyrimidine base in the polyribonucleotide. Thus an A–T pair (or T–A) would determine the location of A or U, and G–C (or C–G) in the DNA would control the sequence of G or C in the RNA. Similarly, reconstruction of a double helical DNA from single stranded RNA using the same coding system can be envisaged. However, since the chains run in opposite directions in the DNA duplex, it is difficult to imagine simultaneous formation of deoxynucleotide pairs unless two mechanisms of enzymic polymerisation are involved.

A simpler mechanism for the transfer of coding sequences from DNA to RNA (and vice versa) is directly analogous to the original replication hypothesis, except that after separation of the polydeoxynucleotide strands intermediate duplexes containing a deoxynucleotide polymer chain specifically paired with a ribonucleotide chain are formed. Separation, followed by further synthesis of DNA or RNA molecules, then provides material for DNA double helices or RNA suitable for protein synthesis. A slight modification of this concept suggests intermediate formation of RNA–DNA two stranded complexes followed by synthesis of a third strand (polydeoxynucleotide) of opposite polarity to the DNA strand in the complex. The triple stranded structure, less stable than a double helix by analogy with the behaviour of enzymically synthesised polymers, then breaks down to the RNA strand and the usual double helix. (The behaviour of hybrid complexes as possible primers for DNA, or RNA, polymerase has not been reported as yet).

Some evidence has been presented for the existence of a single stranded stage of T2 bacteriophage DNA during replication. The approach is based on the difference in ultraviolet action spectra between single stranded DNA (minimum efficiency at 2400 Å) and double stranded material (minimum efficiency at 2350 Å). Changes in the action spectra occur at three minutes after infection (to the single stranded type) and back again at eleven minutes suggesting a conversion of double into single strands, which subsequently form double helical structures.

A general hypothesis of genetic coding and cellular differentiation has been advanced.[73] The three main concepts are: (1) Two genetic codes for RNA formation from DNA exist, one in certain microorganisms and the other in the somatic cells of higher organisms. (2) Histone proteins act as gene regulators by their ability to stabilise one polynucleotide strand and depolymerise the complementary strand. (3) In the differentiated cells of higher organisms, part of the histone allows the RNA templates to act in protein synthesis; another form of histone has the function of suppressing the template role of the associated RNA.

In animal and plant cells it is possible that the coding system involves formation of template single strand RNA from the double helical form of DNA. In contrast with this double strand coding, single strand coding between polydeoxynucleotide and polyribonucleotide chains may be involved in certain unicellular organisms. Another view of the mechanism of synthesis of messenger RNA has been advanced[87] in which a third strand is formed along the deep groove of the intact double helical DNA. Two kinds of triple stranded structures can result by cleavage of one hydrogen bond in each DNA base pair to permit bonding with the RNA component. In animal cells T–A, C–G, A–T, and G–C give rise to C, U, G, and A respectively (i.e., the A + T content of the DNA is paralleled by the G + C content of the RNA) whereas in microbial cells T–A, C–G, A–T, and G–C specify A, G, U, and C respectively to give RNA that reflects the sequence in one strand of the DNA and is complementary to the other (i.e., A + T in the DNA is paralleled by A + U in the RNA). The polymerase enzyme specifies which kind of coding is employed; after synthesis the RNA strand dissociates from the triple stranded structure to restore the double helical DNA template.

Further hypothetical elaboration has suggested that each strand of the DNA duplex forms a complementary strand of RNA. One of the two RNA strands then encounters a specific protein to form microsomes. The second RNA strand forms ribonucleoprotein of a different kind in which parts of the polynucleotide are unprotected by complex formation with the peptide chain; these naked parts are cleaved and modified to give amino acid transfer RNA (possibly in combination with the amino acid activating enzyme) with base sequences complementary to a large part of the ribosomal RNA. In such cases synthesis of transfer RNA should not occur without the dependent synthesis of ribosomal RNA.[74]

EXPERIMENTAL EVIDENCE OF
INFORMATION TRANSFER FROM DNA TO RNA

In addition to biochemical evidence such as the requirement shown by RNA polymerases for primer DNA, and the similarity in base composition and sequence of DNA primer and RNA product, various physical studies offer confirmation of the transfer of information from DNA to RNA. Although the product is initially single stranded (using RNA polymerase from *M. lysodeikticus* and T2 DNA as template) the RNA is self complementary and can assume an ordered double helical structure during isolation and purification, i.e. with respect to *in vitro* processes, both strands of the DNA are operative.[93] Formation of complementary RNA–DNA helical complexes (these are resistant to attack by ribonucleases and deoxyribonucleases) has been demonstrated by heating and then slowly cooling mixtures of DNA and RNA isolated from the same bacteria. A significant alteration of the density band pattern on centrifugation in a density gradient was observed.[75] This effect appeared to be fairly specific for RNA from the same bacterial species. Related methods have been used to demonstrate at least partial sequence complementarity of T2 DNA and the specific RNA synthesised after infection of the host cell.[76] This T2 RNA (labelled with ^{32}P) was added to heat denatured T2 DNA (labelled with tritium), the mixture was reheated and then cooled slowly. Gradient centrifugation revealed the presence of new bands containing both ^{32}P and tritium, suggestive of specific complex formation between complementary strands of RNA and DNA. No such hybrid formation was observed with heterologous DNA even when this possessed the same over-all base composition as T2 DNA. The double labelling technique has also been used (in conjunction with equilibrium centrifugation in caesium chloride gradients) to demonstrate the occurrence of natural DNA–RNA complexes in *Escherichia coli* infected with T2 bacteriophage.[77] Selective biosynthesis of " informational " RNA (this is very heterogeneous in size) is readily achieved in bacteria by using step down cultures from a rich to a synthetic medium. In the absence of growth, RNA with a composition similar to that of the cellular DNA also accumulates in yeast.[81] This material appears to be a precursor (without breakdown to the mononucleotide level) of stable ribosomal RNA. It may be noted that in addition to the formation of specific hybrid complexes with complementary " messenger " type RNA, *E. coli* DNA also possesses sequences that are complementary to the ribosomal RNA. Use of sufficiently sensitive methods (permitting detection of 0·01% of the total genome in *E. coli*) has indicated specific hybrid formation between the ribosomal RNA and homologous DNA.[92] The base composition of bacterial ribosomal RNA implies that only one of the two DNA strands is used in the region transcribed.

CONCLUSIONS

The present status of the molecular biology of nucleic acids is such that attempts to draw precise but generalised conclusions must inevitably prove meretricious in greater or lesser degree. Indeed, while DNA, RNA, and protein are undoubtedly of major significance, it is not entirely clear that these three polymers (together with necessary precursors and energy source) represent the minimum components for a living reproducing system, however attractive such a hypothesis may be. To go still further by introducing hierarchical concepts would seem even less justified either for present day processes or for speculations of a possible origin of life. Although no precise molecular mechanisms for genetic processes can be considered rigidly proven, it is certain that the major genetic material is DNA, and that the information contained therein (by whatever coding system, and many have been devised)* is translated into specific amino acid sequences in proteins via ribonucleic acids, which in certain cases can also act as the chemical basis of heredity. A number of experimental studies, including detailed analysis of genetic fine structure, further suggest that linearity not only of genes, but also within a given gene area, is directly applicable to the deoxynucleic acids and that alteration of a single nucleotide in a particular sequence can result in protein in which a single amino acid specified by this sequence is changed. Specific chemical control of heredity, while yet distant, is now a distinct possibility; as is an even more ambitious objective.

* Recent genetic experiments with coliphage T4 mutants suggest that the code is probably a degenerate, " comma-less ", non-overlapping, triplet type (i.e. each amino acid can be coded by one of several sets of three nucleotides), the sequence being read from a fixed starting point.[78]

REFERENCES

1. Brachet, J., *Nature*, **186**, 194 (1960).
2. Hoagland, M. B., Zamecnik, P. C., and Stephenson, M. L., *Symposium on Molecular Biology*, p. 105 (University of Chicago Press, 1959).
3. Tsugita, A., and Fraenkel-Conrat, H., *Proc. Natl. Acad. Sci. U.S.A.*, **46**, 636 (1960).
4. Brenner, S., Jacob, F., and Meselson, M., *Nature*, **190**, 576 (1961).
5. Gros, F., Hiatt, H., Gilbert, W., Kurland, C. G., Risebrough, R. W., and Watson, J. D., *Nature*, **190**, 581 (1961).
6. Nirenberg, M. W., and Matthaei, J. H., *Proc. Natl. Acad. Sci. U.S.A.*, **47**, 1588 (1961).
7. Martin, R. G., Matthaei, J. H., Jones, O. W., and Nirenberg, M. W., *Biochem. Biophys. Research. Communs.*, **6**, 410 (1961–62).
8. Speyer, J. F., Lengyel, P., Basilio, C., and Ochoa, S., *Proc. Natl. Acad. Sci. U.S.A.*, **48**, 63 (1962).
9. Nirenberg, M. W., Matthaei, J. H., and Jones, O. W., *Proc. Natl. Acad. Sci. U.S.A.*, **48**, 104 (1962).
10. Wood, W. B., and Berg, P., *Proc. Natl. Acad. Sci. U.S.A.*, **48**, 94 (1962).
11. Beljanski, M., *Biochim. et Biophys. Acta*, **41**, 104, 111 (1960).
12. Beljanski, M., Beljanski, M., and Lovingny, T., *Biochim. et Biophys. Acta*, **56**, 559 (1962).
13. Maekawa, S., *Igaku to Seibutsugaku*, **40**, 227 (1956). [*Chemical Abstracts*, **52**, 7384 (1958)].
14. Tanaka, K., Hayashi, T., and Maekawa, S., *J. Biochem. (Tokyo)*, **45**, 97 (1958).
15. Tanaka, K., Egami, F., Hayashi, T., and Maekawa, S., *J. Biochem. (Tokyo)*, **45**, 593 (1958).
16. Asano-Sato, K., Hayashi, T., and Egami, F., *J. Biochem. (Tokyo)*, **48**, 292 (1960).
17. Shugar, D., Tomerska, H., and Michelson, A. M., unpublished work.
18. Nomura, M., and Yoshikawa, H., *Biochim. et Biophys. Acta*, **31**, 125 (1959).
19. Pinchot, G. B., *J. Biol. Chem.*, **229**, 25 (1957); *Biochem. Biophys. Research Communs.*, **1**, 17 (1959).

20. Shibko, S., and Pinchot, G. B., *Arch. Biochem. Biophys.*, **94**, 257 (1961).
21. Allfrey, V. G., and Mirsky, A. E., *Proc. Natl. Acad. Sci. U.S.A.*, **43**, 589 (1957).
22. Kuzin, A. M., and Budilova, E. V., *Doklady Akad. Nauk. U.S.S.R.*, **120**, 361 (1958).
23. Hanson, J. B., *J. Biol. Chem.*, **234**, 1303 (1959).
24. Stern, K. G., Goldstein, G., and Albaum, H. G., *J. Biol. Chem.*, **188**, 273 (1951).
25. Elson, D., and Tal, M., *Biochim. et Biophys. Acta*, **36**, 281 (1959).
26. Elson, D., *Biochim. et Biophys. Acta*, **36**, 372 (1959).
27. Tashiro, Y., *J. Biochem. (Tokyo)*, **45**, 937 (1958).
28. Zillig, W., Krone, W., and Albers, M., *Z. physiol. Chem.*, **317**, 131 (1959).
29. Tal, M., and Elson, D., *Biochim. et Biophys. Acta*, **53**, 227 (1961).
30. Wade, H. E., *Biochem. J.*, **78**, 457 (1961).
31. Wade, H. E., and Lovett, S., *Biochem. J.*, **81**, 319 (1961).
32. Cowie, D. B., Spiegelman, S., Roberts, R. B., and Duerksen, J. D., *Proc. Natl. Acad. Sci. U.S.A.*, **47**, 114 (1961).
33. Waller, J.-P., and Harris, J. I., *Proc. Natl. Acad. Sci. U.S.A.*, **47**, 18 (1961).
34. Lewis, U. J., Rickes, E. L., McClelland, L., and Brink, N. G., *J. Am. Chem. Soc.*, **81**, 4115 (1959).
35. Lewis, U. J., Rickes, E. L., Williams, D. E., McClelland, L., and Brink, N. G., *J. Am. Chem. Soc.*, **82**, 5178 (1960).
36. Benitez, H. H., Murray, M. R., and Chargaff, E., *J. Biophys. Biochem. Cytol.*, **5**, 25 (1959).
37. Niu, M. C., Cordova, C. C., and Niu, L. C., *Proc. Natl. Acad. Sci. U.S.A.*, **47**, 1689 (1961).
38. Smith, J. D., and Matthews, R. E. F., *Biochem. J.*, **66**, 323 (1957).
39. Mandel, H. G., and Markham, R., *Biochem. J.*, **69**, 297 (1958).
40. Mandel, G., Markham, R., and Matthews, R. E. F., *Biochim. et Biophys. Acta*, **24**, 205 (1957).
41. Jeener, R., *Biochim. et Biophys. Acta*, **23**, 351 (1957).
42. Horowitz, J., and Chargaff, E., *Nature*, **184**, 1213 (1959).
43. Gordon, M. P., and Staehelin, M., *J. Am. Chem. Soc.*, **80**, 2340 (1958).
44. Francki, R. I. B., and Matthews, R. E. F., *Biochim. et Biophys. Acta*, **34**, 570 (1959).
45. Gordon, M. P., and Staehelin, M., *Biochim. et Biophys. Acta*, **36**, 351 (1959).
46. Prusoff, W. H., *J. Biol. Chem.*, **226**, 901 (1957).
47. Dunn, D. B., and Smith, J. D., *Biochem. J.*, **67**, 494 (1957).
48. Zamenhof, S., Rich, K., and de Giovanni, R., *J. Biol. Chem.*, **234**, 2960 (1959).
49. Eidinoff, M. L., Cheong, L., and Rich, M. A., *Science*, **129**, 1550 (1959).
50. Hakala, M. T., *J. Biol. Chem.*, **234**, 3072 (1959).
51. Littlefield, J. W., and Gould, E. A., *J. Biol. Chem.*, **235**, 1129 (1960).
52. Ephrati-Elizur, E., and Zamenhof, S., *Nature*, **184**, 472 (1959).
53. Szybalski, W., Opara-Kubinska, Z., Lorkiewicz, Z., Ephrati-Elizur, E., and Zamenhof, S., *Nature*, **188**, 743 (1960).
54. Litman, R. M., and Pardee, A. B., *Biochim. et Biophys. Acta*, **42**, 117, 131 (1960).
55. Lorkiewicz, Z., and Szybalski, W., *Biochem. Biophys. Research Communs.*, **2**, 413 (1960).
56. Greer, S., *J. Gen. Microbiol.*, **22**, 618 (1960).

57. Opara-Kubinska, Z., Lorkiewicz, Z., and Szybalski, W., *Biochem. Biophys. Research Communs.*, **4,** 288 (1961).
58. Erikson, R. L., and Szybalski, W., *Biochem. Biophys. Research Communs.,* **4,** 258 (1961).
59. Kaplan, H. S., Smith, K. C., and Tomlin, P., *Nature,* **190,** 794 (1961).
60. Hsu, T. C., and Somers, C. E., *Proc. Natl. Acad. Sci. U.S.A.,* **47,** 396 (1961).
61. Kit, S., and Hsu, T. C., *Biochem. Biophys. Research Communs.,* **5,** 120 (1961).
62. Baldwin, R. L., Inman, R. B., and Wake, R. G., *Federation Proc.,* **20,** 354 (1961).
63. Shapiro, H. S., and Chargaff, E., *Nature,* **188,** 62 (1960).
64. Frisch, D. M., and Visser, D. W., *Biochim. et Biophys. Acta,* **43,** 546 (1960).
65. Dmochowski, L., *Science,* **133,** 551 (1961).
66. Meselson, M., and Stahl, F. W., *Proc. Natl. Acad. Sci. U.S.A.,* **44,** 671 (1958).
67. Chun, E. H. L., and Littlefield, J. W., *J. Mol. Biol.,* **3,** 668 (1961).
68. Cavalieri, L. F., and Rosenberg, B. H., *Biophys. J.,* **1,** 337 (1961).
69. Alexander, P., Lett, J. T., and Parkins, G., *Biochim. et Biophys. Acta,* **48,** 423 (1961).
70. Lawley, P. D., and Brookes, P., *Nature,* **192,** 1081 (1961).
71. Mahler, H. R., and Fraser, D., *Nature,* **189,** 948 (1961).
72. Chamberlin, M., and Berg, P., *Proc. Natl. Acad. Sci. U.S.A.,* **48,** 81 (1962).
73. Leslie, I., *Nature,* **189,** 260 (1961).
74. Stanley, W. M., and Bock, R. M., *Nature,* **190,** 299 (1961).
75. Schildkraut, C. L., Marmur, J., Fresco, J. R., and Doty, P., *J. Biol. Chem.,* **236,** PC2 (1961).
76. Hall, B. D., and Spiegelman, S., *Proc. Natl. Acad. Sci. U.S.A.,* **47,** 137 (1961).
77. Spiegelman, S., Hall, B. D., and Storck, R., *Proc. Natl. Acad. Sci. U.S.A.,* **47,** 1135 (1961).
78. Crick, F. H. C., Barnett, L., Brenner, S., and Watts-Tobin, R. J., *Nature,* **192,** 1227 (1961).
79. Lengyel, P., Speyer, J. F., Basilio, C., and Ochoa, S., *Proc. Natl. Acad. Sci. U.S.A.,* **48,** 282 (1962).
80. Burton, K., *Biochim. et Biophys. Acta,* **55,** 412 (1962).
81. Kitazume, Y., Ycas, M., and Vincent, W. S., *Proc. Natl. Acad. Sci. U.S.A.,* **48,** 265 (1962).
82. Tsugita, A., and Fraenkel-Conrat, H., *J. Mol. Biol.,* **4,** 73 (1962).
83. Speyer, J. F., Lenygel, P., Basilio, C., and Ochoa, S., *Proc. Natl. Acad. Sci. U.S.A.,* **48,** 441 (1962).
84. Basilio, C., Wahba, A. J., Lengyel, P., Speyer, J. F., and Ochoa, S., *Proc. Natl. Acad. Sci. U.S.A.,* **48,** 613 (1962).
85. Matthaei, J. H., Jones, O. W., Martin, R. G., and Nirenberg, M. W., *Proc. Natl. Acad. Sci. U.S.A.,* **48,** 666 (1962).
86. Trautner, T. A., Swartz, M. N., and Kornberg, A., *Proc. Natl. Acad. Sci. U.S.A.,* **48,** 449 (1962).
87. Zubay, G., *Proc. Natl. Acad. Sci. U.S.A.,* **48,** 456 (1962).
88. Chapeville, F., Lipmann, F., Ehrenstein, G., Weisblum, B., Ray, W. J., and Benzer, S., *Proc. Natl. Acad. Sci. U.S.A.,* **48,** 1086 (1962).
89. Okamoto, H., Ann. Report of the Research Institute of Tuberculosis. Kanazawa University (Japan), **19,** 165 (1962).
90. Lerman, S., Doyle, J., and Doyle, R. F., *Nature,* **194,** 986 (1962).

91. Perkins, E. S., Wood, R. M., Sears, M. L., Prusoff, W. H., and Welch, A. D., *Nature*, **194**, 985 (1962).
92. Yankofsky, S. A., and Spiegelman, S., *Proc. Natl. Acad. Sci. U.S.A.*, **48**, 1069 (1962).
93. Geiduschek, E. P., Moohr, J. W., and Weiss, S. B., *Proc. Natl. Aca. Sci. U.S.A.*, **48**, 1078 (1962).
94. Rudner, R., Shapiro, H. S., and Chargaff, E., *Nature*, **195**, 143 (1962).
95. Weisblum, B., Benzer, S., and Holley, R. W., *Proc. Natl. Acad. Sci. U.S.A.*, **48**, 1449 (1962).
96. Doskočil, J., and Šorm, F., *Biochim. et Biophys. Acta*, **55**, 953 (1962).
97. Lunt, M. R., and Burton, K., *Biochim. et Biophys. Acta*, **55**, 1005 (1962).
98. Fleisner, E., and Borek, E., *Proc. Natl. Acad. Sci. U.S.A.*, **48**, 1199 (1962).

AUTHOR INDEX

Numbers in brackets are reference numbers and are included to
assist in locating references in which the authors' names are not
mentioned in the text. Numbers in *italics* indicate the page on
which the reference is listed.

A

Abraham, E. P., 161 (76), *239*
Acs, G., 188 (295), *245*, 333 (434), 375
(434), *396*
Ademiec, A., 373 (426), *396*, 455 (58),
545
Adler, E., 160 (68), *239*
Adler, J., 362 (383), *395*
Adler, M., 12 (53), *88*, 347 (252), *391*
Agashe, B. D., 209 (398), 221 (398), *248*
Agranoff, B. W., 219 (435), *249*
Albaum, H. G., 568 (24), *582*
Albers, H., 158 (51), *239*, 353 (306), *393*
Albers, M., 568 (28), *582*
Alberts, B. M., 472 (121), 535 (357, 359),
536 (359), *546*, *553*
Alexander, P., 375 (441), 383 (515),
396, *398*, 574 (69), *583*
Algranati, I. D., 167 (143), *241*
Alivasatos, S. G. A., 165 (114), *240*
Al-Khalidi, U., 45 (209, 210), *92*
Allen, E. H., 530 (344), 531 (344), 534
(344), *552*
Allen, F. W., 4 (4), 12 (50, 56, 57), 13
(58), *87*, 142 (226), 145 (233), *152*,
310 (19), 319 (92), 320 (94), 330 (92),
331 (150), 332 (158), 333 (158), 339
(192), 347 (250), 349 (250, 261, 262,
263), *385*, *387*, *389*, *390*, *391*, *392*
Alles, J., 38 (170), *91*, 352 (293), *392*
Allfrey, V. G., 98 (8), *147*, 333 (160),
376 (452), *389*, *396*, 568 (21), *582*
Allison, W. S., 37 (164), *91*, 519 (314),
551
Altman, K. I., 359 (361), *394*
Altmann, R., 2 (2), *3*
Alver, E., 106 (66), *148*
Ames, B. N., 383 (526, 528), *398*
Amos, H., 12 (51), *88*, 347 (249), *391*
Anand, N., 116 (111), 138 (199), *149*,
151, 233 (447), *249*

Andersen, W., 4 (8), 16 (62), *87*, *88*
Anderson, C. D., 80 (345, 347, 348), *96*
Anderson, E. P., 166 (129), *241*
Anderson, G. W., 235 (454), 236 (454),
249
Anderson, L., 165 (121), *240*
Anderson, S. M., 29 (121), *90*, *152*
Anderson, W. A., 476 (156), *547*
Andrews, K. J. M., 25 (97), *89*, 114
(107), *149*, 234 (450), *249*
Andrews, W., 345 (229), 346 (229), *391*
Anfinsen, C. B., 322 (112), 328 (142),
388
Angell, C. L., 12 (47), *88*
Angelos, A., 452 (37, 48, 55), *544*, *545*
Antonovich, E. G., 193 (340), *247*
Anwar, R. A., 174 (201), *243*
Apgar, J., 309 (17), 311 (17, 51, 53, 55,
57), 336 (182), 346 (55), *385*, *386*,
389, *399*
Apicella, M., 30 (124), *90*
Appleby, C. A., 480 (190), *548*
Åqvist, S. E. G., 322 (112), *388*
Armstrong, J. J., 179 (222), *243*
Arnold, J., 139 (238), *152*
Arnold, J. T., 476 (156), *547*
Asahi, T., 184 (266, 267), *245*
Asano-Sato, K., 568 (16), *581*
Ascoli, F., 499 (262), 503 (269), *550*
Ashwell, G., 170 (173), *242*
Astbury, W. T., 316 (74), *387*, 473
(126, 127), *547*
Astrachan, L., 363 (388), *395*
Atherton, F. R., 112 (95), 113 (100),
149, 212 (408), *248*
Atkinson, M. R., 158 (54), *239*
Aubanel, M., 192 (330), *246*
Aubel-Sadron, G., 509 (277, 278, 279),
550, *551*
Austrian, R., 169 (160), *242*
Avison, A. W. D., 204 (373), *247*
Axelrod, J., 168 (151, 156), *241*

10 (36), 24 (85), *87, 88, 89,* 101 (41),
116 (114), 118 (126, 127, 130), *148,
149, 150,* 356 (345), 365 (402), 375
(432), 376 (446, 447), *394, 395, 396*
Brenner, D., 565 (4), 581 (78), *581,* 583
Bresler, D. E., 522 (330), 525 (330), *552*
Breslow, E., 468 (105), 471 (118), 472
(118), *546*
Brigl, P., 112 (96), *149,* 364 (391), *395*
Brink, N. G., 353 (304), *393,* 569 (34,
35), *582*
Brintzinger, H., 156 (43), *239*
Brookes, P., 30 (367), 32 (146), 33 (146),
90, 97, 347 (254), 348 (254), 375 (438,
440), *391, 396,* 574 (70), *583*
Brown, A. D., 193 (337), *246*
Brown, D. H., 170 (168, 170), *242*
Brown, D. M., 11 (40), 18 (67, 68), 22
(67, 68, 76), 23 (78), 26 (78), 44 (68),
69 (324), 75 (334), 76 (334, 336), *88,
89, 95, 96,* 102 (47, 50, 51, 52, 53),
103 (57), 104 (57, 62), 105 (64), 106
(52, 53, 65, 69), 107 (69), 118 (47, 50,
57, 64), 119 (51), 130 (158, 160), 135
(187), 143 (47), 144 (52, 158, 231),
145 (158, 232), 146 (160), *148, 150,
151, 152,* 234 (451), *249,* 293 (22),
307, 317 (81, 85, 86), 318 (81, 86, 87),
320 (101), 321 (87, 105), 337 (185,
187), 348 (256), 358 (81), 365 (406),
375 (430), *387, 390, 391, 395, 396,* 419
(29), *442*
Brown, F., 310 (37), *386*
Brown, G. B., 31 (137, 138), 32 (139),
33 (152, 153), 34 (152, 153, 155), 37
(162), 39 (182), 51 (243), 54 (262, 278),
57 (284), 83 (354), *90, 91, 93, 94, 96,*
140 (210), 141 (223), *152,* 323 (135),
388
Brown, G. L., 313 (63), 354 (332, 333),
387, 393, 530 (346), 534 (346, 403),
552, 554
Brown, G. M., 154 (20), 163 (88, 89),
164 (102), *238, 240*
Brown, R. A., 309 (13), 352 (298), 354
(322), *385, 393*
Brownhill, T. J., 309 (10), *385*
Bryan, R. F., 465 (96), *546*
Buchanan, J. G., 38 (171, 173), 64
(309, 310, 311), 65 (313, 314), *91,
95,* 122 (148), 142 (148), 145 (235),

150, 176 (213, 214, 216), 177 (217,
219, 220), 178 (217), 179 (222), 203
(369, 370), 208 (393), 209 (394), 214
(415), 236 (415), *243, 247, 248*
Buchanan, J. M., 251 (1), 296 (26),
297 (27), *306, 307*
Buchi, J., 159 (61), *239*
Budilova, E. V., 568 (22), *582*
Budowsky, E. I., 132 (170), *151,* 216
(427), *249*
Buettner-Janusch, V., 98 (9), *147,* 154
(23), 181 (238), *238, 244*
Bunce, B. H., 486 (230), *549*
Bunville, L. G., 508 (274), *550*
Burchenal, J. H., 69 (326), *95*
Burckhalter, J. H., 85 (360), *97*
Burger, A., 138 (200, 201, 203), *151*
Burger, M., 182 (247), *244*
Burger, W. C., 351 (273), *392*
Burgi, E., 478 (170), 480 (185), *548*
Burke, D. C., 8 (25), *87*
Burness, A. T. H., 310 (25), 352 (25),
385
Burton, K., 369 (414, 415), 370 (416,
417), *395,* 571 (80), 577 (97), *583, 584*
Burton, R. M., 182 (247), *244*
Butler, D. N., 67 (317), *95*
Butler, G. C., 8 (28), 98 (16), *147,* 322
(119), 340 (119, 193), 341 (119), 353
(318), 378 (475), 380 (475), *388, 390,
393, 397,* 445 (10), *544*
Butler, J. A. V., 353 (312), 375 (439),
382 (504), 383 (504), *393, 396, 398,*
452 (36), 477 (163, 165), 485 (225),
486 (225), *544, 548, 549*
Bynum, B. S., 384 (540), *398*

C

Cabib, E., 167 (131, 132, 143), 169
(163), 179 (225), *241, 242, 243*
Cairns, J., 477 (400), 480 (187), *548, 554*
Cammaroti, M. S., 47 (225), *92*
Canellakis, E. S., 331 (148), 350 (270),
389, 392
Cantero, A., 154 (24), *238*
Cantoni, G. L., 16 (61), 48 (228, 229),
50 (236), *88, 93,* 311 (58), 331 (147),
334 (171), *386, 389,* 533 (353), *552*
Caputto, R., 100 (36), *147,* 162 (81,

518 (310), 521 (238, 326), 522 (238, 326), 525 (238), 527 (339), 529 (238, 339), 534 (355), 535 (359), 536 (359), 538 (339), 543 (382), *545, 546, 548, 549, 550, 551, 552, 553, 554,* 580 (75), *583*

Dounce, A. L., 193 (339), *247,* 309 (5), 375 (431), 382 (509), 383 (525), *385, 396, 398,* 519 (315), *551*

Dove, W. F., 385 (543), *399,* 507 (273), 508 (273), *550*

Downie, I. M., 132 (175), *151*

Doyle, J., 572 (90), *583*

Doyle, R. F., 572 (90), *583*

Drabikowski, W., 191 (312), *246*

Drell, W., 43 (201), *92*

Drummond, G. I., 108 (78), 109 (78), 122 (78), 141 (78), *148*

Druyan, R., 352 (297), *392*

Dub, M., 51 (239), *93*

Dubin, D. T., 383 (526, 528), *398*

Ducay, E. D., 382 (547, 548), *399*

Dudek, G. O., 293 (23), *307*

Duerksen, J. D., 569 (32), *582*

Duggan, E. L., 385 (545), *399,* 482 (214), 510 (289), 514 (299), *549, 551*

Dunham, E. K., 45 (214), *92*

Dunn, D. B., 5 (9, 10, 15), 12 (9, 48, 49), *87, 88,* 341 (200), 347 (247, 248, 253, 255), 349 (258, 259, 268), 376 (460), *390, 391, 392, 396,* 569 (47), *582*

Durant, G. J., 403 (4), *442*

Durell, J., 50 (236), *93*

Durr, G. J., 54 (267), *94*

Duschinsky, R., 58 (286), 60 (298), 69 (326), 83 (355), *94, 95, 96,* 133 (183), *151*

Dutton, G. J., 168 (150, 152), *241*

Dydnska, M., 191 (312), *246*

E

Ebel, J. P., 192 (326), *246,* 509 (277, 278, 279, 318), *550, 551*

Edelman, I. S., 353 (302), *393*

Eden, M., 486 (228), *549*

Egami, F., 139 (240), *152,* 323 (122), 334 (166, 167, 169, 172), 335 (174), 341 (202), 342 (213), *388, 389, 390,* 568 (15, 16), *581*

Ehrenberg, J., 116 (114), *149*

Ehrenstein, G., 567 (88), *583*

Ehrlich, P., 485 (218), 486 (218), *549*

Eichhorn, G. L., 489 (391), *553*

Eidinoff, M. L., 37 (162), 83 (354), *91, 96,* 570 (49), *582*

Eigner, J., 495 (256), *550*

Eiler, J. J., 141 (224), *152*

Eisenberg, H., 310 (21), *385,* 527 (337), 528 (337), *552*

Eissinger, J., 385 (544), *399*

Ellem, K. A. O., 354 (322), *393*

Ekert, B., 30 (127), *90*

Ellfolk, N., 193 (341), *247*

Elliott, W. H., 187 (285), *245*

Elmes, P. C., 452 (54), *545*

Elmore, D. T., 4 (6), 5 (13), *87,* 203 (366), 206 (366), 221 (366), *247,* 319, (89), 376 (458), *387, 396,* 400 (1), 407 (9), *442*

Elson, D., 98 (11), *147,* 343 (222), 344 (232, 234, 236), 345 (224), 346 (224), 351 (282), *390, 391, 392,* 568 (25), 26, 29), *582*

Embden, G., 2 (13), *3,* 98 (4), *147*

Emery, A. J., 382 (508), *398*

Emmanuel, C. F., 504 (270), *550*

Emmerson, P., 383 (513), *398*

England, S., 161 (77), *239*

Ephrati-Elizur, E., 570 (52, 53), *582*

Epstein, L. F., 452 (52), *545*

Erikson, R. L., 570 (58), *583*

Euler, H. von, 158 (48, 50, 51, 53), 159 (55, 58), 160 (67, 68), *239*

Evans, D. D., 68 (322), *95*

Evans, J. S., 163 (85), *240*

Everett, G. A., 311 (56, 57), *386*

F

Fairley, J. L., 344 (238), *391*

Falcone, A. B., 187 (276), *245*

Falconer, R., 2 (10), *3,* 43 (200), 46 (219), *92*

Falkenheim, R., 359 (361), *394*

Fanconneau, G., 179 (227), *243*

Fanshier, D., 166 (127), *241*

Farkas, W. G., 133 (183), *151*

Farr, R. S., 452 (44), *545*

Farrar, K. R., 7 (20), *87*

Farrow, J., 309 (17), 311 (17), *385*

G

Huennekens, F. M., 187 (277), 205 (385), 209 (407), *245, 248*

Hughes, N. A., 27 (234), 50 (234), *93*, 122 (147), *150*, 206 (389), 207 (389), 209 (403), 216 (430), *248, 249,* 285 (31), *307*

Hughes, T. R., 155 (30), 158 (45), *238, 239*

Hull, R., 51 (240), *93*

Hummel, J. P., 328 (141, 144), *388*, 527 (336), *552*

Hunter, W. H., 24 (91), *89,*

Hurlbert, R. B., 98 (5), *147,* 154 (13, 14), *238*

Hurlen, E., 364 (394), 365 (394), *395*

Hurst, R. O., 98 (16), *147,* 353 (315), 376 (449, 450), 378 (475), 380 (475), *393, 396, 397*

Hurwitz, J., 359 (371), *394*

Hutchings, B. L., 40 (193), 41 (193), *92*

Hutchinson, D. W., 234 (449), *249*

Hutchinson, S. A., 39 (177), *91*

Huwyler, S., 54 (254), *93*

Huzino, A., 209 (405), *248*

I

Iacono, L. C., 133 (183), *151*

Idler, D. R., 185 (273), *245*

Imai, K., 216 (428), 237 (428), *249*

Ikehara, M., 58 (287), 63 (307), *94, 95,* 131 (165), 140 (165, 208, 209), *151, 152,* 203 (371), *247*

Ingraham, L. L., 299 (28), *307*

Inman, R. B., 482 (213), 502 (268), 515 (304), *549, 550, 551,* 571 (62), *583*

Inscoe, J. K., 168 (151), *241*

Intrieri, O. M., 54 (262), *94*

Irani, R. R., 295 (25), *307*

Irie, M., 58 (288), *94,* 132 (171), *151,* 323 (121, 130), *388*

Irvin, E. M., 452 (43), *545*

Irvin, J. L., 452 (43), *545*

Ishihara, H., 191 (313), *246,* 341 (202), 376 (444), *390, 396*

Ishikawa, F., 131 (165), 140 (165), *151*

Ishimoto, N., 173 (196), *243*

Isono, K., 39 (181), *91*

Isselbacher, K. J., 166 (128, 129), *241*

Ito, E., 173 (192, 193, 196), *242, 243,* 376 (443), *396*

J

Jachimowicz, T., 112 (91), *149,* 154 (5), *238*

Jackson, A., 61 (304), *95*

Jackson, E. M., 2 (10), *3,* 315 (72), *387*

Jacob, F., 565 (4), *581*

Jacob, M., 154 (18), *238*

Jacobs, W. A., 4 (1, 2), 7 (18), *87,* 100 (25), 110 (80), 142 (225), *147, 149, 152,* 365 (397), *395*

Jacobson, B., 237 (462), *250,* 476 (155, 156), *547*

Jaenicke, F., 24 (81), *89*

James, A. L., 179 (228), 216 (430), *244, 249*

James, D. W. F., 353 (312), 375 (439), *393, 396*

James, T. W., 155 (26), *238*

Jamieson, G. A., 16 (61), 47 (223), 48 (223, 229, 230), 49 (232), *88, 92, 93*

Janion, C., 323 (133), *388,* 449 (26), 450 (26), *544*

Jansen, E. F., 53 (250), *93*

Jardetzky, C. D., 37 (166, 167, 168), 38 (167, 169), *91*

Jardetzky, O., 37 (166), *91*

Jeener, R., 569 (41), *582*

Jefford, C. W., 348 (257), *391*

Jencks, W. P., 187 (283), 190 (301), 204 (417), *245, 248*

Jenkins, R. J., 384 (541), *398,* 505 (271), *550*

Jensen, L. H., 100 (38), *147*

Jesaitis, M. A., 377 (468), *397*

Jezewska, M. M., 43 (199), *92*

Jochmann, I., 376 (446), *396*

Jönsson, B., 322 (112), *388*

Johnson, A. W., 27 (213), 45 (213), 55 (281), *92, 94*

Johnson, E. A., 445 (17), 540 (374), *544, 553*

Johnson, J. A., 54 (273), *94*

Johnson, M. J., 171 (178), *242*

Johnson, T. B., 52 (249), 53 (249), *93*

Jones, A. S., 36 (159), *91,* 309 (10), 314 (64), 370 (419, 420), 372 (421, 424, 425), 374 (424), 376 (445), *385, 387, 395, 396,* 485 (219), 509 (276), 528 (340), *549, 550, 552*

S

152, 153, 406), 529 (343), 531 (351), 534 (351), *547, 552, 554*

Watkins, W. M., 167 (136), *241*

Watson, B. E., 372 (421), *396*

Watson, J. D., 352 (283), 378 (481), *392, 397,* 465 (99), 466 (99), 474 (136), 475 (136), 491 (241), 493 (241), *546, 547, 550,* 565 (5), *581*

Watson, M., 354 (332), *393*

Watson, R. W., 174 (201), *243*

Watts-Tobin, R. J., 581 (78), *583*

Waugh, D. F., 451 (33), *544*

Waugh, J. S., 155 (29), *238*

Way, J. L., 117 (122, 123), *150,* 206 (388), *248*

Wazer, J. R. V., 295 (25), *307*

Webb, R. F., 196 (353), 205 (386), 212 (408, 409), 213 (409), *247, 248,* 403 (6), *442*

Weber, G., 160 (73), 162 (79), *239*

Webster, L. T., 188 (293), *245*

Weed, L. L., 377 (469), *397*

Weil, J. H., 192 (326), *246,* 509 (318), *551*

Weimann, G., 138 (192), *151,* 213 (464), *250,* 411 (18), 412 (18), 417 (46), *442, 443*

Weinstein, C., 192 (329), *246*

Weisblum, B., 567 (88, 95), *583, 584*

Weiss, J., 30 (126, 128), *90,* 140 (219), 141 (219, 220), *152,* 383 (513), *398*

Weiss, M. J., 51 (242), 54 (264, 268, 269), 58 (264, 285), *93, 94*

Weiss, S. B., 175 (202, 204), 176 (202), 190 (302), *243, 246,* 579 (93), *584*

Weissman, N., 452 (40), *545*

Weissmann, B., 12 (53), *88,* 347 (252), *391*

Weitzel, G., 155 (33), *238*

Welch, A. D., 572 (91), *584*

Weliky, V. S., 31 (137), 39 (182), 54 (278), *90, 91, 94*

Wempen, I., 26 (99), 27 (99), 37 (162), 43 (202), 58 (294), 60 (300), 83 (350, 354, 355), *89, 91, 92, 94, 95, 96*

Wende, G., 310 (44), *386*

Wendt, G., 46 (216), *92*

Westheimer, F. H., 293 (23), *307*

Westphal, O., 309 (11), *385*

Weyand, F., 46 (218), *92*

Weymouth, F. J., 114 (106), *149,* 196

(352, 353), 203 (366), 206 (366), **221** (366), *247,* 407 (9), *442*

Wheeler, C. M., 30 (126), *90*

White, D. M., 154 (14), *238*

White, J. C., 452 (54), *545*

Whitehead, C. W., 51 (241), *93*

Whitehouse, M., 187 (284), 204 (**378**), *245, 248*

Whitfeld, P. R., 145 (234), *152,* **321** (103, 104), 332 (572), 337 (186, **188**), *387, 390, 399*

Wiberg, J. S., 352 (292), *392*

Wieczotkowski, J., 27 (234), 50 (234), *93*

Wieland, T., 24 (81, 82), *89,* 164 (108), *240,* 285 (17), *306*

Wierzchowski, K. L., 37 (163), *91,* **119** (139), 140 (217, 218), *150, 152,* **449** (27, 28,) 459 (27, 72), *544, 545*

Wiggins, L. F., 365 (407), *395*

Wilken, D. R., 192 (328), 193 (342), *246, 247*

Wilkins, M. H. F., 474 (139, 141), **475** (139), 476 (142, 143, 144, 145, **146)** 487 (232, 233), 516 (307), 528 (342), 529 (342), 534 (403), 537 (360, **361**), 537 (365, 394), 538 (365), *547, 549, 551, 552, 553, 554*

Wilkins, M. J., 310 (24), *385*

Wilkinson, G. R., 476 (148, 149), **477** (149), 537 (392, 393), *547, 554*

Williams, D. E., 569 (35), *582*

Williams, J. H., 40 (193), 41 (193, 194), 43 (194), 55 (282), *92, 94*

Williams, R. C., 521 (320), *552*

Williams, W. L., 163 (90), *240*

Williams-Ashman, H. G., 176 (208), *243*

Williamson, A. R., 36 (159), *91*

Wilson, D. V., 67 (318), *95*

Wilson, H. R., 474 (139, 141), **475** (139), 476 (142, 144, 145), 537 (360, 361), *547, 553*

Wilson, L. G., 184 (262, 265, 266, **267**), 185 (272), *244, 245*

Wilson, W., 403 (4, 5), *442*

Windmueller, H. G., 33 (151), *91,* 237 (463), *250*

Winstein, S., 78 (340), *96*

Winter, M., 234 (452), *249*

Wiseman, A., 191 (465), 192 (466), *250*

Wittmann, R., 138 (194), *151,* 213 (**411**), 232 (446), *248, 249,* 411 (17), *442*

Witz, J., 529 (420), *554*

Witzel, H., 133 (176), *151*, 323 (124, 125), 324 (561), 340 (195, 197), 342 (210), *388, 390, 399*

Wizerkaniuk, M., 184 (258), *244*

Woessner, J. F., 204 (372), *247*

Wold, F., 224 (441), *249*

Wolf, M. K., 452 (49), *545*

Wolff, M. E., 138 (200, 201, 203), *151*

Wolfrom, M. L., 54 (265, 266, 271), *94*

Wollmann, M., 165 (115), *240*

Wood, R. M., 572 (91), *584*

Wood, W. B., 567 (10), *581*

Woodhouse, D. L., 376 (445), *396*

Woodward, R. B., 237 (460), *250*

Woolf, D. O., 39 (184), *91*

Woolfson, M. M., 106 (65), *148*

Woolley, D. M., 341 (208), *390*

Work, T. S., 345 (243), *391*

Wright, R. S., 56 (283), *94*, 116 (116, 117), *149*

Wulff, D. L., 459 (79), *545*

Wyatt, G. R., 5 (12, 14), *87*, 376 (454, 456), 377 (462), 378 (479), 379 (492), 380 (484), 381 (479), *396, 397*, 474 (138), *547*

Y

Yagi, K., 63 (307), *95*, 140 (208), *151*, 203 (371), *247*

Yamana, K., 310 (29, 30), *386*

Yamane, T., 314 (568), *399*, 455 (60), *545*

Yamazaki, H., 345 (240), *391*

Yankofsky, S. A., 580 (92), *584*

Yčas, M., 346 (228), *391*, 580 (81), *583*

Yemm, E. W., 191 (307, 320), *246*

Yoshikawa, H., 162 (80), *239*, 568 (18), *581*

Young, R. J., 332 (564), *399*

Young, W. J., 158 (46), *239*

Yphantis, D., 461 (82), *546*

Yu, C., 12 (56), *88*, 339 (189), 349 (262), *390, 392*

Yünsten, H., 39 (186, 187), *92*

Yung, N. C., 18 (69, 70, 73), 24 (73), 43 (202), 44 (69), 57 (284), 58 (294, 295), 60 (298, 300), 69 (325, 326, 327, 328), 73 (328), 75 (328), *89, 92, 94, 95*

Z

Zabin, I., 204 (379), *248*

Zabolotsky, N. N., 191 (315), *246*

Zachau, H. G., 24 (83, 84), *89*, 190 (302), *246*, 285 (18, 19), *306, 307*, 311 (52), 312 (52), 333 (434), 375 (434), *386, 396*

Zaluska, H., 191 (312), *246*

Zamecnik, P. C., 154 (19), 187 (288, 289), 188 (288), *238, 245*, 309 (15), 310 (43), 312 (43, 60), 339 (189), *385, 386, 390*, 563 (2), *581*

Zamenhof, S., 8 (24), 33 (149), *87, 90*, 354 (325), 363 (386, 389), 375 (433), 378 (478), 379 (491, 493), 380 (486), *393, 395, 396, 397*, 445 (18), 488 (236), *544, 549*, 569 (48), 570 (52, 53), *582*

Zetsche, F., 205 (382), *248*

Zillig, W., 188 (296), *245*, 331 (149), 343 (220, 221), 353 (306), 384 (221), *389, 390, 393*, 530 (345), *552*, 568 (28), *582*

Zilliken, F., 174 (197), 209 (400), *243, 248*

Zimm, B. H., 496 (257), 497 (257), 517 (312), 519 (257), *550, 551*

Zimmerman, S. B., 168 (145), *241*

Zimmermann, M., 2 (13), *3*, 98 (4), *147*

Zöllner, N., 320 (97), *387*

Zorbach, W. W., 54 (267), *94*

Zubay, G., 312 (566), 382 (507), 383 (507, 521), 384 (537, 539), *398, 399*, 484 (215), 516 (307), 528 (342), 529 (342), 530 (346), 534 (346), 537 (361, 365, 394), 538 (365), *549, 551, 552, 553, 554*, 579 (87), *583*

Zubkoff, P. L., 311 (55), 346 (55), *386*

Zussman, J., 11 (44), 15 (44), 16 (44), *88*

SUBJECT INDEX

A

Acetyl muramic acid, 171
Active methionine, 45, 47
  hydrolysis, 50
  synthesis, 47, 48
Active sulphate, 184
  synthesis, 203, 228
Adenine myonic acid dinucleotide, 162
Adenine thiomethyl pentoside, 45
Adenosine-3′,5′ cyclic phosphate, 107, 156
Adenosine oxide, 33
Adenosine-5′ phosphoramidate, 215
Adenosine-3′,5′ pyrophosphate, 185
Adenosine-5′ pyrophosphate, 154
  synthesis, 194, 197, 214, 216, 224
Adenosine-5′ triphosphate, 153
  alkaline degradation, 156
  conformation, 154
  phosphorus magnetic resonance, 158
  synthesis, 194, 195, 214, 216, 224
Adenosine-2′ uridine-5′ phosphate, 407
Adenylyl diphosphoglyceric acid, 162
Adenylyl sulphate, 184, 218
  synthesis, 203
Amicetin, 39, 40
Analogues, nucleoside, 54, 58
Analogues, nucleotide, 138
Analogues, polynucleotides, 419, 431, 569
Angustmycin A, 39, 40
Angustmycin C, 39, 40
Anhydrides, 153, 272
  acyl, 186, 282, 439
    properties, 189
    synthesis, 203, 227
  amino acid, 187
    properties, 189
    synthesis, 209, 227, 232
  anion exchange, 276
  biochemical aspects, 295
  biosynthesis, 261
  hypochromic effect, 447

Anhydrides—cont.
  mixed, 119, 124, 202, 221, 272, 276, 400, 418
    properties, 274, 435
    synthesis, 194, 204, 216, 221
Antibiotics, 39
Apurinic acid, 364
  alkaline hydrolysis, 372
  neutral hydrolysis, 373
Apyrimidinic acid, 374
Azides, 65

B

Bacterial ribonuclease, 335
Bacteriophage T2, 557
Base composition,
  deoxynucleic acid, 376
  ribonucleic acid, 343
Benzylidene nucleosides, 24
Benzyl phosphorous diphenyl phosphoric anhydride, 114, 123, 127, 196
Biological properties of nucleoproteins, 568
Biological properties of polynucleotides, 568
Biology of nucleic acids, 555
Biosynthesis of nucleotide anhydrides, 261
  purines, 251
  pyrimidines, 254
Bromoguanosine, 34

C

Carboxylic anhydrides, 282, 439
Catabolism of nucleotides, 306
Coenzyme A, 162
  biosynthesis, 164
  synthesis, 219, 228
Coenzyme I, 158
  interplanar interaction, 160
  synthesis, 203, 206
Coenzyme II, 158, 160
Coenzyme III, 160

arabocytin